Lecture Notes in Computer Science 14868

Founding Editors

Gerhard Goos
Juris Hartmanis

Editorial Board Members

Elisa Bertino, *Purdue University, West Lafayette, IN, USA*
Wen Gao, *Peking University, Beijing, China*
Bernhard Steffen, *TU Dortmund University, Dortmund, Germany*
Moti Yung, *Columbia University, New York, NY, USA*

The series Lecture Notes in Computer Science (LNCS), including its subseries Lecture Notes in Artificial Intelligence (LNAI) and Lecture Notes in Bioinformatics (LNBI), has established itself as a medium for the publication of new developments in computer science and information technology research, teaching, and education.

LNCS enjoys close cooperation with the computer science R & D community, the series counts many renowned academics among its volume editors and paper authors, and collaborates with prestigious societies. Its mission is to serve this international community by providing an invaluable service, mainly focused on the publication of conference and workshop proceedings and postproceedings. LNCS commenced publication in 1973.

De-Shuang Huang · Chuanlei Zhang ·
Qinhu Zhang
Editors

Advanced Intelligent Computing Technology and Applications

20th International Conference, ICIC 2024
Tianjin, China, August 5–8, 2024
Proceedings, Part VII

Editors
De-Shuang Huang
Eastern Institute of Technology
Ningbo, China

Chuanlei Zhang
Tianjin University of Science and Technology
Tianjin, China

Qinhu Zhang
Eastern Institute of Technology
Ningbo, China

ISSN 0302-9743   ISSN 1611-3349 (electronic)
Lecture Notes in Computer Science
ISBN 978-981-97-5599-8   ISBN 978-981-97-5600-1 (eBook)
https://doi.org/10.1007/978-981-97-5600-1

© The Editor(s) (if applicable) and The Author(s), under exclusive license
to Springer Nature Singapore Pte Ltd. 2024

This work is subject to copyright. All rights are solely and exclusively licensed by the Publisher, whether the whole or part of the material is concerned, specifically the rights of translation, reprinting, reuse of illustrations, recitation, broadcasting, reproduction on microfilms or in any other physical way, and transmission or information storage and retrieval, electronic adaptation, computer software, or by similar or dissimilar methodology now known or hereafter developed.
The use of general descriptive names, registered names, trademarks, service marks, etc. in this publication does not imply, even in the absence of a specific statement, that such names are exempt from the relevant protective laws and regulations and therefore free for general use.
The publisher, the authors and the editors are safe to assume that the advice and information in this book are believed to be true and accurate at the date of publication. Neither the publisher nor the authors or the editors give a warranty, expressed or implied, with respect to the material contained herein or for any errors or omissions that may have been made. The publisher remains neutral with regard to jurisdictional claims in published maps and institutional affiliations.

This Springer imprint is published by the registered company Springer Nature Singapore Pte Ltd.
The registered company address is: 152 Beach Road, #21-01/04 Gateway East, Singapore 189721, Singapore

If disposing of this product, please recycle the paper.

Preface

The International Conference on Intelligent Computing (ICIC) was started to provide an annual forum dedicated to emerging and challenging topics in artificial intelligence, machine learning, pattern recognition, bioinformatics, and computational biology. It aims to bring together researchers and practitioners from both academia and industry to share ideas, problems, and solutions related to the multifaceted aspects of intelligent computing.

ICIC 2024, held in Tianjin, China, August 5–8, 2024, constituted the 20th International Conference on Intelligent Computing. It built upon the success of ICIC 2023 (Zhengzhou, China), ICIC 2022 (Xi'an, China), ICIC 2021 (Shenzhen, China), ICIC 2020 (Bari, Italy), ICIC 2019 (Nanchang, China), ICIC 2018 (Wuhan, China), ICIC 2017 (Liverpool, UK), ICIC 2016 (Lanzhou, China), ICIC 2015 (Fuzhou, China), ICIC 2014 (Taiyuan, China), ICIC 2013 (Nanning, China), ICIC 2012 (Huangshan, China), ICIC 2011 (Zhengzhou, China), ICIC 2010 (Changsha, China), ICIC 2009 (Ulsan, South Korea), ICIC 2008 (Shanghai, China), ICIC 2007 (Qingdao, China), ICIC 2006 (Kunming, China), and ICIC 2005 (Hefei, China).

This year, the conference concentrated mainly on the theories and methodologies as well as the emerging applications of intelligent computing. Its aim was to unify the picture of contemporary intelligent computing techniques as an integral concept that highlights the trends in advanced computational intelligence and bridges theoretical research with applications. Therefore, the theme for this conference was "Advanced Intelligent Computing Technology and Applications". Papers that focused on this theme were solicited, addressing theories, methodologies, and applications in science and technology.

ICIC 2024 received 2189 submissions from 15 countries and regions. All papers went through a rigorous single-blind peer-review procedure and each paper received at least three review reports. Based on the review reports, the Program Committee finally selected 863 high-quality papers for presentation at ICIC 2024, included in twenty-one volumes of proceedings published by Springer: thirteen volumes of Lecture Notes in Computer Science (LNCS), six volumes of Lecture Notes in Artificial Intelligence (LNAI), and two volumes of Lecture Notes in Bioinformatics (LNBI).

In addition, this year we selected 134 Poster papers from the remaining papers, which will be made accessible on the open access website http://poster-openaccess.com/.

This volume of LNCS_14868 includes 41 papers.

The organizers of ICIC 2024, including Eastern Institute of Technology, Ningbo, China; Tianjin University of Science and Technology, China; China University of Mining & Technology (Beijing), China; China University of Mining and Technology (Xuzhou), China; and North China University of Science and Technology, China, made an enormous effort to ensure the success of the conference. We hereby would like to thank the members of the Program Committee and the referees for their collective effort in reviewing and soliciting the papers. In particular, we would like to thank all the authors for contributing their papers. Without the high-quality submissions from the authors, the success of the conference would not have been possible. Finally, we are especially grateful to the International Neural Network Society and the National Science Foundation of China for their sponsorship.

De-Shuang Huang
Fuping Lu

Organization

General Co-chairs

De-Shuang Huang   Eastern Institute of Technology, China
Fuping Lu   Tianjin University of Science and Technology, China

Program Committee Co-chairs

Prashan Premaratne   University of Wollongong, Australia
Xiankun Zhang   Tianjin University of Science and Technology, China
Chuanlei Zhang   Tianjin University of Science and Technology, China
Wei Chen   China University of Mining and Technology, China
Jair Cervantes Canales   Autonomous University of Mexico State, Mexico
Yijie Pan   Eastern Institute of Technology, China
Qinhu Zhang   Eastern Institute of Technology, China
Jiayang Guo   Xiamen University, China

Organizing Committee Co-chairs

Zhanjun Si   Tianjin University of Science and Technology, China
Xiaoyue Liu   North China University of Science and Technology, China
Fan Zhang   China University of Mining and Technology (Beijing), China

Organizing Committee Members

Yarui Chen   Tianjin University of Science and Technology, China
Jing Su   Tianjin University of Science and Technology, China

Shuo Yang	Tianjin University of Science and Technology, China
Jing Han	Tianjin University of Science and Technology, China
Yiying Zhang	Tianjin University of Science and Technology, China
Jucheng Yang	Tianjin University of Science and Technology, China
Qian Long	Tianjin University of Science and Technology, China
Yongjun Ma	Tianjin University of Science and Technology, China
Lin Sun	Tianjin University of Science and Technology, China
Guoliang Gong	Tianjin University of Science and Technology, China

Award Committee Chair

Kang-Hyun Jo	University of Ulsan, South Korea

Tutorial Co-chairs

Abir Hussain	Liverpool John Moores University, UK
Michal Choras	Bydgoszcz University of Science and Technology, Poland

Publication Co-chairs

Jair Cervantes Canales	Autonomous University of Mexico State, Mexico
Chenxi Huang	Xiamen University, China

Special Session Co-chairs

Valeriya Gribova	Far Eastern Branch of Russian Academy of Sciences, Russia
M. Michael Gromiha	Indian Institute of Technology Madras, India

Special Issue Co-chairs

Yu-Dong Zhang	University of Leicester, UK
Yoshinori Kuno	Saitama University, Japan
Phalguni Gupta	Indian Institute of Technology Kanpur, India

International Liaison Chair

Prashan Premaratne   University of Wollongong, Australia

Workshop Co-chairs

Kyungsook Han	Inha University, South Korea
Laurent Heutte	Université de Rouen Normandie, France

Publicity Co-chairs

Chun-Hou Zheng	Anhui University, China
Dhiya Al-Jumeily	Liverpool John Moores University, UK
Han Huang	Nanjing University of Information Science and Technology, China

Program Committee Members

Antonio Brunetti	Polytechnic University of Bari, Italy
Bin Liu	Beijing Institute of Technology, China
Bin Qian	Kunming University of Science and Technology, China
Bin Yang	Zaozhuang University, China
Bing Wang	Anhui University of Technology, China
Bingqiang Liu	Shandong University, China
Binhua Tang	Hohai University, China
Bo Li	Wuhan University of Science and Technology, China
Caihong Mu	Xidian University, China
Changqing Shen	Soochow University, China
Chao Song	University of South China, China
Cheng Tang	Kyushu University, Japan

Chin-Chih Chang	Chung Hua University, Taiwan, RoC
Chuanlei Zhang	Tianjin University of Science and Technology, China
Chunhou Zheng	Anhui University, China
Chunmei Liu	Howard University, USA
Chunquan Li	University of South China, China
Cong Shen	Tianjin University of Technology, China
Daowen Qiu	Sun Yat-sen University, China
Delong Yang	First People's Hospital of Foshan, China
Dian Ding	Shanghai Jiao Tong University, China
Dong Wang	University of Jinan, China
Duo Chen	Nanjing University of Chinese Medicine, China
Eros Gian Alessandro Pasero	Politecnico di Torino, Italy
Fa Zhang	Beijing Institute of Technology, China
Fei Guo	Central South University, China
Fei Luo	Wuhan University, China
Fei Shen	Nanjing University of Science and Technology, China
Feng Liu	East China Normal University, China
Feng Zou	Huaibei Normal University, China
Fengfeng Zhou	Jilin University, China
Fudong Nian	Hefei University, China
Fuxue Li	Yingkou Institute of Technology, China
Gang Li	Qilu University of Technology, China
Gaoxiang Ouyang	Beijing Normal University, China
Guanghui Gong	Eastern Institute of Technology, Ningbo, China
Guohui Ding	Shenyang Aerospace University, China
Guoliang Li	Huazhong Agricultural University, China
Han Zhang	Nankai University, China
Hao Huang	Hubei University, China
Hao Lin	University of Electronic Science and Technology of China, China
Haodi Feng	Shandong University, China
Haodong Zhu	Zhengzhou University of Light Industry, China
Heng Li	Southern University of Science and Technology, China
Hoang-Anh Ngo	The University of Waikato, New Zealand
Hongjie Wu	Suzhou University of Science and Technology, China
Hongmin Cai	South China University of Technology, China
Hulin Kuang	Central South University, China
Jiahui Pan	South China Normal University, China

Jian Huang	University of Electronic Science and Technology of China, China
Jian Shen	Beijing Institute of Technology, China
Jiang Xie	Shanghai University, China
Jianrong Li	Tianjin University of Science and Technology, China
Jiawei Luo	Hunan University, China
Jiayang Guo	Xiamen University, China
Jing Chen	Suzhou University of Science and Technology, China
Jing Hu	Wuhan University of Science and Technology, China
Jintian Lu	Jishou University, China
Jin-Xing Liu	University of Health and Rehabilitation Sciences, China
Jipeng Wu	First People's Hospital of Foshan, China
Joaquin Torres-Sospedra	Universidade do Minho, Portugal
Juan Liu	Wuhan University, China
Junfeng Xia	Anhui University, China
Jungang Lou	Huzhou University, China
Junqing Li	Yunnan Normal University, China
Junyi Li	Harbin Institute of Technology (Shenzhen), China
Ka-Chun Wong	City University of Hong Kong, China
Kangning Zhang	Academy of Mathematics and Systems Science, CAS, China
Ke Niu	Beijing Information Science and Technology University, China
Laurent Heutte	Université de Rouen Normandie, France
Le Zhang	Sichuan University, China
Lei Wang	Guangxi Academy of Sciences, China
Lejun Gong	Nanjing University of Posts and Telecommunications, China
Liang Gao	Huazhong University of Science & Technology, China
Lida Zhu	Huazhong Agriculture University, China
Lin Wang	University of Jinan, China
Lin Yuan	Qilu University of Technology, China
Liqiang Liu	Xi'an Technological University, China
Li-Wei Ko	National Yang Ming Chiao Tung University, Taiwan, RoC
Long Shao	Beijing Institute of Technology, China
Long Xu	Ningbo University, China
Meiyan Xu	Minnan Normal University, China

Meng Liu	National University of Defense Technology, China
Michael Gromiha	Indian Institute of Technology Madras, India
Michal Choras	Bydgoszcz University of Science and Technology, Poland
Mingyong Li	Chongqing Normal University, China
Mohd Helmy Abd Wahab	Universiti Tun Hussein Onn Malaysia, Malaysia
Nicola Altini	Polytechnic University of Bari, Italy
Nier Wu	Inner Mongolia University of Technology, China
Peipei Gu	Zhengzhou University of Light Industry, China
Peng Chen	Anhui University, China
Pengjiang Qian	Jiangnan University, China
Pengwei Hu	Xinjiang Technical Institute of Physics and Chemistry, CAS, China
Prashan Premaratne	University of Wollongong, Australia
Pu-Feng Du	Tianjin University, China
Qi Sun	Hangzhou Nuowei Information Technology Co., Ltd., China
Qi Zhao	University of Science and Technology Liaoning, China
Qifang Luo	Guangxi University for Nationalities, China
Qinhu Zhang	Eastern Institute of Technology, Ningbo, China
Qiuzhen Lin	Shenzhen University, China
Quan Zou	University of Electronic Science and Technology of China, China
Rong Wang	Sichuan Normal University, China
Rong-Qiang Zeng	Chengdu University of Information Technology, China
Rui Wang	National University of Defense Technology, China
Saiful Islam	Aligarh Muslim University, India
Shanfeng Zhu	Fudan University, China
Shitong Wang	Jiangnan University, China
Shixiong Zhang	Xidian University, China
Sungshin Kim	Pusan National University, South Korea
Taisong Jin	Xiamen University, China
Tian Wu	Nanchang University, China
Tieshan Li	University of Electronic Science and Technology of China, China
Valeria Gribova	Far Eastern Branch of Russian Academy of Sciences, Russia
Wangren Qiu	Jingdezhen Ceramic University, China
Waqas Haider Bangyal	Kohsar University Murree, Pakistan

Wei Chen	China University of Mining and Technology (Xuzhou), China
Wei Chen	Chengdu University of Traditional Chinese Medicine, China
Wei Jiang	Fujian Medical University, China
Wei Wang	Henan Normal University, China
Wei Xu	East China Normal University, China
Weichao Wu	Beijing Institute of Technology, China
Weiwei Kong	Xi'an University of Posts and Telecommunications, China
Weixiang Liu	Shenzhen University, China
Wen Jiang	Ctrip Computer Technology (Shanghai) Co., Ltd., China
Wen-Sheng Chen	Shenzhen University, China
Wenzheng Bao	Xuzhou University of Technology, China
Xiangtao Li	Jilin University, China
Xiaodi Li	Shandong Normal University, China
Xiaofeng Wang	Hefei University, China
Xiaoke Ma	Xidian University, China
Xiaolei Zhu	Anhui Agricultural University, China
Xiaoli Lin	Wuhan University of Science and Technology, China
Xiaoqing Li	Capital University of Economics and Business, China
Xin Zhang	Jiangnan University, China
Xingjian Xu	Inner Mongolia Normal University, China
Xingquan Cai	North China University of Technology, China
Xingtao Wang	Harbin Institute of Technology, China
Xinguo Lu	Hunan University, China
Xingyu Feng	City University of Hong Kong, China
Xinlu Li	Hefei University, China
Xinzheng Xu	China University of Mining and Technology (Xuzhou), China
Xiufen Zou	Wuhan University, China
Xiujuan Lei	Shaanxi Normal University, China
Xiwei Liu	Tongji University, China
Xiyuan Chen	Southeast University, China
Xizhao Luo	Soochow University, China
Xulong Zhang	Ping An Technology (Shenzhen) Co., Ltd., China
Yang Yang	Hubei University, China
Yansen Su	Anhui University, China
Yijie Pan	Eastern Institute of Technology, Ningbo, China
Yiming Tang	Hefei University of Technology, China

Yizhang Jiang	Jiangnan University, China
Yong Wang	Academy of Mathematics and Systems Science, CAS, China
Yong Wu	Anhui Normal University, China
Yonggang Lu	Lanzhou University, China
Yu Lu	Shenzhen Technology University, China
Yu Xue	Huazhong University of Science and Technology, China
Yunxia Liu	Zhengzhou Normal University, China
Yupei Zhang	Northwestern Polytechnical University, China
Yushan Qiu	Shenzhen University, China
Yuyan Zheng	Shandong Normal University, China
Zhan-Li Sun	Anhui University, China
Zhen Shen	Nanyang Institute of Technology, China
Zhendong Liu	Shandong Jianzhu University, China
Zhenran Jiang	East China Normal University, China
Zhenyi Shen	Zhejiang University, China
Zhi-Hong Guan	Huazhong University of Science and Technology, China
Zhi-Ping Liu	Shandong University, China
Zhong-Qiu Zhao	Heifei Institute of Technology, China
Zhuangzhuang Chen	Hong Kong University of Science and Technology, China
Zhuo Lei	City Cloud Technology China Co., Ltd., China
Zixiao Kong	University of International Relations, China

Contents – Part VII

Image Processing

Light-Dark: A Novel Lightweight Self-supervised Monocular Depth
Estimation in the Dark 3
   Qi Liang, Lizhe Wang, Lanmei Wang, Xiang Liu, and Guibao Wang

Non-homogeneous Image Dehazing with Edge Attention Based
on Relative Haze Density 15
   *Ruting Deng, Zhan Li, Yifan Deng, Hang Long, Zhanglu Chen,
Zhiqing Kang, and Zhichao Qiu*

Contrastive Learning for Silent Face Liveness Detection Based
on A Hybrid Framework 29
   *Ying Tang, Zhongyue Chen, Minchao Ye, Zhaojuan Zhang, Yaping Qi,
Huijuan Lu, and Wanli Huo*

BS2CL: Balanced Self-supervised Contrastive Learning for Thyroid
Cytology Whole Slide Image Multi-classification 41
   *Wensi Duan, Juan Liu, Lang Wang, Yu Jin, Peng Jiang, Cheng Li,
Dehua Cao, and Baochuan Pang*

Unsupervised Domain Adaptation Method for Medical Image
Segmentation Using Fourier Feature Decoupling and Multi-scale Feature
Fusion 53
   *Wei Hu, Qiaozhi Xu, Zhe Lian, Yanjun Yin, Min Zhi, Na Yang,
Wentao Duan, and Lei Yu*

LVMUM: Toward Open-World Object Detection with Large Vision
Models and Unsupervised Modeling 65
   Yangyang Huang, Xing Xi, Weiye Wu, and Ronghua Luo

Implementation and Application of Violence Detection System Based
on Multi-head Attention and LSTM 77
   Fengping Cao, Yi Miao, and Wangyi Zhang

GFFNet: An Efficient Image Denoising Network with Group Feature Fusion ... 89
   Lijun Gao, Youzhi Zhang, Xiao Jin, Qin Xin, Zeyang Sun, and Suran Wang

End-to-End Object Detection with YOLOF 101
   Xing Xi, Yangyang Huang, Weiye Wu, and Ronghua Luo

BiRGAN: Bi-directional Deep Image Retargeting 113
  Di Sun, Yunxiang Wang, Tingting Yang, Yijing Mei, and Gang Pan

MulTIR: Deep Multi-Target Image Retargeting 124
  Di Sun, Yitong Guo, Chaojie Yao, Yijing Mei, Dufeng Chen, and Gang Pan

PAAM (Parameter-free Attentional Aggregation Model) 134
  Xuan-Hao Qi, Min Zhi, Zeng Mi, Wei Hu, Yan-Jun Yin, Yue-Ning Zhang, Wen-Tao Duan, and Zhe Lian

FRFT Domain Watermarking Algorithm Based on GA Adaptive
Optimization 147
  Qiaoqiao Du, Yanchen Zhao, Weijie Hao, and Wenyin Zhang

Joint Semantic Feature and Optical Flow Learning for Automatic
Echocardiography Segmentation 160
  Juan Lyu, Jinpeng Meng, Yu Zhang, Sai Ho Ling, and Lin Sun

FMUnet: Frequency Feature Enhancement Multi-level U-Net
for Low-Dose CT Denoising with a Real Collected LDCT Image Dataset 172
  Yu Zhang, Xinqi Yang, Guoliang Gong, Xianghong Meng, Xiaoliang Wang, and Zhongwei Zhang

Research on Intelligent Recognition Algorithm of Container Numbers
in Ports Based on Deep Learning 184
  Zhehao Lin, Chen Dong, and Yuxuan Wan

Dr-SAM: U-Shape Structure Segment Anything Model for Generalizable
Medical Image Segmentation 197
  Xiangzuo Huo, Shengwei Tian, Bingming Zhou, Long Yu, and Aolun Li

Aerial Multi-object Tracking via Information Weighting 208
  Pengnian Wu, Bangkui Fan, Ruiyu Zhang, Yulong Xu, and Dong Xue

Optimization Method for Fractal Image Compression Based
on Self-similarity Evaluation and Gradient Bisection Algorithm 218
  Caixu Xu, Di Xie, Hui Guo, Jie He, and Minglang Chen

DiffGIC: Diffusion Prior Based Null-Space Correction for High
Resolution Grayscale Image Colorization 234
  Yachao Li, Yutian Fu, Feng Dong, and Dong Liang

Chinese Character Image Inpainting with Skeleton Extraction
and Adversarial Learning 246
  Di Sun, Tingting Yang, Xiangyu Pan, Jiahao Wang, and Gang Pan

The Weakly Supervised Network of Hierarchical Attention Mechanism
for Fine-Grained Classification 257
   Qian Long, Gaihua Wang, Hongwei Qu, Jingxuan Yao, and Bolun Zhu

CS-KD: Confused Sample Knowledge Distillation for Semantic
Segmentation of Aerial Imagery 266
   Yue Sun, Lingfeng Huang, Qi Zhu, and Dong Liang

CD-Font: One-Shot Font Generation via Conditional Diffusion Model
with Disentangled Guidance 279
   Siyi Chen, Zhenhua Li, and Dong Liang

Image Super-Resolution Reconstruction Based on Dual-Branch Channel
Attention 291
   Jinyu Shi, Zhanjun Si, Yingxue Zhang, and Xinbin Yang

A Flipped Reversible Information Hiding Method Based on AMP 300
   Yaowen Fu, Haoshan Shi, Tianyang Qi, Xueyan Gao, and Yifei Zou

Decoupling Control in Text-to-Image Diffusion Models 312
   Shitong Cao, Xuejie Zhang, Jin Wang, and Xiaobing Zhou

Arbitrary Scale Texture Synthesis with Feature Map Swapping 323
   *Di Sun, Yangde Lin, Sheng Shen, Zhiliang Zeng, Shizhao Zhang,
   and Qihang Wang*

A 3D-2D Hybrid Network with Regional Awareness and Global Fusion
for Brain Tumor Segmentation 333
   Wenxiu Zhao, Changlei Dongye, and Yumei Wang

GLAD: A Global-Attention-Based Diffusion Model for Infrared
and Visible Image Fusion 345
   Haozhe Guo, Mengjie Chen, Kaijiang Li, Hao Su, and Pei Lv

An Approach for Extracting Road Network from Remote Sensing Images 357
   Zhihui Wang, Yu Wang, and Yuliang Ni

Sparse Point Cloud Upsampling Based on Neural Implicit Functions 369
   Wenjun Wang, Xiangyu Kong, Daole Wang, and Xiuyang Zhao

Adaptive Non-local Means Filter Based on Multi-kernel for Complicated
Noise 381
   Qian long, Hongwei Qu, Yiping Wang, Gaihua Wang, and Bolun Zhu

One-Stage Lightweight Network of Object Detection for Rectangular
Panoramic Images 390
   Yingying Lu, Yun Tie, and Lin Qi

ISE-UFDS: A Dataset for Detecting the Degree of Danger to Vehicles
in Urban Flooding and Performance Assessment 402
   Jiwu Sun, Cheng Zhang, Cheng Xu, Pengfei Wang, and Hongzhe Liu

Convergence and Divergence: A New Paradigm for Pedestrian Detection 414
   Yueyan Zhu, Hai Huang, Shan Yue, Shu Zhang, and Aoran Chen

Improved YOLOv8-Based Lightweight Object Detection on Drone Images 426
   Maoxiang Jiang, Zhanjun Si, Ke Yang, and Yingxue Zhang

A Multi-dimensional Camera Image Stitching Method Under Large
Parallax Conditions 435
   *Chuanlei Zhang, Yubo Li, Tianxiang Cheng, Jianrong Li, Haifeng Fan,
   Zhiqiang Zhao, Zhanjun Si, and Hui Ma*

Harmonizing Stable Diffusion and GPT-4 for Mural Expansion
with ArtExtend 446
   *Dufeng Chen, Yuqing Yang, Zehua Wang, Zishan Xu, Jueting Liu,
   Tingting Xu, and Wei Chen*

MuralRescue: Advancing Blind Mural Restoration via SAM-Adapter
Enhanced Damage Segmentation and Integrated Restoration Techniques 456
   *Zishan Xu, Dufeng Chen, Qianzhen Fang, Wei Chen, Tingting Xu,
   Jueting Liu, and Zehua Wang*

Full-Range Fusion Network with Local-Global Attention for Change
Detection in Remote Sensing Images 464
   Shuting Niu, Yingxue Zhang, and Zhanjun Si

Author Index 473

Image Processing

Light-Dark: A Novel Lightweight Self-supervised Monocular Depth Estimation in the Dark

Qi Liang[1], Lizhe Wang[1], Lanmei Wang[1(✉)], Xiang Liu[2], and Guibao Wang[3]

[1] School of Physics, Xidian University, Xi'an 710071, China
lmwang@mail.xidian.edu.cn
[2] Institute of Science and Technology Innovation, Dongguan University of Technology, Dongguan 523808, China
[3] School of Electronic Information and Artificial Intelligence, Shaanxi University of Science and Technology, Xi'an 710021, China

Abstract. Self-supervised monocular depth estimation has been widely studied in recent years. In nighttime scenes where the photometric consistency assumption is not met, several solutions have emerged to address this challenge. However, existing monocular depth estimation algorithms for nighttime often require a large-scale model and a significant number of floating-point operations, making it challenging to apply them to practical problems such as autonomous driving. In this paper, we propose a lightweight monocular depth estimation algorithm tailored for nighttime scenes, named Light-Dark. Specifically, we design a lightweight Depth-Net incorporating Feature-Fusion blocks and Cross-connections. Additionally, in response to the low-light and high-noise issues in nighttime scenes, we introduce a Noise-Constrained Adaptive Image Enhancement (NCAIE) module. We deploy our model on the edge device Jetson AGX Orin to validate its real-world performance. A series of experiments conducted on nighttime datasets, Robot-Car and nuScenes, indicate the effectiveness of our proposed Light-Dark and the equilibrium between lightweight design and accuracy.

Keywords: Monocular depth estimation · Lightweight · Nighttime

1 Introduction

Monocular depth estimation is a vital task in the field of computer vision and essential for applications such as autonomous driving, robotic navigation and 3D reconstruction [1]. Self-supervised monocular depth estimation, which leverages photometric constraints between monocular image sequences without the need for collecting real depth maps, is gaining increasing attention. In addition to research on daytime datasets such as KITTI [2] and Make 3D [3], some self-supervised methods are attempting to be applied in nighttime scenarios [4, 5]. Meanwhile, lightweighting of models in monocular depth estimation has garnered attention. Recent researches often focus on reducing model parameters through techniques such as knowledge distillation [6] and exploring new convolution operations [7]. This allows models to be deployed on edge devices to solve real-world problems.

However, few lightweight methods are proposed to address the challenges posed in more complex nighttime scenarios. The DepthNet in current nighttime methods is primarily adapted from Monodepth2 [8], exhibiting a relatively high model complexity. Existing lightweight methods are primarily trained and evaluated on daytime scenes. Nighttime scenes disrupt the photometric consistency between adjacent frames, making the reconstruction of the target frame challenging and resulting in higher training loss. Meanwhile, in low-light and high-noise environments, depth prediction maps may exhibit irregularities such as non-smooth regions and large holes [4].

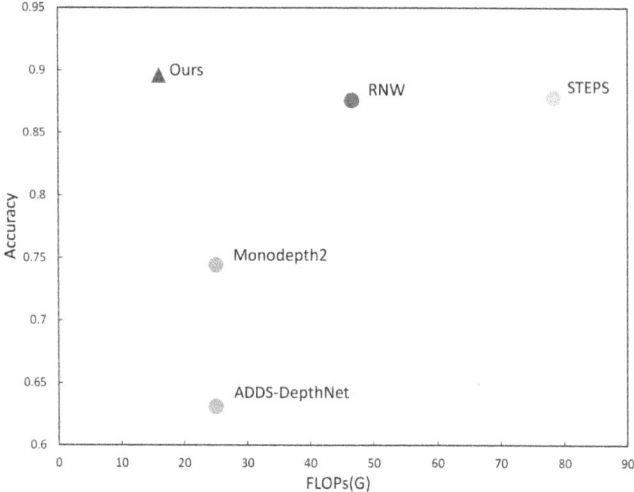

Fig. 1. Comparison graph of FLOPs (Floating Point Operations) and Accuracy(δ_1) for different models. All models were tested on the 576 × 320 RobotCar dataset. Smaller FLOPs is better, and higher Accuracy(δ_1) is better.

To address the aforementioned issues, this paper propose a lightweight self-supervised monocular depth estimation method tailored for nighttime scenes. Firstly, we design a lightweight depth estimation network by adopting a shallower network to reduce model complexity. To better capture and process both local and global features of the images, we introduce Feature-Fusion blocks by combining CNNs and Transformers. Within these blocks, cross-covariance attention (XCA) [9] is employed to reduce computational complexity. We also utilize Cross-connections to enhance the propagation of features. Secondly, we introduce a Noise-Constrained Adaptive Image Enhancement (NCAIE) module, which enhances image contrast while suppressing noise. Finally, we test our model on edge devices at different power levels to demonstrate its real-time inference performance. In summary, our model achieves a favorable equilibrium between lightweight design and accuracy compared to other nighttime methods (see Fig. 1). Our contributions can be summarized in three aspects:

(1) We propose a lightweight DepthNet and fuse it into the nighttime self-supervised depth estimation architecture.

(2) We employ the Noise-Constrained Adaptive Image Enhancement module to address the low-light and high-noise problem in nighttime scenes.
(3) We test the inference speed of our model on Nvidia Titan V and an edge device Jetson AGX Orin to confirm the practicality of our lightweight model.

2 Method

2.1 Nighttime Self-supervised Depth Estimation Architecture

In self-supervised monocular depth estimation, the system is primarily composed of a depth estimation network Φ_d and a pose network Φ_p [8]. However, due to the specificity of nighttime scenes, relying solely on the above methods can result in numerous abnormal depth values. To address this issue, we follow [4] by pretraining DepthNet $\Phi_{d'}$ on the daytime dataset and then utilizing an adversarial neural network to guide nighttime training. We utilize a Patch-GAN discriminator to differentiate between the nighttime depth map D_t generated by Φ_d and the daytime depth map D_d generated by Φ'_d. Figure 2 illustrates the fundamental architecture of our proposed Light-Dark model.

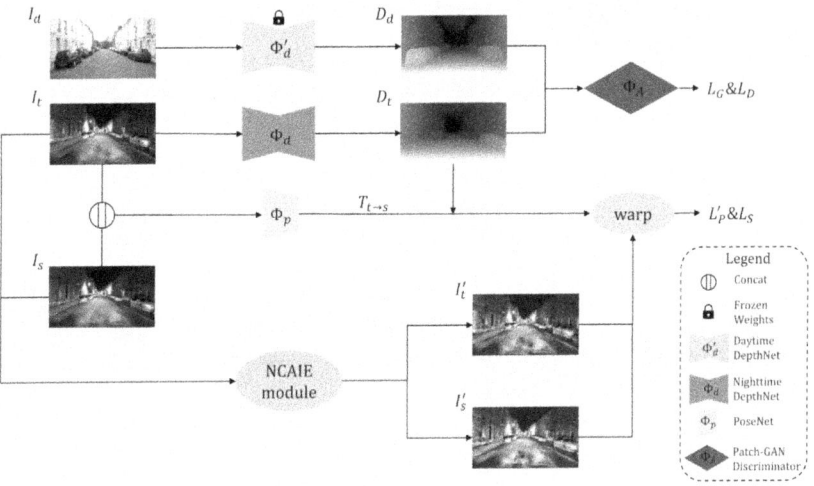

Fig. 2. Overview of our Light-Dark architecture. DepthNet Φ_d and Φ'_d share the same network, which serves as the core module in our lightweight approach. The NCAIE module represents the image enhancement module in our work.

Given a RGB image I_t, a depth map D_t can be predicted using a trainable network Φ_d: $D_t = \Phi_d(I_t)$. To achieve self-supervision, it's necessary to reconstruct the target frame I_t from the source frame I_s using geometric relationships: $T_{t \to s} = \Phi_p(I_t, I_s)$. The reconstruction process involves using the pose network to obtain the relative pose $T_{t \to s}$ between I_s and I_t. Then, we can project the point p_t in D_t onto the point p_s in I_s:

$$p_s \sim K T_{t \to s} D_t(p_t) K^{-1} p_t \tag{1}$$

where $\sim$ represents a homogeneous equivalence relationship, and K denotes the camera intrinsics. Then, I_s obtains the reconstructed target frame $\hat{I}_t$ through the differentiable bilinear sampling operation $s(\cdot, \cdot)$:

$$\hat{I}_t = s(I_s, p_s) \quad (2)$$

Following [8], we combine l_1 and SSIM (structural similarity) loss as the photometric loss L_P, the formula is:

$$L_P(I_t, \hat{I}_t) = \frac{\alpha}{2}(1 - SSIM(I_t, \hat{I}_t)) + (1 - \alpha)\|I_t - \hat{I}_t\|_1 \quad (3)$$

where $\|\cdot\|_1$ represents the L1 norm, and the parameter α is set to 0.85 in all experiments. In addition, we apply edge-aware smoothness loss to reduce the noise and discontinuity of the depth map or surface normal vector, making the depth estimation results more accurate and stable. The expression is as follows:

$$L_S = |\partial_x D_t|e^{-|\partial_x I_t|} + |\partial_y D_t|e^{-|\partial_y I_t|} \quad (4)$$

where ∂_x and ∂_y are the image gradients in the horizontal and vertical directions respectively. Finally, we train the generator Φ_d and the discriminator Φ_A by minimizing the loss function of LSGAN, expressed as:

$$L_D = \frac{1}{2|I_d|}\sum_{D_d}(\Phi_A(D_d) - 1)^2 + \frac{1}{2|I_t|}\sum_{D_t}(\Phi_A(D_t))^2 \quad (5)$$

$$L_G = \frac{1}{2|I_t|}\sum_{D_t}(\Phi_A(D_t) - 1)^2 \quad (6)$$

where $|I_d|$ represents the number of daytime training images, and $|I_t|$ represents the number of nighttime training images. It's important to note that I_t and I_d do not correspond one-to-one to daytime and nighttime images, so the generated depth maps $D_d = \Phi'_d(I_d)$ and $D_t = \Phi_d(I_t)$ are not required to be paired.

2.2 Lightweight DepthNet

After training with the Light-Dark architecture, our subsequent inference only requires the use of the DepthNet. Therefore, designing a lightweight DepthNet can help us effectively reduce the model's complexity and inference speed. Inspired by recent research [10], we design a lightweight depth estimation network that incorporates Feature-Fusion blocks and Cross-connections, as shown in Fig. 3.

Depth Encoder. Using a shallower network can effectively reduce model complexity, hence we adopted a four-stage encoder. The Conv-stem consists of a 3×3 convolution with a stride of 2 followed by two 3×3 convolutions with a stride of 1, and the downsample module is a 3×3 convolution with a stride of 2. Due to the high requirements of depth estimation tasks for perceiving local details and scene structure, we introduce a Feature-Fusion block that can simultaneously integrate both local and global image features. First, the Feature-Fusion block utilizes a 3 × 3 dilated convolution to expand the receptive field, achieving the extraction of local features. Assuming a feature map x with dimensions $H \times W \times C$, this process can be represented as:

$$L(x) = Pw_2(Pw_1(BN(Dconv(x)))) + x \tag{7}$$

where $Dconv(\cdot)$ represents dilated convolution, BN stands for batch normalization, and $Pw1(\cdot)$ and $Pw2(\cdot)$ respectively signify the pointwise operations for dimensionality expansion and reduction. In the Feature-Fusion blocks of the encoder, the operation of extracting local features $L(\cdot)$ is repeated N times, with the respective counts being 3, 3 and 9 from top to bottom.

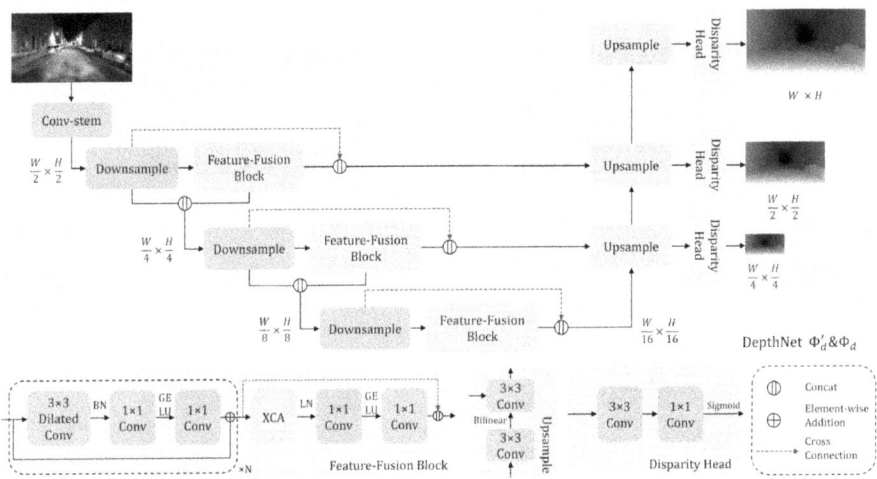

Fig. 3. DepthNet used in Light-Dark. The DepthNet adopts an encoder-decoder structure, where the encoder utilizes Feature-Fusion blocks and Cross-connections to merge local and global features.

Then, we replace the original self-attention [11] with the lower computational complexity Cross-Covariance Attention (XCA) [9] to model global context more efficiently. We denote this operation as $G(\cdot)$, and its expression is given by:

$$G(x') = Pw_2(Pw_1(LN(XCA(x')))) \tag{8}$$

where x' is the input feature, and LN represents layer normalization. To enhance the integration and propagation of local and global features, we utilized Cross-connections in both the Downsample module and Feature-Fusion blocks. The final output y of the Feature-Fusion block can be expressed as:

$$y = Concat[N \cdot L(x), G(N \cdot L(x))] \tag{9}$$

Depth Decoder. To reduce the complexity of the model, we follow [10] by using a decoder consisting only of convolutional layers, as illustrated in Fig. 3. The upsample module employs bilinear interpolation for upsampling, followed by a disparity head connected to each output. These outputs are generated at $\frac{1}{4}$, $\frac{1}{2}$, and full resolution, respectively.

2.3 Noise-Constrained Adaptive Image Enhancement

In nighttime images, the photometric consistency between the target frame I_t and the source frame I_s often does not hold, accompanied by low-light and high-noise levels. Therefore, inspired by Adaptive Histogram Euqalization, we propose the Noise-Constrained Adaptive Image Enhancement (NCAIE) module. This avoids the use of additional image enhancement networks, aligning with the goal of model lightweight design. Figure 4 illustrates the processing flow of NCAIE.

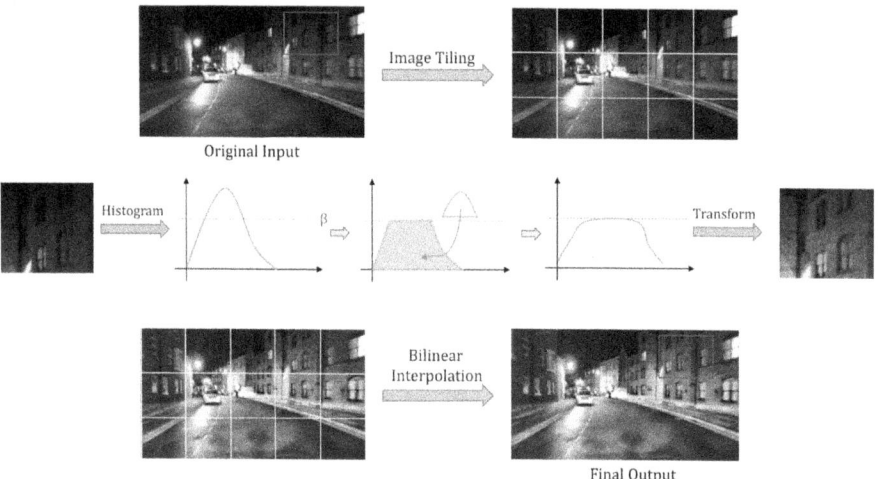

Fig. 4. Flowchart of Noise-Constrained Adaptive Image Enhancement (NCAIE). The main steps include image block tiling, histogram equalization for each block, and concatenation of blocks using interpolation methods.

We initially divide the target frame I_t and the source frame I_s into $I \times J$ small blocks. Each block from the partition of I_t is denoted as $t_{i,j}$, and each block from the partition of I_s is represented as $s_{i,j}$. Assuming each block has M pixels and N grayscale levels, we calculate the histogram $h_{i,j}(n)$ for each small block, where $n = 1, 2, \ldots, N-1$. Simultaneously, to control the noise amplification resulting from excessive contrast, we introduce a contrast limitation parameter β, obtaining the clipped histogram $h'_{i,j}(n)$. Then, we compute the cumulative distribution function (CDF) of the histogram as follows:

$$f_{i,j}(n) = \frac{(N-1)}{M} \cdot \sum_{k=0}^{n} h'_{i,j}(k) \tag{10}$$

The above expression represents the histogram equalization operation for each small block. Finally, we use bilinear interpolation to smoothly concatenate the processed blocks, obtaining the enhanced target frame I'_t and source frame I'_s. In our experiments, the size of each small block $I \times J$ is set to 8×8, and the contrast limitation parameter β is set to 4. The entire enhancement process can be expressed as:

$$I'_t = \varepsilon(I_t), I'_s = \varepsilon(I_s) \tag{11}$$

Here, ε represents the mapping function for image enhancement. Therefore, we can obtain the reconstructed frame $\hat{I}'_t$ from I'_s:

$$\hat{I}'_t = s(I'_s, p_s) \tag{12}$$

In conclusion, our photometric loss function is modified as follows:

$$L'_P(I'_t, \hat{I}'_t) = \frac{\alpha}{2}(1 - SSIM(I'_t, \hat{I}'_t)) + (1-\alpha)\|I'_t - \hat{I}'_t\|_1 \tag{13}$$

From Fig. 4, it is visually evident that there is a significant improvement in the contrast of the final output image, especially in the region highlighted in the red box. Additionally, the background noise in the enhanced image is effectively constrained.

2.4 Loss Function

In summary, the expression for the total loss function is:

$$L_{total} = mL'_P + \rho L_S + \sigma L_D + \varsigma L_G \tag{14}$$

where ρ, σ and ς are hyperparameters. The parameter m is the auto-mask introduced following the approach proposed by Wang et al. [4].

3 Experiments

3.1 Datasets

Robotcar. The Oxford RobotCar Dataset [12] is a large autonomous driving dataset that includes driving videos captured under various environmental conditions. Following the setup in [4], we selected a portion of the '2014-12-09-13-21-02' and '2014-12-16-18-44-24' datasets as daytime and nighttime data, respectively. This resulted in approximately 41,000 images for training and 570 images for testing. To eliminate the influence of the car hood, we cropped the images to 1152×672.

nuScenes. nuScenes [13] is a large-scale outdoor autonomous driving dataset that comprises 1000 video clips captured in diverse road and weather conditions. This dataset is more challenging than RobotCar. We selected daytime and nighttime scenes from nuScenes, cropped the images to 1536×768, and utilized them for both training and testing.

3.2 Implementation Detail

Our model is trained for 50 epochs using the Adam optimizer on a single Nvidia Titan V. Our training process consists of two steps. Initially, we train the DepthNet Φ'_d using the daytime dataset. Subsequently, we train the entire network using the nighttime dataset, during which the DepthNet Φ'_d trained in the first step is frozen. The batch size is set to 4, and the learning rate is set to $1e^{-4}$. When training with the RobotCar dataset, the hyperparameters in the total loss are set as follows: $\rho = 1e^{-3}, \sigma = 2.5e^{-4}, \varsigma = 2.5e^{-4}$. When using the nuScenes dataset, they are set as: $\rho = 1e^{-3}, \sigma = 4e^{-4}, \varsigma = 4e^{-4}$. The input resolutions for RobotCar and nuScenes are 576×320 and 768×384, respectively.

3.3 Evaluation Results

Comparison with Prior Work. Table 1 presents the comparison results between our model and previous nighttime depth estimation methods. Figure 5 illustrates more visualization results. In the evaluation, the maximum depths for the RobotCar and nuScenes datasets are set to 40 m and 60 m, respectively. We reproduced the latest models RNW [4] and STEPS [5] on our own device, while the quantitative results for the remaining models follow those reported in previous papers [14]. Quantitative results (see Table 1) show that our model achieved SOTA performance on the RobotCar dataset and outperformed most competitors on the nuScenes dataset. Below, we select the Sq Rel metric as a representative error measure for analysis. In the RobotCar and nuScenes datasets, our method reduced the error of Monodepth2 [8] by 91.4% and 88.6%, while achieving a reduction of 15.5% and 0.7% compared to STEPS. Moreover, our model maintains a comparable level of accuracy to STEPS while exhibiting significantly lower complexity (see Fig. 1).

Figure 5 illustrates the qualitative comparison results between our model and others. All methods are trained on the same dataset, and the best checkpoints are utilized to generate depth maps. The red boxes highlight some regions with low-light conditions or overexposure, as well as moving cars. It can be observed that our model performs well

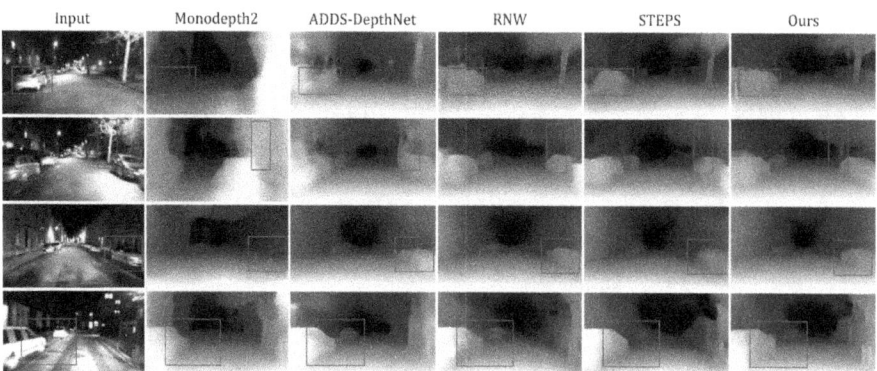

Fig. 5. Visualization results of the RobotCar dataset. Our model is compared with Monodepth2 [8], ADDS-DepthNet [14], RNW [4], and STEPS [5]. The leftmost column represents the RGB input image to the model.

Table 1. Quantitative results. We compare our model with previous SOTA methods on the RobotCar and nuScenes datasets. Smaller Depth Error is better, and higher Depth Accuracy is better.

Method	Depth Error($\downarrow$)				Depth Accuracy($\uparrow$)		
	Abs Rel	Sq Rel	RMSE	RMSE log	δ_1	δ_2	δ_3
RobotCar(Max Depth = 40m)							
Monodepth2 [8]	0.400	7.451	6.642	0.443	0.744	0.892	0.928
DeFeat-Net [15]	0.393	4.896	6.343	0.424	0.626	0.829	0.899
ADFA [16]	0.201	2.575	7.172	0.278	0.735	0.883	0.942
ADDS-DepthNet[14]	0.233	2.344	6.859	0.270	0.631	0.908	0.962
RNW [4]	0.124	0.712	3.368	0.172	0.876	0.961	**0.987**
STEPS [5]	0.121	0.757	3.321	0.173	0.878	0.959	0.983
Light-Dark(Ours)	**0.118**	**0.640**	**3.136**	**0.165**	**0.896**	**0.962**	**0.987**
nuScenes (Max Depth = 60m)							
Monodepth2 [8]	1.185	42.306	21.613	1.567	0.184	0.360	0.504
FeatDepth [17]	1.138	41.617	20.848	1.148	0.238	0.425	0.565
RNW [4]	0.371	5.956	11.261	0.432	0.499	0.767	0.879
STEPS [5]	0.348	4.873	**9.980**	0.425	**0.531**	0.765	0.886
Light-Dark(Ours)	**0.340**	**4.838**	10.136	**0.414**	0.526	**0.772**	**0.889**

in estimating the depth of objects in regions with low-light conditions or overexposure. Additionally, when facing moving objects like cars, our model can generate detailed contours.

Complexity and Speed Evaluation. We compared the complexity of the models, which includes the number of parameters and floating point operations (FLOPs). Table 2 illustrates that our model has significantly reduced the number of parameters by approximately 85% compared to previous models. Simultaneously, compared to recent nighttime models RNW and STEPS, our model achieves a significant reduction in FLOPs by 65.5% and 79.5%, respectively.

Considering limited computing resources in practical aplications, we ran our model on the edge device Jetson AGX Orin. Jetson AGX Orin is an embedded computing module introduced by Nvidia, offering various power modes. Generally, lower power consumption results in lower GPU and CPU frequencies, leading to slower inference speeds. We evaluated the average inference speed and frame rate of the model at different power levels and compared the results with those on Titan V. Table 3 displays the evaluation results on the nighttime test set of 411 images from RobotCar, where the first 10 images were used for warm-up and are not included in the statistics. Experiments indicate that our model achieves rapid inference across various power modes on edge

Table 2. Model complexity assessment. We compared the parameters and FLOPs during inference for each model, including the encoder, decoder, and full model. The input size is 576 × 320.

Method	Encoder		Decoder		Full Model	
	Params	FLOPs	Params	FLOPs	Params	FLOPs
Monodepth2 [8]	23.51M	15.18G	9.01M	9.82G	32.52M	25.00G
ADDS-DepthNet [14]	23.51M	15.18G	9.01M	9.82G	32.52M	25.00G
RNW [4]	23.51M	15.33G	9.33M	31.25G	32.84M	46.58G
STEPS[5]	23.52M	46.99G	9.33M	31.25G	32.85M	78.24G
Light-Dark(Ours)	**2.84M**	**6.47G**	**2.03M**	**9.60G**	**4.87M**	**16.07G**

Table 3. The evaluation of the average inference speed and frame rate for our model. The first three rows show the results under different power modes on Jetson AGX Orin, and the last row displays the results on Titan V. The batch size is set to 1.

Platform(Power Mode)	Input Size	Inference Speed	Frame Rate
Jetson AGX Orin (30W)	576 × 320	42.9ms	23.3 fps
Jetson AGX Orin (50W)	576 × 320	37.1ms	27.0 fps
Jetson AGX Orin (MaxN)	576 × 320	25.5ms	39.2 fps
Titan V	576 × 320	9.1ms	110.3 fps

devices. Even in the 30W mode, which operates at less than half of the maximum power consumption, the frame rate still meets the real-time requirement of 20 fps.

3.4 Ablation Study

We conducted ablation experiments on the RobotCar and nuScenes datasets, removing Feature-Fusion blocks, Cross-connections, and NCAIE modules from the Light-Dark model. The results in Table 4 show that each component enhances performance. Feature-Fusion blocks are crucial, as their removal increases Sq Rel by 18.8% (RobotCar) and 20.2% (nuScenes), highlighting their role in feature integration. The NCAIE module reduces the impact of inconsistent photometry and complex lighting, with Sq Rel increasing by 15.2% and 18.7% upon removal. Cross-connections facilitate feature propagation, with their removal leading to a 10.9% and 6.9% increase in Sq Rel.

Table 4. Quantitative results of ablation experiments on the RobotCar and nuScenes datasets.

Method	Depth Error(↓)				Depth Accuracy(↑)		
	Abs Rel	Sq Rel	RMSE	RMSE log	δ_1	δ_2	δ_3
RobotCar(Max Depth = 40 m)							
Light-Dark(Ours)	0.118	0.640	3.136	0.165	0.896	0.962	0.987
w/o Feature-Fusion	0.146	0.760	3.522	0.194	0.828	0.953	0.985
w/o Cross-conn	0.119	0.710	3.279	0.169	0.883	0.959	0.985
w/o NCAIE	0.138	0.737	3.418	0.189	0.850	0.956	0.983
nuScenes(Max Depth = 60 m)							
Light-Dark(Ours)	0.340	4.838	10.136	0.414	0.526	0.772	0.889
w/o Feature-Fusion	0.412	5.816	11.580	0.508	0.419	0.678	0.807
w/o Cross-conn	0.361	5.170	10.572	0.430	0.500	0.749	0.868
w/o NCAIE	0.374	5.741	10.578	0.429	0.498	0.758	0.882

4 Conclusions

In this paper, we propose a lightweight architecture for monocular depth estimation in nighttime conditions, named Light-Dark. We design a shallow DepthNet with low computational Feature-Fusion blocks and Cross-connections responsible for facilitating feature propagation. Considering the characteristics of nighttime scenes, we introduce the Noise-Constrained Adaptive Image Enhancement (NCAIE) module. Experiments demonstrate that Light-Dark achieves an excellent balance between model complexity and accuracy, making it particularly suitable for application on resource-constrained edge devices.

Acknowledgments. This work was supported by the National Natural Science Foundation of China under Grant 62071122, the Outstanding Youth Project of Guangdong Basic and Applied Basic Research Foundation under Grant 2023B1515020064, and the Key Research and Development Program Projects of Shaanxi Province under Grant 2024QCY-KXJ-168.

References

1. Ming, Y., Meng, X., Fan, C., Yu, H.: Deep learning for monocular depth estimation: a review. Neurocomputing **438**, 14–33 (2021)
2. Geiger, A., Lenz, P., Stiller, C., Urtasun, R.: Vision meets robotics: the kitti dataset. The Int. J. Robot. Res. **32**(11), 1231–1237 (2013)
3. Saxena, A., Sun, M., Ng, A.Y.: Make3d: Learning 3d scene structure from a single still image. IEEE Trans. Pattern Anal. Mach. Intell. **31**(5), 824–840 (2008)
4. Wang, K., Zhang, Z., Yan, Z., Li, X., Xu, B., Li, J., Yang, J.: Regularizing nighttime weirdness: efficient self-supervised monocular depth estimation in the dark. In: Proceedings of the IEEE/CVF International Conference on Computer Vision, pp. 16055–16064 (2021)

5. Zheng, Y., Zhong, C., Li, P., Gao, H.a., Zheng, Y., Jin, B., Wang, L., Zhao, H., Zhou, G., Zhang, Q., et al.: Steps: Joint self-supervised nighttime image enhancement and depth estimation. arXiv preprint arXiv:2302.01334 (2023)
6. Hu, J., Fan, C., Jiang, H., Guo, X., Gao, Y., Lu, X., Lam, T.L.: Boosting lightweight depth estimation via knowledge distillation. In: Jin, Z., Jiang, Y., Andrei Buchmann, R., Bi, Y., Ghiran, A.-M., Ma, W. (eds.) Knowledge Science, Engineering and Management: 16th International Conference, KSEM 2023, Guangzhou, China, August 16–18, 2023, Proceedings, Part I, pp. 27–39. Springer Nature Switzerland, Cham (2023). https://doi.org/10.1007/978-3-031-40283-8_3
7. Wofk, D., Ma, F., Yang, T.J., Karaman, S., Sze, V.: Fastdepth: Fast monocu- lar depth estimation on embedded systems. In: 2019 International Conference on Robotics and Automation (ICRA), pp. 6101–6108. IEEE (2019)
8. Godard, C., Mac Aodha, O., Firman, M., Brostow, G.J.: Digging into self-supervised monocular depth estimation. In: Proceedings of the IEEE/CVF international conference on computer vision, pp. 3828–3838 (2019)
9. Ali, A., et al.: Xcit: Cross-covariance image transformers. Adv. Neural. Inf. Process. Syst. **34**, 20014–20027 (2021)
10. Zhang, N., Nex, F., Vosselman, G., Kerle, N.: Lite-mono: A lightweight cnn and transformer architecture for self-supervised monocular depth estimation. In: Proceedings of the IEEE/CVF Conference on Computer Vision and Pattern Recognition, pp. 18537–18546 (2023)
11. Dosovitskiy, et al.: An image is worth 16x16 words: Transformers for image recognition at scale. arXiv preprint arXiv:2010.11929 (2020)
12. Maddern, W., Pascoe, G., Linegar, C., Newman, P.: 1 year, 1000 km: the ox-ford robotcar dataset. Int. J. Robot. Res. **36**(1), 3–15 (2017)
13. Caesar, H., et al.: nuscenes: A multimodal dataset for autonomous driving. In: Proceedings of the IEEE/CVF conference on computer vision and pattern recognition, pp. 11621–11631 (2020)
14. Liu, L., Song, X., Wang, M., Liu, Y., Zhang, L.: Self-supervised monocular depth estimation for all day images using domain separation. In: Proceedings of the IEEE/CVF International Conference on Computer Vision, pp. 12737–12746 (2021)
15. Spencer, J., Bowden, R., Hadfield, S.: Defeat-net: General monocular depth via simultaneous unsupervised representation learning. In: Proceedings of the IEEE/CVF Conference on Computer Vision and Pattern Recognition, pp. 14402–14413 (2020)
16. Vankadari, M., Garg, S., Majumder, A., Kumar, S., Behera, A.: Unsupervised monocular depth estimation for night-time images using adversarial domain feature adaptation. In: Computer Vision–ECCV 2020: 16th European Conference, Glasgow, UK, 23–28 Aug 2020, Proceedings, Part XXVIII 16, pp. 443–459. Springer (2020)
17. Shu, C., Yu, K., Duan, Z., Yang, K.: Feature-metric loss for self-supervised learning of depth and egomotion. In: Vedaldi, A., Bischof, H., Brox, T., Frahm, J.-M. (eds.) Computer Vision – ECCV 2020: 16th European Conference, Glasgow, UK, 23–28 Aug 2020, Proceedings, Part XIX, pp. 572–588. Springer International Publishing, Cham (2020). https://doi.org/10.1007/978-3-030-58529-7_34

Non-homogeneous Image Dehazing with Edge Attention Based on Relative Haze Density

Ruting Deng[1], Zhan Li[1(✉)], Yifan Deng[1], Hang Long[1], Zhanglu Chen[1], Zhiqing Kang[2], and Zhichao Qiu[3]

[1] Department of Computer Science, Jinan University, Guangzhou 510632, China
`lizhan@jnu.edu.cn`
[2] KingSoft Office Software, Wuhan, China
[3] Fesco Adecco Co. Ltd, Shenzhen, China

Abstract. Image dehazing is a widely used technology for recovering clear images from hazy inputs. However, most dehazing methods are designed to target a specific haze concentration, without considering the varying degrees of image degradation. Removing non-homogeneous haze from real-world images is challenging. To address this issue, this study proposes a dual-cycle framework based on relative haze density, in which inputs are regarded as both hazy images to be recovered by a restoration network (RNet) and clear images to be deteriorated by a degradation network (DNet). Edge attention blocks and multi-order derivative loss are proposed for RNet to enhance the details and colors. Furthermore, two multi-class discriminators are designed to distinguish between relative levels of haze density. Extensive experiments on both real-world and synthetic datasets demonstrate that the proposed method is superior to state-of-the-art approaches for non-homogeneous image dehazing using either supervised or unsupervised learning. This code is available at https://github.com/lizhangray/EARHD.

Keywords: Image Dehazing · Haze Density · Edge Attention · Multi-class Discriminator

1 Introduction

Images captured in hazy and foggy weather often suffer from color attenuation, limited visibility, and blurry edges, which adversely affect subsequent high-level computer vision tasks such as object detection, recognition, tracking, and semantic segmentation. Aiming to recover clear images from hazy inputs, image dehazing technology has broad application prospects.

Traditional prior-based methods approximate dehazed images according to the atmospheric scattering model [1] by incorporating handcrafted priors, such as the dark channel prior (DCP) [2] and non-local prior (NLP) [3]. However, these physical priors frequently result in inaccurate parameter estimation and unsatisfactory results [4, 5]. Recent advancements in deep learning have led to the development of learning-based methods [5–11] that have demonstrated remarkable performance in image dehazing challenges.

However, most networks have limitations in removing haze from real-world images with non-homogeneous haze [5, 10] because of their uniform processing of different haze densities without considering the diversity of image degradation.

In this study, we propose a dual-cycle framework for non-homogeneous image dehazing based on relative haze density. Because the haze concentrations are comparative, an input image is regarded as both a hazy image compared with clearer images, and a clear image compared with images with denser haze. As illustrated in Fig. 1, an image is always dehazed using a restoration network (RNet) and degraded using a degradation network (DNet). In cycle learning, image I_{in} is restored to a clear image I_{de}^A and then degraded to I_{cyc} in the upper branch, whereas it is degraded to an image with dense haze I_{add} and subsequently restored to a clear image I_{de}^B in the lower branch. Moreover, two multi-class discriminators, D_{clear} and D_{dense}, are designed to distinguish images with different haze levels generated by RNet or DNet, relative to clear or dense reference images. Furthermore, to recover details and colors, edge attention blocks and a multi-order derivative loss are proposed to construct and train the RNet, respectively. Guided by the dual-cycle framework, the RNet learns the image features of different degrees of degradation to remove thin or dense haze from the images.

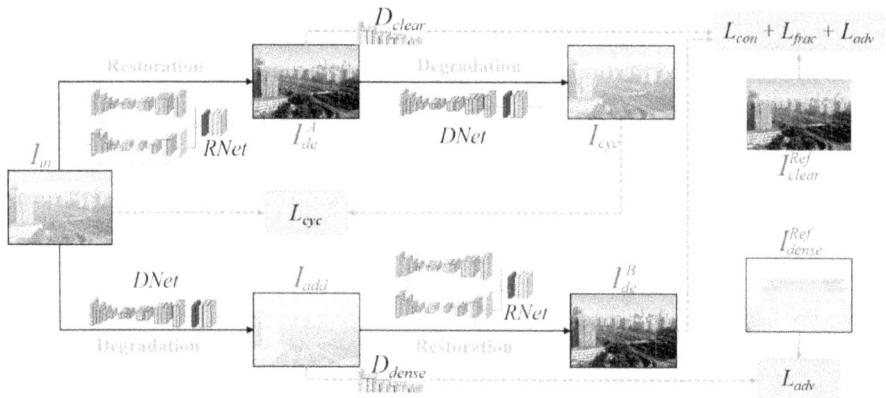

Fig. 1. Dual-cycle framework based on relative haze density.

The contributions of this study can be summarized as follows:

- We propose a dual-cycle framework based on relative haze density for non-homogeneous image dehazing, in which an input image is both dehazed by the RNet and added with haze by the DNet. The proposed framework is applicable for both supervised and unsupervised learning.
- We design an edge attention branch and a super-resolution branch to enhance details covered by haze. Moreover, we introduce a multi-order derivative loss to constrain dehazed images for recovering rich textures and bright colors.
- Distinguished from typical binary discriminators that determine if samples are real or fake, we design two novel multi-class discriminators to differentiate relative levels of haze density, which guide the RNet and DNet to produce haze-removed and haze-added images, respectively.

2 Related Works

Learning-based methods train neural network models to map hazy inputs to dehazed outputs in an end-to-end manner, divided into supervised and unsupervised dehazing.

Supervised dehazing networks learn from paired hazy and haze-free images to achieve an impressive performance. An all-in-one network for dehazing (AOD) [6] has been proposed to directly output clear images instead of estimating the parameters of the atmospheric scattering model [1]. A gated context aggregation network (GCA) [12] incorporates a gated sub-network for multi-scale feature fusion, which eliminates grid artifacts. A feature fusion attention network (FFA) [13] and an end-to-end network (T-Net) [7] have been proposed to overcome the bottleneck of conventional dehazing models using attention mechanisms. A fast dehazing model for 4K resolution images (4Kdehazing) [8] and a Laplacian pyramid dehazing network (LDN) [9] have been proposed to restore high-definition dehazed images. A trident dehazing network (TDN) [5] has been proposed as a coarse-to-fine model for automatic haze-density recognition. A knowledge transfer dehazing network (KTDN) [10] utilizes the teacher–student framework to calculate high-frequency features from hazy images. A principled synthetic-to-real dehazing (PSD) [4] network was pre-trained on synthetic datasets and fine-tuned to real-world images. A self-paced semi-curricular attention network (SCANet) [14] has been proposed to learn features between non-homogeneous haze and underlying scenes. An additional self-attention transformer (ASAT) [11] and a detail-enhanced attention network (DEA) [15] helps the model acquire more detailed information.

Dehazing methods based on unsupervised learning do not require paired haze-free images for training. Inspired by the CycleGAN [16], Cycle-Dehaze [17] employs a cycle structure and a perceptual loss constraint to train two generators. A deep DCP [18] network was trained by minimizing DCP-based loss. Visual quality-driven dehazing (VQDD) [19] combines deep and shallow features to compensate for the missing information. A zero-shot dehazing network named "you only look yourself" (YOLY) [20] combines three sub-networks to disentangle the parameters of the atmospheric scattering model. A self-guided disentangled representation learning (SGDRL) [21] model has been proposed to evaluate the degree of feature decomposition and guide the feature fusion for reconstruction. Although these models make improvements, they do not consider the impact of haze concentrations on image dehazing.

3 Proposed Method

3.1 Dual-Cycle Framework Based on Relative Haze Density

To learn image features with different degradation levels, this study proposes a dual-cycle framework that incorporates both supervised dehazing and unsupervised haze addition based on relative haze density. Considering the haze density as a relative variable, an image is recovered to a dehazed image by supervised learning, constrained by its corresponding clear reference image. Simultaneously, the image is degraded to a state containing dense haze through unsupervised learning using an unpaired reference image with dense haze, as illustrated in Fig. 1. In this dual-cycle framework, two networks, RNet and DNet, are employed for the restoration and degradation of images, respectively, and are trained and refined simultaneously.

Restoration Network. Figure 2 illustrates the architecture of the RNet, which consists of an edge attention (EA) branch, a super-resolution (SR) branch, and a feature compression (FC) module.

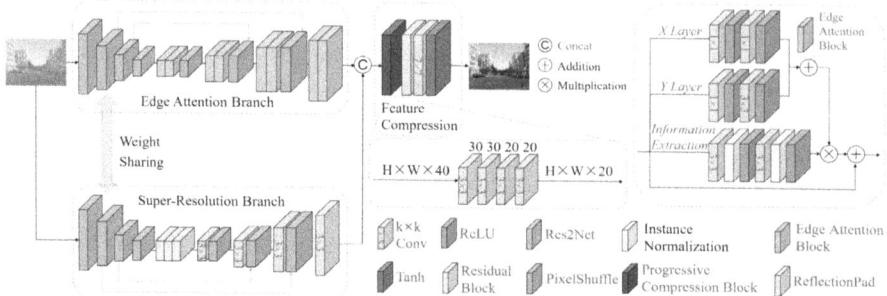

Fig. 2. Architecture of the restoration network RNet.

Edge Attention Branch. High-frequency components of images generally receive more attention, because they are related to rich and intricate details. Inspired by the Sobel edge detection operator [22] and attention mechanisms [13], we designed EA branch to capture more edges from hazy inputs. As illustrated in Fig. 2, an EA block comprises the X layer, Y layer, and information extraction layer with a residual connection. The X and Y layers are designed to learn the edge weights of the images in the X- and Y-directions, respectively. An EA map is produced by pixel-wise addition and multiplication of the outputs of the three layers. Composed of several EA blocks, the RNet is guided to focus on the edges.

Super-Resolution Branch. When training with high-resolution images, preprocessing steps including cropping and downsampling are commonly conducted to reduce the image size. However, these routines generally result in coarse textures and degrade the visual quality. To address this issue, we designed an SR branch to improve the resolution of the images and recover lost details. The SR branch adopts an encoder–decoder structure, wherein the encoder shares weights with Res2Net blocks in the EA branch, and the decoder incorporates three residual blocks and pixel shuffle layers [23].

Feature Compression Module. An FC module was designed to concatenate the feature maps produced by the EA and SR branches, producing a dehazed image. The progressive compression block is depicted in Fig. 2, where H and W are the height and width of the feature maps, respectively, and the number of convolution kernels is marked above each convolution layer, which has a stride of 1 and a padding of 1. Distinguished from commonly used post-processing blocks that compress channels of feature maps through a single convolution layer, the FC module compresses and merges features by progressive convolutions, which reduces information loss and enhances the capability of the feature representation of the RNet.

Degradation Network. Considering the function of the DNet, we constructed it as a simplified version of the RNet, which is composed of only the EA branch and the FC module of the RNet. DNet is trained to add haze to images, causing them to deteriorate from clear to containing thin haze or from containing thin haze to dense haze. The DNet is jointly trained with the RNet to enhance its performance, which removes haze at various concentrations from images.

3.2 Multi-class Discriminator

A discriminator was employed in the GAN to distinguish the real data from the results created by the generator. However, these binary classifiers are insufficient for categorizing images with different haze levels. To address this issue, we propose two multi-class discriminators: a clear image discriminator D_{clear} and a dense haze discriminator D_{dense}. Using adversarial learning, D_{clear} guides the RNet to generate clear images with lower haze concentrations and richer details. Conversely, D_{dense} guides the DNet to produce degraded images with higher haze density and lower clarity.

Figure 3 illustrates the structure of the D_{clear}. As the discriminator of the RNet, D_{clear} outputs the probabilities of four types of images: clear reference, input, dense haze reference, and dehazed image. Correspondingly, the discriminator of DNet, D_{dense} has the same structure as D_{clear}; however, it classifies the dense haze reference, input, clear reference, and haze-added images generated by DNet. Our ablation study demonstrates that employing multi-class discriminators improves the dehazing results because the capabilities of RNet and DNet are boosted.

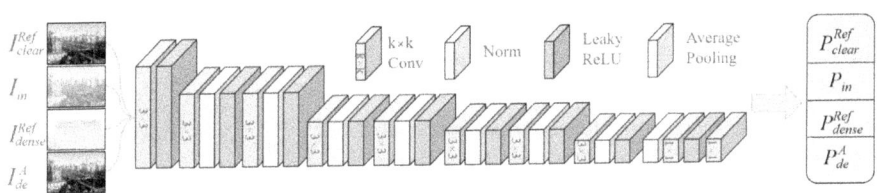

Fig. 3. The structure of a multi-class discriminator D_{clear}, which outputs the predicted probabilities of four types of input images.

3.3 Loss Function

In the proposed dual-cycle framework, our networks are trained by minimizing a total loss, which is a combination of the content (L_{con}), cycle-consistency (L_{cyc}), adversarial (L_{adv}), and multi-order derivative (L_{frac}) losses:

$$L_{total} = \lambda_1 L_{con} + \lambda_2 L_{cyc} + \lambda_3 L_{adv} + \lambda_4 L_{frac}, \tag{1}$$

where $\lambda_1, \lambda_2, \lambda_3, \lambda_4$ are the hyperparameters that balance the different losses.

Content Loss. The content loss is computed as the mean absolute errors between the clear reference image I_{clear}^{Ref} and the two dehazed images I_{de}^A and I_{de}^B generated by RNet, which are dehazed from the input and haze-added images, respectively. In this section, the images are labeled as shown in Fig. 1. N represents the number of training images.

$$L_{con} = \frac{1}{N} \sum_{i=1}^{N} (|I_{clear}^{Ref} - I_{de}^{A}| + |I_{clear}^{Ref} - I_{de}^{B}|). \tag{2}$$

Cycle-Consistency Loss. As illustrated in Fig. 1, $I_{in} \rightarrow I_{de}^{A} \rightarrow I_{cyc} \approx I_{in}$, where I_{cyc} is the hazy image degraded from dehazed image I_{de}^{A}. Therefore,

$$L_{cyc} = \frac{1}{N} \sum_{i=1}^{N} |I_{in} - I_{cyc}|. \tag{3}$$

Adversarial Loss. To distinguish clear images, the ratio of the clear image class is increased compared with the other three classes for training the multi-class discriminator D_{clear}, which is set as 3:1:1:1. Similarly, to train D_{dense}, the ratio is set to 1:1:3:1 to highlight the class of images with dense haze. For these two multi-class discriminators, cross-entropy (CE) loss is applied:

$$\begin{aligned} L_{adv}(D_{clear}) = &\tfrac{3}{4} CE(D_{clear}(I_{clear}^{Ref}), C_{clear}^{Ref}) + \tfrac{1}{4} CE(D_{clear}(I_{in}), C_{in}) \\ &+ \tfrac{1}{4} CE(D_{clear}(I_{dense}^{Ref}), C_{dense}^{Ref}) + \tfrac{1}{4} CE(D_{clear}(I_{de}^{A}), C_{de}^{A}), \end{aligned} \tag{4}$$

$$\begin{aligned} L_{adv}(D_{dense}) = &\tfrac{1}{4} CE(D_{dense}(I_{clear}^{Ref}), C_{clear}^{Ref}) + \tfrac{1}{4} CE(D_{dense}(I_{in}), C_{in}) \\ &+ \tfrac{3}{4} CE(D_{dense}(I_{dense}^{Ref}), C_{dense}^{Ref}) + \tfrac{1}{4} CE(D_{dense}(I_{add}), C_{add}), \end{aligned} \tag{5}$$

where C_x denotes the class of the corresponding image I_x; I_{dense}^{Ref} is the reference image with dense haze; and I_{add} is the image added with haze by DNet.

During the adversarial training process, RNet aims to generate I_{de}^{A} that approaches class C_{clear}^{Ref}, and DNet generates I_{add} that approaches class C_{dense}^{Ref}. The adversarial losses of RNet and DNet are defined as follows:

$$L_{adv}(RNet) = CE\left(D_{clear}\left(I_{de}^{A}\right), C_{clear}^{Ref}\right), L_{adv}(DNet) = CE(D_{dense}(I_{add}), C_{dense}^{Ref}). \tag{6}$$

Multi-order Derivative Loss. The integer-order derivatives of an image, such as Sobel (first-order) and Laplacian (second-order) operators, are commonly used for edge detection. By capturing both the edges and other information, fractional-order derivatives extract rich nonlinear features from images related to their contrasts, colors, and edges.

To better match dehazed images with clear images, we propose a multi-order derivative loss function based on the fractional-order derivative [24], which improves the visual quality of the dehazed outputs. The multi-order derivatives are computed using Tiansi convolution templates [25]. In addition, the fractional-order features of the dehazed images are constrained to be consistent with the clear images as follows:

$$L_{frac} = \frac{1}{N} \sum_{i=1}^{N} \sum_{v \in V}^{V} \left(\left| F_v\left(I_{clear}^{Ref}\right) - F_v\left(I_{de}^{A}\right) \right| + \left| F_v\left(I_{clear}^{Ref}\right) - F_v\left(I_{de}^{B}\right) \right| \right), \tag{7}$$

where N is the number of images; v represents the order of the derivative in the list of selected orders V; and F_v is the v th-order derivative convolution.

4 Experiments

4.1 Experimental Setup

Training Details. All the experiments were performed on an NVIDIA RTX3090 GPU using PyTorch 1.12.1. For data augmentation, rotations (90, 180, or 270°), horizontal flips, and cropping to a size of 512 × 512 were performed randomly for the training images. An Adam optimizer with settings $\beta_1 = 0.9$ and $\beta_2 = 0.999$ was employed to optimize the framework. The initial learning rate was set to 0.0001 and halved every 50 epochs. The parameters of the loss function were $\lambda_1 = 1.0$, $\lambda_2 = \lambda_3 = \lambda_4 = 0.1$.

Datasets. To test the dual-cycle framework by supervised learning, datasets NH-HAZE20, NH-HAZE21, and NH-HAZE23 [32] were used for non-homogeneous dehazing, which contain 55, 30, and 40 real-world image pairs of hazy and haze-free outdoor scenes, respectively. In addition to the original size, bicubic downsampling of 2× and 4× was also applied to the input images to evaluate the performance in dehazing for low-resolution hazy images. In particular, NH-HAZE23 is a high-definition image set containing images of extremely large size (6000 × 4000), which cannot be processed directly by most dehazing methods with the original size. Therefore, we only trained and tested the models on this dataset by downsampled images. To evaluate our method for unsupervised learning, we use three subsets of the benchmark dataset RESIDE [26]: the outdoor training set (OTS), synthetic objective testing set (SOTS), and hybrid subjective testing set (HSTS). Similar to most dehazing methods [4, 19, 21], our networks were trained on OTS and tested on outdoor scenes from SOTS and synthetic images from HSTS, which contain 500 and 10 hazy and haze-free image pairs, respectively.

4.2 Evaluation of Supervised Learning

Our method was compared with several state-of-the-art dehazing approaches, including DCP [2], AOD [6], GCA [12], FFA [13], KTDN [10], TDN [5], 4Kdehazing [8], SCANet [14], T-Net [7], LDN [9], ASTA [11], and DEA [15]. Two commonly used full-reference metrics were calculated: the peak signal-to-noise ratio (PSNR) [27] and structural similarity (SSIM) [28], which evaluate the recovery accuracy compared with the corresponding haze-free images. Meanwhile, no-reference indexes, namely the learned perceptual image patch similarity (LPIPS) [29] and fog aware density evaluator (FADE) [30], were used to measure the visual quality for real-world hazy images.

For a quantitative evaluation for real-world images with non-homogeneous haze, Tables 1 and 2 report the average metrics on the NH-HAZE series datasets. For a fair comparison, all the networks were retrained on the three NH-HAZE datasets. Notably, as indicated by the highest values in Table 2 and the best metrics in Table 1, our network generally outperforms other dehazing models for low-resolution images (sizes of 2× and 4× downsampling) with degradation introduced by both haze and downsampling. These experimental results demonstrate that our model is superior to its competitors in terms of dehazing performance, as measured by the FADE, recovery accuracy, as reflected by PSNR and SSIM values, and the perceptual quality as indicated by the LPIPS.

Table 1. Quantitative comparison of dehazing methods. **Bold** and underline indicate the rankings of 1st and 2nd, respectively. "↑" ("↓") indicates the larger (smaller) the better.

Method			DCP '10	AOD '17	GCA '19	FFA '20	4Kdehazing '21	T-Net '22	SCANet '23	LDN '24	ASTA '24	DEA '24	Ours
NH-HAZE20	1×	PSNR↑	13.28	16.00	17.00	18.16	17.37	19.06	19.50	17.79	18.85	19.39	**19.79**
		SSIM↑	0.479	0.533	0.559	0.638	0.469	0.644	0.650	0.618	0.652	0.656	**0.663**
		LPIPS↓	0.517	0.481	0.336	0.359	0.683	0.329	0.422	0.392	0.338	0.324	**0.304**
		FADE↓	0.358	0.595	0.492	0.298	0.530	0.331	0.306	0.318	0.311	0.318	**0.296**
	2×	PSNR↑	13.41	15.88	17.00	18.29	17.48	17.46	18.82	17.99	18.25	18.54	**19.66**
		SSIM↑	0.430	0.465	0.558	0.586	0.472	0.575	0.501	0.594	0.578	0.566	**0.607**
		LPIPS↓	0.643	0.634	0.507	0.555	0.682	0.526	0.602	0.505	0.585	0.537	**0.454**
		FADE↓	0.519	0.790	0.472	0.488	0.631	0.555	0.493	0.518	0.495	0.539	**0.459**
	4×	PSNR↑	13.22	15.61	17.63	16.96	17.21	16.35	16.97	16.15	16.57	16.52	**18.83**
		SSIM↑	0.337	0.362	0.447	0.432	0.406	0.424	0.343	0.437	0.416	0.395	**0.470**
		LPIPS↓	0.794	0.787	0.689	0.767	0.812	0.770	0.834	0.744	0.779	0.784	**0.666**
		FADE↓	0.819	1.167	0.736	0.839	0.875	0.911	0.955	0.719	0.885	1.017	**0.637**
NH-HAZE21	1×	PSNR↑	11.68	16.08	18.47	20.27	18.28	18.98	**21.12**	17.85	20.15	19.71	19.82
		SSIM↑	0.647	0.698	0.738	0.800	0.652	0.786	0.769	0.772	0.803	0.794	**0.814**
		LPIPS↓	0.448	0.378	0.327	0.264	0.548	0.259	0.364	0.310	0.275	0.281	**0.255**
		FADE↓	0.395	0.578	0.441	0.454	0.630	0.479	0.442	0.395	**0.355**	0.389	0.394
	2×	PSNR↑	11.80	15.83	18.55	19.29	18.00	18.60	**20.20**	17.77	19.53	19.22	19.56
		SSIM↑	0.564	0.597	0.672	0.690	0.600	0.678	0.555	0.614	0.694	0.660	**0.722**
		LPIPS↓	0.583	0.551	0.506	0.491	0.616	0.453	0.572	0.484	0.514	0.507	**0.439**
		FADE↓	0.491	0.725	0.592	0.519	0.702	0.583	0.651	0.517	**0.447**	0.439	0.473
	4×	PSNR↑	11.56	15.37	18.05	18.06	17.44	17.16	18.27	16.23	18.27	17.91	**18.80**
		SSIM↑	0.417	0.442	0.507	0.507	0.471	0.477	0.373	0.514	0.491	0.449	**0.530**
		LPIPS↓	0.761	0.756	0.711	0.748	0.792	0.742	0.868	0.721	0.775	0.791	**0.662**
		FADE↓	0.727	1.059	0.799	0.793	0.948	0.848	1.171	0.779	0.712	0.888	**0.693**

Table 2. Quantitative comparison of dehazing methods on NH-HAZE23 dataset.

Method		DCP '10	AOD '17	GCA '19	KTDN '20	TDN '20	4Kdehazing '21	T-Net '22	LDN '24	DEA '24	Ours
2×	PSNR↑	11.11	14.31	16.45	18.18	14.28	14.32	18.13	17.85	18.12	**18.19**
	SSIM↑	0.496	0.584	0.535	0.590	0.562	0.532	0.614	0.613	0.604	**0.620**
4×	PSNR↑	11.15	14.16	16.70	17.34	16.96	14.25	17.57	17.26	17.27	**17.79**
	SSIM↑	0.470	0.544	0.559	0.549	0.532	0.507	0.544	0.563	0.538	**0.565**

Figure 4 illustrates the dehazed images of the various methods when the input hazy image is downsampled by a factor of 2 (first two rows) and 4 (the 3rd and 4th rows), in which local regions in red boxes are enlarged below the global images. As shown in Fig. 4, DCP, 4Kdehazing, and LDN restores images with significant color distortions of the overall bluish, greenish, and reddish colors, respectively, whereas DCP, AOD, 4Kdehazing, and LDN suffer from insufficient haze removal. Generally, learning-based networks generate dehazed images of higher quality than prior-based models such as DCP. By employing the EA blocks, SR branch, and multi-order derivative loss, our RNet recovers the finest details and most vivid colors when the input images are degraded by both haze effects and downsampling.

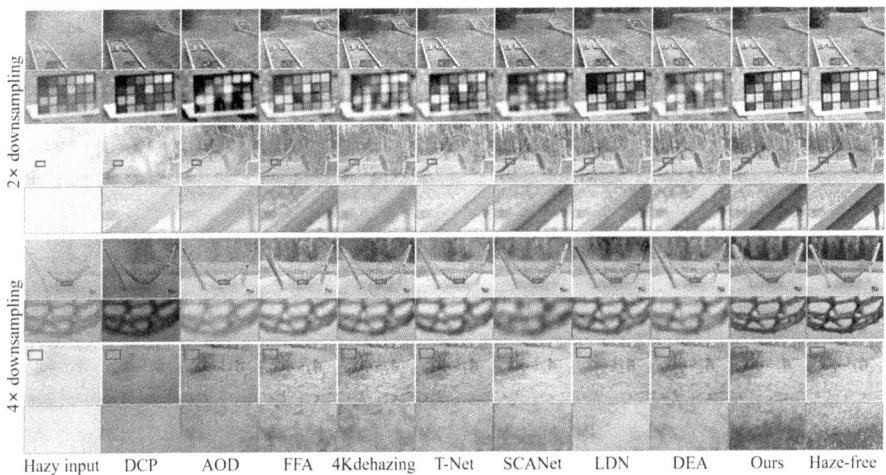

Fig. 4. Comparison of visual quality on the NH-HAZE20 and NH-HAZE21 datasets.

4.3 Ablation Study

To demonstrate the effectiveness of the components introduced in the proposed method, we conducted ablation experiments on the NH-HAZE20 dataset. The results are summarized in Table 3. Replacing the traditional channel attention (CA) or pixel attention (PA) with our EA blocks in RNet increases both PSNR and SSIM significantly, indicating a better quality of image recovery. Meanwhile, by gradually adding the SR branch, multi-class discriminator, and multi-order derivative loss, both metrics were further increased. The multi-class discriminator better constrains the types of output images, while the SR branch recovers lost details, resulting in better image quality restored by the RNet. Therefore, all the proposed components contribute to the performance improvement for haze removal from real-world images.

Table 3. Ablation study of components in our framework on the NH-HAZE20 dataset.

Components	Alternatives					
Attention block (CA/PA/EA)	CA	PA	EA	EA	EA	EA
SR branch	✓	✓	×	✓	✓	✓
Classification of discriminator	multi	multi	multi	binary	multi	multi
Multi-order derivative loss	✓	✓	✓	✓	×	✓
PSNR↑	18.12	17.66	19.08	19.36	19.51	**19.79**
SSIM↑	0.619	0.618	0.648	0.645	0.643	**0.663**

4.4 Evaluation of Unsupervised Learning

Based on prior knowledge, the proposed dual-cycle framework can be adapted for unsupervised learning by replacing the clear reference images. In our experiments, a simple yet effective linear function, i.e., Z-score normalization [31], was applied to the intensity of the pixels in a hazy image to produce a contrast-enhanced version of the input, as a substitute for the clear reference image in supervised learning.

Table 4 presents a quantitative comparison of the SOTS and HSTS datasets. Trained using hazy images with unpaired dense reference images, our network was compared with several prior-based, supervised, and unsupervised methods. The proposed method outperforms all others on the HSTS dataset and is the second best on the SOTS dataset for outdoor scenes, achieving impressive performance in terms of PSNR and SSIM.

Figure 5 presents an example in HSTS dataset, in which local regions are enlarged below. As shown in Fig. 5, methods of DCP, AOD, YOLY, and SGDRL output images too dark with a low saturation, whereas PSD produces a dehazed image too bright with significant color distortions. Notably, the output of ours is most approximate to the ground-truth haze-free image with clear edges and color fidelity.

Table 4. Quantitative comparison of dehazing methods on SOTS and HSTS datasets.

Method		Prior			Supervised			Unsupervised					Ours
		Z-score '07	DCP '10	NLP '16	AOD '17	PSD '21	Cycle GAN'18	Cycle-Dehaze'20	Deep DCP'20	YOLY '21	VQDD '23	SGDRL '24	
SOTS	PSNR↑	14.57	18.38	18.07	20.08	20.49	17.38	18.60	20.99	20.39	22.25	**23.28**	22.76
	SSIM↑	0.527	0.819	0.802	0.861	0.844	0.706	0.797	0.893	0.889	0.847	**0.919**	0.912
HSTS	PSNR↑	15.27	17.01	17.62	19.68	19.37	16.05	17.96	21.21	21.02	22.53	22.01	**22.91**
	SSIM↑	0.567	0.803	0.798	0.835	0.824	0.703	0.777	0.871	0.905	0.875	0.888	**0.909**

Fig. 5. Comparison of visual quality by unsupervised learning on the HSTS dataset.

5 Conclusion

This study proposes a dual-cycle framework based on relative haze density for non-homogeneous image dehazing, in which RNet and DNet are designed to remove and add haze. Composed of EA and SR branches and guided by multi-order differential loss, RNet recovers sharp edges and bright colors for haze scenes. Multi-classification discriminators are designed to distinguish the relative levels of haze density, helping RNet and DNet gradually learn the image features of different haze concentrations. Qualitative and quantitative evaluations of both supervised and unsupervised learning demonstrate the superiority of our method for image dehazing. In future work, we will extend the dual-cycle framework to other tasks such as low-light image enhancement.

Acknowledgments. This work was supported by the National Natural Science Foundation of China (No. 62071201), and the Guangdong Basic and Applied Basic Research Foundation (No. 2024A1515011762, No. 2022A1515010119).

References

1. Narasimhan, S.G., Nayar, S.K.: Chromatic framework for vision in bad weather. In: Proceedings of the IEEE Conference on Computer Vision and Pattern Recognition (CVPR), pp. 598–605. IEEE (2000)
2. He, K., Sun, J., Tang, X.: Single image haze removal using dark channel prior. IEEE Trans. Pattern Anal. Mach. Intell. 33(12), 2341–2353 (2010)
3. Berman, D., Treibitz, T., Avidan S.: Non-local image dehazing. In: Proceedings of the IEEE Conference on Computer Vision and Patter Recognition (CVPR), pp. 1674–1682. IEEE (2016)
4. Chen, Z., Wang, Y., Yang, Y., Liu, D.: PSD: principled synthetic-to-real dehazing guided by physical priors. In: Proceedings of the IEEE/CVF Conference on Computer Vision and Pattern Recognition (CVPR), pp. 7180–7189. IEEE (2021)
5. Liu, J., Wu, H., Xie, Y., Qu, Y., Ma, L.: Trident dehazing network. In: Proceedings of the IEEE/CVF Conference on Computer Vision and Pattern Recognition Workshops (CVPRW), pp. 430–431. IEEE (2020)
6. Li, B., Peng, X., Wang, Z., Xu, J., Feng, D.: AOD-Net: all-in-one dehazing network. In: Proceedings of the IEEE International Conference on Computer Vision (ICCV), pp. 4770–4778. IEEE (2017)

7. Zheng, L., Li, Y., Zhang, K., Luo, W.: T-Net: deep stacked scale-iteration network for image dehazing. IEEE Trans. Multimedia **25**, 6794–6807 (2023)
8. Zheng, Z., Ren, W., Cao, X., Hu, X., Wang, T., Song, F., et al.: Ultra-high-definition image dehazing via multi-guided bilateral learning. In: Proceedings of the IEEE/CVF Conference on Computer Vision and Pattern Recognition (CVPR), pp. 16180–16189. IEEE (2021)
9. Xiao, B., Zheng, Z., Zhuang, Y., Lyu, C., Jia, X.: Single UHD image dehazing via interpretable pyramid network. Signal Process. **214**, 109225 (2024)
10. Wu, H., Liu, J., Xie, Y., Qu, Y., Ma, L.: Knowledge transfer dehazing network for nonhomogeneous dehazing. In: Proceedings of the IEEE/CVF Conference on Computer Vision and Pattern Recognition Workshops (CVPRW), pp. 478–479. IEEE (2020)
11. Cai, Z., Ning, J., Ding, Z., Duo, B.: Additional self-attention transformer with adapter for thick haze removal. IEEE Geosci. Remote Sens. Lett. **21**, 1–5 (2024)
12. Chen, D., He, M., Fan, Q., Liao, J., Zhang, L., Hou, D., et al.: Gated context aggregation network for image dehazing and deraining. In: Winter Conference on Applications of Computer Vision (WACV), pp. 1375–1383. IEEE (2019)
13. Qin, X., Wang, Z., Bai, Y., Xie, X., Jia, H.: FFA-Net: feature fusion attention network for single image dehazing. In: Proceedings of the AAAI Conference on Artificial Intelligence, vol. 34, pp. 11908–11915. AAAI (2020)
14. Guo, Y., Gao, Y., Liu, W., Lu, Y., Qu, J., He, S., et al.: SCANet: self-paced semi-curricular attention network for non-homogeneous image dehazing. In: Proceedings of the IEEE/CVF Conference on Computer Vision and Pattern Recognition Workshops (CVPRW), pp. 1884–1893. IEEE (2023)
15. Chen, Z., He, Z., Lu, Z.M.: DEA-Net: single image dehazing based on detail-enhanced convolution and content-guided attention. IEEE Trans. Image Process. **33**, 1002–1015 (2024)
16. Zhu, J.Y., Park, T., Isola, P., Efros, A.A.: Unpaired image-to-image translation using cycle-consistent adversarial networks. In: Proceedings of the IEEE International Conference on Computer Vision (ICCV), pp. 2223–2232. IEEE (2017)
17. Engin, D., Genç, A., Kemal Ekenel, H.: Cycle-Dehaze: enhanced CycleGAN for single image dehazing. In: Proceedings of the IEEE Conference on Computer Vision and Pattern Recognition Workshops (CVPRW), pp. 825–833. IEEE (2018)
18. Golts, A., Freedman, D., Elad, M.: Unsupervised single image dehazing using dark channel prior loss. IEEE Trans. Image Process. **29**, 2692–2701 (2019)
19. Yang, A., Liu, Y., Wang, J., Li, X., Cao, J., Ji, Z., et al.: Visual-quality-driven unsupervised image dehazing. Neural Netw. **167**, 1–9 (2023)
20. Li, B., Gou, Y., Gu, S., Liu, Z., Zhou, T., Peng, X.: You Only Look Yourself: unsupervised and untrained single image dehazing neural network. Int. J. Comput. Vision **129**, 1754–1767 (2021)
21. Jia, T., Li, J., Zhuo, L., Zhang, J.: Self-guided disentangled representation learning for single image dehazing. Neural Netw. **172**, 106107 (2024)
22. Gao, W., Zhang, X., Yang, L., Liu, H.: An improved Sobel edge detection. In: International Conference on Computer Science and Information Technology, vol. 5, pp. 67–71. IEEE (2010)
23. Shi, W., Caballero, J., Huszár, F., Totz, J., Aitken, A.P., Bishop, R., et al.: Real-time single image and video super-resolution using an efficient sub-pixel convolutional neural network. In: Proceedings of the IEEE Conference on Computer Vision and Pattern Recognition (CVPR), pp. 1874–1883. IEEE (2016)
24. Podlubny, I., Chechkin, A., Skovranek, T., Chen, Y., Jara, B.M.V.: Matrix approach to discrete fractional calculus ii: partial fractional differential equations. J. Comput. Phys. **228**(8), 3137–3153 (2009)
25. Yang, Z., Zhou, J., Huang, M.: Edge detection based on fractional differential. J. Sichuan Univ. (Eng. Sci. Ed.) **40**(1), 152 (2008)

26. Li, B., Ren, W., Fu, D., Tao, D., Feng, D., Zeng, W., et al.: Benchmarking single-image dehazing and beyond. IEEE Trans. Image Process. **28**(1), 492–505 (2018)
27. Wang, Z., Li, Q.: Information content weighting for perceptual image quality assessment. IEEE Trans. Image Process. **20**(5), 1185–1198 (2011)
28. Wang, Z., Bovik, A.C., Sheikh, H.R., Simoncelli, E.P.: Image quality assessment: from error visibility to structural similarity. IEEE Trans. Image Process. **13**(4), 600–612 (2004)
29. Zhang, R., Isola, P., Efros, A.A., Shechtman, E., Wang, O.: The unreasonable effectiveness of deep features as a perceptual metric. In: Proceedings of the IEEE Conference on Computer Vision and Pattern Recognition (CVPR), pp. 586–595. IEEE (2018)
30. Choi, L.K., You, J., Bovik, A.C.: Referenceless prediction of perceptual fog density and perceptual image defogging. IEEE Trans. Image Process. **24**(11), 3888–3901 (2015)
31. Abdi, H.: Z-scores. Encycl. Meas. Stat. **3**, 1055–1058 (2007)
32. Ancuti, C.O., Ancuti, C., Vasluianu, F.A., Timofte, R., Zhou, H., Dong, W., et al.: NTIRE 2023 HR nonhomogeneous dehazing challenge report. In: Proceedings of the IEEE/CVF Conference on Computer Vision and Pattern Recognition Workshops (CVPRW), pp. 1808–1825. IEEE (2023)

Contrastive Learning for Silent Face Liveness Detection Based on A Hybrid Framework

Ying Tang[1], Zhongyue Chen[1], Minchao Ye[1], Zhaojuan Zhang[1], Yaping Qi[1], Huijuan Lu[1,2], and Wanli Huo[1(✉)]

[1] China Jiliang University, Hangzhou 310018, Zhejiang, China
huowl@cjlu.edu.cn
[2] Drore Information and Technology Co., Ltd., Hangzhou 310000, Zhejiang, China

Abstract. Face liveness detection is essential to ensuring the security of face recognition systems. Most current models rely on convolutional neural networks to achieve domain generalization through complete representations on common modules. The limitations of receptive field prevent model getting global context and capturing long-range dependencies, which ignores the global face semantic information and lacks the local focus of the face on more fine-grained features. To tackle these challenges, this paper proposes a silent face liveness detection domain generalization model based on the fusion of convolutional neural network (CNN) and Swin Transformer features, namely, CLCSN. Then, a contrastive learning technique is suggested to highlight liveness-related style aspects, which improves the generalization capacity, in order to generate a generalized representation. Experimental results demonstrate our approach's effectiveness in solving the face liveness detection domain generalization problems.

Keywords: Silent Face Liveness Detection · Domain Generalization · CNN-Swin Transformer · Contrastive Learning

1 Introduction

Recently, computer vision advancements have spurred widespread adoption of face recognition technology across real-world applications. However, presentation attacks (Pas) such as print attacks, video replay attacks, 3D masks, and potential future unknown attack methods are also emerging. To address these concerns, researchers have developed various face liveness detection (FLD) methods, ranging from those based on hand-crafted descriptors [1] to which based on deep representations [2].

Previous domain-specific FLD approaches have demonstrated high accuracy. However, they also exhibit significant degradation in performance when handling cross-domain data or facing novel adversarial attacks. The overfitting due to dataset bias limited by training dataset results in poor generalization to new domains. Domain Adaptation (DA) techniques [4] are employed to reduce distributional differences between source and target domains. However, in many FLD scenarios, collecting large amounts of unlabeled target data, specifically for spoofing attacks, is a challenging and costly task. Additionally, due to privacy concerns, it is typically hardly to access source face data when deploying FLD models in the target domain.

Therefore, the emergence of domain generalization FLD methods [5] solves above problems and ensures the validity of trained model across different domains. In researching domain generalization, it is assumed that the model is trained on datasets from D1 to DK and applied in a zero-shot manner to the unknown target domain dataset DK + 1. The model's insensitivity to domain changes allows it to be successful applicated in unknown domains.

The essence of FLD is to distinguish between real and fake faces, however, many current methods use domain generalization (i.e., CNN-BN-ReLU) on a common module. This approach does not fully consider local and global fine-grained features. Recent studies have utilized the Transformer architecture as the backbone for models employing FLD domain generalization. Since Transformers can provide larger receptive fields than CNN and are adept at capturing remote dependencies [8] and extracting global semantic features. Additionally, the authors [18] discovered reasonably high performance on domain generalization FLD using only a simple concentration loss to centrally embed real faces in space due to powerful entire face feature extraction of Transformer models.

We propose a new framework for FLD domain generalization. Considering that CNN has local relational coding characteristics which is better at extracting local fine-grained features, while Transformer is good at extracting global semantic information and capturing dependencies between long distances. We combine two frameworks, CNN and Swin Transformer, to extract global semantic face features while capturing local key features with differentiation. Therefore, this model can extract key facial features more accurately to classify facial images with unknown attacks. Discriminative information that enhances the distinction between living and spoofing is retained for extracted localized key information. A contrastive learning method is employed to reduce domain-specific style elements and emphasize liveness-related ones, which achieves the purpose of enhancing the generalization ability.

In comparison to previous domain generalization approaches, our contributions can be summarized as follows:

•We propose a novel network architecture that fuses CNN and Swin Transformer for silent face liveness detection.
•The local feature extraction network captures intrinsic detailed patterns by aggregating the intensity and gradient information, which improves the network's ability to discriminate between fine-grained images of faces.
•The proposed method involves comparing different features and placing emphasis on liveness-related style features. This effectively reduces the domain gap between similar samples, thereby enhancing the model's domain generalization capability.

2 Related Work

2.1 RGB Image-Based FLD

FLD methods are broadly classified into two types: traditional methods and methods based on deep learning. In the early stages of research, most traditional approaches heavily relied on manually designed local descriptors like local binary patterns [1] and directed gradient histograms [10]. However, handcrafted features have certain drawbacks such as limited generalization, time-consuming feature extraction, and applicability in specific scenarios only. Since the success of deep learning, CNN approaches have been widely used to solve liveness detection problems. Dual-stage Feature Learning FLD [12] model using generative adversarial training by removing deception traces from images, improving the interpretability of model decisions.

This paper aims to contribute to the field of domain generalization for silent face liveness detection. The aforementioned methods demonstrate satisfactory performance, but only in cases where the difference in distribution between the training and testing domains is relatively minor. As a result, many methods for domain generalization have been proposed. FGHV [13] was proposed with the aim of handling distributional shifts between real faces and known attacks. By utilizing Gaussian inputs to align the generated face features with the assumptions created by the feature generation network, FGHV aims to produce more robust and reliable features that can effectively counter attacks in unknown domains. IADG [14] introduced Asymmetric Instance Adaptive Whitening (AIAW), which improves the feature by adaptively whitening the feature correlations that are sensitive to the domains in question.

2.2 Transformers and FLD

Transformers are gaining popularity in computer vision and natural language processing (NLP). Dosovitskiy et al. [15] proposed the Vision Transformer (ViT) as a method for reducing processing resources and dividing an image into several small portions for projection onto a low-dimensional feature space. MobileViT [17] combines convolution and transformation in a single module to effectively collect local and global data. The model performs well even in shallow scenarios with this module, making visual translator more suitable for edge devices.

The transformer model has only been used in a few previous studies in FLD tasks. To avoid overfitting, Huang et al. [18] proposed a novel Multi-Level Attention Module DropBlock (MAMD) to enrich discriminative features while removing irrelevant spatial features. The enriched convolutional feature sets were combined and fed into the MTSS network for face spoofing. DiVT [9] used converter model to propose domain-invariant concentration loss and attack separation loss to deal with cross-domain FAS problem, which can achieve higher performance than previous methods on domain-generalized FLD problem with better resource consumption efficiency.

3 Method

3.1 Overview

In this section, we introduce our approach shown in Fig. 1. It avoids the interference of external ambient light by using the improved MobileNetV2 as backbone. A Swin Transformer-based network is also employed to facilitate the extraction of global key information. Its sophisticated sliding window module is utilized to effectively accomplish inter-pane interaction and global attention. Contrastive learning is applied to hide style information unique to a domain and highlight liveliness-related ones. In order to optimize the network for consistent and dependable training, the overall loss is finally integrated.

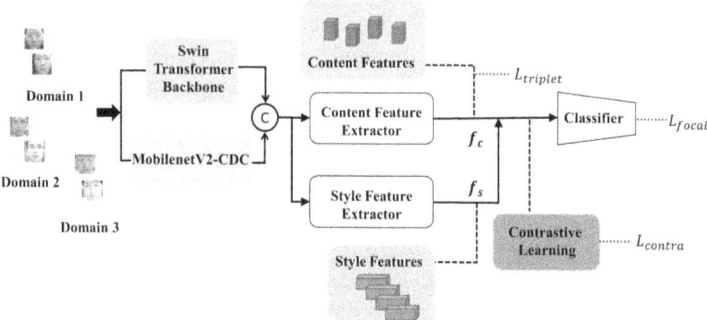

Fig. 1. The overall architecture of our Contrastive Learning based on CNN-Swin Trans-former network (CLCSN).

3.2 Network Architecture

Local Feature Extraction. Current algorithms used for the FLD (fine-grained texture description) task have faced challenges in adequately capturing detailed texture information and often exhibit instability when the environmental conditions, such as lighting levels, change. Our suggested local feature extraction network chooses mobilenetV2 [19] as CNN backbone, which combines Inverted Residuals and Linear Bottlenecks. The model complexity and training time by convolutional substitution while maintaining model performance to make it widely used in real-world scenarios. Specifically, the central difference convolution (CDC) [11] is utilized to replace depthwise separable convolution in mobilenetV2 due to its remarkable ability to represent invariant fine-grained features in different environments, especially its better robustness under ambient light changes. Without introducing any additional parameters, a central differential convolution network is formed with more powerful modeling capabilities as follows:

$$y(p_0) = \theta \sum_{p_n \in R} \omega(p_n) \cdot (x(p_0 + p_n) - x(p_0)) + (1 - \theta) \sum^{\omega}(p_n) \cdot x(p_0 + p_n) \quad (1)$$

where x, y is convolution input and feature map output, p_0 is current input position, p_n is the index of the current position as center neighborhood R, ω is convolution kernel, and θ is hyperparameter. The CDC degenerates into a simple convolution when θ is set to 0, indicating that CDC contains richer information than simple convolution.

Global Feature Extraction. The global feature extractor uses Swin Transformer as backbone in this study [16], which is a network model that includes shifted windows and hierarchical architecture. To achieve global modeling capability, shifted windows operation combines non-overlapping local windows with overlapping cross-windows. It significantly reduces computational load and captures face global features accurately. Patch Partition, Linear Embedding, and four stages make up the Swin Transformer. Multiple Patch Merging and Swim Transformer Block structures are included in each stage. As illustrated in Fig. 2, the output feature maps of Stages 2, 3, and 4 are H/8 × W/8 × 2C, H/16 × W/16 × 4C, and H/32 × W/32 × 8C, respectively. After each Patch Merging, the height and width are cut in half and the depth is doubled.

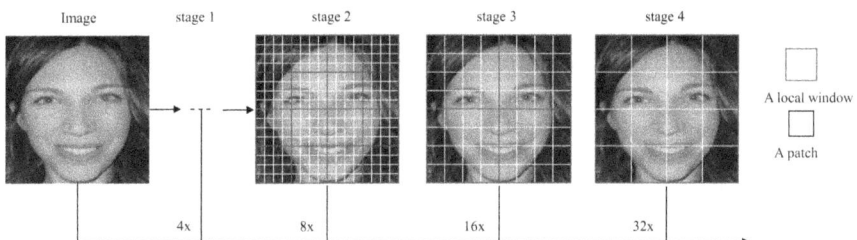

Fig. 2. Hierarchical feature map of Swin Transformer.

In FLD tasks, locating local key discriminatory information is essential. Self-attention or Multi-headed Self-attention (MSA) is used under the assumption that there is a correlation in any portion of the data. Through modeling this correlation, the complete face features can be obtained. Swin Transformer has superior performance in computer vision by using shifted windows instead of conventional Multi-head Self-attention (MSA). Before calculating W-MSA, the second Transformer module uses spatial shuffle, which can prevent the impact of data input order on network training effectively while simultaneously increasing network's randomness and improving its generalization. Shifted Windows Multi-Head Self Attention (SW-MSA) efficiently implements window interaction and global attention with linear computational complexity for image size and a more flexible hierarchical architecture.

Contrastive Learning of Features. One of key challenges when looking at local features is that in cross-domain scenarios, liveness-related style elements could be hidden by domain-specific elements, which could cause mistakes in judgment. We suggest a contrastive learning strategy to suppress domain-specific style elements and highlight liveness-related elements to figure out this problem. We aggregate extracted style and content features. The content features primarily capture physical and global semantic features, such as the size and shape of real or fake faces, which feature space with similar shared semantics. The style features maintain some discriminant information that can be used to improve differentiation between real and fake faces, and also describing certain distinguishing cues.

We hypothesize that, for content feature aggregation, there are only slight differences between attributes based on content information in different domains, but distributional differences between deceptive and real faces are large due to the complexity and variety of deceptive faces as well as various methods used in face database collection. In order to facilitate class boundary optimization for invisible target domains, we employ asymmetric triplet loss [20] to aggregate all real faces to make their distribution in the feature space more compact and to separate deceptive faces from various source domains in order to make their distribution more decentralized. The specific expression is as follows:

$$L_{triplet}(X,Y;G) = \sum_{\forall y_a = y_p, y_a = y_n} \left(G(x_a) - G(x_p)_F^2 - G(x_a) - G(x_n)_F^2 + m \right) \quad (2)$$

where $\|\cdot\|_F^2$ represents the square of Frobenius paradigm, m represents the boundary, x_a has the same label as the positive example x_p, but a different label than the negative example x_n.

Because style features with diverse scales, we use a pyramidal [14] strategy for style features aggregation in order to gather multi-layer features as well as hierarchical structures. For example, the scene brightness is mainly concerned with broad-scale features, while a rendered material texture usually focuses on local-scale regions.

For $f_c(x_i)$, we input it to classifier and supervise them using binary real signals with loss function L_{focal}. For $f_s(x_i)$, we use the cosine similarity to measure their difference from $f_c(x_i)$:

$$Sim(a, b) = -{a}/{\|a\|_2} \cdot {b}/{\|b\|_2} \quad (3)$$

where $\|\cdot\|_2$ is l_2-norm, a and b represent two compared features.

As shown in Fig. 3, content features are set as anchors in the style features space. Motivated by [21], a stop-gradient (stop-grad) operation is implemented to fix their position in the feature space. Then, face liveness information extracted from the feature network guides style features away from or close to their corresponding anchors. And this process further aggregates the style information associated with faces. Consequently, the contrastive loss is described as follow:

$$L_{contra} = \sum_{i=1}^{N} Eq(x_i, x_{i*}) \cdot Sim(stopgrad(a), b) \quad (4)$$

where $a = f_c(x_i)$ and $b = f_s(x_i)$. $Eq(x_i, x_{i*})$ measures the consistency of liveness labels between x_i and x_{i*}, which can be formulated as follows:

$$Eq(x_i, x_{i*}) = \begin{cases} +1, & label(x_i) == label(x_{i*}), \\ -1, & otherwise \end{cases} \quad (5)$$

Loss Function. Following the explanation of our network's operation, we gathered the total loss function for stable and reliable training to improve model generalization while addressing positive and negative sample imbalances, which is able to be expressed as follows:

$$L_{overall} = L_{focal} + \lambda_1 \cdot L_{triplet} + \lambda_2 \cdot L_{contra} \quad (6)$$

where λ_1 and λ_2 are hyperparameters used to balance the proportions of different loss functions. We substitute focal loss [22] function for cross-entropy loss function.

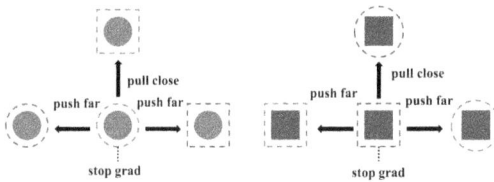

Fig. 3. The illustration of contrastive learning between different features.

4 Experiment

4.1 Datasets and Evaluation Metrics

Within-dataset type protocols, across-dataset intra-type protocols, within-dataset cross-type protocols, and across-dataset cross-type protocols have been developed to assess the efficacy of FLD approaches. In particular, the majority of procedures only include one or two datasets, which can make it more difficult to assess various data distributions. For this reason, the domain generalization performance across different domains is assessed using the OCIM protocol. To assess our method, we used four publicly available world-wide datasets: CASIA-FASD (C) [26], MSU-MFSD (M) [24], Idiap Replay-Attack (I) [27] and OULU-NPU (O) [28]. The quantity of real and fraudulent videos used in our studies is displayed in Table 1. Area Under Curve (AUC) and Half Total Error Rate (HTER) are evaluation metrics used in all of our experiments.

Table 1. Dataset

Dataset	Real videos	Fake videos
CASIA-FASD [26]	150	450
MSU-MFSD [24]	70	210
Replay-Attack [27]	140	700
OULU-NPU [28]	720	2880

4.2 Implementation Details

During the image preprocessing stage, we used all image data directly and employed MTCNN [23] method for face detection on all of the video frames. After that, we cropped facial region and resize it to 256 × 256 as RGB input. We used the same training setup as in [7], that is, randomly sampling one frame as training data from each video because variations between various frames in the videos are not very great. The equal quantity of fake and real data was sampled from all training datasets in every training phase. The proposed models are conducted on Pytorch platform and Ubuntu system, and all the experiments are conducted on a single NVIDIA GTX4090 GPU. The learning rate and weight decay parameters of 1e-4 and 5e-5 were used, respectively, the Adam optimizer was applied after pretraining model on ImageNet1K dataset.

4.3 Domain Generalized Evaluation

Experiment in Leave-One-Out (LOO) Setting. In order to evaluate method performance in Domain Generalization FLD for an overall evaluation, we perform cross-dataset testing using the LOO strategy: three datasets are selected for training and the others remain for testing. We follow this setting principle and show performance comparison between our method and previous competing methods (each dataset is represented using its prefix) in Table 2. The algorithm in this paper is compared with several representative traditional FLD methods in cross-domain FLD performances, including MS-LBP [1], Binary CNN [3], Auxiliary (Depth) [2] and IDA [24]. Performances of recent cross-domain face live detection techniques, including MADDG [6], ANRL [25], and FGHV [13]. Table 2 shows that the algorithm performance proposed in this paper provides more excellent results on four datasets in the cross-dataset scenario, which proves the domain generalization capability of our approach. We provide two figures to better illustrate our results, as shown in the figure of Figs. 4 and 5.

Table 2. The results of cross-dataset testing on OULU-NPU, CASIA-MFSD, Replay-attack, and MSU-MFSD.

Method	O&C&M to I		O&C&I to M		I&C&M to O		O&M&I to C	
	HTER	AUC	HTER	AUC	HTER	AUC	HTER	AUC
MS-LBP [1]	50.30	51.64	29.76	78.50	50.29	49.31	54.28	44.98
Binary CNN [3]	34.47	65.88	29.25	82.87	29.61	77.54	34.88	71.94
IDA [24]	28.35	78.25	66.67	27.86	54.20	44.59	55.17	39.05
Auxiliary [2]	29.14	71.69	22.72	85.88	30.17	77.61	33.52	73.15
MADDG [6]	22.19	84.99	17.69	88.06	27.98	80.02	24.50	84.51
ANRL [25]	16.03	91.04	10.83	96.75	15.67	91.90	17.85	89.26
FGHV [13]	9.17	96.92	12.47	93.47	16.29	90.11	13.59	93.55
Ours	8.16	98.99	7.39	97.66	13.39	93.10	9.46	96.98

Experiment on Limited Source Domains. In this experiment, the algorithms will be evaluated under challenging conditions where the available source domains are extremely limited. Specifically, a smaller training dataset will be used for evaluation purposes, selecting MSU-MFSD and Replay-Attack as the source domains for training. The remaining two domains, CASIA-MFSD and OULU-NPU, will serve as the target domains for testing the algorithms. As shown in Table 3, despite the limited source data, the algorithm proposed in this paper still performs well in more challenging situations. These results strongly verify our network generalization on invisible target domain.

Table 3. Comparison results on limited source domains.

Methods	M&I to C		M&I to O	
	HTER	AUC	HTER	AUC
ANRL [26]	31.06	72.12	30.73	74.10
SSAN-M [5]	30.00	76.20	29.44	76.62
Ours	29.43	79.13	27.35	79.48

4.4 Ablation Study

To demonstrate the superiority of our CLCSN and evaluate the impact of each component, we constructed several incomplete models by varying different variables. All results were measured using the same method, as depicted in Table 4.

Table 4. Evaluations of different components for the method with different architectures.

Method	O&C&M to I		O&C&I to M		I&C&M to O		O&M&I to C	
	HTER	AUC	HTER	AUC	HTER	AUC	HTER	AUC
CLCSN w/o CDC	9.64	94.87	8.24	95.54	14.41	91.94	10.67	94.58
CLCSN w/o Swin Transformer	10.36	93.14	10.37	94.91	15.59	91.39	12.33	93.97
CLCSN w/o L_{contra}	9.49	95.42	9.54	95.24	15.36	91.27	11.67	94.78
Ours (CLCSN)	8.16	98.99	7.39	97.66	13.39	93.10	9.46	96.98

Effectiveness of Different Components. We performed ablation experiments on different backbone branches and components using publicly available datasets to give a thorough and efficient evaluation of our approach. At first, we performed CLCSN w/o CDC experiments. Specifically, the improved CNN network is more conducive to emphasizing local face information through the incorporation of CDC. The CNN is more efficient in capturing fine-grained face features, which is essential for FLD systems deployed in real-world application scenarios. Then, we performed CLCSN w/o Swin Transformer tests to illustrate the significance of the sliding window in the Swin Transformer module and to realize the interaction between panes and the global attention for global feature capture. Quantitative results show that the global feature extraction network using Swin Transformer as backbone is beneficial to improve performance of cross-domain FLD task.

Analysis of Contrastive Learning. The approach in this paper is to perform contrastive learning between global style features and local content features. In previous work, all FLD implemented classical supervised contrastive learning (SCL) on complete representations (CNN-BN-ReLU). To compare them, we conducted w/o L_{contra} experiments. The final experimental results show the effectiveness of the feature space constructed by content features and style features in contrastive learning.

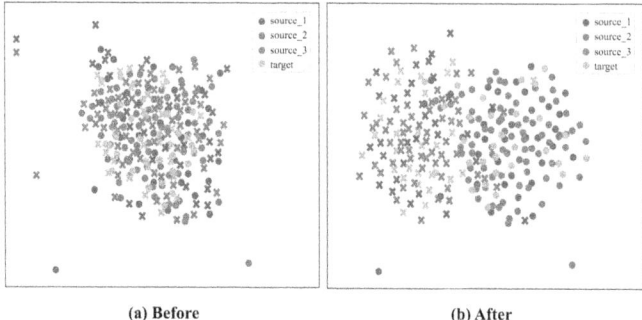

Fig. 4. The various features under protocol O&C&I to M are visualized using t-SNE.

Fig. 5. Feature maps generated at different stages. (a): Original images. (b): Visualizations for content features generation. (c): Visualizations for content and style features generation.

5 Conclusion

In this work, we have proposed a generalizable silent face liveness detection contrastive learning network that combined CNN and Swin Transformer. The enhanced CNN and Swin transformer model were in charge of extracting global semantic features and local fine-grained features, respectively. We used central difference convolution to reduce the impact of ambient light on feature extraction. Considering the attributes of content and style features were distinct, we treated them separately from the prior complete implementation of domain generalization strategy on the common module. For content features, we used asymmetric triplet loss to make them more compact in feature space and promote class boundary optimization in invisible target domain. For style features, to highlight liveliness-related style features, a contrastive learning technique was applied. Experiments conducted using current assessment standards showed our method's superiority.

Acknowledgments. his work was supported by research fundings from National Science Foundation of China (No.82303675, No.61272315 and No.12305404), the National Key R&D Program of China (No.2023YFF0613504), Zhejiang Provincial Major Science and Technology Project (No.2023C01040), Natural Science Foundation of Zhejiang Province (No. LY21F020028, No. LY22F010010 and No. LQ22F020021), Fundamental Research Funds for the Provincial Universities of Zhejiang (No. 2022YW52) and National Platform for basic conditions of science and technology (No.APT2301–7).

Disclosure of Interests. Disclosure of interests. the authors have no competing interests to declare that are relevant to the content of this article.

References

1. Määttä, J., Hadid, A., Pietikäinen, M.: Face spoofing detection from single images using micro-texture analysis. In: 2011 International Joint Conference on Biometrics (IJCB), pp. 1–7. IEEE (2011)
2. Liu, Y., Jourabloo, A., Liu, X.: Learning deep models for face anti-spoofing: Binary or auxiliary supervision. In: Proceedings of the IEEE Conference on Computer Vision and Pattern Recognition, pp. 389–398. IEEE (2018)
3. Yang, J., Lei, Z., Li, S. Z.: Learn convolutional neural network for face anti-spoofing. arxiv preprint arxiv: 1408.5601 (2014)
4. Li, H., Li, W., Cao, H., Wang, S., Huang, F., Kot, A.C.: Unsupervised domain adaptation for face anti-spoofing. IEEE Trans. Inform. Forens. Secur. **13**(7), 1794–1809 (2018)
5. Wang, Z., Wang, Z., Yu, Z., Deng, W., Li, J., Gao, T., Wang, Z.: Domain generalization via shuffled style assembly for face anti-spoofing. In: Proceedings of the IEEE/CVF Conference on Computer Vision and Pattern Recognition, pp. 4123–4133. IEEE (2022)
6. Shao, R., Lan, X., Li, J., Yuen, P.C.: Multi-adversarial discriminative deep domain generalization for face presentation attack detection. In: Proceedings of the IEEE/CVF Conference on Computer Vision and Pattern Recognition, pp. 10023–10031. IEEE (2019)
7. Jia, Y., Zhang, J., Shan, S., Chen, X.: Single-side domain generalization for face anti-spoofing. In: Proceedings of the IEEE/CVF Conference on Computer Vision and Pattern Recognition, pp. 8484–8493. IEEE (2020)
8. Muzammal, N.M.: Intriguing properties of vision transformers. Adv. Neural Info. Process. Syst. **34** (2021)
9. Liao, C. H., Chen, W. C., Liu, H. T., Yeh, Y. R., Hu, M. C., Chen, C. S.: Domain invariant vision transformer learning for face anti-spoofing. In: Proceedings of the IEEE/CVF Winter Conference on Applications of Computer Vision, pp. 6098–6107. IEEE (2023)
10. Komulainen, J., Hadid, A., Pietikäinen, M.: Context based face anti-spoofing. In: 2013 IEEE Sixth International Conference on Biometrics: Theory, Applications and Systems (BTAS), pp. 1–8. IEEE (2013)
11. Yu, Z., Zhao, C., Wang, Z., Qin, Y., Su, Z., Li, X., Zhou, F., Zhao, G.: Searching central difference convolutional networks for face anti-spoofing. In: Proceedings of the IEEE/CVF Conference on Computer Vision and Pattern Recognition, pp. 5295–5305. IEEE (2020)

12. Wang, Y.C., Wang, C.Y., Lai, S.H.: Disentangled representation with dual-stage feature learning for face anti-spoofing. In: Proceedings of the IEEE/CVF Winter Conference on Applications of Computer Vision, pp. 1955–1964. IEEE (2022)
13. Liu, S., Lu, S., Xu, H., Yang, J., Ding, S., Ma, L.: Feature generation and hypothesis verification for reliable face anti-spoofing. Proc. AAAI Conf. Intell. **36**(2), 1782–1791 (2022)
14. Zhou, Q., Zhang, K.Y., Yao, T., Lu, X., Yi, R., Ding, S., Ma, L.: Instance-aware domain generalization for face anti-spoofing. In: Proceedings of the IEEE/CVF Conference on Computer Vision and Pattern Recognition, pp. 20453–20463. IEEE (2023)
15. Dosovitskiy, A., et al.: An image is worth 16×16 words: Transformers for image recognition at scale. arxiv preprint arxiv: 2010.11929 (2020)
16. Liu, Z., et al.: Swin transformer: Hierarchical vision transformer using shifted windows. In: Proceedings of the IEEE/CVF International Conference on Computer Vision, pp. 10012–10022. IEEE (2021)
17. Mehta, S., Rastegari, M.: Mobilevit: Light-weight, general-purpose, and mobile-friendly vision transformer. arxiv 2021. arxiv preprint arxiv: 2110.02178. IEEE (2021)
18. Huang, Y.H., Hsieh, J.W., Chang, M.C., Ke, L., Lyu, S., Santra, A.S.: Multi-teacher single-student visual transformer with multi-level attention for face spoofing detection. In: BMVC, p. 125. IEEE (2021)
19. Sandler, M., Howard, A., Zhu, M., Zhmoginov, A., Chen, L.C.: Mobilenetv2: Inverted residuals and linear bottlenecks. In: Proceedings of the IEEE Conference on Computer Vision and Pattern Recognition, pp. 4510–4520. IEEE (2018)
20. Schroff, F., Kalenichenko, D., Philbin, J.: Facenet: A unified embedding for face recognition and clustering. In: Proceedings of the IEEE Conference on Computer Vision and Pattern Recognition, pp. 815–823. IEEE (2015)
21. Chen, X., He, K.: Exploring simple siamese representation learning. In: Proceedings of the IEEE/CVF Conference on Computer Vision and Pattern Recognition, pp. 15750–15758. IEEE (2021)
22. Lin, T. Y., Goyal, P., Girshick, R., He, K., Dollár, P.: Focal loss for dense object detection. In: Proceedings of the IEEE International Conference on Computer Vision, pp. 2980–2988. IEEE (2017)
23. Xiang, J., Zhu, G.: Joint face detection and facial expression recognition with MTCNN. In: 2017 4th International Conference on Information Science and Control Engineering (ICISCE), pp. 424–427. IEEE (2017)
24. Wen, D., Han, H., Jain, A.K.: Face spoof detection with image distortion analysis. IEEE Trans. Inform. Forensic. Secur. **10**(4), 746–761 (2015)
25. Liu, S., et al.: Adaptive normalized representation learning for generalizable face anti-spoofing. In: Proceedings of the 29th ACM International Conference on Multimedia, pp. 1469–1477. IEEE (2021)
26. Zhang, Z., Yan, J., Liu, S., Lei, Z., Yi, D., Li, S.Z.: A face antispoofing database with diverse attacks. In: 2012 5th IAPR International Conference on Biometrics (ICB), pp. 26–31. IEEE (2012)
27. Chingovska, I., Anjos, A., Marcel, S.: On the effectiveness of local binary patterns in face anti-spoofing. In: 2012 BIOSIG-Proceedings of the International Conference of Biometrics Special Interest Group (BIOSIG), pp. 1–7. IEEE (2012)
28. Boulkenafet, Z., Komulainen, J., Li, L., Feng, X., Hadid, A.: Oulu-npu: A mobile face presentation attack database with real-world variations. In: 2017 12th IEEE International Conference on Automatic Face & Gesture Recognition (FG 2017), pp. 612–618. IEEE (2017)

BS2CL: Balanced Self-supervised Contrastive Learning for Thyroid Cytology Whole Slide Image Multi-classification

Wensi Duan[1], Juan Liu[1(✉)], Lang Wang[1], Yu Jin[1], Peng Jiang[1], Cheng Li[2], Dehua Cao[2], and Baochuan Pang[2]

[1] Institute of Artificial Intelligence, School of Computer Science, Wuhan University, Wuhan, China
liujuan@whu.edu.cn
[2] Landing Artificial Intelligence Center for Pathological Diagnosis, Wuhan, China

Abstract. Thyroid cytology whole slide images (WSIs) hold vital information essential for precise diagnosis. Given the huge size of WSIs, multiple instance learning (MIL) is an effective solution for the WSI classification task when only slide-level labels are accessible. The embedding-based MIL uses a feature extractor pretrained with the self-supervised contrastive learning framework to eliminate the dependence on patch-level labels. However, the distribution of class in thyroid patches is unbalanced, and most existing self-supervised contrastive learning methods take little account of the data imbalance, which makes the features not discriminative enough. To address this problem, we propose a novel balanced self-supervised contrastive learning (BS2CL) framework for pretraining. It first clusters the patches to preserve the class structure of the patches and then assigns the clustering centers to a set of pre-computed uniformly distributed optimal locations. This constraint creates a more uniform distribution of different classes in the feature space which leads to clearer class boundaries between different classes, an unbiased feature space, and more discriminative features. Furthermore, a bag-level data augmentation strategy is introduced to increase bag quantities and improve classification performance. Extensive experiments show that the proposed method outperforms other latest methods on the thyroid cytology WSI dataset.

Keywords: Whole Slide Image · Thyroid Cytology · Self-Supervised Contrastive Learning · Multiple Instance Learning

1 Introduction

Thyroid cancer has seen the fastest growth in incidence of any malignancy worldwide in recent years, and this rising trend continues [1]. Fine-needle aspiration biopsy (FNAB) is the most commonly used preoperative diagnostic technique for thyroid malignancies [2]. Cytopathologists look at the morphology of cells on a liquid-based preparation slide collected by FNAB using a microscope and make a diagnostic classification according to the Thyroid Bethesda System (TBS) [3]. TBS is the universally recognized system for reporting thyroid FNAB, and it is structured into six distinctive categories, from TBS1 to TBS6. TBS 1 is assigned to inadequately prepared slides and is beyond the scope of this work. TBS 2 suggests benign conditions. The next categories, TBS 3 to 5, indicate abnormalities, which escalate from mild to severe as the category number increases. Lastly, TBS 6 is indicative of malignancy. However, the examination process for professional cytopathologists is both time-consuming and strenuous. Additionally, the complex nature of biological specimens results in a certain level of subjectivity and non-repeatability. To improve diagnostic efficiency and accuracy, computer-aided diagnosis is critically important. The development of digital pathology and the widespread adoption of whole slide imaging (WSI) make it possible to employ computerized methods for diagnostic assistance. This can provide more objective and repeatable results and substantially ease the cytopathologists' workload.

Due to the high pixel count of WSIs, reaching up to a trillion, it's hard to analyze a WSI directly limited by computational resources. A common process is to divide a WSI into smaller images called patches. Many studies are based on labeled patches [4–7], and tend to focus on a specific disease like papillary thyroid carcinoma [6, 7]. As for thyroid WSI classification, most approaches follow the multiple instance learning (MIL) setting to the natural structure of WSIs. WSIs serve as labeled bags, while the extracted patches function as the unlabeled instances within these bags. MIL could be modeled in two ways: 1) instance-based approach [8, 9]. Instances are first assigned pseudo-labels or are labeled to train an instance-level classifier in a supervised manner and the instance-level classification aggregates the bag-level classification results. 2) embedding-based approach [10, 11]. Instances are first mapped to feature embeddings through a feature extractor. The instance-level embeddings are then aggregated into a bag-level feature embedding for classification through MIL pooling operators which are typically the mean pooling or max pooling operator, while the latter is mostly used [12–15].

Instance-level labeling is a prerequisite for instance-based MIL, however, the large size of WSI makes the process of detailed annotation both costly and time-consuming. Additionally, the accuracy of diagnosis is heavily dependent on the clinical expertise and medical insight of cytopathologists. For embedding-based MIL, training a feature extractor in an unsupervised way removes the dependency on instance-level labels. Self-supervised contrastive learning has grown rapidly in recent years, even outperforming supervised learning methods. However, most embedding-based MIL methods directly use existing self-supervised contrastive learning frameworks like SimCLR [16], MoCo [17] and DINO [18]. Classical self-supervised contrastive learning explicitly pulls the representations of different transformations or views of the same instance closer and pushes the representations of different instances apart. This may lead to distances of instances belonging to the same class being pulled apart. What's more, these frameworks are pretrained on the class-balanced ImageNet dataset [19] and fail to learn discriminative features when the dataset is imbalanced [20]. Classes with high numbers can dominate the feature space, leading to unclear class boundaries. Figure 1 shows the class distribution of 41077 randomly selected instances annotated by cytopathologists. In a thyroid WSI, the class distribution of follicular cells or clusters is unbalanced but the critical classes for classification tend to be few.

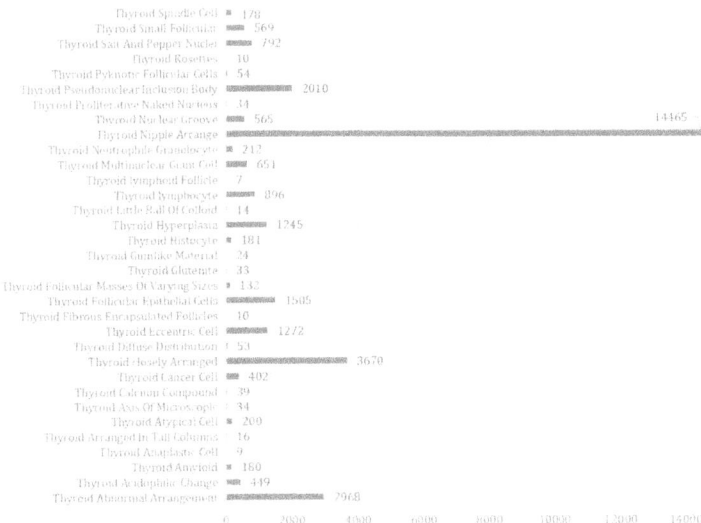

Fig. 1. The class distribution of follicular cells or clusters from 41077 randomly selected instances.

In this paper, we propose a novel **b**alanced **s**elf-**s**upervised **c**ontrastive **l**earning (**BS2CL**) framework based on clustering. When pretraining the feature extractor, we cluster all the instance features and treat each cluster as a class to form the contrastive loss that preserves the semantic structure among instances. Meanwhile, we match the cluster centers to the optimal locations that are generated in advance. These locations are uniformly distributed in the feature space to avoid the feature space being biased and dominated by classes with high numbers. Moreover, deep learning networks are inherently data-intensive, exhibiting enhanced performance metrics when trained on extensive and heterogeneous annotated data which are expensive to collect especially for thyroid cytology WSIs. Therefore, we propose a bag-level data augmentation strategy that amplifies the volume of bags and further improves the utilization of instance features and classification performance. The contributions of this study are as follows:

1) We propose a novel balanced self-supervised contrastive learning framework that captures the implicit semantic structure of instances and avoids the biased feature space.
2) We introduce a bag-level data augmentation strategy to expand the count of thyroid WSIs and improve classification performance further.
3) We further show that our method achieves state-of-the-art thyroid cytology WSI classification performance on the in-house dataset.

2 Related Work

2.1 Self-Supervised Contrastive Learning in MIL

Self-supervised contrastive learning methods have shown promising results in medical imaging [21, 22] and most MIL methods utilize available networks like SimCLR [16], MoCo [17] and DINO [18] For instance, Li *et al.* [21] applied SimCLR [16] as a feature extractor for WSI classification following the MIL setting. Yet existing self-supervised contrastive learning methods are pretrained on class-balanced datasets such as ImageNet [19] while the instances of the thyroid WSI dataset are unbalanced which may lead to significant drops in performance. To address this problem, we propose a novel BS2CL framework that balances the feature space and makes the class boundaries clearer.

2.2 Thyroid Cytology WSI Classification

Most methods for thyroid WSI classification follow the MIL setting and can be classified into instance-based methods [8, 9] and embedding-based methods [10, 11]. Instance-based methods focus on training an instance-level classifier and studying the instance-level informativeness. For example, Dov *et al.* propose a maximum likelihood estimation to analyze the instances' contribution beyond the MIL setting [9]. These methods are limited by their dependence on instance-level labels. Using a pretrained feature extractor, embedding-based methods only require WSI labels. However, most works ignore the importance of data augmentation while it's expensive to collect and annotate thyroid WSIs (bags). In this paper, we propose a bag-level data augmentation strategy that increases the quantity of bags.

3 Method

This section introduces our method for thyroid cytology WSI classification including the BS2CL framework and the bag-level data augmentation strategy.

3.1 Preliminary: Problem Description

Given a dataset composed of N thyroid WSIs $W = \{W_1, W_2 \cdots W_N\}$, where each W_i is associated with a corresponding label $Y_i \in \{2, 3, 4, 5, 6\}$ which indicates the TBS category annotated by a cytopathologist. W_i is patched into a bag of small patches (instances) $W_i = \{x_{i,j}, j \in \{1, 2, \ldots n_i\}\}$ without overlapping where n_i is the number of patches in the i-th WSI. Our goal is to predict the label $\widehat{Y}_i$ of W_i, given by:

$$\widehat{Y}_i = c(g(f(x_{i,1}), f(x_{i,2}), \ldots, f(x_{i,j}), \ldots, f(x_{i,n_i}))) \quad (1)$$

where $f(\cdot)$ is the pretrained feature extractor that corresponds to the proposed BS2CL framework. And its output $f(x_{i,j}) \in R^d$ refers to a latent feature vector of d-dimensions. $g(\cdot)$ is an aggregator that integrates instance features. $c(\cdot)$ is a linear classifier that outputs a bag prediction.

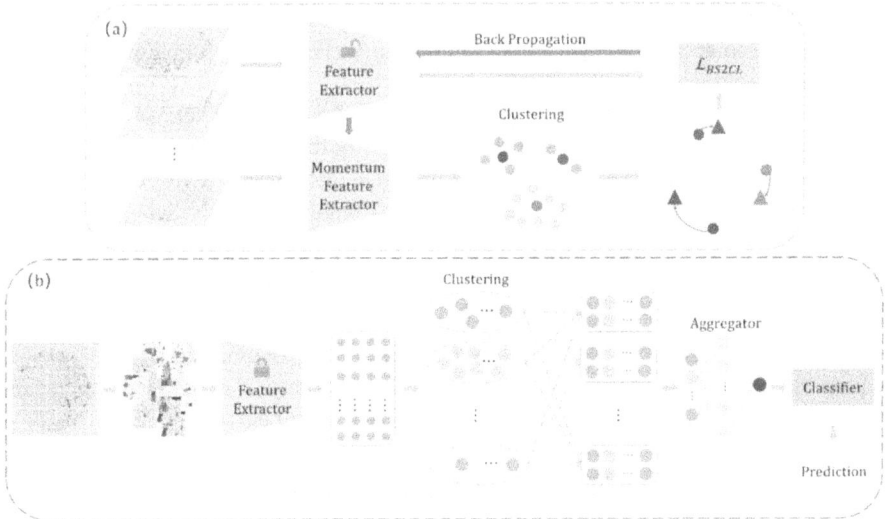

Fig. 2. (a) The overview of the proposed Balanced Self-Supervised Contrastive Learning framework. (b) The pipeline of the thyroid cytology WSI classification based on multiple instance learning.

3.2 Balanced Self-Supervised Contrastive Learning

Within a pertaining set $X = \{x_1, x_2, \ldots, x_n\}$ consisting of n patches extracted from various WSIs, the aim of self-supervised learning is to develop a feature extractor $f_\theta(\cdot)$ that transforms X into a corresponding set of feature vectors $V = \{v_1, v_2, \ldots, v_n\}$, where each $v_i = f_\theta(x_i)$ is generated without utilizing any patch labels. Traditional self-supervised contrastive learning fulfills this goal by minimizing a contrastive loss function such as InfoNCE [23], which is articulated as follows:

$$\mathcal{L}_{InfoNCE} = \sum_{i=1}^{n} -\log \frac{\exp(v_i \cdot v_i'/\tau)}{\exp(v_i \cdot v_i'/\tau) + \sum_{j=1}^{r} \exp(v_i \cdot v_j'/\tau)} \tag{2}$$

where v_i' is extracted from a random augmentation of x_i, and v_j' is extracted from r other patches, and τ is a temperature hyper-parameter [24].

Minimizing the loss function drives the feature of x_i to align more closely with the feature of its randomly augmented counterpart, while simultaneously repelling the feature of x_i from the features of other patches within the training set. But it may lead to pushing apart the features of patches from the same class. What's more, the class distribution of thyroid patches is unbalanced which causes the biased feature space and unclear class boundaries. Uniformity is a fundamental characteristic of contrastive learning. It implies that features from different classes are evenly spread across a hypersphere $S^{d-1} = \{u \in R^d : ||u|| = 1\}$. However, an imbalanced dataset can undermine uniformity. When certain classes have a significantly larger number compared to others, the majority classes occupy a larger portion of the hypersphere in the feature space, while the minority classes are sparsely distributed. This imbalanced distribution disrupts the clear boundaries between classes in the feature space, making it more challenging for the model to accurately distinguish the minority classes which may be critical for classification.

To solve these problems, we proposed the **BS2CL** framework shown in **Fig. 2(a)**. BS2CL is a framework that improves the uniformity of the feature space. It first extracts features from all patches. Then it clusters all the patch features into K clusters to preserve the class structure avoiding the problem of pulling features from the same class closer together. We define $C = \{c_i\}_{i=1}^{K}$ as the cluster centers and $P = \{p_i^*\}_{i=1}^{K}$ as the points of the optimal positions that are uniformly distributed on the hypersphere. To obtain clear class boundaries, we should assign C to P.

Position Generation and Assignment Computing the optimal positions does not require access to the dataset, and only requires the dimension d of the feature space and the number of classes. We calculate $\{p_i^*\}_{i=1}^{K}$ by gradient descent on

$$\mathcal{L}_u(\{p_i\}_{i=1}^{K}) = \frac{1}{K}\sum_{i=1}^{K} \log \sum_{j=1}^{K} exp(p_i \cdot p_j/\tau) \tag{3}$$

where p_i is restricted to be on the hypersphere and $\{p_i^*\}_{i=1}^{K}$ corresponds to the minimum loss.

Then we should assign each cluster to a corresponding position. Due to the different distances between two optimal positions, random assignment may ruin the semantics of the feature space. The ideal situation is that clusters with semantic proximity close to each other should be assigned to positions that are equally proximate. However, the ground truth of the training set is unknown and it's hard to quantify the semantic proximity. To match a cluster to the corresponding optimal position while keeping semantic similarity between clusters is difficult. To solve this, we compute the assignment during pretraining instead of using a settled assignment. In each epoch, we compute the assignment $\{\sigma_i^*\}_{i=1}^{K}$ with the Hungarian Algorithm [25], defined as:

$$\{\sigma_i^*\}_i = \arg\min_{\{\sigma_i\}_i} \frac{1}{K} \sum_{i=1}^{K} ||p_{\sigma_i} - c_i||. \tag{4}$$

The computed assignment minimizes the distance between cluster centers and the optimal positions.

Balanced Self-Supervised Contrastive Loss. To make the class boundaries clearer and the feature space less biased, we compute the uniformly distributed positions $\{p_i^*\}_{i=1}^{K}$ and the assignment $\{\sigma_i^*\}_{i=1}^{K}$ that matches the clusters to the corresponding positions. Additionally, in order to preserve the property of local smoothness and to facilitate the bootstrap of clustering, we add InfoNCE loss to our balanced self-supervised contrastive Loss $\mathcal{L}_{BS2CL}$, which is defined as:

$$\mathcal{L}_{BS2CL} = \sum_{i=1}^{n} -\left(\log \frac{exp(v_i \cdot v_i'/\tau)}{exp(v_i \cdot v_i'/\tau) + \sum_{j=1}^{r} exp(v_i \cdot v_j'/\tau)} \right. \\ \left. + \log \frac{exp(v_i \cdot p_{\sigma_{k_i}}/\tau)}{exp(v_i \cdot p_{\sigma_{k_i}}/\tau) + \sum_{j=1}^{r} exp(v_i \cdot p_{\sigma_{k_j}}/\tau)} \right) \tag{5}$$

where $p_{\sigma_{k_i}}$ is the position corresponding to the centroid c_{k_i} of the cluster to which v_i belongs.

After pertaining the feature extractor $f(\cdot)$ with the BS2CL framework, we freeze its parameters in the stage of classification for thyroid WSIs.

3.3 Bag-Level Data Augmentation Strategy

Considering the cost of collecting and annotating thyroid WSIs, appropriate data augmentation is necessary. We propose a bag-level data augmentation strategy to increase the number of bags.

Figure 2(b) shows the pipeline of thyroid WSI classification. Given a WSI W_i (bag), we split it into small patches $\{x_{i,j}\}_{j=1}^{n_i}$ (instances) which are sent into the pretrained feature extractor. In traditional MIL, the output $\{v_{i,j}\}_{j=1}^{n_i}$ are then aggregated into a bag feature through the aggregator. In this paper, before aggregation, we cluster all instance features $\{v_{i,j}\}_{j=1}^{n_i}$ from W_i and sample random instances from each cluster. After repeating the sampling process M times, we get M pseudo bags $X_i = \{X_i^m | m = 1, 2, \ldots, M\}$ with $n_{i'}$ instances from a bag X_i and each pseudo X_i^m bag is assigned the label of X_i, i.e., $Y_i^m = Y_i$. As instances in the same cluster share similar semantic properties, the $n_{i'}$ instances in a pseudo bag approximate the representation of a bag with n_i instances. Then, we feed these pseudo bags into the aggregator to get the bag features. A bag-level classifier is trained with bag features in a supervised way for thyroid cytology WSI classification.

4 Experiments

Our experiment is conducted on the in-house dataset and demonstrates the superior performance of the proposed method.

4.1 Thyroid Cytology Dataset

We conducted a retrospective analysis and collected 461 thyroid FNAB WSIs from multiple healthcare institutions. Table 1 shows the distribution of the 461 WSIs, wherein each WSI corresponds to a single participant, with liquid-based cytologic preparation. This dataset was labeled by professional cytopathologists and only the TBS category is used for training. 80% of the dataset is used for training and validation and 20% for testing. We divide a WSI into patches with a size of 1024 × 1024 without overlapping.

This study conforms to the ethical standards of the institutional research committee and the tenets of the Helsinki Declaration. As the nature of this study is anonymized and retrospective, the requirement for informed consent has been exempted.

4.2 Experiment Details and Evaluation Metrics

Feature Extractor Pretraining. When pretraining the feature extractor, we build a pretraining dataset consisting of 500629 patches from 56 thyroid WSIs. The self-supervised contrastive methods in this study are all pretrained on this dataset for 200 epochs with four

Table 1. The thyroid cytology WSI dataset description.

	TBS Category	WSI count
1	Nondiagnostic or unsatisfactory	-
2	Benign	33
3	Atypia of undetermined significance or follicular lesion of undetermined significance	18
4	Follicular neoplasm or suspicious for a follicular	6
5	Suspicious for malignancy	67
6	Malignant	337

NVIDIA GeForce GTX 3090Ti GPUs. To ensure an equitable evaluation, our pretraining procedure for the feature extractor mirrors the setting of MoCo [17]. A ResNet-50 [26] is adopted as the feature extractor and its last fully connected layer outputs a 128-dimensional feature that undergoes ℓ_2-normalization. The optimizer is conducted using SGD with a weight decay set at 0.0001, momentum of 0.9, and a batch size of 128. In the initial 20 epochs, we use InfoNCE loss only to warm up the network for better clustering. The learning rate initiates at 0.03 and is scaled down by a factor of 0.1 at epoch 120 and epoch 160. We set the temperature hyper-parameter $\tau = 0.2$ and set $r = 16384$. For each epoch, we utilize the FAISS [27] library for efficient K-means clustering. We set $K = 1000$ and design an ablation experiment to explore the effects of the value of K.

WSI Classification. In this stage, we freeze the parameters of the pretrained feature extractor. We cluster a bag into 100 clusters and randomly sample 5 instances from each cluster to form a pseudo bag. We train the aggregator for 100 epochs and use the Adam [28] optimizer with a cosine decay learning rate scheduler.

Evaluation Metrics. We report the balanced accuracy (ACC) and macro area under the curve (AUC) scores for the task of WSI classification.

Baselines. We utilize 2 classical self-supervised learning frameworks (DINO [18], MoCoV3 [29]) and 6 commonly used aggregators (max poling, mean pooling, ABMIL [15], DSMIL [21], CLAM-SB, CLAM-MB [22]) for experiments. A feature extractor and an aggregator form a combination to perform comparative experiments.

Table 2. Classification results on thyroid cytology dataset

Framework	Max Pooling		Mean Pooling		DSMIL [21]		ABMIL [15]		CLAM-SB [22]		CLAM-MB [22]	
	ACC	AUC	ACC	AUC	ACC	AUC	ACC	AUC	ACC	AUC	ACC	AUC
MoCoV3 [29]	0.258	0.600	0.200	0.500	0.206	0.575	0.200	0.500	0.200	0.500	0.200	0.500
DINO [18]	**0.404**	0.700	0.320	0.675	0.431	0.700	0.341	0.600	0.350	0.600	0.361	0.675
ours	0.356	**0.750**	**0.499**	**0.800**	**0.521**	**0.975**	**0.494**	**0.725**	**0.535**	**0.800**	**0.487**	**0.800**

4.3 Classification Results

The classification results are summarized in Table 2. By examining the quantitative results outlined in Table 2, it is readily apparent that our proposed approach outperformed other existing methods on the task of WSI classification. Surprisingly, we find that certain frameworks utilizing a feature extractor pretrained with MoCoV3 demonstrate performance comparable to random classification. This finding strongly suggests the impact of class imbalance within the instance level on self-supervised learning models. When combined with different aggregators, our proposed approach consistently yields improved performance which validates the robustness of our method as well as its ability to learn discriminative representations suited for the classification task.

Figure 3 (a) and (c) show two example confusion matrices of DINO and our BS2CL combined with the same aggregator CLAM-SB, respectively. For DINO, the off-diagonal values indicate a higher level of misclassification between classes, which suggests that it is not extracting distinguishing features. In contrast, the matrix for BS2CL shows higher diagonal and lower off-diagonal values, demonstrating it can better distinguish different classes attributed to more discriminative features learned through the proposed balanced self-supervised contrastive learning framework.

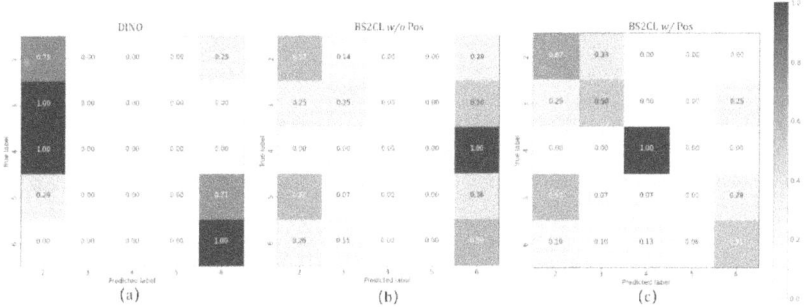

Fig. 3. The example confusion matrices from three compositions: (a) DINO [18] + CLAM-SB [22], (b) BS2CL without positions + CLAM-SB [22], (c) BS2CL(ours) + CLAM-SB [22].

4.4 Ablation Study

We conducted ablation experiments to analyze the impact of the optimal positions in our proposed BS2CL framework. We assign the cluster centers to the optimal positions in our study. This helps alleviate the bias towards majority classes in the learned feature space and yields clearer class boundaries.

As shown in Table 3, classification performance with the optimal positions is better than without applying the positions. This optimization enhances the separability and discrimination of the extracted features. We visualize the features extracted from the pretrained feature extractors in Fig. 4. It can be observed that the boundaries of features from BS2CL with optimal positions are clearer, which further confirms the effectiveness of our approach.

Table 3. Accuracy of BS2CL with/without positions with different values of K

Framework		$K = 500$	$K = 1000$	$K = 5000$
w/o Position Assignment	Max Pooling	0.333	0.238	0.298
	Mean Pooling	0.321	0.340	0.308
	DSMIL [21]	0.374	0.358	0.471
	ABMIL [15]	0.27	0.319	0.39
	CLAM-SB [22]	0.282	0.353	0.363
	CLAM-MB [22]	0.381	0.358	0.466
w Position Assignment	Max Pooling	0.230	**0.356**	0.292
	Mean Pooling	0.277	**0.499**	0.408
	DSMIL [21]	0.444	**0.521**	0.425
	ABMIL [15]	0.452	**0.494**	0.375
	CLAM-SB [22]	0.477	**0.535**	0.411
	CLAM-MB [22]	**0.523**	0.487	0.397

(a) BS2CL w/o Pos   (b) BS2CL w/ Pos

Fig. 4. The t-SNE [30] visualization of instance features from a thyroid WSI: (a) features extracted by BS2CL without positions and (b) features extracted by BS2CL with positions.

We also investigate the impact of the number of clusters K on the classification results. Excessive clustering can have some benefits, but it can also lead to loss of the internal structure of the class when exceeding a certain limit. Therefore, different K values should be adopted for different datasets. For the thyroid dataset used in this study, $K = 1000$ is found to perform best. The confusion matrices shown in Fig. 3 are a further demonstration of our previous experiments.

5 Conclusion

In this study, we propose a balanced self-supervised contrastive learning (BS2CL) framework and a bag-level data augmentation strategy for thyroid cytology WSI multi-classification. The BS2CL framework captures the intrinsic semantic relationships between patches while avoiding biased feature space. The bag-level augmentation strategy is introduced to expand the size of the training dataset effectively. Experimental results on an in-house thyroid cytology WSI dataset demonstrate that the proposed method achieves state-of-the-art classification performance and can be combined with different aggregators. The current work focuses on evaluating the proposed approach at a single-resolution level, future work will explore experiments involving multi-resolution feature learning and classification.

References

1. Cabanillas, M.E., McFadden, D.G., Durante, C.: Thyroid cancer. The Lancet **388**(10061), 2783–2795 (2016)
2. Haugen, B.R., Alexander, E.K., Bible, K.C., et al.: 2015 American Thyroid Association management guidelines for adult patients with thyroid nodules and differentiated thyroid cancer: the American Thyroid Association guidelines task force on thyroid nodules and differentiated thyroid cancer. Thyroid **26**(1), 1–133 (2016)
3. Cibas, E.S., Ali, S.Z.: The 2017 Bethesda system for reporting thyroid cytopathology. Thyroid **27**(11), 1341–1346 (2017)
4. Cochand-Priollet, B., Koutroumbas, K., Megalopoulou, T.M., et al.: Discriminating benign from malignant thyroid lesions using artificial intelligence and statistical selection of morphometric features. Oncol. Rep. **15**(4), 1023–1026 (2006)
5. Gopinath, B., Shanthi, N.: Development of an automated medical diagnosis system for classifying thyroid tumor cells using multiple classifier fusion. Technol. Cancer Res. Treat. **14**(5), 653–662 (2015)
6. Chain, K., Legesse, T., Heath, J.E., et al.: Digital image-assisted quantitative nuclear analysis improves diagnostic accuracy of thyroid fine-needle aspiration cytology. Cancer Cytopathol. **127**(8), 501–513 (2019)
7. Guan, Q., Wang, Y., Ping, B., et al.: Deep convolutional neural network VGG-16 model for differential diagnosing of papillary thyroid carcinomas in cytological images: a pilot study. J. Cancer **10**(20), 4876 (2019)
8. Hirokawa, M., Niioka, H., Suzuki, A., et al.: Application of deep learning as an ancillary diagnostic tool for thyroid FNA cytology. Cancer Cytopathol. **131**(4), 217–225 (2023)
9. Dov, D., Kovalsky, S.Z., Assaad, S., et al.: Weakly supervised instance learning for thyroid malignancy prediction from whole slide cytopathology images. Med. Image Anal. **67**, 101814 (2021)
10. Qiu, S., Guo, Y., Zhu, C., et al.: Attention based multi-instance thyroid cytopathological diagnosis with multi-scale feature fusion. In: 2020 25th International Conference on Pattern Recognition (ICPR), pp. 3536–3541 (2021)
11. Yu, B., Yin, P., Chen, H., et al.: Pyramid multi-loss vision transformer for thyroid cancer classification using cytological smear. Knowl.-Based Syst. **275**, 110721 (2023)
12. Feng, J., Zhou, Z.H.: Deep MIML network. In: Proceedings of the AAAI conference on artificial intelligence, pp. 1884–1890 (2017)
13. Pinheiro, P.O., Collobert, R.: From image-level to pixel-level labeling with convolutional networks. In: Proceedings of the IEEE Conference on Computer Vision and Pattern Recognition, pp. 1713–1721 (2015)
14. Zhu, W., Lou, Q., Vang, Y.S., et al.: Deep multi-instance networks with sparse label assignment for whole mammogram classification. In: Descoteaux, M., Maier-Hein, L., Franz, A., Jannin, P., Collins, D.L., Duchesne, S. (eds) MICCAI 2017. LNCS, vol. 10435, pp. 603–611. Springer, Cham (2017). https://doi.org/10.1007/978-3-319-66179-7_69

15. Ilse, M., Tomczak, J., Welling, M.: Attention-based deep multiple instance learning. In: International Conference on Machine Learning, pp. 2127–2136 (2018)
16. Chen, T., Kornblith, S., Norouzi, M., et al.: A simple framework for contrastive learning of visual representations. In: International Conference on Machine Learning, pp. 1597–1607 (2020)
17. He, K., Fan, H., Wu, Y., et al.: Momentum contrast for unsupervised visual representation learning. In: Proceedings of the IEEE/CVF Conference on Computer Vision and Pattern Recognition, pp. 9729–9738 (2020)
18. Caron, M., Touvron, H., Misra, I., et al.: Emerging properties in self-supervised vision transformers. In: Proceedings of the IEEE/CVF Conference on Computer Vision and Pattern Recognition, pp. 9650–9660 (2021)
19. Deng, J., Dong, W., Socher, R., et al.: Imagenet: a large-scale hierarchical image database. In: 2009 IEEE Conference on Computer Vision and Pattern Recognition, pp. 248–255 (2009)
20. Assran, M., Balestriero, R., Duval, Q., et al.: The hidden uniform cluster prior in self-supervised learning. arXiv preprint arXiv:2210.07277 (2022)
21. Li, B., Li, Y., Eliceiri, K.W.: Dual-stream multiple instance learning network for whole slide image classification with self-supervised contrastive learning. In: Proceedings of the IEEE/CVF Conference on Computer Vision and Pattern Recognition, pp. 14318–14328 (2021)
22. Lu, M.Y., Williamson, D.F., Chen, T.Y., et al.: Data-efficient and weakly supervised computational pathology on whole-slide images. Nat. Biomed. Eng. **5**(6), 555–570 (2021)
23. Oord, A.v.d., Li, Y., Vinyals, O.: Representation learning with contrastive predictive coding. arXiv preprint arXiv:1807.03748 (2018)
24. Wu, Z., Xiong, Y., Yu, S.X., et al.: Unsupervised feature learning via non-parametric instance discrimination. In: Proceedings of the IEEE Conference on Computer Vision and Pattern Recognition, pp. 3733–3742 (2018)
25. Kuhn, H.W.: The Hungarian method for the assignment problem. Naval Res. Logistics Q **2**(1–2), 83–97 (1955)
26. He, K., Zhang, X., Ren, S., et al.: Deep residual learning for image recognition. arXiv preprint arXiv:1512.03385 (2015)
27. Johnson, J., Douze, M., Jégou, H.: Billion-scale similarity search with GPUs. IEEE Trans. Big Data **7**(3), 535–547 (2019)
28. Kingma, D.P., Ba, J.: Adam: a method for stochastic optimization. arXiv preprint arXiv:1412.6980 (2014)
29. Chen, X., Xie, S., He, K.: An empirical study of training self-supervised vision transformers. arXiv preprint arXiv:2104.02057 (2021)
30. Van der Maaten, L., Hinton, G.: Visualizing data using t-SNE. J. Mach. Learn. Res. **9**(11), 2579–2605 (2008)

Unsupervised Domain Adaptation Method for Medical Image Segmentation Using Fourier Feature Decoupling and Multi-scale Feature Fusion

Wei Hu[1], Qiaozhi Xu[1(✉)], Zhe Lian[1], Yanjun Yin[1], Min Zhi[1], Na Yang[1], Wentao Duan[1], and Lei Yu[2]

[1] School of Computer Science and Technology, Inner Mongolia Normal University, Hohhot 010022, China
`ciecxqz@imnu.edu.cn`
[2] People's Hospital of Inner Mongolia Autonomous Region, Hohhot 010022, China

Abstract. Unsupervised Domain Adaptation (UDA) is an effective technique for utilizing labeled data from a source domain alongside unlabeled data from a target domain, aiming to mitigate the impact of domain shift on model performance. Feature decoupling-based UDA methods have garnered significant attention due to their ability to address specific challenges, offering superior performance. However, existing methods that employ cycle-consistency and adversarial losses need improvements to better maintain content consistency and preserve the style information of medical images. To address these issues, we propose UDA-F4, an improved UDA method based on the feature decoupling of Fourier transform and multi-scale feature fusion. Experiments on the MICCAI 2017 MM-WHS cardiac dataset demonstrate that our method not only generates higher quality synthetic images and achieves more precise medical segmentation results. Additionally, our method significantly improves both the Dice and ASD metrics compared to traditional methods.

Keywords: Unsupervised Domain Adaptation · Cross-Medical Image Segmentation · Feature Decoupling · Fourier Transform · Multi-Scale Feature Fusion

1 Introduction

In recent years, medical image segmentation models based on deep learning have rapidly evolved [1, 2]. These models typically assume that the training and testing data are independent and identically distributed (i.i.d.) [3]. However, the problem of domain shift challenges this assumption and may lead to a significant decline in model performance upon actual deployment. Consequently, addressing domain shift is crucial for the practical application of these models.

Domain Adaptation (DA) techniques can adapt models to an unseen target domain using knowledge learned from the source domain, offering effective solutions to the domain shift problem. Among these, Unsupervised Domain Adaptation (UDA) technology, which does not require labeled target data, has proven to be an effective approach for addressing cross-domain medical image segmentation tasks where target domain labels are scarce. In recent years, UDA methods based on feature decoupling [4–6] have shown exceptional performance which employed a similar or identical feature decoupling framework to enhance the domain adaptability of models, and we call them Traditional Feature Decoupling Method (TFDM) in this paper. However, these methods had some limitations: firstly, the cycle-consistency loss used by them was less effective in maintaining the content consistency between original and reconstructed images; secondly, the decoupling process, which solely utilizes adversarial loss, might fail to preserve the style information of medical images fully; lastly, the shared content encoder in the feature extraction process may lead to the loss of some crucial semantic information. These limitations led to the inability of traditional methods to effectively preserve the content and style features of original images, which resulted in the poor quality of synthetic images and impacted adaptability in the target domain.

To address these issues, we propose a novel UDA method for medical image segmentation, dubbed UDA-F4. The primary contributions of our work are threefold:

(1) We replace the traditional cycle-consistency loss, which maintains the fidelity between the original and reconstructed images in feature decoupling methods, with a Fourier-based content consistency loss. This approach more effectively preserves content consistency.
(2) We have designed a Fourier-based style transfer loss and incorporated it into the traditional feature decoupling framework. This innovation effectively addresses the challenge of aligning multi-style features in medical images, achieving style consistency.
(3) By introducing a multi-scale feature fusion strategy within a shared content encoder, we merge features across different scales to generate synthesized images that retain more semantic information. This promotes domain adaptation of the model.

2 Related Work

Domain Adaptation (DA) technology can transfer knowledge learned in the source domain to the target domain and enhance adaptation in the target domain by minimizing distribution differences between the source and target domains. Depending on whether the target domain contains labels or not, domain adaptation methods are classified into Supervised Domain Adaptation (SDA), Semi-supervised Domain Adaptation (SSDA), and Unsupervised Domain Adaptation (UDA) [7].

UDA methods, which do not require labels in the target domain, have shown excellence in addressing the scarcity of labels in cross-domain medical image segmentation tasks. Image alignment and feature alignment are the mainstream strategies in this area currently [8–11]. These methods primarily employ Cycle-Consistent Generative Adversarial Networks (CycleGAN) [12] for image alignment strategy. However, CycleGAN can cause content distortion during the image translation process, limiting model adaptability. The feature alignment strategy mainly utilizes adversarial learning, which presents its own challenges, such as training instability, mode collapse, and difficulties in model evaluation [13].

Feature decoupling is an enhanced feature alignment method that can effectively alleviate the aforementioned issues by decomposing input data into multiple meaningful components. Medical images are complex mixtures of anatomical structures and modality factors [14]. Feature decoupling methods separate the medical images of the source and target domains into anatomical structures (content features, which are domain-invariant) and modality factors (style features, which are domain-specific). Then, different features are combined and synthesized into cross-domain medical images that have the content features of the source domain and the style features of the target domain. These synthetic images share labels with their corresponding source domain images, thus improving the adaptability of models in the target domain [15, 16].

3 Method Overview

UDA methods involve two domains with different distributions: the source domain D^s and the target domain D^t. The source domain $D^s = \{(x_i, y_i)\}_{i=1}^{n}$ contains n data samples and their corresponding labels, whereas the target domain $D^t = \{(x_j)\}_{j=1}^{m}$ comprises m data samples and no labels.

The UDA-F4 framework is divided into two stages:

(1) Data alignment: A feature decoupling approach based on the Fourier Transform is designed and integrated with a multi-scale feature fusion strategy. This approach can effectively capture the semantic and style information of the original images and generate high-quality synthetic images.
(2) Network Training: The segmentation model is trained using the high-quality synthetic images mentioned above and learns the knowledge of the target domain to enhance its generalization ability in the target domain.

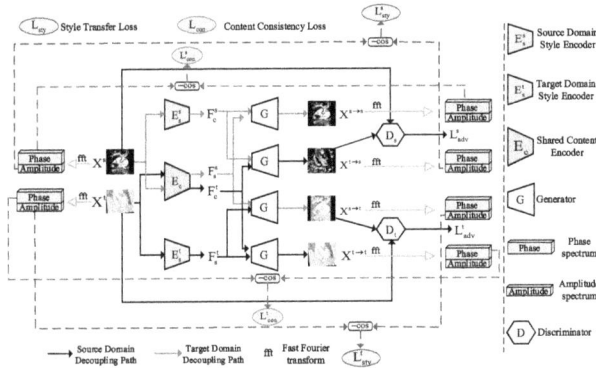

Fig. 1. Structure of the Feature Decoupling based on Fourier Transform.

3.1 Fourier Transform-Based Feature Decoupling Method

In this stage, medical images are decoupled into domain-invariant content features and domain-specific style features using the Feature Decoupling Method based on the Fourier

Transform (FDFF), as shown in Fig. 1. The blue solid line represents the decoupling path for images from the source domain, while the red solid line indicates the decoupling path for images from the target domain. Initially, images from both the source and target domains are input into a shared content encoder E_c and two distinct style encoders (E_s^s, E_s^t) to extract their content features (F_c^s, F_c^t) and style features (F_s^s, F_s^t) respectively. Subsequently, the style and content features are combined and fed into a decoder to generate reconstructed images ($X^{s \to s}, X^{t \to t}$,,) as well as synthetic images ($X^{t \to s}, X^{s \to t}$).

Thereafter, two style discriminators (D_s, D_t) are used to differentiate between real and synthetic images, aiming to make the synthetic images ($X^{t \to s}, X^{s \to t}$) have a similar style to the original images (X^s, X^t). The discrimination loss for the target domain is shown in Eq. (1), where D_t needs to maximize the loss function L_{adv}^t in order to accurately discriminate between the real and synthetic images. Conversely, E_s^t, E_c, and G need to minimize the loss function L_{adv}^t and ensure that the style of the synthetic images $X^{s \to t}$ closely aligns with that of the real target domain images X^t.

$$L_{adv}^t(E_c, E_s^t, G, D_t) = E_{x^t \in D^t}[\log(D_t(x^t))] + E_{x^s \in D^s, x^t \in D^t} \\ [\log(1 - D_t(G(E_c(x^s), E_s^t(x^t))))] \quad (1)$$

Content Consistency Loss and Style Transfer Loss. The amplitude spectrum and phase spectrum of the Fourier Transform can respectively capture the low-level distributional features of images (such as style) and high-level distributional features (such as content) [17]. The phase spectrum contains substantial semantic content. Therefore, by minimizing the phase difference loss between the original image and its corresponding reconstructed image, the strict constraints of pixel-level loss can be relaxed. This encourages the shared content encoder to extract more content features and generate reconstructed images that preserve more semantic content, thereby achieving content consistency. Variations in the amplitude spectrum significantly impact the image style [18]. The style similarity between synthetic and original images is further enhanced by reducing the differences in the amplitude spectrum, which pushes the style encoder to extract more style features.

Based on the analyses above, we propose the Content Consistency Loss (CCL) and Style Transfer Loss (STL) based on the Fourier Transform. Firstly, we apply the Fourier Transform to the original, synthetic, and reconstructed images using Eq. (2) (as shown by the gray solid line in Fig. 1), where H, W, and C represent the height, width, and channels of the ith image, respectively.

$$F(x_i^k)(u, v, c) = \sum_{h=0}^{H-1} \sum_{w=0}^{W-1} x_i^k(h, w, c) e^{-j2\pi(\frac{h}{H}u + \frac{w}{W}v)} \quad (2)$$

Subsequently, the frequency domain signal $F(x_i^k)$ can be further decomposed into its phase spectrum $P_i^k \in \mathbb{R}^{h \times w \times d}$ and amplitude spectrum $A_i^k \in \mathbb{R}^{h \times w \times d}$ [19]. Equation (3) represents the negative cosine of the phase difference between the source domain image and its reconstructed image, where $< \cdot >$ denotes the dot-product, and $|| \cdot ||_2$ represents the L2 norm. Minimizing Eq. (3) can reduce the discrepancies in the phase spectrum, thereby enhancing the consistency of semantic content.

$$L_{con}^s(x^s, x^{s \to s}) = -\frac{1}{N} \sum_{i=1}^{N} \frac{< F(x^s)_i^P, F(x^{s \to s})_i^P >}{||F(x^s)_i^P||_2 \cdot ||F(x^{s \to s})_i^P||_2} \quad (3)$$

The final CCL is shown in Eq. (4), which corresponds to the red dashed line in Fig. 1.

$$\underset{\theta(E_s^s, E_c, G), \theta(E_s^t, E_c, G)}{min} L_{con}\big((E_s^s, E_c, G), (E_s^t, E_C, G)\big) = L_{con}^s(x^s, x^{s \to s}) + L_{con}^t(x^t, x^{t \to t}) \tag{4}$$

Finally, a Style Transfer Loss based on the Fourier Transform is added to the base of the adversarial loss, which corresponds to the blue dashed line in Fig. 1. The STL is applied to the amplitude spectrum of the original and synthetic images to further maintain the style similarity.

$$L_{sty}^s(x^s, x^{t \to s}) = -\frac{1}{N} \sum_{i=1}^{N} \frac{< F(x^s)_i^A, F(x^{t \to s})_i^A >}{||F(x^s)_i^A||_2 \cdot ||F(x^{t \to s})_i^A||_2} \tag{5}$$

Equation (5) represents the negative cosine of the amplitude difference between the source domain image and its synthetic image. Minimizing this difference can reduce disparities in the amplitude spectrum and enhance style consistency. The final STL is shown in Eq. (6).

$$\underset{\theta(E_s^s, E_c, G), \theta(E_s^t, E_c, G)}{min} L_{sty}\big((E_s^s, E_c, G), (E_s^t, E_C, G)\big) = L_{sty}^s(x^s, x^{t \to s}) + L_{sty}^t(x^t, x^{s \to t}) \tag{6}$$

3.2 Multi-scale Feature Fusion Strategy

Many studies have shown that generating synthetic images that preserve more semantic information is significant for improving the generalization of models [20, 21]. The CCL can help models generate synthetic images with more semantic content, but the fundamental reason for losing important semantic information is the multi-layer convolutional processing during feature extraction. Therefore, we introduce a multi-scale feature fusion strategy (MSFFS) into the shared encoder to preserve and transmit early feature information to subsequent convolutional layers, ultimately reducing the loss of crucial semantic information.

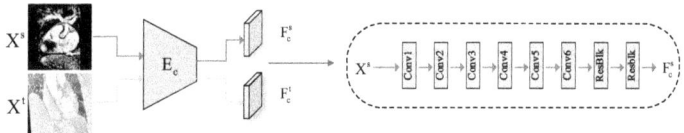

Fig. 2. Detailed Structure of the Content Encoder.

Multi-scale Feature Extraction. The shared content encoder E_c is composed of six two-dimensional convolutional blocks and two residual blocks, as illustrated in Fig. 2.

The kernel size for the first convolutional block is 7×7, whereas the kernel sizes for the subsequent blocks are 4×4. The inclusion of the two residual blocks aims to address the issues of gradient vanishing and slow convergence during the training of the network.

Lower-dimensional features contain more positional and detail information and have a higher resolution but may lack some semantic information because they pass through fewer convolutional layers. Conversely, higher-dimensional features contain stronger semantic information as they pass through more convolutional layers. Therefore, we perform multi-scale feature extraction on the last three layers of the content encoder, as shown in Fig. 3(a).

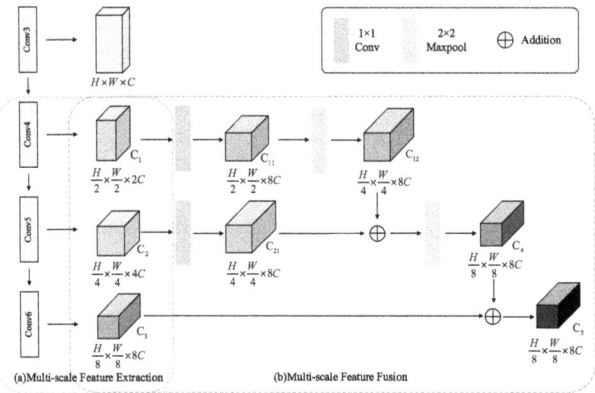

Fig. 3. Multi-scale Feature Fusion Strategy.

Multi-scale Feature Fusion. Multi-scale feature fusion can fully utilize semantic information at various levels to achieve a more comprehensive, richer, and representative feature representation. By integrating features at different scales, it captures more accurate edges and details of the target and synthesizes images that preserve more semantic features, thereby enhancing the precision and robustness of models.

Firstly, a 1×1 convolution is applied to the lower-level features (C_1, C_2) to increase dimensionality, thereby aligning their dimensions with those of the higher-level features, as shown in Eqs. (7) and (8).

$$C_{11} = Reshape\left(c_1, size = \left(\frac{H}{2} \times \frac{W}{2} \times 8C\right)\right), Reshape = conv1 \times 1, c_1 \in \mathbb{R}^{\frac{H}{2} \times \frac{W}{2} \times 2C} \quad (7)$$

$$C_{21} = Reshape\left(c_2, size = \left(\frac{H}{4} \times \frac{W}{4} \times 8C\right)\right), Reshape = conv1 \times 1, c_2 \in \mathbb{R}^{\frac{H}{4} \times \frac{W}{4} \times 4C} \quad (8)$$

Secondly, a 2×2 max pooling layer is employed to reduce the size of the lower-level features ($C_{11}, C_{12} + C_{21}$) by half, as shown in Eqs. (9–10).

$$C_{12} = Reshape\left(c_{11}, size = \left(\frac{H}{4} \times \frac{W}{4} \times 8C\right)\right), Reshape = Maxpool2 \times 2 \quad (9)$$

$$C_4 = Reshape\left(c_{12} + C_{21}, size = \left(\frac{H}{8} \times \frac{W}{8} \times 8C\right)\right), Reshape = Maxpool2 \times 2 \quad (10)$$

Finally, features from different layers are fused to obtain a representation that preserves more semantic information, as shown in Eq. (11). The detailed implementation scheme is illustrated in Fig. 3(b).

$$C_5 = C_3 + C_4, \ C_3 \in \mathbb{R}^{\frac{H}{8} \times \frac{W}{8} \times 8C} \tag{11}$$

The fused features C_5 are then input into a residual block. Residual blocks only need to learn the differences between inputs and outputs, effectively mitigating the problem of gradient vanishing and obtaining content features that preserve more semantic content.

3.3 Model Training and Testing

After the first phase, UDA-F4 has obtained synthetic images $x^{s \to t}$, and their content features come from the source domain while their style features come from the target domain. Consequently, the labels from the source domain can be shared with the synthetic target domain images [15]. This approach can be used to train the model and enhance its generalization in the target domain, as shown in Fig. 4(a).

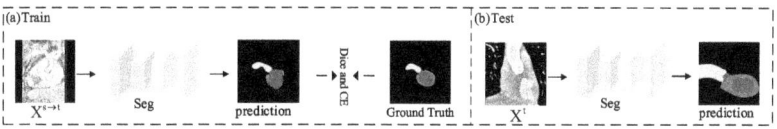

Fig. 4. Training and Testing Process of the Segmentation Network.

The training process uses Dice loss and cross-entropy loss, as shown in Eq. (12). The loss function takes into account both pixel-level and region-level relationships, enabling the model to comprehend the target areas more accurately and produce more precise segmentation results. The total loss is shown in Eq. (13). After training, the real target domain images (x^t) are used for testing, as shown in Fig. 4(b).

$$L_{seg} = Dice\bigl(y^s, seg\bigl(X^{s \to t}\bigr)\bigr) + CE(y^s + Seg(X^{s \to t})) \tag{12}$$

$$L = L_{adv}^s + L_{adv}^t + L_{con} + L_{style} + L_{seg} \tag{13}$$

4 Experiments

4.1 Dataset and Evaluation Metrics

To validate the effectiveness of the UDA-F4 framework, we utilize the MICCAI 2017 Multi-Modality Whole Heart Segmentation (MM-WHS) dataset [22] for testing, which includes 20 unpaired 3D cardiac MRI images and 20 3D cardiac CT images. For training, sixteen labeled 3D cardiac MRI images are selected, and the remaining four are used for testing segmentation performance. The division of CT images is identical to that of MRI images. Initially, the region of interest (the cardiac area) is cropped from the original 3D images, then the 3D images are sliced into 2D sections, and the cropped images from both datasets are normalized. The slice size during the data augmentation phase is 512 × 512 × 1, and in the segmentation phase, it is 256 × 256 × 1.

The experiment targets four anatomical structures for segmentation, including the Ascending Aorta (AA), Left Atrial Cavity (LAC), Left Ventricular Cavity (LVC), and Myocardium (MYO). We employed the Dice coefficient (Dice) and Average Surface Distance (ASD) as evaluation metrics. The Dice coefficient ranges from 0 to 1, with higher values indicating better segmentation outcomes, while a lower ASD signifies superior model performance at the boundaries.

4.2 Validation of Model Adaptability in the Target Domain

To validate adaptability, experiments were conducted in two directions: CT (source domain) to MRI (target domain) and MRI (source domain) to CT (target domain). To compare the segmentation accuracy of different models, optimal (Supervised) and worst (Without Domain Adaptation, WoDA) performance thresholds were established. The optimal threshold was obtained through supervised training in the target domain, while the worst threshold resulted from testing the target domain data directly on the source domain model without domain adaptation. The WoDA performance is extremely low in both directions due to significant domain shifts between CT and MRI images.

Table 1. Comparison of average Dice & ASD (CT to MRI).

Method name	Dice (%)					ASD (%)				
	AA	LAC	LVC	MYO	Avg	AA	LAC	LVC	MYO	Avg
Supervised	82.8	80.5	92.4	78.8	83.6	3.6	3.9	2.1	1.9	2.9
WoDA	5.4	30.2	24.6	2.7	15.7	15.4	16.8	13.0	10.8	14.0
CyCADA [25]	60.5	44.0	77.6	47.9	57.5	7.7	13.9	4.8	5.2	7.9
CycleGAN [12]	64.3	30.7	65.0	43.0	50.7	5.8	9.8	6.0	5.0	6.6
PnPAdaNe t[23]	43.7	47.0	77.7	48.6	54.3	11.4	14.5	4.5	5.3	8.9
SynSegNet [24]	41.3	57.5	63.6	36.5	49.7	8.6	10.7	5.4	5.9	7.6
SIFA [8]	65.3	62.3	78.9	47.3	63.4	7.3	7.4	3.8	4.4	5.7
TFDM	66.7	63.9	77.4	46.7	**63.7**	5.7	6.5	4.1	4.7	**5.3**
UDA-F4(ours)	**68.8**	**64.7**	**79.0**	**48.1**	**65.2**	**5.2**	**5.9**	**3.8**	**4.5**	**4.9**

We compare UDA-F4 with CycleGAN, PnP-AdaNet [23], SynSegNet [24], SIFA, CyCADA [25], and the TFDM, which utilized cycle-consistency loss and adversarial loss, among others. These methods had performed well on the MM-WHS dataset. Table 1 presents the results from CT (source domain) to MRI (target domain), and Table 2 shows results for MRI (source domain) to CT (target domain). The results indicate that UDA-F4 outperforms other methods, with the average Dice score increasing to 65.2% and 76.6% in both directions, respectively, and the average ASD decreasing to 4.9 and 5.8. This narrows the gap to a 14% difference from supervised training Dice scores. Figure 5 presents the visual results, demonstrating that, apart from the supervised training method, the segmentation results of UDA-F4 are closer to the labels and exhibit better adaptability and effectiveness in the unlabeled target domain.

Table 2. Comparison of average Dice & ASD (MRI to CT).

Method name	Dice(%)					ASD(%)				
	AA	LAC	LVC	MYO	Avg	AA	LAC	LVC	MYO	Avg
Supervised	92.7	91.1	91.9	87.7	90.9	1.5	3.5	1.7	2.1	2.2
WoDA	28.4	27.7	4.0	8.7	17.2	20.6	16.2	N/A	48.4	N/A
CyCADA [25]	72.9	77.0	62.4	45.3	64.4	9.6	8.0	9.6	10.5	9.4
CycleGAN [12]	73.8	75.7	52.3	28.7	57.6	11.5	13.6	9.2	8.8	10.8
PnPAdaNet [23]	74.0	68.9	61.9	50.8	63.9	12.8	6.3	17.4	14.7	12.8
SynSegNet [24]	71.6	69.0	51.6	40.8	58.2	11.7	7.8	7.0	9.2	8.9
SIFA [8]	81.3	79.5	73.8	61.6	74.1	7.9	6.2	5.5	8.5	7.0
TFDM	83.4	81.3	74.2	62.4	**75.3**	6.8	6.0	4.7	7.7	**6.3**
UDA-F4(ours)	**84.1**	**83.4**	**74.7**	**64.1**	**76.6**	**6.3**	**5.5**	**4.6**	**6.8**	**5.8**

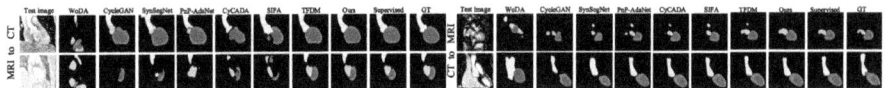

Fig. 5. Visual Results Comparison of Various Methods.

4.3 Ablation Experiment

This experiment incrementally integrates the Fourier Transform-based Content Consistency Loss (CCL), Style Transfer Loss (STL), and Multi-Scale Feature Fusion Strategy (MSFFS) into the TFDM to evaluate the effectiveness of each component.

Table 3. Comparison of average Dice & ASD under different CCL and STL (MRI to CT).

TFDM	CCL	STL	Dice (%)					ASD (%)				
			AA	LAC	LVC	MYO	Avg	AA	LAC	LVC	MYO	Avg
1	×	×	83.4	81.3	74.2	62.4	75.3	6.8	6.0	4.7	7.7	6.3
2	✓	×	84.0	82.6	74.7	62.4	75.9	6.6	5.9	4.7	7.8	6.2
3	×	✓	83.8	81.5	74.2	62.5	75.5	6.6	6.0	4.8	7.4	6.2
4	✓	✓	84.0	83.2	75.1	63.1	76.4	6.4	5.7	4.6	7.3	6.0

Effectiveness of CCL and STL. Firstly, we replace the cycle-consistency loss in the TFDM with the CCL. Figure 6(A) illustrates the visualization results of the reconstruction effects on MRI images (top row) and CT images (bottom row) using two different loss functions. The first column shows the original images, serving as a baseline. The second and third columns display the reconstructed images using cycle-consistency loss and content consistency loss, respectively. Notably, images reconstructed with cycle-consistency loss show discrepancies with the original ones, while those reconstructed using content consistency loss maintain semantic consistency more effectively, as highlighted in the red-boxed areas. These results underscore the effectiveness of content consistency loss in preserving the inherent content features of the images.

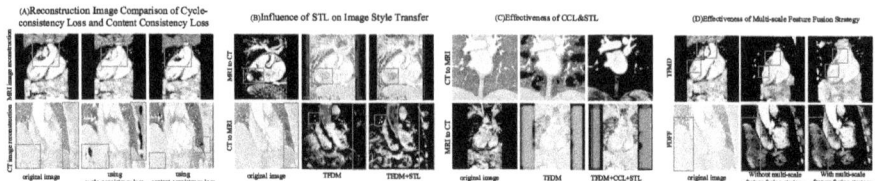

Fig. 6. Visualization of ablation experiment results.

Secondly, the STL is incorporated into the TFDM, and Fig. 6(B) presents the visualization results of style transfer between MRI and CT images. It is observed that images produced with the style transfer loss exhibit enhanced clarity and realism compared to those produced with the TFDM alone.

Finally, the TFDM was enhanced by embedding both the CCL and the STL. Figure 6(C) shows the visual results, which demonstrate that the CCL and STL can successfully accomplish the style shift while preserving more substantial semantic content. The detailed experimental results, shown in Table 3, reveal that, compared to cycle consistency loss, content consistency loss facilitates an improvement of 0.6% in average Dice and a reduction of 0.1 in average ASD. Moreover, the style transfer loss further enhances average Dice and ASD. Their combination results in an increase of 1.1% in the average Dice and a decrease of 0.3 in ASD.

Table 4. Effectiveness of MSFFS on Dice & ASD (MRI to CT)

Method name	Dice(%)					ASD(%)				
	AA	LAC	LVC	MYO	Avg	AA	LAC	LVC	MYO	Avg
TFDM	83.4	81.3	74.2	62.4	75.3	6.8	6.0	4.7	7.7	6.3
TFDM + MSFFS	83.7	82.2	74.3	63.0	75.8	6.6	5.9	4.7	7.4	6.1
FDFF	84.0	83.2	**75.1**	63.1	76.4	6.4	5.7	4.6	7.3	6.0
FDFF + MSFFS	**84.1**	**83.4**	74.7	**64.1**	**76.6**	**6.3**	**5.5**	**4.6**	**6.8**	**5.8**

Validation of the Effectiveness of MSFFS. We add the MSFFS into the TFDM and FDFF respectively, and Fig. 6(D) illustrates the results. It is evident that the MSFFS can preserve more semantic information, thereby significantly enhancing the quality of the generated images. The results in Table 4 also prove the effectiveness of the MSFFS, which enhances the average Dice score of the TFDM by nearly 0.5% and reduces the average ASD by 0.2. When applied to FDFF, there is an increase of 0.2% in the average Dice score and a decrease of 0.3 in ASD.

5 Conclusion

To address the problems of cycle consistency loss in feature decoupling methods, which cannot effectively maintain semantic consistency between the original and reconstructed images, unsatisfactory style preservation between the original and synthesized images, and semantic information loss caused by shared encoders, we propose UDA-F4, a UDA framework based on the feature decoupling of the Fourier transform and multi-scale feature fusion. First, in the feature decoupling process, the content consistency loss based on the Fourier transform is used to replace the cycle consistency loss, enhancing semantic consistency between the original and reconstructed images. Second, a style transfer loss based on the Fourier transform is proposed to effectively address the preservation of diverse styles in medical datasets. Finally, a multi-scale feature fusion strategy is introduced into the shared content encoder to generate synthesized images with richer semantic features. The experimental results based on the MICCAI 2017 MM-WHS cardiac dataset demonstrate the effectiveness and superiority of UDA-F4.

Acknowledgments. This study was funded by Science and Technology Program of Inner Mongolia Autonomous Region (2022YFSH0010) and Natural Science Foundation of Inner Mongolia Autonomous Region (2021MS06031).

References

1. Du, X., Liu, Y.: Constraint-based unsupervised domain adaptation network for multi-modality cardiac image segmentation. IEEE J. Biomed. Health Inform. **26**(1), 67–78 (2021)
2. Yang, F., Liang, F., Lu, L., Yin, M.: Dual attention-guided and learnable spatial transformation data augmentation multi-modal unsupervised medical image segmentation. Biomed. Signal Process. Control **78**, 103849 (2022)
3. Xu, H., Xie, H.T., Zhang, Y.D.: Review of domain generalization in vision. J. Guangzhou Univ. (Nat. Sci. Edn.) **21**(02), 42–59 (2022)
4. Xie, Q., Li, Y., He, N., Ning, M., Ma, K., Wang, G., Zheng, Y.: Unsupervised domain adaptation for medical image segmentation by disentanglement learning and self-training. IEEE Trans. Med. Imag. **43**, 4–14 (2022)
5. Peng, L., Lin, L., Cheng, P., Huang, Z., Tang, X.: Unsupervised domain adaptation for cross-modality retinal vessel segmentation via disentangling representation style transfer and collaborative consistency learning. In: 2022 IEEE 19th International Symposium on Biomedical Imaging (ISBI), pp. 1–5. IEEE (2022)
6. Yao, K., et al.: A novel 3D unsupervised domain adaptation framework for cross-modality medical image segmentation. IEEE J. Biomed. Health Inform. **26**(10), 4976–4986 (2022)
7. Tian, Q., Zhu, Y., Ma, C.: Review on Domain Adaptation Methods Based on Deep Learning Data Collection and Processing **37**(03) (2022)
8. Chen, C., Dou, Q., Chen, H., Qin, J., Heng, P.-A.: Synergistic image and feature adaptation: Towards cross-modality domain adaptation for medical image segmentation. Proc. AAAI Conf. Artif. Intell. **33**(01), 865–872 (2019). https://doi.org/10.1609/aaai.v33i01.3301865

9. Dong, S., et al.: Partial unbalanced feature transport for cross-modality cardiac image segmentation. IEEE Trans. Med. Imaging **42**(6), 1758–1773 (2023)
10. Wang, S., Fu, Z., Wang, B., Hu, Y.: Fusing feature and output space for unsupervised domain adaptation on medical image segmentation. Int. J. Imaging Syst. Technol. **33**(5), 1672–1681 (2023)
11. Cui, H., Yuwen, C., Jiang, L., Xia, Y., Zhang, Y.: Bidirectional cross-modality unsupervised domain adaptation using generative adversarial networks for cardiac image segmentation. Comput. Biol. Med. **136**, 104726 (2021)
12. Zhu, J.Y., Park, T., Isola, P., Efros, A. A.: Unpaired image-to-image translation using cycle-consistent adversarial networks. In: Proceedings of the IEEE international conference on computer vision, pp. 2223–2232 (2017)
13. Hu, W., Xu, Q.Z., Ge, X.W.: A review of unsupervised domain adaptation in medical image segmentation. Comput. Eng. Appl. **60**(06), 10–26 (2024)
14. Chartsias, A., Joyce, T., Papanastasiou, G., Semple, S., Williams, M., Newby, D.E., Tsaftaris, S.A.: Disentangled representation learning in cardiac image analysis. Med. Image Anal. **58**, 101535 (2019)
15. Isola, P., Zhu, J. Y., Zhou, T., Efros, A.A.: Image-to-image translation with conditional adversarial networks. In: Proceedings of the IEEE conference on computer vision and pattern recognition, pp. 1125–1134 (2017)
16. Wang, R., Zhou, Q., Zheng, G.: EDRL: entropy-guided disentangled representation learning for unsupervised domain adaptation in semantic segmentation. Comput. Methods Programs Biomed. **240**, 107729 (2023)
17. Liu, Q., Chen, C., Qin, J., Dou, Q., Heng, P.A.: Feddg: Federated domain generalization on medical image segmentation via episodic learning in continuous frequency space. In: Proceedings of the IEEE/CVF Conference on Computer Vision and Pattern Recognition, pp. 1013–1023 (2021)
18. Zhang, Z., Li, Y., Shin, B.S.: C2-GAN: Content-consistent generative adversarial networks for unsupervised domain adaptation in medical image segmentation. Med. Phys. **49**(10), 6491–6504 (2022)
19. Frigo, M., Johnson, S.G.: FFTW: An adaptive software architecture for the FFT. In: Proceedings of the 1998 IEEE International Conference on Acoustics, Speech and Signal Processing, ICASSP'98 (Cat. No. 98CH36181), vol. 3, pp. 1381–1384. IEEE (1998)
20. Jiang, Z., et al.: O2M-UDA: unsupervised dynamic domain adaptation for one-to-multiple medical image segmentation. Knowl.-Based Syst. **265**, 110378 (2023)
21. Liu, X., et al.: Attentive continuous generative self-training for unsupervised domain adaptive medical image translation. Med. Image Anal. **88**, 102851 (2023)
22. Zhuang, X., Shen, J.: Multi-scale patch and multi-modality atlases for whole heart segmentation of MRI. Med. Image Anal. **31**, 77–87 (2016)
23. Dou, Q., et al.: Pnp-adanet: plug-and-play adversarial domain adaptation network at unpaired cross-modality cardiac segmentation. IEEE Access **7**, 99065–99076 (2019)
24. Huo, Y., et al.: Synseg-net: synthetic segmentation without target modality ground truth. IEEE Trans. Med. Imaging **38**(4), 1016–1025 (2018)
25. Hoffman, J., et al.: Cycada: Cycle-consistent adversarial domain adaptation. In: International Conference on Machine Learning, pp. 1989–1998. Pmlr (2018)

LVMUM: Toward Open-World Object Detection with Large Vision Models and Unsupervised Modeling

Yangyang Huang, Xing Xi, Weiye Wu, and Ronghua Luo[✉]

South China University of Technology, Guangdong 510006, GZ, China
huangyangy@whu.edu.cn

Abstract. Open-world object detection (OWOD), as an emerging and challenging task in object detection, requires the model to have the ability to detect known and unknown objects in dynamic environments. Furthermore, it should have the capability to perform incremental learning based on newly acquired knowledge. However, current OWOD methods focus on labeling regions with high objectness scores as unknown objects. These heuristic annotation methods rely entirely on the supervision of known objects, thus leading to the issue of label bias. To solve this problem, we propose the Object Reconstruction-based Weibull Model (ORWM) method, which uses object-level semantic information for feature reconstruction to perform unsupervised modeling of the foreground and background. In the modeling process, another challenge to detecting unknown objects is the limited annotations for unknown objects. Therefore, we propose an Unsupervised Region Proposal Generation method based on SAM (SAM-URPG) to generate original pseudo labels for unknown objects and use the zero-shot ability of the large visual model to generate pseudo labels for unknown objects. Experimental results show that our proposed method significantly improves the ability to detect unknown objects on the MS-COCO dataset. It increases U-Recall by 14.0, surpassing the previous state-of-the-art (SOTA) method by **34%**, re-aching **50.9** U-Recall, while maintaining competitive performance in detecting known objects. Additionally, in terms of inference speed, our method constructs the model using a pure convolutional neural network, rather than employing a dense attention mechanism. This approach surpasses the SOTA deformable DETR-based method with a speed of **9.95 FPS**, while maintaining an inference speed advantage of the SOTA Faster R-CNN-based methods.

Keywords: Unsupervised · Open World · Incremental Learning · Object Detection

1 Introduction

In the early phase, there has been significant advancement in object detection using deep learning techniques [13, 14, 16, 23]. However, conventional object detection models usually work in a closed set, focusing only on detecting known categories with manual annotations, ignoring other unlabeled objects. However, in specific scenarios, identifying unknown categories is crucial. For example, self-driving cars and robots must be able to identify unexpected obstacles to prevent accidents and maintain safety.

Previous research [2] investigated Open Set Object Detection (OSOD), which involves training detectors with known category labels but requires them to identify unknown categories during testing. Recent research has expanded the OSOD task to a more dynamic situation referred to as OWOD [11], in which the model needs to identify both known and unknown categories and can learn incrementally based on the new knowledge introduced. Prior methods tackled the OWOD challenge [7, 11, 15, 25] through the strategy of assigning pseudo-labels to regions that exhibit high objectness scores and do not intersect with known objects. These methods successfully detected unknown categories with features similar to those of known categories. However, they suffer from a severe label bias issue for known categories, tending to detect all regions as part of the background if they are dissimilar to known categories.

Several prior approaches [3, 15] have investigated the application of unsupervised region proposal generation techniques [1, 17, 18, 24] to enhance the adaptability of OWOD models. These unsupervised region proposals are typically derived from hand engineered low-level attributes such as colour, texture, shape, and contour. These proposals offer preliminary knowledge and physical limitations concerning areas where unknown objects may be located. Nonetheless, these unsupervisedly generated region proposals still necessitate pseudo-labels based on objectness for calibration. Consequently, the issue of label bias, which impedes the detection of unknown objects in OWOD tasks, persists.

To address the label bias problem, we propose a novel method named LVMUM. The primary implementation process is as follows: Firstly, to model unknown objects in an unsupervised manner, we delve into the rapidly emerging Large Vision Models (LVM), such as the Segment Anything Model (SAM) [12]. Leveraging SAM's capability to segment any object, we generate class-agnostic masks for all objects in the image. By identifying the maximum and minimum coordinates x, y, we can obtain the bounding boxes of the objects. Subsequently, we generate pseudo-labels for potential targets, providing the model with supervision for potential unknown objects. However, the generated pseudo-labels contain Ground Truth information and noise. Therefore, we propose an Unsupervised Region Proposal Generation method based on SAM (SAMURPG) to generate original pseudo-labels for unknown objects.

To identify true unknown objects from the original pseudo-labels of unknown objects generated by SAM-URPG, we find that generic background areas (such as walls, sky, and ground) often appear in images, exhibiting repetitive and low-level patterns. On the contrary, foreground areas appear less frequently and have diverse features. Therefore, from the perspective of feature frequency, the background and foreground form two different distributions. Inspired by out-of-distribution (OOD) detection [10, 22] based on data reconstruction, it is observed that the encoder-decoder framework trained on In-Distribution (ID) data exhibits a larger reconstruction error for Out-Of-Distribution (OOD) data. Therefore, during inference, ID and OOD samples can be distinguished based on their reconstruction errors. However, the current reconstruction-based OOD detection methods [4, 5, 10], which compute reconstruction errors at the pixel level, have high training costs and are unable to capture semantic information adequately. We propose the Object Reconstruction-based Weibull Model (ORWM), which utilizes the ability of SAM to segment any object, generating object-level semantic information for feature reconstruction to model foreground and background in an unsupervised manner, thereby improving the model's accuracy in identifying unknown objects, and it significantly reduces the training cost of the model. Compared to previous SOTA methods, the experimental results demonstrate that the proposed method substantially improves over previous leading techniques in identifying unknown objects within the MS-COCO dataset while maintaining competitiveness Performance in detecting known object categories. Furthermore, our model, constructed using a pure convolutional neural network and utilizing fewer parameters, showcases significant advantages in terms of inference speed. We summarize our methods and contributions as follows:

- We propose an Unsupervised Region Proposal Generation method based on SAM (SAM-URPG) to generate original pseudo-labels for unknown objects, providing the model with supervision for potential unknown objects.
- We propose an Object Reconstruction error Weibull Model (ORWM), which utilizes the prior knowledge of object occurrence frequency for unsupervised modeling, enhancing the model's accuracy in identifying unknown objects. Moreover, our modeling method based on object reconstruction error significantly reduces the training cost of the model.
- Through experimental research, it was found that our proposed method, when evaluated on the OWOD task on the MS-COCO dataset, significantly outperforms contemporaneous SOTA methods in terms of recall rate for unknown categories, achieving a U-Recall of **50.9**. At the same time, it maintains competitive performance in detecting known object categories. In terms of inference speed, our method can reach **34.04 FPS**.

2 Methodology

To tackle the previously mentioned issue of label bias for known categories, we propose a method named LVMUM aimed at the unsupervised modeling of unknown objects in the original pseudo-labels generated by the unsupervised region proposal generation method. For this purpose, our method proposes several modules, including the SAM-based Unsupervised Region Proposal Generation method (SAM-URPG) discussed in Sect. 2.2, and the Weibull model based on object reconstruction error (ORWM) discussed in Sect. 2.3. As shown in Fig. 1, SAM-URPG uses SAM to generate original pseudo-labels for unknown objects, providing the model with supervision for potential unknown objects. ORWM uses the prior knowledge of object occurrence frequency for unsupervised modeling, improving the model's accuracy in identifying unknown objects. We use Faster-RCNN [16] as the base detector because Faster-RCNN has a natural advantage [2] in detecting unknown categories, and it has been used as the baseline network for many open vocabulary and open world object detection tasks [6, 11, 21].

2.1 Problem Description

In OWOD defined by ORE [11], the model M_t at time t is tasked not only with detecting the known classes $KN_t = \{1, 2, ..., C\}$, but also with identifying previously unlearned target instances as unknown classes $UN = \{C+1, ...\}$. Subsequently, users can selectively label n new interesting classes and annotate the corresponding unknown instances to train the model, incorporating this new set of classes into the known categories, denoted as $KN_{t+1} = KN_t + \{C + 1, ..., C + n\}$. Finally, the model M_t undergoes incremental learning on KN_{t+1}, avoiding training on the entire dataset to detect all target categories within KN_{t+1}.

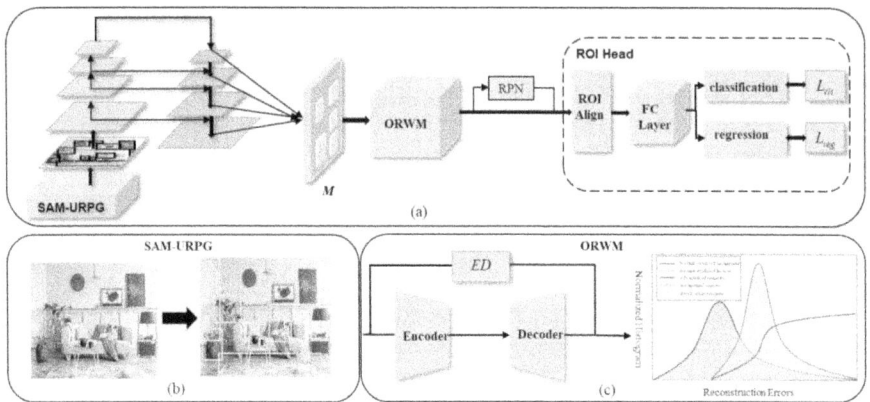

Fig. 1. The overall structure of our model. The proposed method is based on the standard Faster R-CNN [16] with FPN [9]. We first propose SAM-URPG, using the SAM to generate raw pseudo-labels for unknown objects, enhancing the model's recognition of unknown objects. Then, we propose ORWM, which utilizes object-level semantic information generated by SAM for feature reconstruction, improving the model's accuracy in recognizing unknown objects.

2.2 SAM-URPG: SAM Unsupervised Region Proposal Generation

Existing unsupervised region extraction methods can generate a large number of regions, which may contain various types of known and unknown objects. Therefore, region proposals that do not overlap with Ground Truth objects can serve as pseudo-labels for unknown objects. However, these pseudo-labels for unknown objects are coarse and are likely to be non-object bounding boxes of background areas.

To generate accurate initial pseudo-labels for unknown objects in images, we propose an Unsupervised Region Proposal Generation method based on SAM (SAM-URPG). Specifically, as shown in Fig. 2, we first use the SAM model to segment the entire image X to obtain a class-agnostic mask, represented as:

$$M_{sam}(X) = \left\{ i \in [1, nm] | \left(\left(x_1^i, y_1^i\right), ..., \left(x_{np}^i, y_{np}^i\right) \right) \right\} \quad (1)$$

where *nm* and *np* represent the number of masks and the pixel count of the current mask, respectively, subsequently, we calculate the maximum x and y coordinates for each mask to obtain the bounding box set for each mask:

$$Bb_i = \left(\min_{j \in [1,np]} \left(x_j^i, y_j^i \right), \max_{j \in [1,np]} \left(x_j^i, y_j^i \right) \right) \tag{2}$$

$$B_{set} = \{Bb_1, Bb_2, ..., Bb_{nm}\} \tag{3}$$

These bounding boxes may contain Ground Truth information and noise. To generate pseudo-labels for unknown objects, we first filter through Non-Maximum Suppression (NMS) and Intersection Over Union (IOU). We use NMS to filter out duplicate bounding boxes, then calculate the IOU of the object bounding boxes generated by SAM with the annotated object bounding boxes. If the IOU is greater than a set threshold IOU_a, it is considered a known object; otherwise, it is an unknown object:

$$B_{rough} = \left(Bb_j \in B_{set} | \left\langle \max_{i \in [1,n_{gt}]} IOU(Bb_j, gt_i) \right\rangle < IOU_a \right) \tag{4}$$

where gt_i is an instance of a known class. Despite SAM's strong zero-shot capability, it still has noise bounding boxes. Upon observation, SAM often predicts new masks for some internal pixels of already segmented objects. If a mask's bounding box has a length-to-width ratio that is too large or too small, then this object may be due to noise or detection errors. Therefore, we can apply appropriate thresholds to effectively filter out noise. If the length-to-width ratio is between thresholds Ba_{min} and Ba_{max}, we consider it as a pseudo-label for an unknown object:

$$B_{uk} = \left\{ Bb_j \in B_{rough} | Ba_{\min} < \frac{|x_2^i - x_1^i|}{|y_2^i - y_1^i|} < Ba_{\max} \right\} \tag{5}$$

where x_1^i, x_2^i, y_1^i, y_2^i are the bounding box coordinates generated by Eq. (2). Please refer to Sect. 3.3 for the experimental parameter settings.

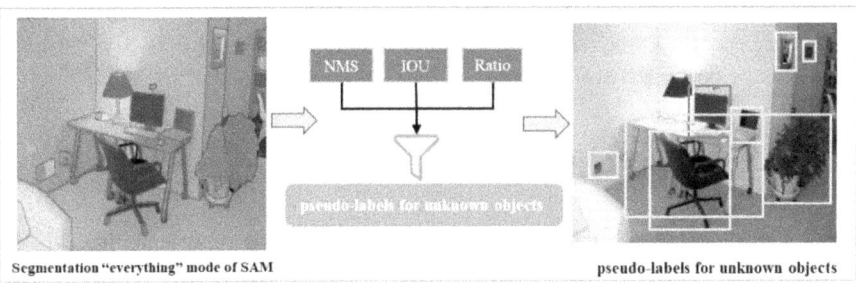

Fig. 2. The process by which SAM generates pseudo-labels, where the yellow box represents an unknown category and the red box represents a known category.

2.3 ORWM: Object Reconstruction Error Weibull Model

Current OOD detection methods based on reconstruction utilize the encoding and decoding process of autoencoders, which present the following issues: Firstly, pixel-level feature reconstruction requires the computation of reconstruction errors for all pixels, leading to high training costs. Secondly, pixel features cannot adequately represent the semantic information of known and unknown objects. To address these issues, we propose an unsupervised modeling method based on object reconstruction.

Specifically, ORWM first uses SAM to segment all objects in the image and generates object bounding boxes based on the mask, as shown in Eq. (3), Bset = {Bb1, Bb2,..., Bbnm}. Then, it extracts the feature map M = [M1, M2, M3, M4] from the input image $X \in R^{H \times W \times C}$ through the backbone network. In order to fully represent the semantic information of objects, the object bounding boxes generated by SAM are mapped to the feature map. That is, referring to the technical details of RoIAlign [8] is used to extract features from the feature map that correspond to the target area in the original image:

$$O_F = R_A(M, B_{set}) = [of_1, of_2, of_3, ..., of_{nm}] \tag{6}$$

Here, R_A represents the features extracted by ROIAlign [18], and of_{nm} represents the feature representation of each object on the feature map. Since the object-level features of_{nm} can fully represent the semantic information of objects (whether foreground or background), we perform feature reconstruction for each object's features generated on the feature map through an autoencoder. The autoencoder consists of an encoder $Ed(.)$ and a decoder $Dd(.)$. The encoder first maps all objects in the feature map to a low-dimensional latent space representation:

$$Ed(of_{nm}) = [of_E^1, of_E^2, ..., of_E^{nm}] \tag{7}$$

Here, of_{nm} represents the original features of each object in the object feature map, and of i represents the features after encoding. Then, the decoder reconstructs all objects in the latent space back to their original dimensions:

$$Dd(of_E^{nm}) = [of_D^1, of_D^2, ..., of_D^{nm}] \tag{8}$$

We use the Euclidean Distance (ED) to calculate the reconstruction error of each object, which serves as the reconstruction loss function for the autoencoder. The above process can be described as follows:

$$L_{ORWM} = \frac{1}{nm} \sum_{i=1}^{nm} \left\| of_E^i - of_D^i \right\|^2 \tag{9}$$

Here, $\|.\|$ represents the Euclidean norm. The formula above represents the square of the ED between the original data of_E^i and the reconstructed data of_D^i.

Each object region feature represents the features of the corresponding bounding box, thus assigning foreground or background labels to each object based on the corresponding bounding box. Since the background region appears more frequently and is easier to reconstruct, its reconstruction error is smaller compared to foreground objects. By arbitrarily extracting object representations from known object regions and background parts in the MS-COCO training dataset, we collected a set of object reconstruction errors, represented as ε_{kn} and ε_{bg}. As shown in part (c) of Fig. 1, we visualized the histogram of object reconstruction errors extracted from known object regions and background parts. The comparison found that the reconstruction error of the background part is smaller than the reconstruction error of the known object region because the frequency of the background region appearing is higher than the frequency of the known object region. Therefore, we can use the reconstruction error extracted from the known object region to estimate the probability distribution of all foreground regions.

Due to the inherent advantage of the Weibull distribution in fitting the shape distribution of many scenarios, it is used as the prior model in ORWM. The forms of the Weibull distributions for known regions and background regions (denoted as ft_{kn} and ft_{bg} respectively) are as follows:

$$ft(L_{ORWM}; k, g) = \frac{g}{k}(\frac{L_{ORWM}}{k})^{g-1}e^{-(L_{ORWM}/k)^g} \qquad (10)$$

Here, L_{ORWM} represents the magnitude of the object's reconstruction error, and ft is the probability distribution function of the Weibull distribution. k and g serve as the scale and shape parameters of ft. The most suitable k and g are calculated using least squares estimation (LS) based on the sampled reconstruction errors from the foreground region (ε_{kn}) and the background part (ε_{bg}).

After establishing the probability distribution models for the background region and foreground objects, we use the probability functions (ft_{kn} and ft_{bg}) to evaluate the likelihood of a pseudo-unknown object being a real unknown object. Equation (5) calculates the pseudo-label B_{uk} of an unknown object in image X. The following equation is used to calculate the soft label, which estimates the likelihood score of the pseudo-object becoming a real unknown object:

$$s(B_{uk}) = \left(\frac{ft_{kn}(L_{ORWM}(B_{uk}))}{ft_{bg}(L_{ORWM}(B_{uk})) + ft_{kn}(L_{ORWM}(B_{uk}))}\right)^{\gamma} \qquad (11)$$

Here, ft_{kn} and ft_{bg} respectively represent the Weibull functions of the known object area and the background part. γ is a hyperparameter used for score calculation. When $\gamma \to \infty$, the probability of all unknown object pseudo-labels is very low, which can be considered close to 0. However, when $\gamma \to 0$, we consider these pseudo-labels as real unknown objects. Then, the score from Eq. (11) is used as a parameter and added to the loss function of the base detector as a supervisory signal, thereby learning known and unknown objects. The optimized loss function is as follows:

$$L(P_{rpj}) = \frac{1}{N_{cls}} \sum_{rpj} w_{rpj} L_{cls}\left(P_{rpj}, P^*_{rpj}\right) \qquad (12)$$

where w_{rpj} is the loss weight for region proposals rpj. When rpj belongs to a region of pseudo-unknown objects, w_{rpj} equals $s(rpj)$; otherwise, it equals 1. p_{rpj} represents the predicted probability for region proposals rpj, while p^*_{rpj} represents its ground truth, and L_{cls} represents the cross-entropy loss.

3 Experiment

3.1 Dataset

To substantiate our proposed method's efficacy, we evaluated our model on the OWOD benchmark, as proposed by OWOD [11] and OW-DETR [7]. As defined by PROB [25], there exist two benchmarks, namely S-OWODB and M-OWODB. Given that S-OWODB is superclass-separated and the semantics of unknown objects are more challenging to extend, our experiment pertains to the S-OWODB benchmark. We formulated four distinct tasks with 80 categories from the MS-COCO dataset, with the number of training images and instances for each task being: T1 (89490, 421243), T2(55870, 163512), T3(39402, 114452), T4(38903, 160794) respectively. Task one encompasses the categories of PASCAL VOC, and subsequently, each task incorporates 20 new categories based on the preceding task for incremental experiments. The test set comprises all categories with 4952 images and 36781 test instances.

3.2 Metric

We adhere to the standard evaluation metrics for the OWOD task [11]. The widely accepted object detection metric evaluates the model's performance on known categories, Mean Average Precision (mAP). The model's performance on objects without annotations is evaluated using the Unknown Class Recall (U-Recall) for unknown classes. Previously known mAP represents the detection accuracy for classes seen in previous tasks, denoted as mAP_pk. The current known mAP represents the detection accuracy for newly introduced classes in the current task, denoted as mAP_ck. Both indicate the detection accuracy for all categories seen in the current task, denoted as mAP_bo. In the incremental learning tasks (T2 − T4), the performance of known classes is divided into two parts: classes seen before and the classes introduced in the current task.

3.3 Details

Our experiments are built based on Detectron2 [20]. We use ResNet50-FPN [9] as our backbone network, and the base detector adopts Faster-RCNN [16]. The Stochastic Gradient Descent (SGD) is used as the optimizer. Our parameter settings include a learning rate of 0.02, a momentum parameter of 0.9, and a weight decay of e − 4. The model undergoes a standard training schedule for 32 training cycles, with each round consisting of a 6-cycle self-training process. Our experiments utilize 2 NVIDIA RTX3090 GPUs, with a batch size of 16. In this experiment, the hyperparameter $\gamma = 4$ is set by default. In the process of handling pseudo-labels in SAM-URPG, our experiment adopts a data processing strategy to filter Ground Truth information and noise bounding boxes. Firstly, the generated bounding boxes use NMS for deduplication, setting IOUa to 0.8. We calculate the IOU of the object-bounding boxes generated by SAM and the annotated object-bounding boxes. If the IOU is greater than the set threshold IOUa, it is considered a known object. Otherwise, it is an unknown object. Then we proceed to denoise, setting the maximum aspect ratio threshold of the bounding box Bamax to 4 and the minimum threshold Bamin to 0.25. Bounding boxes that do not satisfy the aspect ratio size between 0.25 and 4 are considered noise bounding boxes. Finally, we obtain the pseudo-labels of unknown objects.

3.4 Comparison with State-of-the-Art Models

To provide a clear demonstration of the experimental to provide a clear demonstration of the experimental results of our method, we compared it with several of the latest models in the field of OWOD, including ORE [11], OW-DETR [7], PROB [25], CAT [15] and MEPU [4]. We removed the energy model (EBUI) from ORE, as it could potentially lead to data leakage due to its use of fully annotated categories. All the data used in the papers above originate from the data in the original papers.

Table 1. Compare state-of-the-art of OWOD models

Task IDs ($\rightarrow$)	Task 1		Task 2			Task 3				Task 4		
	U-Recall ($\uparrow$)	mAP ($\uparrow$) Current known	U-Recall ($\uparrow$)	mAP ($\uparrow$) Previously known	Current known	Both	U-Recall ($\uparrow$)	mAP ($\uparrow$) Previously known	Current known	Both	mAP ($\uparrow$) Previously known	Current known	Both
ORE-EBUI(CVPR2021)	1.5	71.4	3.9	61.0	30.9	45.6	3.6	43.1	32.2	39.5	33.6	26.3	31.8
OW-DETR(CVPR2022)	5.7	73.1	6.2	65.0	29.0	46.0	6.9	46.7	25.7	39.7	38.2	28.1	33.1
PROB(CVPR2023)	17.6	73.5	22.3	66.3	36.0	50.4	24.8	47.8	30.4	42.0	42.6	31.7	39.9
CAT(CVPR2023)	24.0	74.2	23.0	67.6	35.5	50.7	24.6	**51.2**	32.6	45.0	**45.4**	**35.1**	**42.8**
MEPU	37.9	**74.3**	35.8	68.0	1.9	**54.3**	35.7	50.2	**38.3**	**46.2**	43.7	33.7	41.2
Ours(LVMUM)	**50.9**	73.5	**50.7**	**68.2**	37.8	52.3	**43.6**	48.8	36.6	44.1	42.1	32.2	39.8

Identifying Potential Unknown Objects (T_1). As shown in Table 1, our method has achieved a comprehensive lead in the recall rate of unknowns. In terms of the performance of recalling unknown objects, it reached the highest unknown recall rate of 51.9. The closest to this result is MEPU, and our model significantly leads with a recall rate advantage of 34.3% (50.9 vs 37.9). For CAT, the advantage reaches 112.1% (50.9 vs 24.0), and for PROB, the advantage reaches 189.2% (50.9 vs 17.6). In terms of the performance of known categories, the mAP has slightly decreased, lagging behind MEPU's mAP by 0.8 and CAT's mAP by 0.7. This decline in performance is acceptable because the additional unknown supervision makes it more difficult for the model to distinguish known objects.

Incremental Learning ($T_2 - T_4$). As shown in Table 1, our method maintains an advantage in U-Recall (T_2: 141.6% MEPU, T_3: 122.1% MEPU). As the number of known categories increases, the mAP of our model on known categories gradually falls behind that of MEPU. This result is acceptable because the model recalls more unknown targets, which reduces the proportion of seen categories in the top 100 predictions of standard post-processing and faces serious challenges in the classification head (RoI Head).

3.5 Ablation Study

We conducted experiments to compare the model's performance with and without adding these modules to the tasks to validate the effectiveness of the two modules, SAM-URPG and ORWM, in our proposed approach.

Table 2. Different unsupervised region proposal methods generate pseudo labels

Unsupervised Region Propoasl Genenration	U-Recall	mAP_ck
Baseline	33.4	73.2
Selective Search	34.2	73.7
GOP	37.1	73.4
FreeSOLO	37.9	**74.3**
SAM-URGP	**50.9**	73.5

SAM-URGP Effectiveness. We evaluated the effectiveness of unsupervised region proposal generation methods on our model, as shown in Table 2. In Task 1, we compared four unsupervised region proposal generation methods with a baseline method that does not use any proposal generator. These methods are Selective Search [17], DETReg [1], FreeSOLO [18], and SAM-URGP. We found that all proposal generation methods typically produce better results than the baseline method, especially regarding unknown recall (a gain of + 17.5 can be achieved using SAM-URGP), significantly improving the detection results of unknown objects. It is worth noting that although the earliest method, such as Selective Search, generates lower-quality region proposals, it still improves. Our ORWM module can identify true unknown classes from cluttered environments.

ORWM Effectiveness. We conducted a performance analysis of ORWM on the MSCOCO dataset, reporting mAP for known classes and U-Recall for unknown classes in Task 1–4, as shown in Table 3. Without ORWM, the method is equivalent to using proposals generated by the SAM-URGP method directly as pseudo-labels for training Faster-RCNN on unknown objects. Few inaccuracies exist in the pseudo-labels for unknown objects, leading to confusion between foreground and background regions in the detector. The modeling mechanism of ORWM for unknown objects contributes to improving the accuracy of recognizing known and unknown objects. In Task 1, U-Recall improved by 4.6, and mAP_ck improved by 4.1. In Task 2, U-Recall increased by 7.5, and mAPck increased by 2, and there were varying degrees of improvement in other tasks as well.

Table 3. Our complete model with its variants

	Task 1		Task 2		Task 3		Task 4
ORWM	U-Recall	mAP_ck	U-Recall	mAP_ck	U-Recall	mAP_ck	mAP_ck
×	46.3	69.1	43.2	35.8	37.1	**34.7**	31.7
√	**50.9**	**73.5**	**50.7**	**37.8**	**43.6**	34.6	**32.2**

4 Conclusions

In response to the existing label bias problem in OWOD, we propose a novel method to address this problem. Initially, we model unknown objects unsupervised, effectively resolving the label bias problem. Simultaneously, we leverage popular Large Visual.

Models (LVM), such as the SAM model, which can segment any object to extend the effective detection of unknown objects. Experimental findings reveal that our model has significantly improved the detection of unknown objects, substantially surpassing current SOTA methods. At the same time, it maintains competitive performance in detecting known object categories. Our method can inspire insights into OWOD, especially in detecting unknown objects.

Acknowledgements. This work was also partially supported by Guangdong Artificial Intelligence and Digital Economy Laboratory (Guangzhou).

References

1. Bar, A., et al.: Detreg: unsupervised pretraining with region priors for object detection. In: Proceedings of the IEEE/CVF Conference on Computer Vision and Pattern Recognition, pp. 14605–14615 (2022)
2. Dhamija, A., Gunther, M., Ventura, J., Boult, T.: The overlooked elephant of object detection: Open set. In: Proceedings of the IEEE/CVF Winter Conference on Applications of Computer Vision, pp. 1021–1030 (2020)
3. Dong, N., Zhang, Y., Ding, M., Lee, G.H.: Open world detr: transformer based open world object detection. arXiv preprint arXiv:2212.02969 (2022)
4. Fang, R., Pang, G., Zhou, L., Bai, X., Zheng, J.: Unsupervised recognition of unknown objects for open-world object detection. arXiv preprint arXiv:2308.16527 (2023)
5. Graham, M.S., et al.: Denoising diffusion models for out-of-distribution detection. In: Proceedings of the IEEE/CVF Conference on Computer Vision and Pattern Recognition, pp. 2947–2956 (2023)
6. Gu, X., Lin, T.Y., Kuo, W., Cui, Y.: Open-vocabulary object detection via vision and language knowledge distillation. arXiv preprint arXiv:2104.13921 (2021)
7. Gupta, A., et al.: Ow-detr: Open-world detection transformer. In: Proceedings of the IEEE/CVF Conference on Computer Vision and Pattern Recognition, pp. 9235–9244 (2022)
8. He, K., Gkioxari, G., Dollár, P., Girshick, R.: Mask r-cnn: In: Proceedings of the IEEE international conference on computer vision, pp. 2961–2969 (2017)

9. He, K., Zhang, X., Ren, S., Sun, J.: Deep residual learning for image recognition. In: Proceedings of the IEEE conference on computer vision and pattern recognition, pp. 770–778 (2016)
10. Jiang, W., et al.: Read: Aggregating reconstruction error into out-of-distribution detection. In: Proceedings of the AAAI Conference on Artificial Intelligence, vol. 37, pp. 14910–14918 (2023)
11. Joseph, K., Khan, S., Khan, F.S., Balasubramanian, V.N.: Towards open world object detection. In: Proceedings of the IEEE/CVF conference on computer vision and pattern recognition, pp. 5830–5840 (2021)
12. Kirillov, A., et al.: Segment anything. arXiv preprint arXiv:2304.02643 (2023)
13. Lin, T.Y., Goyal, P., Girshick, R., He, K., Dollár, P.: Focal loss for dense object detection. In: Proceedings of the IEEE international conference on computer vision, pp. 2980–2988 (2017)
14. Lu, Y., Chen, X., Wu, Z., Yu, J.: Decoupled metric network for single-stage few-shot object detection. IEEE Transactions on Cybernetics **53**(1), 514–525 (2022)
15. Ma, S., et al.: Cat: Localization and identification cascade detection transformer for open-world object detection. In: Proceedings of the IEEE/CVF Conference on Computer Vision and Pattern Recognition, pp. 19681–19690 (2023)
16. Ren, S., He, K., Girshick, R., Sun, J.: Faster r-cnn: Towards real-time object detection with region proposal networks. Advances in neural information processing systems 28 (2015)
17. Uijlings, J.R., Van De Sande, K.E., Gevers, T., Smeulders, A.W.: Selective search for object recognition. Int. J. Comput. Vision **104**, 154–171 (2013)
18. Wang, X., et al.: Freesolo: Learning to segment objects without annotations. In: Proceedings of the IEEE/CVF Conference on Computer Vision and Pattern Recognition, pp. 14176–14186 (2022)
19. Wei, F., Gao, Y., Wu, Z., Hu, H., Lin, S.: Aligning pretraining for detection via object-level contrastive learning. Adv. Neural. Inf. Process. Syst. **34**, 22682–22694 (2021)
20. Wu, Y., Kirillov, A., Massa, F., Lo, W., Girshick, R.: Detectron2 [www document] (2019). URL https://github.com/facebookresearch/detectron2. Accessed 3 March 2021
21. Zhao, X., et al.: Revisiting open world object detection. IEEE Transactions on Circuits and Systems for Video Technology (2023)
22. Zhou, Y.: Rethinking reconstruction autoencoder-based out-of-distribution detection. In: Proceedings of the IEEE/CVF Conference on Computer Vision and Pattern Recognition, pp. 7379–7387 (2022)
23. Zhu, X., et al.: Deformable detr: Deformable transformers for end-to-end object detection. arXiv preprint arXiv:2010.04159 (2020)
24. Zitnick, C.L., Dollár, P.: Edge boxes: Locating object proposals from edges. In: Computer Vision–ECCV 2014: 13th European Conference, Zurich, Switzerland, September 6–12, 2014, Proceedings, Part V 13, pp. 391–405. Springer (2014)
25. Zohar, O., Wang, K.C., Yeung, S.: Prob: probabilistic objectness for open world object detection. In: Proceedings of the IEEE/CVF Conference on Computer Vision and Pattern Recognition, pp. 11444–11453 (2023)

Implementation and Application of Violence Detection System Based on Multi-head Attention and LSTM

Fengping Cao(✉), Yi Miao, and Wangyi Zhang

Southeast University Chengxian College, Nanjing 210000, JS, China
cfp423@126.com

Abstract. The extensive expansion of surveillance has enabled the identification of numerous threats in advance. By examining surveillance footage, violent activities can be identified in time to prevent disastrous repercussions. In this paper, a method for detecting violence is proposed. Initially, GoogLeNet is chosen for feature extraction in time and space based on the loss of pre-trained CNN feature extraction results and the running efficiency of each model. Some convolutional layers of GoogLeNet are frozen in accordance with the concept of migration learning to meet the demand for accurate feature extraction on tiny data sets. Multi-head Attention (MHA) was used in order to increase the model's precision and operating efficiency by focusing on key features. The results are then input into the long short-term memory (LSTM) violence detection model. In addition, an ablation study on the input characteristics was carried out, comparing the outcomes with and without the MHA. It revealed that including the MHA enhanced the outcomes by 7.31%. Finally, the model obtains 100% accuracy on the Daily Violence and Movies Fight datasets and 94.36% accuracy on the RWF-2000 dataset, which is commendable. As can be seen, our model on daily violence and Movies Fight has produced the best results, and it is 4% more accurate than the best method currently available for RWF-2000. To put the model in this paper to use in practice, we also created an Android application (APP). Violence in hospitals is common, but not all hospitals can deal with it promptly. Our APP can detect violent behavior in hospital surveillance videos in real time and promptly alert security officers. The usefulness is excellent.

Keywords: Violence Detection · Application · Multi-head Attention · LSTM

1 Introduction

Identification of human behavior is a topic of intense interest in computer vision. The detection of anomalies in contemporary intelligent video surveillance systems has a significant research value [1]. Violence detection, a key component of anomaly detection, has become an active study subject in computer vision, drawing a large number of researchers [2].

Research [3, 4] has shown that action recognition and behavior detection of videos using deep learning techniques are more efficient and accurate than manual monitoring.

With the progress of artificial intelligence, it is now possible to detect violence by convolutional neural networks (CNN) to extract and classify data at temporal and spatial levels [5]. To predict violent acts, Ullah FUM [6] et al. utilized lightweight CNN and an improved 3D-CNN model. CNN was employed as a spatial feature extractor and Long Short Term Memory Network (LSTM) [7] as a temporal feature extractor for a real-time violence detector by Abdali et al. [8]. For violence detection, Pang et al. [9] utilized an audiovisual dependency attention (AVD-attention) module. Nevertheless, the currently available approaches for violence detection cannot combine efficiency and precision.

In this paper, we use a pre-trained GoogLeNet to extract spatiotemporal video features. Then classify using LSTM. Subsequently, MHA is added to improve the model's precision and efficiency. Finally, we obtain a violence detection model. Using this model, a violence detection software application was designed for use in hospitals.

The rest of the paper is laid out as follows: Sect. 2 provides an overview of related works on abnormal behavior and violence detection. Section 3 demonstrates the proposed method in detail. Section 4 explains experiments, results, and application. Finally, Sect. 5 concludes our work.

2 Related Work

2.1 Abnormal Behavior Detection

Analysis and monitoring, recognition, and detection of abnormal human behavior have become one of the hot spots in the field of computer vision, which plays a crucial role in freeing up labor and boosting productivity. Researchers usually define aberrant behavior as unusual, unexpected, and unpredictable behavior that deviates from existing patterns [10]. Currently, approaches to abnormal behavior recognition are divided into two groups, one based on manual feature extraction and the other on deep network learning features.

The method based on manual feature extraction frequently employs traditional machine learning techniques. Its advantages lie in need-based orientation, strong pertinence, and simple implementation. However, as the necessity for recognizing aberrant activity develops, manual feature extraction can become increasingly time-consuming and ineffective.

Nowadays, deep feature-based models have achieved tremendous success in a variety of nonlinear high-dimensional data applications [11], including activity recognition and video summarization, etc. In the study of abnormal behavior detection, Deng et al. [12] presented a model of a "spatiotemporal auto-encoder". Deep neural networks were used to extract the movie's temporal and spatial data and learn the film's motion characteristics. Ma et al. [13] used YOLO for real-time detection and feature extraction of specified surveillance targets and then LSTM to make the final behavioral discrimination of behavioral action sequences. Zhou et al. [14] present a behavior recognition model based on spatiotemporal convolution (ST-CNN) and attention-based LSTM (ATT-LSTM). Integrating spatial information at a granular level into each network segment increases network recognition performance.

2.2 Violence Detection

As part of deviant behavior, violent acts, such as fights, assaults, and knife wounds, are included. Traditional methods for violence identification have largely centered on manually generated characteristics that indicate motion trajectory, limb orientation, local appearance, inter-frame variations, etc. Deniz et al. [15] proposed a hybrid "handcrafted/learned" feature framework, which used the Hough Forests classifier and 2DCNN.

Li et al. [16] suggested a 3D CNN based on the DenseNet architecture that requires fewer parameters and is more efficient. Halder et al. [17] used a Convolutional Neural Network-based Bidirectional LSTM for violence detection. This demonstrates that LSTM is a more prevalent classification method for violent behaviors. Mumtaz et al. [18] propose a deep representation-based violence scene detection model that uses the concept of transfer learning to identify human aggressive behavior. Results show the highest accuracies of 99.28% and 99.97% on Hockey Fight [19] and Movies Fight [20] datasets respectively. This demonstrates that migration learning and LSTM can yield superior results in the detection of violence.

3 Method

Each frame of the video is transformed into a 240 × 240 RGB picture with three channels. For temporal space feature extraction, the processed video frames are fed into a CNN model with partially frozen convolutional layers. The results are entered into a Long short-term memory (LSTM) model for the classification of violent and non-violent behaviors. To improve the accuracy of the model, we identify many significant video frame elements utilizing multi-headed attention (MHA) [21]. The outputs are fused with spatiotemporal information for feature fusion and then fed into an LSTM classifier. The overall model structure of this paper is shown in Fig. 1 In addition, the procedure is discussed in detail below.

3.1 Feature Extraction

Feature extraction is the main core in classification, clustering, recognition, and detection. Using useful feature variables can result in high performance, even if the machine learner is simple. In contrast, using unhelpful feature variables with an advanced complex machine learner might lead to decreased performance [22]. Therefore, it is important to choose a suitable feature extraction method to obtain features for each frame. There are numerous approaches to extracting features. Common methodologies in deep learning include Recurrent Neural Networks (RNNs), Autoencoders (AE), Convolutional Neural Networks (CNNs), Generative Adversarial Networks (GANs), and others.

Research [8, 22]indicates that CNNs perform better at behavior recognition. Meanwhile, the CNN models that performed well on ImageNet for glomerulus classification, mineral prospectivity prediction, object detection, etc. can also perform better. Transfer learning [23] is the process of transferring knowledge from one domain to another, in order to improve learning outcomes in the target domain. This paper utilizes a pre-trained CNN model for temporal and spatial information extraction from violent video clips.

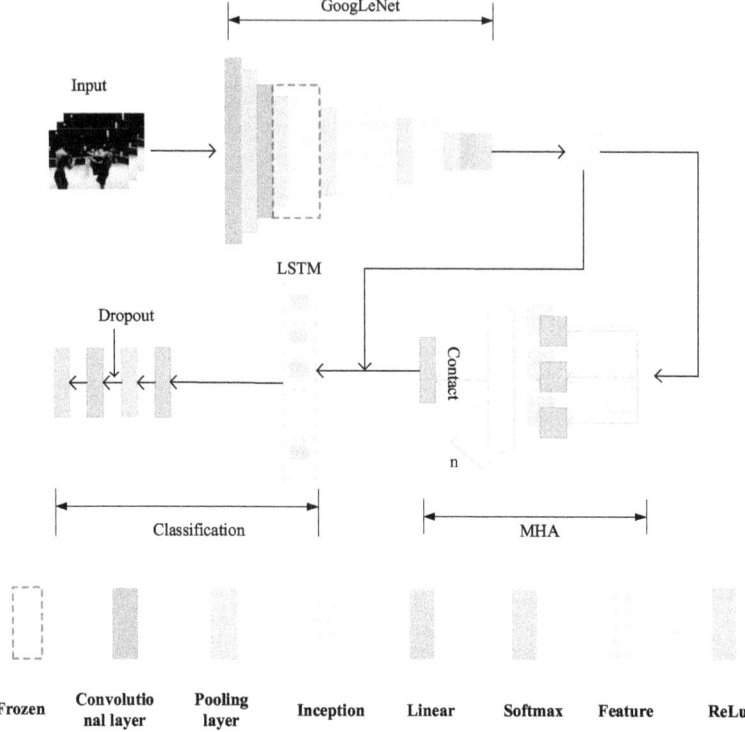

Fig. 1. Overall model structure

According to the requirement of real-time surveillance video monitoring, consideration is given to which pre-trained CNNs will be utilized for migration learning. In this study, VGG, which has more parameters and higher computational demand, was not selected as the pre-trained CNN model. Initially, ResNet, GoogLeNet, and DenseNet were chosen for training. They have excellent performance and consume less memory than VGG computation. ResNet is capable of avoiding gradient disappearance and preserving the original characteristics. GoogLeNet's global average pooling layer reduces parameters, while inception raises recognition accuracy and decreases overfitting. DenseNet uses dense connectivity to enhance feature reuse and mitigate gradient disappearance.

However, in some tiny datasets, it is inappropriate to employ large and deep models. In addition to causing arithmetic overload, it may also overfit the network and fail to produce a widely applicable model. Thus, in this paper, we consider frozen convolutional layers when employing a pre-trained CNN model. For smaller datasets, more convolutional layers are frozen to minimize the model depth, whereas, on larger datasets, fewer or no convolutional layers are frozen to place greater emphasis on precise feature extraction.

3.2 Optimization Using Attention Mechanism

The attention mechanism [24] is capable of focusing on the most important aspects of a huge amount of information while paying less attention to irrelevant details. After Vaswani et al. [21] proposed the Transformer structure in 2017, the attention mechanism is frequently implemented in models of neural network architectures. Attention mechanisms are present in domains such as picture caption creation, text categorization, action recognition, image-based analysis, etc. In this study, after employing CNN for feature extraction, we use an attention mechanism to zero out the most salient elements of violent actions.

Each frame offers a variety of information regarding the recognition of violence, such as knives, swinging fists, firearms, etc. It is not scientific to recognize only the smallest amount of information in a frame, as this will drastically lower the accuracy and applicability of the model. MHA enables the model to simultaneously attend to multiple sections of the input sequence, which can enhance the model's capacity to grasp complex dependencies and interactions within the data. Additionally, using MHA can provide greater flexibility in modeling different types of relationships within the data, like capturing both local and global dependencies. This can increase the efficiency of model detection while maintaining the model's precision. So, we employ MHA to concentrate on the most important information in each frame. Hence, the model's retrieved features are more representative.

The subsequent part will provide a concise overview of the concept of MHA. The specific steps are shown in the Fig. 2.

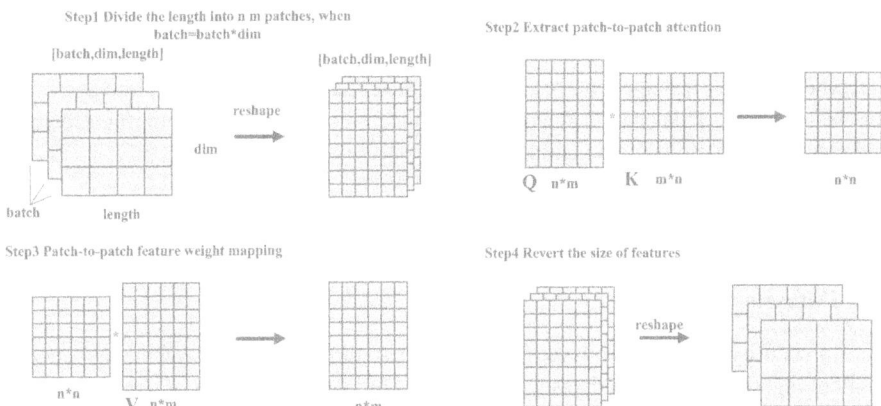

Fig. 2. Step in MHA

In The first step, the feature matrix that GoogleNet has extracted is entered into MHA. Its length is divided into n patches of length m. At this time, the batch becomes batch*dim. The input is divided into matrices that can be computed with MHA in this step. Additionally, a preliminary depiction of the violent behavior's characterization QVK is obtained. In the second step, the features between patches are extracted. Each layer comprises n blocks and each patch is of length m. To create a n*n feature matrix, multiply the Q matrix by its transposed K matrix. The inter-patch features are represented by this matrix. In the third step, doing the mapping of features to weights between patches. The V matrix is used to multiply the second step's outcome. In the second and third steps, the original features are split to get more detailed features. The relevance of the features is "ranked" by weighting them, emphasizing the primary features while ignoring the supporting ones. For instance, if swinging a fist is the primary characteristic of violent conduct, the higher weight is multiplied by its matrix. More focus is placed on it in the future detection process so that it is simpler to identify the occurrence of violent conduct using the many traits of human behavior.

After getting the extracted features, their dimensions are finally lifted to the input dimensions. The model can better focus on the key characteristics of a violent act thanks to feature extraction by MHA, which improves violence detection.

3.3 Classification

LSTM is a temporal recurrent neural network that processes time-dependent information well.

These are the specific phases of the original categorization presented in this research. First, the extracted features from the pre-trained CNN are used as the prediction input for the LSTM. The results of the prediction are input into the fully connected layer. With the Relu activation function, increase each neuron's expressiveness. Using the gradient descent process, the loss function's lowest point is identified. The results are then projected in two dimensions to the fully linked layer. Finally, the prediction is generated using the softmax function.

In this paper, the model is once again optimized to improve its precision. Using the MHA technique, the crucial information in the retrieved characteristics is extracted. The outcomes are then reshaped, merged with the retrieved features, and sent into an LSTM for classification. This enables the model to concentrate on the most important features and enhances the model's precision.

4 Experiment and Analysis

4.1 Datasets

Due to security and privacy issues, access to surveillance footage of the violence is challenging. The following datasets are frequently used in the field of violence detection: Crowd Violence [25], Hockey Fight [19], Movies Fight [20], and RWF-2000 [26]. Specific information for each dataset is shown in Table 1.

Crowd Violence Dataset is comprised of 246 segments of violent and non-violent activities in crowded, low-resolution situations. With the advancement of modern surveillance technologies, the resolution of surveillance video is now greater than that of Violent Flow, making its use for training models impractical. Hockey Fight Dataset is video captured from National Hockey League games, which contains some of the moves that might be involved in the fight. The Movies Fight Dataset contains footage of double fights from movies. RWF-2000 is a collection of 2,000 videos collected by surveillance

Table 1. The dataset used in this paper

Dataset	Data Scale	Resolution	Scenario
Movies Fight [20]	200 Clips	720*480	Movie
RWF-2000 [26]	2000 Clips	Variable	Surveillance
Hockey Fight [19]	1000 Clips	Variable	Hockey
Daily Violence	42 Clips	Variable	Natural

cameras in real-world circumstances, containing a variety of violent actions that are consistent with real-world scenarios. A model generated from it as a training dataset is capable of detecting a variety of violent behaviors in daily life.

To improve the detection of violent behavior, this study collects behavioral patterns from the web to produce a Dataset titled Daily Violence, which spans numerous scenarios. It contains both violent and non-violent behaviors in a crowded area and activities involving two combatants. Videos are captured from real-life security footage or from movies that show daily life. For example, in the same scene, we artificially distinguish its violent and non-violent actions.

The successful identification of these behaviors has positive implications for the application of the model in this paper.

4.2 Experiment

The hardware environment used for the experiment is as follows:

- CPU: i7-10710U 1.10 GHz
- GPU: NVIDIA Geforce MX350; P100 on Kaggle

We utilized Restnet34, DenseNet121, and GoogLeNet for feature extraction on the Movies Fight dataset, respectively, to determine a suitable CNN model. Since there are only 200 clips in Movies Fight, we freeze the same proportion of convolutional layers for each training model. Given that freezing different convolutional layers could result in different feature extraction outcomes, we evaluated each model multiple times and then calculated the mean. The final cross-entropy loss was used to judge which model had superior results for feature extraction.

Figure 3 displays the results, with the loss of GoogLeNet being the lowest at 0.36. GoogLeNet is therefore selected for feature extraction in this work.

In the process of behavioral classification, various activation functions and hidden layers provide various outcomes. Numerous experiments have shown that, in short-batch datasets, a mere 40 hidden layers are needed for accurate video classification. Stated differently, detecting violence in tiny areas can yield greater results with fewer resources. Whereas in RWF-2000, more hidden layers are used for classification. However, adding more hidden layers all at once does not provide desirable outcomes. 200 hidden layers were employed in one experiment, which not only wasted a lot of resources but also produced subpar results.

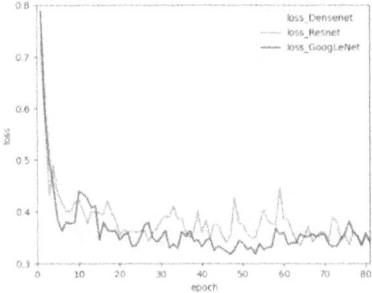
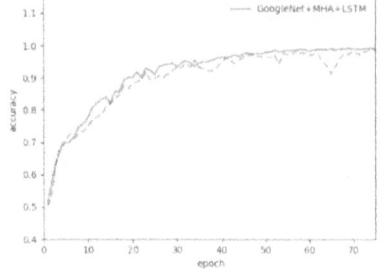

Fig. 3. Losses with different CNNs

Fig. 4. Model accuracy before and after enhancement in RWF-2000

To assess the performance of our model, it was implemented on three datasets. After dividing the dataset into training (80%) and testing (20%), the model was used for detection. Finally, the accuracy of the tests for Daily Violence and Movies Fight both reached 100 percent. Nonetheless, the outcomes of RWF-2000 were disappointing. So, we added the MHA module and retested it. Figure 4 shows a line graph depicting the change in accuracy before and after the improvement.

As seen in Fig. 4, the addition of attention somewhat improves the model's convergence speed. What's more, the mean recall rate before improvement was 0.951 after improvement was 0.967. In the meantime, the accuracy rate rises from 87.05 percent to 94.36 percent. As seen in Table 2, our model outperforms others.

Table 2. Comparison of accuracy on datasets

Model/Dataset	RWF-2000	Movie Fights	Hockey Fight	Daily Violence
ConvLSTM [3]	77%	100%	97.10%	-
I3D (Optical-flow only) [27]	75.50%	100%	-	-
Cheng et al. (P3D) [26]	87.20%	100%	98%	-
SSHA model (RGB only) [28]	90.40%	99%	98%	-
SSHA model (Optical-flow only) [28]	76%	98.50%	86.20%	-
Ours	94.30%	100%	98%	100%

The above accuracy rates are explained in this study. Movies Fight is easier to categorize because it only consists of one scene, has a small amount of high-definition clips overall, and primarily features two people performing violent activities in a single scene. Therefore, most approaches produce superior outcomes. The above accuracy rates are examined in this study.

Movie Fights is easier to categorize because it only consists of one scene, has a small amount of high-definition clips overall, and primarily features two people performing violent activities in a single scene. Therefore, most approaches produce superior outcomes. The accuracy percentage is greater in Hockey Fight because the majority of the videos feature two-person incidents of violence in lesser resolution.

Nonetheless, the majority of the movies in RWF-2000 have diverse settings, colors, and definitions. The span is very large, which is a good reproduction of the diversity of video sources in daily life. Owing to the wide range of movies, it is required to convert the videos to the same size and color. The information currently has a certain loss, which affects the outcome as well. Despite having a tiny sample size, Daily Violence offers a wide variety of video formats. High-resolution films of individuals acting violently or peacefully in pairs, multiples, and masses were gathered. It is also clearly detectable by our model. We will also gather more information for the dataset in the future so that we can finish this job more effectively.

4.3 Application

The purpose of violence detection is to reduce damage. When violence happens, if the relevant staff notices it in a timely manner and takes the necessary steps to prevent it from continuing, or if the victim is treated in a timely way. Then, violence would not divide so many families from one another.

Thus, we design an app for hospitals that detects violence based on the model presented in this research. Use this model to detect surveillance video. When an odd incident is identified, the app will notify hospital security officers in time for them to respond. With the app, security staff can view the location details of the violent occurrence and

(a)Login UI   (b)Alarm UI   (c)Address UI

Fig. 5. The main UI of the application

the live scenario map, allowing them to make more informed decisions about how to respond.

The Android application is built using the GSON framework and Android Jetpack. Focusing on the user experience, it satisfies use criteria while being simple and straightforward. The main UI of the APP is shown in Fig. 5. The web-facing management information of the backend is developed using Spring Boot. Within the application, the administrator can manage the content of notifications, user information, alarm information, etc.

The database connects the detection model and APP to create a three-tier design. When the model identifies violence, the location and site information are saved to the database, and the APP is refreshed every 0.1s to receive the database information. This enables the detection of violence in surveillance footage in real-time and the notification of the appropriate staff for processing.

5 Conclusion

In this paper, a methodology for detecting violence is laid out and applied practically. The model's processing phases are as follows. In terms of picture recognition, models like GoogLeNet, DenseNet, ResNet, and others perform well. Based on the concept of transfer learning, we apply it to the detection of violent behavior in surveillance videos. We perform feature extraction separately using them and conclude that GoogLeNet is the most effective in this regard based on the loss. To improve model accuracy on smaller datasets such as Movies Fight, we freeze part of the convolutional layer of GoogLeNet for feature extraction. The extracted features are then subjected to ablation experiments to compare the effect of including or excluding the multi-headed attention mechanism on the results. Finally, we use LSTM to classify whether an act is violent or not. Our model achieved 100% accuracy on datasets containing daily violence and Movies Fight. An accuracy of 94.36% was achieved on RWF-2000, which contains many types of violent behaviors, which is about 4% higher than that of Mohammadi et al. [28].

Our model does not process facial recognition for tracking. Future research could include a face recognition module to better reduce the impact of violent events and expand our model's range of applications, such as helping police officers identify ongoing violent incidents and targeting them for tracking.

References

1. Mabrouk, A.B., Zagrouba, E.: Abnormal behavior recognition for intelligent video surveillance systems: A review. Expert Syst. Appl. **91**, 480–491 (2018)
2. Ramzan, M., et al.: A review on state-of-the-art violence detection techniques. IEEE Access **7**, 107560–107575 (2019)
3. Sudhakaran, S., Lanz, O.: Learning to detect violent videos using convolutional long short-term memory. In: 2017 14th IEEE international conference on advanced video and signal based surveillance (AVSS), pp. 1–6. IEEE (2017)
4. Tran, D., Bourdev, L., Fergus, R., Torresani, L., Paluri, M.: Learning spatiotemporal features with 3d convolutional networks. In: Proceedings of the IEEE international conference on computer vision, pp. 4489–4497 (2015)

5. Traoŕe, A., Akhloufi, M.A.: Violence detection in videos using deep recurrent and convolutional neural networks. In: 2020 IEEE International Conference on Systems, Man, and Cybernetics (SMC), pp. 154–159. IEEE (2020)
6. Ullah, F.U.M., Ullah, A., Muhammad, K., Haq, I.U., Baik, S.W.: Violence detection using spatiotemporal features with 3d convolutional neural network. Sensors **19**(11), 2472 (2019)
7. Hochreiter, S., Schmidhuber, J.: Long short-term memory. Neural Comput. **9**(8), 1735–1780 (1997)
8. Abdali, A.M.R., Al-Tuma, R.F.: Robust real-time violence detection in video using cnn and lstm. In: 2019 2nd Scientific Conference of Computer Sciences (SCCS), pp. 104–108. IEEE (2019)
9. Pang, W., Xie, W., He, Q., Li, Y., Yang, J.: Audiovisual dependency attention for violence detection in videos. IEEE Transactions on Multimedia, pp. 1–12 (2022)
10. Khaleghi, A., Moin, M.S.: Improved anomaly detection in surveillance videos based on a deep learning method. In: 2018 8th Conference of AI and Robotics and 10th RoboCup Iranopen International Symposium (IRANOPEN), pp. 73–81. IEEE (2018)
11. Ullah, W., Ullah, A., Hussain, T., Khan, Z.A., Baik, S.W.: An efficient anomaly recognition framework using an attention residual lstm in surveillance videos. Sensors **21**(8), 2811 (2021)
12. Zhao, Y., et al.: Spatio-temporal autoencoder for video anomaly detection. In: Proceedings of the 25th ACM international conference on Multimedia, pp. 1933–1941 (2017)
13. Ma, Y., Tan Li, D.X., Chong, Y.C.: Behavior recognition for intelligent surveillance, pp. 282–290 (2019)
14. Zhou, K., Hui, B., Wang, J., Wang, C., Wu, T.: A study on attention-based lstm for abnormal behavior recognition with variable pooling. Image Vis. Comput. **108**, 104120 (2021)
15. Serrano, I., Deniz, O., Espinosa-Aranda, J.L., Bueno, G.: Fight recognition in video using hough forests and 2d convolutional neural network. IEEE Trans. Image Process. **27**(10), 4787–4797 (2018)
16. Li, J., Jiang, X., Sun, T., Xu, K.: Efficient violence detection using 3d convolutional neural networks. In: 2019 16th IEEE International Conference on Advanced Video and Signal Based Surveillance (AVSS), pp. 1–8 (2019)
17. Halder, R., Chatterjee, R.: CNN-BiLSTM model for violence detection in smart surveillance. SN Computer Science **1**(4), 201 (2020)
18. Mumtaz, A., Sargano, A.B., Habib, Z.: Violence detection in surveillance videos with deep network using transfer learning. In: 2018 2nd European Conference on Electrical Engineering and Computer Science (EECS), pp. 558–563 (2018)
19. Bermejo Nievas, E., Deniz Suarez, O., Bueno Garćıa, G., Sukthankar, R.: Violence detection in video using computer vision techniques. In: Computer Analysis of Images and Patterns: 14th International Conference, CAIP 2011, Seville, Spain, August 29–31, 2011, Proceedings, Part II 14, pp. 332–339. Springer (2011)
20. Nievas, E.B., Suarez, O.D., Garcia, G.B., Sukthankar, R.: Movies fight detection dataset. In: Computer Analysis of Images and Patterns, pp. 332–339. Springer (2011)
21. Vaswani, A., et al.: Attention is all you need. Adv. Neural Info. Proc. Sys. **30** (2017)
22. Ko, K.E., Sim, K.B.: Deep convolutional framework for abnormal behavior detection in a smart surveillance system. Eng. Appl. Artif. Intell. **67**, 226–234 (2018)
23. Pan, S.J., Yang, Q.: A survey on transfer learning. IEEE Trans. Knowl. Data Eng. **22**(10), 1345–1359 (2010)
24. Mnih, V., Heess, N., Graves, A., et al.: Recurrent models of visual attention. Adv. Neural Info. Proce. Sys. **27** (2014)
25. Hassner, T., Itcher, Y., Kliper-Gross, O.: Violent flows: Real-time detection of violent crowd behavior. In: 2012 IEEE Computer Society Conference on Computer Vision and Pattern Recognition Workshops, pp. 1–6. IEEE, Providence, RI, USA (2012)

26. Cheng, M., Cai, K., Li, M.: Rwf-2000: an open large scale video database for violence detection. In: 2020 25th International Conference on Pattern Recognition (ICPR), pp. 4183–4190. IEEE (2021)
27. Carreira, J., Zisserman, A.: Quo vadis, action recognition? a new model and the kinetics dataset. In: proceedings of the IEEE Conference on Computer Vision and Pattern Recognition, pp. 6299–6308 (2017)
28. Mohammadi, H., Nazerfard, E.: Video violence recognition and localization using a semi-supervised hard attention model. Expert Syst. Appl. **212**, 118791 (2023)

GFFNet: An Efficient Image Denoising Network with Group Feature Fusion

Lijun Gao[1], Youzhi Zhang[1(✉)], Xiao Jin[1], Qin Xin[2], Zeyang Sun[1], and Suran Wang[1]

[1] College of Computer Science, Shenyang Aerospace University, Shenyang 110136, China
zhangyouzhi@stu.sau.edu.cn
[2] Faculty of Science and Technology, University of the Faroe Islands, Faroe Islands, Denmark

Abstract. Image denoising is a critical pre-processing step for a wide range of image processing and computer vision applications, where the primary goal is to remove noise interference from corrupted images while preserving the essential features of the image. Although recent research has made significant progress in images denoising using deep learning methods, problems such as loss of detail, difficulty in recovering edge textures, and low image processing performance still persist. To tackle these issues, we develop an effective network architecture. This study introduces a Group Feature Fusion (GFF) module, which leverages image feature grouping and fusion techniques to enhance the representation capacity and computational efficiency of features in our network. Additionally, this artical introduce a Cross-Information Integration (CII) Module to enhance the network's ability to utilize input data features by integrating low-level and high-level channel information. Finally, the network was enhanced in its effectiveness for edge texture restoration by optimizing it with the PSNR loss function in conjunction with a novel edge loss function. This architecture achieves significant performance improvements on nine benchmark test datasets for image denoising tasks. Extensive experiments have demonstrated the efficiency and superior performance of this architecture.

Keywords: Image Denoising · Computer Vision · Deep Learning

1 Introduction

Recent advancements in deep learning techniques have greatly enhanced image denoising. Utilizing Convolutional Neural Networks (CNNs) [1–3] and Transformers [23, 33], these models effectively capture complex image features and noise distribution patterns, resulting in more accurate noise removal. Several image denoising methods based on deep learning have yielded remarkable results, including Auto-encoder [2, 4], Generative Adversarial Networks (GAN) [28], and Transformer-based encoder-decoder networks [6, 7, 29], offering innovative solutions for the task.

Preserving image details and texture while removing noise is crucial in image denoising. Although deep learning boosts denoising effectiveness via abundant data and high representation, challenges persist in detail preservation and computational efficiency.

Hence, current research focuses on improving denoising efficiency while retaining image details. This entails exploring efficient network architectures, optimization algorithms, and acceleration techniques to reduce computational load and parameters, thus improving real-time performance and scalability.

In this paper, we propose an enhanced denoising network by incorporating the GFF module and CII module into U-Net architecture and optimizing them with a novel loss function. Major contributions include:

- We introduce the Group Feature Fusion (GFF) module, dividing channels into two subprocesses for joint processing across different channels, leveraging inter-channel correlations to enhance denoising accuracy and computational efficiency.
- We developed a Cross-Information Integration (CII) module to enhance feature transfer across layers and introduce additional pathways for information flow. This module effectively merges low-level features from the encoder with high-level features from the upsampling module, transmitting them to the decoder for enhanced processing. The goal is to enrich captured details and minimize information loss across the network architecture.
- By combining the edge loss function with the PSNR loss function, we've optimized the network to markedly improve its ability to restore intricate edge textures in images.

2 Related Work

2.1 Convolutional Neural Network

Recent advancements in image denoising leveraging deep learning, particularly Convolutional Neural Networks (CNNs), have shown remarkable progress. These models can learn intricate features and noise distributions, leading to more precise and resilient denoising outcomes. For example, Zhang et al. [2] achieved efficient denoising through multi-layer convolution and residual connections, while Guo et al. [3] introduced a CNN-based blind denoising method for real photograph noise, demonstrating strong performance on real-world datasets. However, CNNs employed in denoising may inadvertently blur image edges and details due to the local receptive field of convolution operations and information loss from pooling. Additionally, some complex CNN architectures demand substantial computational resources and memory, limiting real-time application in resource-constrained environments.

2.2 U-Net Network

The U-Net network excels in image denoising due to its robust feature extraction, skip connections for information propagation, and effective contextual information usage. Ronneberger et al.'s U-Net architecture [5] is widely adopted and achieves remarkable denoising results. Researchers have adapted U-Net's structure and concept for denoising tasks, yielding significant improvements. For example, Fan et al. [6] proposed SUNet, integrating Swin Transformer layers into U-Net for enhanced performance. Wang et al. [8] introduced Uformer, replacing convolutional layers with Transformers in a U-Net structure, achieving exceptional results in image restoration. U-Net's flexibility allows customization for various denoising tasks, adjusting model complexity and capacity by adding or removing layers [7, 8, 22, 23, 29].

3 Method

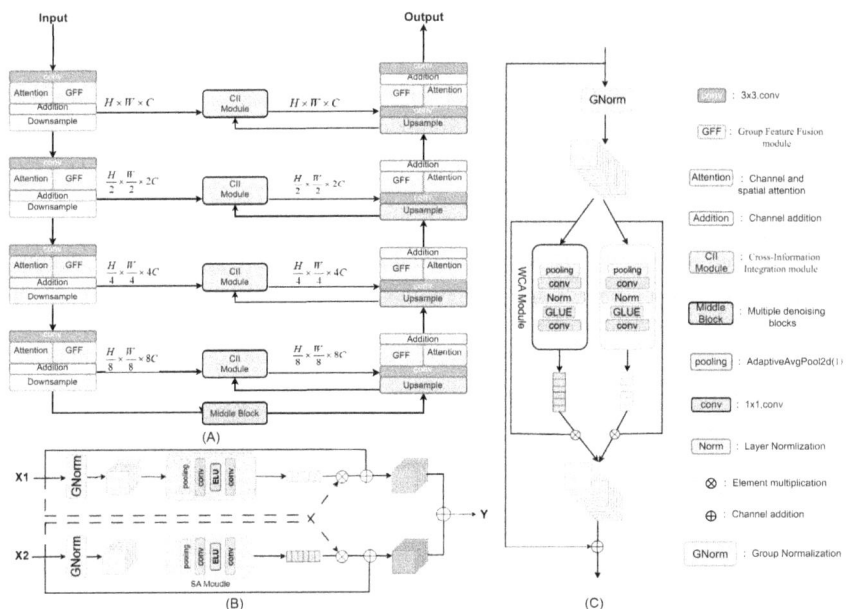

Fig. 1. GFFNet framework diagram. (A) shows the overall framework diagram, (B) shows the CII module and (C) displays the GFF module.

3.1 Network Architecture

In this section, we provide a comprehensive description of our meticulously designed denoising network model for efficient image restoration. As depicted in Fig. 1(A), our model adopts a U-Net-based architecture, consisting of four well-balanced encoder-decoder levels. When presented with a noisy image $I \in \mathbb{R}^{H \times W \times 3}$, we employ convolutions to extract low-level features $F_0 \in \mathbb{R}^{H \times W \times C}$. Subsequently, these features F_0 undergo denoising operations through the integration of Group Feature Fusion (GFF) modules and Attention modules within the encoder. The resulting denoised features from both modules are then fused together. Moreover, the image features F_0 are further processed through downsampling operations to obtain $F_1 \in \mathbb{R}^{\frac{H}{2} \times \frac{W}{2} \times 2C}$. This multi-scale processing is iteratively performed, yielding $F_3 \in \mathbb{R}^{\frac{H}{8} \times \frac{W}{8} \times 8C}$, and so forth. The intermediate layers further refine the features F_3, which are subsequently fed into the decoder for the corresponding operations. Ultimately, the processed features F_3 generate the denoised image $\tilde{I} \in \mathbb{R}^{H \times W \times 3}$.

3.2 Group Feature Fusion (GFF) Module

The Group Feature Fusion (GFF) module is designed for image denoising, aiming to reduce noise and preserve intricate image details through orchestrated operations like normalization, channel segmentation, convolution, weight calculation, and fusion. Shown in Fig. 1(C), this module effectively manipulates feature maps to alleviate noise effects and enhance overall image quality. By intelligently segmenting and combining channel information, along with weight calculation and fusion, the GFF module selectively processes distinct features from different channels, resulting in precise denoising outcomes and preserved intricate image details.

This module initially applies group normalization to the input image to remove redundant information across channels. Subsequently, the normalized image $X \in \mathbb{R}^{H \times W \times C}$ is segmented into $X_1 \in \mathbb{R}^{H \times W \times \frac{C}{2}}$ and $X_2 \in \mathbb{R}^{H \times W \times \frac{C}{2}}$ based on channels.

To determine the importance weights for each group of channels, the WCA module is used to compute these weights. The module extracts and computes the weights of each channel from the input tensor for weighted fusion operations. Firstly, the module performs adaptive average pooling on each channel group by reducing its dimensionality to $X^* \in \mathbb{R}^{1 \times 1 \times C}$. Next, a convolutional layer is used to map the pooled feature map $X^* \in \mathbb{R}^{1 \times 1 \times C}$ to a lower dimensional channel space becoming $X^{**} \in \mathbb{R}^{1 \times 1 \times \frac{C}{2}}$. Following this, the output of the convolutional layer undergoes channel normalization to enhance model stability and generalization. Finally, the normalized features undergo a nonlinear transformation using the GELU activation function. Additionally, the number of channels of the feature map is restored to be consistent with the number of channels of the input tensor by another convolutional layer, i.e., $X^{**} \in \mathbb{R}^{1 \times 1 \times \frac{C}{2}}$ is restored to the form $X^* \in \mathbb{R}^{1 \times 1 \times C}$. The channel weights are computed and then mapped to their corresponding channel groups, resulting in a weighted fusion operation.

$$\overline{X_1} = X_1 \cdot WCA(X_1), \overline{X_2} = X_2 \cdot WCA(X_2) \tag{1}$$

where $\overline{X_1}$ and $\overline{X_2}$ represent the weighted outputs of each group of channels, and $WCA(\cdot)$ represents the module in which the channel weights are calculated.

Finally, the weighted fused channel sets are spliced by channel dimension and added to the original input image through residual linking.

3.3 Cross-Information Integration (CII) Module

The Cross-Information Integration (CII) module begins with normalizing the input to ensure consistent statistical properties. Next, features are extracted via a convolutional layer with a "groups" parameter for feature localization. To enhance information flow and fusion between encoder and decoder, this module normalizes the feature maps of both inputs, reducing redundancy and enhancing stability. It employs the Simple Attention (SA) module to calculate channel weights, reducing dimensionality to 1×1 using average pooling and convolution to halve channel numbers, reducing complexity. ELU activation introduces nonlinearity, handling negative noise and preventing mapping to zero values, aiding detail preservation and mitigating the vanishing gradient problem. A subsequent convolution operation restores the original channel count for precise feature scaling and fusion.

$$ELU(x) = \begin{cases} e^x - 1 & x < 0 \\ x & x \geq 0 \end{cases} \tag{2}$$

$$W_1 = SA(LN(X_1)), W_2 = SA(LN(X_2)) \tag{3}$$

In this network, X_1 and X_2 represent the encoder output and the upsampling module output, respectively. $SA(\cdot)$ calculates the weights of the feature map channels, and $LN(\cdot)$ performs the normalization operation.

Element-wise multiplication is employed to multiply the features from the encoder and upsampling modules by their respective weights following feature scaling and fusion weight acquisition. This process realizes the weighted fusion of encoder and upsampling features. The ultimate output features result from adding the weighted fused features to the original input.

3.4 Network Optimization

To guide the model in the right learning direction, accelerate convergence, and improve generalization ability, we first optimize it using the L_1 loss function, which measures the difference between the reconstructed image and the original clean image. By minimizing this loss, the network is compelled to learn to generate denoised images that closely resemble the clean original images. This encourages the network to learn the details and structure required for denoising tasks, thereby improving the denoising performance.

Our experiments have shown that using L_1 loss as the loss function results in the loss of details and high frequency texture information in the denoised image. To prevent this, we use PSNR loss as the reconstruction loss function and edge loss to preserve edge texture information between X and Y. The overall loss function is designed as follows:

$$Loss = \lambda_1 \cdot L_{PSNR} + \lambda_2 \cdot L_{Edge} \tag{4}$$

By adjusting λ_1 and λ_2, we control the importance of the two loss functions in the composite loss, balancing low-level pixel reconstruction quality (PSNR loss) with high-level structural similarity (edge loss) during network optimization. PSNR loss focuses on pixel-level details, while edge loss emphasizes structural preservation, ensuring clear pixel details and good structural sense. Setting λ_1 to 0.9 and λ_2 to 0.1 in experiments, we tailor the significance of the loss functions, enhancing training effectiveness and generation results.

$$L_{PSNR} = 10 \cdot log_{10}(\frac{MAX_I^2}{MSE}) \tag{5}$$

where, m, n is the spatial dimension of the image, MSE is the mean square error, and PSNR is derived based on MSE, and MAX_I is the maximum value that indicates the color of an image point(If each sampling point is represented by 8 bits, its value is 255.). The edge loss function L_{Edge} is denoted as:

$$L_{Edge} = SmoothL_1(\nabla X, \nabla Y) \tag{6}$$

where, L_{Edge} is mainly derived using $SmoothL_1$ loss and $\nabla X, \nabla Y$ are the edge gradients of the noisy and real images respectively. The L_{Edge} loss adds the consideration of image structure information. By extracting and comparing the blurred edges of the image gradient, the quality of image reconstruction can be effectively measured.

4 Experiment

4.1 Experimental Details

The following is a description of our experimental setup, unless otherwise noted. In the image denoising task, the number of blocks for each stage of the encoder and decoder in this network is set to {2, 2, 4, 8} and {2, 2, 2, 2}. For the Group Feature Fusion (GFF) Module, the number of groups is set to 2 by default. We used the Adam optimizer and the PyTorch framework for training (where $\beta_1 = 0.9$, $\beta_2 = 0.9$, and weight decay is 0). The total number of iterations was 500 K, and the initial learning rate was set to 1e-3 and gradually decreased to 1e-7. We used 256 × 256 training patches and set the batch size to 8. Finally, in our experiments, we used peak signal-to-noise ratio (PSNR) and structural similarity (SSIM) as evaluation metrics. Among them, the best results are marked in bold.

4.2 Gaussian Noise Cancellation

This study utilized the DIV2K dataset for training Gaussian denoising, consisting of 1000 high-resolution images. From these, 256 × 256 sized patches were randomly cropped and Gaussian noise (15–50 range) added for training. The network was trained on 700, validated on 150, and tested on 150 images. Evaluation during testing covered various image types using standard test sets.

Table 1 presents denoising results for grayscale images. We tested on standard sets (Set12, BSD68, Urban100) at noise levels of 15, 25, and 50, evaluating using PSNR and visual inspection, comparing with classical methods. Our approach achieved state-of-the-art performance, particularly outperforming others at high noise levels. Visual comparisons at noise level 25 (Fig. 2) show our network's ability to recover richer details and produce more realistic images than classical methods.

In the context of color image denoising, our experiment evaluated performance on established benchmark datasets: CBSD68, Kodak24, and McMaster. Applying the same

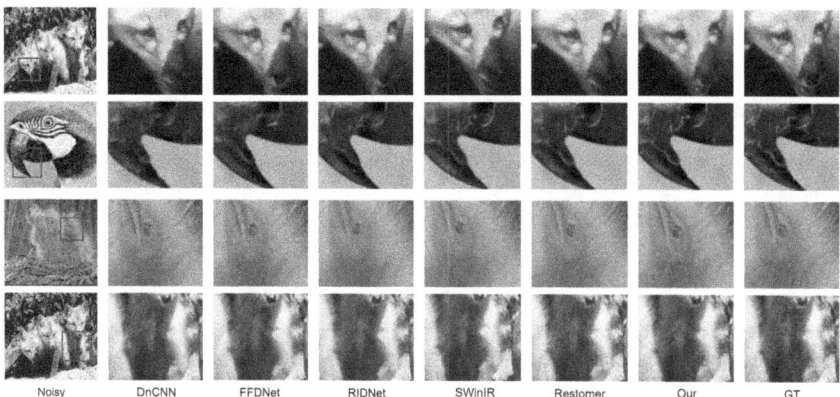

Fig. 2. Gaussian noise removal(where Noisy is the noisy image and GT is the real image)

testing conditions as for grayscale images, we consistently observed commendable denoising performance. Visual results in Fig. 2 vividly illustrate the network's effectiveness in recovering texture information, demonstrating its proficiency in color image denoising.

Table 1. Gaussian gray scale image denoising.

Method	Set12			BSD68			Urban100		
	$\sigma=15$	$\sigma=25$	$\sigma=50$	$\sigma=15$	$\sigma=25$	$\sigma=50$	$\sigma=15$	$\sigma=25$	$\sigma=50$
DnCNN [2]	32.67	30.35	27.18	31.62	29.16	26.23	32.28	29.80	26.35
FFDNet [4]	32.75	30.43	27.32	31.63	29.19	26.29	32.40	29.90	26.50
IRCNN [11]	32.76	30.37	27.12	31.63	29.15	26.19	32.46	29.80	26.22
RIDNet [12]	–	–	–	31.81	29.34	26.40	–	–	–
DRUNet [13]	33.25	30.94	27.90	31.91	29.48	26.59	32.44	31.11	27.96
DRANet [18]	–	–	–	31.79	29.36	26.47	–	–	–
SwinIR [24]	33.36	31.01	27.91	31.97	29.50	26.58	33.70	31.30	27.98
Restomer [29]	**33.42**	31.08	28.00	31.96	29.52	26.62	**33.79**	31.46	28.29
Our	33.41	**31.13**	**28.06**	**32.00**	**29.58**	**26.65**	**33.79**	**31.52**	**28.32**

Table 2. Gaussian color image denoising.

Method	CBSD68			Kodak24			McMaster		
	$\sigma=15$	$\sigma=25$	$\sigma=50$	$\sigma=15$	$\sigma=25$	$\sigma=50$	$\sigma=15$	$\sigma=25$	$\sigma=50$
DnCNN [2]	33.90	31.24	27.95	34.60	32.14	28.95	33.45	31.52	28.62
FFDNet [4]	33.87	31.21	27.96	34.63	32.13	28.98	34.66	32.35	29.18
IRCNN [11]	33.86	31.16	27.86	34.69	32.18	28.93	34.58	32.18	28.91
DRANet [18]	34.18	31.56	28.37	35.02	32.59	29.50	35.09	32.84	29.77
BRDNet [20]	34.10	31.43	28.16	34.88	32.41	29.22	35.08	32.75	29.52
SwinIR [24]	**34.42**	31.78	28.56	35.34	32.89	29.79	35.61	33.20	30.22
Restomer [29]	34.39	31.78	**28.59**	35.44	33.02	30.00	35.55	**33.31**	30.29
AirNet [30]	33.92	31.26	28.01	34.68	32.21	29.06	34.70	32.44	29.26
ADNet [31]	33.99	31.31	28.04	34.76	32.26	29.10	34.93	32.56	29.36
Our	34.41	**31.80**	28.58	**35.48**	**33.05**	**30.03**	**35.65**	**33.31**	**30.33**

4.3 Real Image Denoising

This study trained the network using the SIDD dataset to denoise real images, enabling the model to learn to remove complex real-world noise. Evaluation involved multiple standard test datasets like SIDD, DND, and SenseNoise, covering diverse real-world scenarios and shooting conditions, comprehensively assessing the method's generalization performance.

SIDD. Using the SIDD benchmark with 1280 color images for validation, we assess our method's performance in real-world denoising tasks. Table 3 demonstrates our network's superior results compared to 10 denoising algorithms, particularly outperforming other CNN-based methods. Visual comparisons reveal our network's ability to restore richer colors and texture details, with sharper image edges compared to alternative methods (Table 2 and Fig. 3).

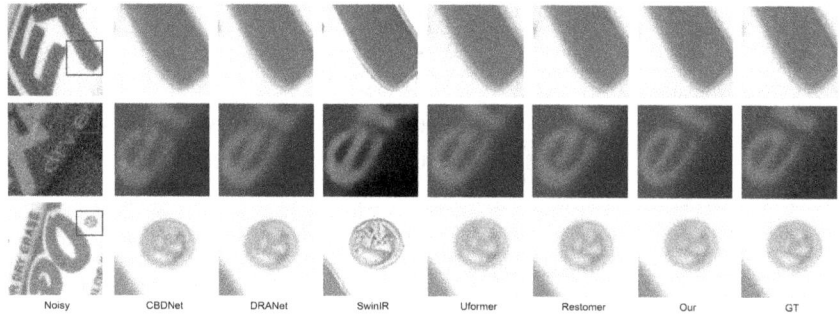

Fig. 3. Visualization and comparison of denoising results on SIDD dataset.

DND. Our method was evaluated on the DND dataset consisting of 50 pairs of real noisy images and corresponding clean references. Since no training data was available in the DND dataset, we trained our model using the SIDD dataset. We employed the same model that performed best on the SIDD benchmark and submitted the results to the DND benchmark. Table 3 shows that our method outperformed other networks on the DND dataset.

SenseNoise. The SenseNoise dataset comprises training and test sets. Training set: 39,345 pairs of real noisy and clean images. Test set: real noisy and clean images from 120 scenes, diverse in types, scenes, and lighting conditions. Our experiments compare denoising techniques' effectiveness in recovering image clarity and detail. Evaluation based on denoised images and quantitative metrics like PSNR and SSIM, alongside visual perception assessment. Results presented in Table 3 and Fig. 4.

Table 3. Denoising results demonstrated on three standard real noisy image test sets.

Method	SIDD		DND		SenseNoise	
	PSNR	SSIM	PSNR	SSIM	PSNR	SSIM
DnCNN [2]	23.66	0.583	32.43	0.790	34.06	0.904
CBDNet [3]	30.78	0.801	38.06	0.942	–	–
NBNet [7]	39.75	0.973	39.89	0.955	–	–
Uformer [8]	39.77	0.956	39.80	0.954	35.43	0.920
RIDNet [12]	38.71	0.951	39.26	0.953	34.88	0.915
BM3D [14]	25.65	0.685	34.51	0.851	–	–
MPRNet [22]	39.71	0.958	39.88	0.956	35.43	0.922
Restomer [29]	40.02	0.960	40.03	0.956	35.52	0.924
MIRNet [32]	39.72	0.956	39.80	0.954	35.30	0.919
SADNet [33]	39.46	0.957	39.59	0.952	–	–
Our	**40.28**	**0.967**	**40.26**	**0.961**	**35.58**	**0.927**

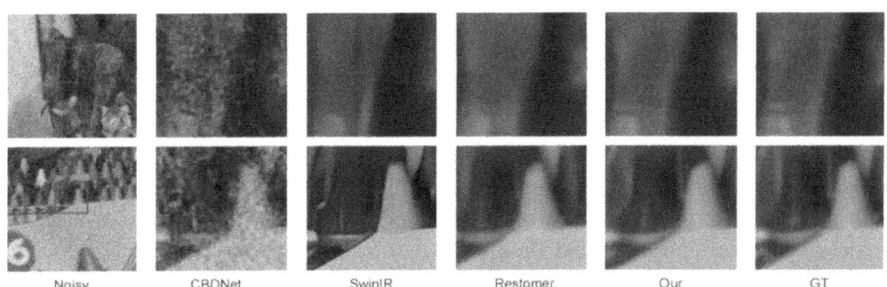

Fig. 4. Comparison of denoising results visualization in SenseNoise dataset.

4.4 Ablation Experiment

We conducted extensive ablation studies to validate the effectiveness of our method. All ablation studies were conducted based on Gaussian denoising. We trained the model for 150,000 iterations. The other training settings were kept consistent with the main experiments of Gaussian denoising on color images.

Group Feature Fusion (GFF) Module. In this experiment, the network architecture incorporating the Group Feature Fusion (GFF) Module was compared with the baseline model for gaussian denoising tasks. As shown in Table 4(a), the peak signal-to-noise ratio(PSNR) significantly increased by 0.11 dB when introducing the Group Feature Fusion (GFF) Module compared to the baseline model.

Table 4. Comparison of each module

Network	PSNR
Baseline	29.36
(a)Baseline + GFF	29.47
(b)Baseline + CII	29.45
(c)Baseline + GFF + CII	29.55
(d)Baseline + GFF + Loss	29.52
(e)Baseline + GFF + CII + Loss	**29.64**

Table 5. Loss function selection

Loss Function	PSNR
PSNR Loss	29.36
L1 Loss	29.19
Edge Loss	29.15
L1 + Edge Loss	29.30
PSNR + Edge Loss	**29.41**

Table 6. The selection of λ_1 and λ_2 in the loss

λ_1	λ_2	PSNR
0.95	0.05	29.39
0.9	0.1	**29.41**
0.85	0.15	29.38
0.8	0.2	29.37
0.5	0.5	29.34

Cross – Information Integration(CII) Module. Comparing the network structure with the addition of the cross-information Integration (CII) Module to the baseline model in gaussian denoising task (Table 4(B)), it's noted that the PSNR has increased by 0.09 dB with the inclusion of the CII Module (Table 6).

Network Optimization. In this experiment, different loss functions were added to the same baseline model for comparing denoising results. As shown in Table 5, it can be observed from the data that the denoising performance of the network significantly improved after incorporating the edge loss function.

The Selection of λ_1 and λ_2 in the Network Optimization. As shown in the table above, we conducted experiments to find optimal values for hyperparameters λ_1 and λ_2. results show $\lambda_1 = 0.9$ and $\lambda_2 = 0.1$ produced the best outcomes. Deviating from these values resulted in reduced PSNR. When λ_2 exceeded 0.1, fine edge details were overly emphasized, diminishing optimization efficiency for non-edge details. Conversely, excessive focus on non-edge details led to significant loss of critical edge details.

5 Conclusion

Our study presents the Group Feature Fusion (GFF) module to enhance computational efficiency and accuracy in image denoising. This module divides image processing into two subprocesses, reducing complexity via channel grouping. Additionally, we introduce the Cross-Information Integration (CII) module, facilitating direct low- to high-level feature connections, enhancing detail retention and quality. After optimizing with an improved loss function, a high-performance image denoiser is developed. Experimental results demonstrate the method's outstanding performance across nine benchmark datasets for image denoising.

References

1. Luo, E., Chan, S.H., Nguyen, T.Q.: Adaptive image denoising by mixture adaptation. IEEE Trans. Image Process. **25**(10), 4489–4503 (2016)
2. Zhang, K., Zuo, W., Chen, Y., Meng, D., Zhang, L.: Beyond a gaussian denoiser: Residual learning of deep cnn for image denoising. IEEE Trans. Image Process. **26**(7), 3142–3155 (2016)
3. Guo, S., Yan, Z., Zhang, K., Zuo, W., Zhang, L.: Toward convolutional blind denoising of real photographs (2018)
4. Zhang, K., Zuo, W., Zhang, L.: Ffdnet: Toward a fast and flexible solution for cnn-based image denoising. IEEE (9) (2018)
5. Ronneberger, O., Fischer, P., Brox, T.: U-net: Convolutional networks for biomedical image segmentation (2015)
6. Fan, C.M., Liu, T.J., Liu, K.H.: Sunet: Swin transformer unet for image denoising (2022)
7. Cheng, S., et al.: Nbnet: Noise basis learning for image denoising with subspace projection. In: Computer Vision and Pattern Recognition (2021)
8. Wang, Z., Cun, X., Bao, J., Liu, J.: Uformer: A general u-shaped transformer for image restoration (2021)
9. Hu, J., Shen, L., Sun, G.: Squeeze-and-excitation networks. In: 2018 IEEE/CVF Conference on Computer Vision and Pattern Recognition (CVPR) (2018)
10. Woo, S., Park, J., Lee, J.Y., Kweon, I.S.: Cbam: Convolutional block attention module (2018)
11. Zhang, K., Zuo, W., Gu, S., Zhang, L.: Learning deep cnn denoiser prior for image restoration. IEEE (2017)
12. Anwar, S.: Real image denoising with feature attention. IEEE (2019)
13. Zhang, K., et al.: Plug-and-play image restoration with deep denoiser prior. IEEE Transactions on Pattern Analysis and Machine Intelligence (01) (2021)
14. Dabov, K., Foi, A., Katkovnik, V., Egiazarian, K.: Image denoising by sparse 3-d transform-domain collaborative filtering. IEEE Trans. Image Process. **16**(8), 2080–2095 (2007)
15. Gu, S., Zhang, L., Zuo, W., Feng, X.: Weighted nuclear norm minimization with application to image denoising. In: 2014 IEEE Conference on Computer Vision and Pattern Recognition (CVPR) (2014)
16. Portilla, J., Strela, V., Wainwright, M.J., Simoncelli, E.P.: Image denoising using scale mixtures of gaussians in the wavelet domain. IEEE (11) (2003)
17. Rudin, L.I., Osher, S., Fatemi, E.: Nonlinear total variation based noise removal algorithms. Physica D **60**(1–4), 259–268 (1992)
18. Wu, W., Liu, S., Xia, Y., Zhang, Y.: Dual residual attention network for image denoising. Pattern Recognition 110291 (2024)

19. Peng, Y., Zhang, L., Liu, S., Wu, X., Zhang, Y., Wang, X.: Dilated residual networks with symmetric skip connection for image denoising. Neurocomputing **345**, 67–76 (2019)
20. Tian, C., Xu, Y., Zuo, W.: Image denoising using deep cnn with batch renormalization. Neural Netw. **121**, 461–473 (2020)
21. Plötz, T., Roth, S.: Neural nearest neighbors networks. Advances in Neural Information Processing Systems 31 (2018)
22. Zamir, S.W., et al.: Multi-stage progressive image restoration. In: Proceedings of the IEEE/CVF conference on computer vision and pattern recognition. pp. 14821–14831 (2021)
23. Chen, L., Chu, X., Zhang, X., Sun, J.: Simple baselines for image restoration. In: European Conference on Computer Vision, pp. 17–33. Springer (2022)
24. Liang, J., et al.: Swinir: Image restoration using swin transformer. In: Proceedings of the IEEE/CVF international conference on computer vision, pp. 1833–1844 (2021)
25. Li, D., et al.: No attention is needed: Grouped spatial-temporal shift for simple and efficient video restorers. arXiv preprint arXiv:2206.10810 (2022)
26. Nah, S., Son, S., Lee, S., Timofte, R., Lee, K.M.: Ntire 2021 challenge on image deblurring. In: Proceedings of the IEEE/CVF Conference on Computer Vision and Pattern Recognition, pp. 149–165 (2021)
27. Zamir, S.W., et al.: Learning enriched features for real image restoration and enhancement. In: Computer Vision--ECCV 2020: 16th European Conference, Glasgow, UK, August 23--28, 2020, Proceedings, Part XXV 16, pp. 492–511. Springer (2020)
28. Cai, Y., et al.: Learning to generate realistic noisy images via pixel-level noise-aware adversarial training (2022)
29. Zamir, S.W., et al.: Restormer: Efficient transformer for high-resolution image restoration. In: Proceedings of the IEEE/CVF conference on computer vision and pattern recognition, pp. 5728–5739 (2022)
30. Tian, C., Xu, Y., Li, Z., Zuo, W., Liu, H.: Attention-guided cnn for image denoising. Neural Netw. **124**, 117–129 (2020)
31. Li, B., et al.: All-in-one image restoration for unknown corruption. In: 2022 IEEE/CVF Conference on Computer Vision and Pattern Recognition (CVPR), pp. 17431–17441 (2022). https://doi.org/10.1109/CVPR52688.2022.01693
32. Zamir, S.W., et al.: Learning enriched features for fast image restoration and enhancement. IEEE Trans. Pattern Anal. Mach. Intell. **45**(2), 1934–1948 (2022)
33. Menteş, S., Kınlı, F., Özcan, B., Kıraç,, F.: [re] spatial-adaptive network for single image denoising. In: ML Reproducibility Challenge 2020 (2021)

End-to-End Object Detection with YOLOF

Xing Xi, Yangyang Huang, Weiye Wu, and Ronghua Luo[✉]

South China University of Technology, Guangzhou, China
xxyzll@yeah.net

Abstract. Within the field of computer vision, object detection is a core issue. A technique extensively utilized in convolution-oriented detectors is Non-Maximum Suppression (NMS), designed to suppress redundant predictions. However, the sequential nature intrinsic to NMS inhibits its capacity for parallel execution, consequently restricting the inference speed. Furthermore, the recall rate of detectors with NMS is also affected in scenes with high object density and overlap. In this paper, we propose a real-time and end-to-end detector with YOLOF (You Only Look One-level Feature). The proposed methods do not introduce additional parameters or attention mechanisms, making them practical for real-time applications. Specifically, we propose the stop-gradient strategy to train only a portion of parameters to address the problem of weak supervision in one-to-one label assignment. We also present auxiliary losses to strengthen the supervision of negative samples during training and use semantic anchor optimization to suppress other anchors in the same location. These techniques allow the improved YOLOF to discard NMS within a 1 mAP gap and achieve faster inference speed. Our YOLOF-CSP-D53-DC5 achieves 42.7 mAP, only 0.5 mAP lower than the original version. Additionally, our YOLOF-R50 achieves a 37.1 mAP at 38 FPS and exceeds state-of-the-art networks by more than 1.5 times in inference speed.

Keywords: YOLOF · End-to-end Detector · Non-Maximum Suppression · Object Detection

1 Introduction

Object detection, a fundamental component of computer vision, is instrumental in a range of real-world applications, including but not limited to autonomous vehicles, security monitoring, and robotic systems. A common obstacle encountered in object detection is the problem of Non-Maximum Suppression (NMS), which is used to discard the reduplicative bounding boxes by the detection algorithm (left in Fig. 1).

Despite the widespread adoption of NMS in standard post-processing workflows, it presents two potential issues: computational burden and recall rate. NMS is a ranking-based algorithm that iteratively suppresses duplicate predictions within the same category. However, the entire computation process is not parallelizable. As a result, it significantly impacts the inference speed of the model, especially on edge devices.

Subsequent work [15, 18, 19] has proposed modifications to its process to achieve higher execution speeds, but the computational burden it brings is still considerable.

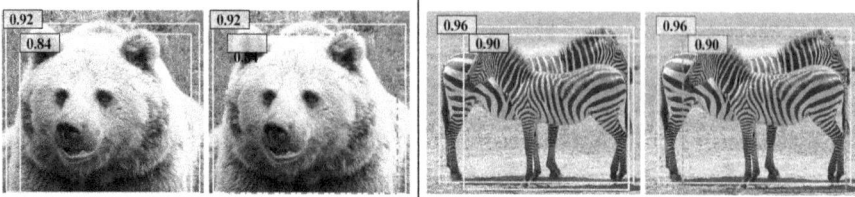

Fig. 1. The purpose and shortcomings of the NMS. The aim of NMS is to suppress redundant predictions with lower scores (left). However, the algorithm exhibits recall issues when two objects are in close proximity (right).

In addition, NMS has the problem of reducing the recall rate (right in Fig. 1). The principle of NMS in suppressing duplicate predictions is to calculate the Intersection over Union (IOU) of two targets of the same class. If this value exceeds a predefined threshold, the one with the lower confidence among them will be suppressed. This flaw is particularly prominent in dense tasks, such as the CrowdHuman [7] task, where the theoretical upper bound of the recall rate using NMS is 95%. Therefore, in this paper, we focus on how to discard NMS in detectors with dense predictions. We adopt YOLOF (You Only Look One-level Feature [3]) as our baseline model because it only uses single-layer features and has an advantage in inference speed.

We noted a substantial reduction in the mean average precision (mAP) by 27.7 when NMS was excluded from YOLOF, suggesting that its NMS-dependent version generated reduplicative predictions. Although PSS [14] and DATE [4] have effectively solved this issue, they have yet to produce satisfactory outcomes in YOLOF, a single-feature-map detector. We attribute the subpar performance of the end-to-end model to the insufficient supervision signal provided by π_{oto}.[1] Consequently, we introduce the stop-gradient strategy, which utilizes only a subset of the model's parameters to fit the results of π_{oto}.

To further narrow the performance gap between $YOLOF_{nms}$ and $YOLOF_{end}$, we conducted an analysis using TIDE [1]. Our investigation disclosed that $YOLOF_{end}$ classifies numerous background regions as positive samples. To diminish the error and enhance model performance, we propose the negative loss and introduce the ranking loss [14] for training. The proposed negative loss function has only one hyperparameter and provides supervision effectively for the background error.

Lastly, given that $YOLOF_{nms}$ is an anchor-based detector, we conducted a visual analysis and discovered that predictions generated by anchors of varying sizes at the same position are similar. π_{oto} allocates only one prediction to each instance in the image, resulting in one anchor being matched as a positive sample while another scale anchors as the negative sample. However, those anchors share similar feature regions; the only difference is their receptive fields. Thus, treating one as positive and the other as negative samples causes an optimized conflict. Therefore, we propose an innovative solution to

---

[1] For simplicity, we use π_{oto} and π_{otm} to denote one-to-one and one-to-many label assignments, respectively. $YOLOF_{nms}$ and $YOLOF_{end}$ represent the NMS-dependent and NMS-independent YOLOF, respectively.

the problem. Specifically, we select an optimal anchor for each position in the feature map to serve as its prediction. The remaining predictions are disregarded and do not participate in model supervision. This approach reduces the number of predictions and prevents optimization conflicts.

Compared to YOLOF$_{nms}$, our proposed method achieves end-to-end object detection with slight sacrifice within one mAP. For instance, the YOLOF-CSP-D53-DC5 implementation yields 43.2 mAP, while its NMS-free counterpart yields 42.7 mAP, just 0.5 mAP gap. Furthermore, the improved YOLOF is NMS-independent and runs approximately 1 FPS faster than the original implementation. Compared with other NMS-free detectors, our proposed YOLOF NMS-free version can attain similar performance with over 1.5 + times the inference speed. It's worth noting that the speed evaluation is based on RTX TAITAN (24). Therefore, on edge devices, the impact of NMS is greater, and our improvements will be more significant. We summarize the contributions of this article as follows:

- In our quest to eliminate the necessity for NMS, we proposed three novel approaches: the Stop-Gradient Strategy, the Auxiliary Loss, and the Semantic Anchor Optimization.
- Notably, these proposed techniques, devoid of any additional parameters or attention mechanisms, successfully achieve YOLOF$_{end}$ while maintaining a marginal 1 mAP disparity and demonstrating superior inference speed.
- By conducting experiments on COCO, the improved model achieves 37.1 mAP at 38 FPS and exceeds other SOTA methods by more than 1.5 times in inferencespeed.

2 Our Approach

2.1 Overall Architecture

Figure 2 illustrates the outline of the proposed model. Firstly, we observed that π_{oto} provided insufficient supervision, greatly compromising the performance. Thus, we propose the Stop-Gradient strategy (Sect. 2.2). Secondly, we noticed that YOLOF$_{end}$ classifies numerous background regions as positive samples. Therefore, we propose the Auxiliary Loss to mitigate this (Sect. 2.3). Finally, we observed that anchors corresponding to different scales share feature regions, and treating one as positive and the other as negative samples causes the optimized conflict. To tackle this, we propose Semantic Anchor Optimization (Sect. 2.4).

2.2 Stop Gradient

The dataset is denoted as $D = \{X, Y\}$, where X and Y represent the input image and corresponding label, respectively. The label of the i-th instance in the k-th image, denoted as y_i^k, is defined as $\{l^k, c_x^k, c_y^k, w^k, h^k\}$, where l^k, c_x^k, c_y^k, w^k and h^k correspond to the category, bounding box center coordinates, width, and height, respectively. Traditional object models often employ π_{otm} to optimize the model:

$$L = \sum_{\pi_{otm}} f_{cls}(p_j^k, y_i^k | \pi_{i,j}) + f_{loc}(p_j^k, y_i^k | \pi_{i,j}). \tag{1}$$

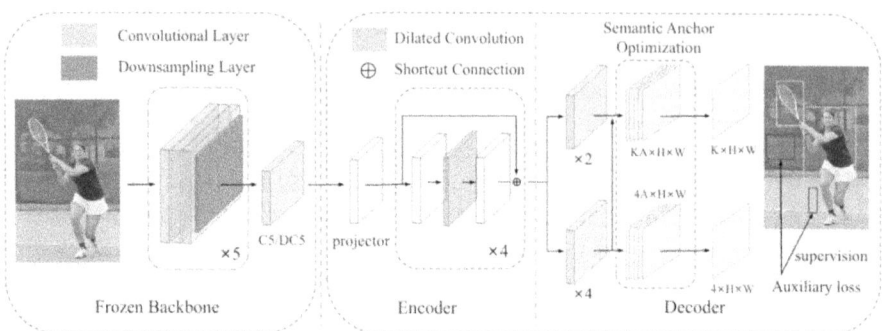

Fig. 2. The overall architecture of the proposed method. Consistent with YOLOF, the model comprises three key components: the Backbone, Encoder, and Decoder. The Backbone serves as the feature extractor for image classification tasks, employing architectures such as ResNet50 [10]. The Encoder incorporates dilated convolutions and residual connections, with the aim of enlarging the receptive field to cover objects of all scales. The Decoder follows a RetinaNet-style [5] prediction head. C5/DC5 represents the output of the Backbone network, while the Project layer is designed to adjust the channel count of feature maps.

Here, $p_j^k \in P^k$ means the j-th prediction in the k-th image, and $\pi_{i,j}$ indicates that the i-th ground truth is assigned to the j-th prediction. The loss functions f_{cls} and f_{loc} correspond to classification and location, respectively. π_{otm} forces the detector to adopt additional post-processing to suppress these redundant predictions. To alleviate the need for NMS, an alternative is π_{otm}. However, YOLOF-ono achieves only 31.6 mAP, indicating a significant performance gap compared to YOLOF$_{nms}$ (Table 1). Furthermore, YOLOF-woNMS attains a mere 10.0 mAP, suggesting a strong reliance on NMS.

In addition, several existing methods have achieved successful end-to-end object detection. DATE [4] introduces an additional π_{otm} branch for training. PSS [14] improves performance by incorporating a sample selector into the regression branch. These methods exhibit competitive performance on FPN-based detectors like FCOS [11] and oneNet [8]. However, these methods do not translate effectively to YOLOF. DATE[4] and PSS [14] achieve mAP values of 31.0 and 23.3, respectively, indicating declines of 6.7 and 14.4 mAP compared to the NMS version of YOLOF.

The question arises: Why do detectors heavily depend on π_{otm} ? We deem that this isdue to the adequate supervisory signal it provides to train the entire model. However, the signal supplied by π_{oto} is insufficient for the training model with numerous parameters.

Thus, we propose the stop-gradient strategy to reduce the number of trainable parameters in the backbone. During training, we employ the encoder and decoder to fit π_{oto} while transferring the knowledge from YOLOF to the backbone (Table 1 YOLOF-detach). YOLOF-detach achieves 35.1 mAP, marking a 3.5 mAP improvement over YOLOF-ono, demonstrating that parameter reduction significantly alleviates the supervisory signal issues.

Table 1. Comparison of various end-to-end methods in object detection. All experiments were conducted using the mmdetection [2].

Method	AP	AP50	AP75	AP_S	AP_M	AP_L
YOLOF	37.7	56.9	40.6	19.1	42.5	53.2
YOLOF-woNMS	10.0	13.3	11.0	12.1	18.9	14.3
YOLOF-ono	31.6	52.6	33.0	16.1	35.6	42.3
YOLOF-PSS	23.3	32.8	25.4	10.2	24.7	37.7
YOLOF-DATE	31.0	51.8	32.0	13.6	34.9	44.5
YOLOF-datach	35.1	55.0	37.3	18.7	39.5	48.2

2.3 Auxiliary Loss

Furthermore, we investigate the impact of π_{oto} and π_{otm} on model prediction. To prevent the Stop-Gradient strategy from introducing noise into the results, we conduct an error analysis using YOLOF-ono and YOLOF, with the results displayed in Fig. 3. The result reveals that YOLOF-ono exhibits a notably higher background prediction error rate, suggesting that YOLOF-ono erroneously categorizes many background samples as positive instances. Thus, we propose an additional loss function to supervise those background predictions to address this.

The post-processing procedure entails three steps: (1) For model predictions P^2, retain predictions P_t that exceed the threshold hyperparameter t, and discard the rest. (2) Sort P_t based on their confidence. (3) Select the top-k samples from P_t as the model's output, denoted as $P_{t,k}$. To reduce the Bkg error, we propose a negative loss to attenuate the confidence of background samples, leading to their filter in step (1):

$$f_{negative}(P, Y | \pi_{oto}) = \frac{1}{n_-} \sum_{i=1}^{n_-} max(e^{t-p_{i_-}+m} - 1, 0). \quad (2)$$

where, n_- is the number of negative samples, and $p_{i_-} \in P$ denotes the negative sample. The hyperparameter $m \in [0, t]$ controls the desired margin between negative samples and t. The parameter t is utilized in step (1) to filter out samples with low scores. It is set in YOLOF$_{nms}$ (0.05). Thus, the proposed loss function contains only a single hyperparameter m.

To further decrease the Bkg error, we introduce the Rank loss [14], which aims to widen the gap between positive and negative samples:

$$f_{rank}\left(P, Y | \pi_{oto}\right) = \frac{1}{n_- n_+} \sum_{i_-}^{n_-} \sum_{j_+}^{n_+} max\left(0, \alpha - p_{j_+} + p_{i_-}\right) \quad (3)$$

where n_+ denote the number of positive samples. α is a hyperparameter used to control the gap between positive and negative samples.

---
[2] For clarity, we omit image indices k.

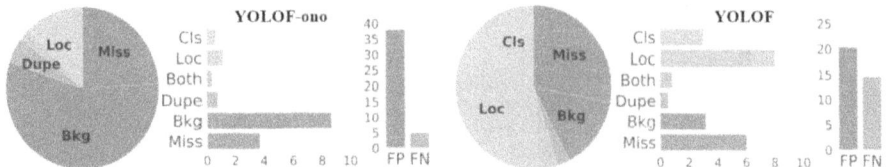

Fig. 3. Error Analysis of TIDE [81]. The image displays six types of errors: Cls (classification error), Loc (location error), Both (both classification and location error), Dupe (duplication error), Bkg (background error), and Miss (missing error).

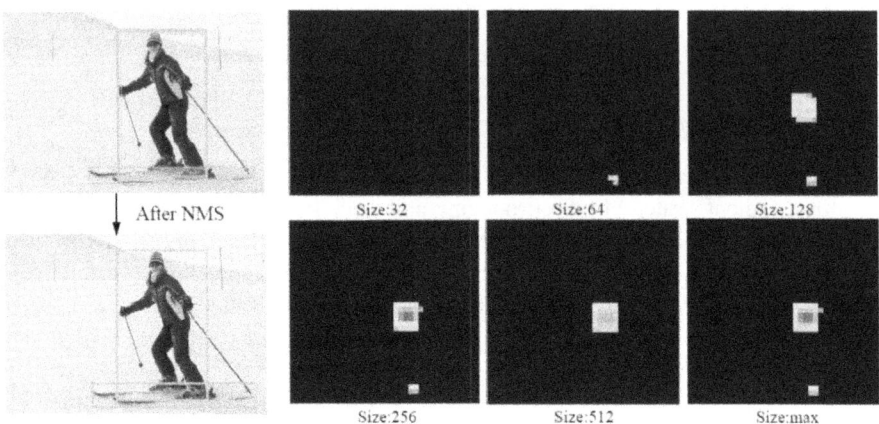

Fig. 4. Visualization of predicted classification scores from different anchors. The input image contains two instances. Size denotes the corresponding anchor scale, while max indicates the maximum value of the proposed channel.

The total loss function is defined as follows:

$$L = f_{cls}(P_{t,k}, Y|\pi_{ono}) + f_{loc}(P_{t,k}, Y|\pi_{ono}) + f_{negative}(P_{t,k}, Y|\pi_{ono}) + f_{rank}(P_{t,k}, Y|\pi_{ono}), \quad (4)$$

where f_{cls} is classification loss, and we use the Focal loss [5] with default setting. The term f_{loc} corresponds to the GIOU [6]. Notably, it is important to emphasize that, in alignment with the conventional post-processing procedure, all loss computations are performed based on $P_{t,k}$ rather than the complete prediction set P.

2.4 Semantic Anchor Optimization

YOLOF operates as an anchor-based detector, employing five preset anchors at each position. The Uniform Match strategy [3] assigns multiple predictions to the same instance based on the bounding box L1 distance. However, replacing it with the one-to-one label assignment introduces optimization conflicts. As illustrated in Fig. 4, anchors of sizes 64, 128, and 256 produce duplicate predictions for the same instance, and similar scenarios also occur with anchors of sizes 54, 128, and 256. However, those anchors share

Table 2. Effect of Different Anchor Sizes on Model Performance. Anchor size denotes the side length of the anchor. ALL indicates the use of pre-set anchors.

Anchor size	AP	AP50	AP75	AP_S	AP_M
32	35.4	53.9	38.0	18.5	40.8
64	36.1	54.5	39.1	18.5	41.2
128	35.7	53.7	39.0	18.3	40.5
256	34.9	52.5	37.9	17.3	39.7
512	36.0	54.1	39.0	18.3	40.7
ALL	35.1	55.0	37.3	18.7	39.5

similar feature regions; the only difference is their receptive field. Consequently, optimization conflicts arise when one anchor is assigned as a positive sample and other anchors are treated as negative samples. To illustrate this, we experimented to assess their impact. Table 2 reveals that using all preset anchors achieved only 35.1 mAP. However, a model with an anchor size of 64 attained 36.1 mAP, marking a 1.0 mAP improvement. Remarkably, all experimental configurations, except for anchor size 256, outperformed the baseline.

To address the optimization conflict, we propose the Semantic Anchor Optimization strategy. As depicted in Fig. 4, we select the most suitable anchor for each position by suppressing non-maximum predictions at the same position:

$$p_i = p_i \cdot I\{\max_{1 \leq j \leq n} (p_i, p_{i+j}) = p_i\}. \tag{5}$$

Here, n denotes the number of preset anchors, and $I()$ denotes the Kronecker delta function, equal to 1 when the input condition holds and 0 otherwise. The confidence of these non-maximum predictions is set to 0, leading to their exclusion in step (1).

3 Experients

3.1 Baseline Settings

Details. All experiments were conducted on the COCO [15]. We utilized the official train2017 split, which contains approximately 118,000 images for training, and the eval2017 split, which includes 5,000 images for evaluation. We adhered to the standard COCO evaluation metric mAP 0.5–0.95 as our evaluation metric, and instances were divided into large (AP_L), medium (AP_M), and small (AP_S) objects to evaluate their performance separately. For clarity, in the table, we only display the current average indicator (AP) for 0.5–0.95 and the mAP at 0.5 (AP50) and 0.75 (AP75). All experiments standard conduct 1x schedule, which total contain 12 epoch.

Table 3. Main Experimental Results.

Model	NMS	FPS	GFLOPs	#par	AP	Gap	AP50	AP75	AP_S	AP_M	AP_L
YOLOF-R50*our*	N	38	88	44.1 M	37.1	0.6	55.2	40.2	18.8	41.9	52.4
YOLOF-R50	Y	37	88	44.1 M	37.3	0.4	57.1	39.6	18.7	42.0	52.9
YOLOF-R50*	Y	37	86	44.1 M	37.7	-	56.9	40.6	19.1	42.5	53.2
YOLOF-R101*our*	N	26	154	63.1 M	39.0	0.8	57.6	42.5	20.5	44.2	53.8
YOLOF-R101	Y	25	154	63.1 M	39.2	0.6	59.4	42.0	20.6	44.3	54.6
YOLOF-R101*	Y	25	151	63.1 M	39.8	-	59.4	42.9	20.5	44.5	54.9
YOLOF-CSP-D53-DC5*our*	N	-	211	48.3 M	42.7	0.5	60.4	46.5	23.0	47.2	59.4
YOLOF-CSP-D53-DC5	Y	-	211	48.3 M	42.8	0.4	62.1	45.9	23.2	47.2	59.4
YOLOF-CSP-D53-DC5*	Y	-	209	48.3 M	43.2	-	62.2	46.6	22.8	47.2	59.8

* denotes the official version, while R50 and R101 denote ResNet50 and ResNet101, respectively. CSP-D53-DC5 indicates the use of DarkNet53 as the backbone with no downsampling performed in the final stage. The FPS for R101 was calculated with a batch size of 1 on TAITAN, based on the total pure inference time reported in Detectron2 [13]. For R50, FPS was calculated using mmdetection [2]. GFLOPs were measured with a shorter edge size of 800 and a longer edge below 1333 using the first 100 images of COCO val2017. #par denotes the number of parameters in the model.

3.2 Main Experimental Results

We conducted experiments to evaluate our proposed method (Table 3). Our approach successfully implements the NMS-free version of YOLOF with an absolute gap of only 1 mAP. In the first section, YOLOF-R50 achieves a mAP of 37.1, which is only 0.6 mAP lower than its NMS-based counterpart. In the last section, YOLOF-CSP-D53-DC5 achieves a mAP of 42.7, which is only 0.5 mAP lower than the NMS-based version.

The original YOLOF relies on traditional NMS to suppress duplicate predictions, and the sorting nature of NMS slows down its detection speed. Our method does not rely on NMS, and the Semantic Anchor Optimization only retains 1/5 of the detection results, which further speeds up the processing speed. Therefore, our method surpasses the original YOLOF in terms of detection speed. In addition, our method realizes end-to-end detection without any additional parameters, adding only 2 GFlops of computational burden during inference. Notably, all inference speed evaluations were conducted on a TAITAN (24 G). When deployed on specific edge devices, the proposed method can achieve significant improvements, as our model does not rely on the non-parallelizable NMS.

3.3 Ablation Experiments

Auxiliary Loss. Due to the limitations of π_{ono}, which provides less supervision, the YOLOF$_{end}$ predicts a large number of background samples as positive samples. To solve the issue, we propose the $f_{negative}$, and introduce the f_{rank}. We analyze their impact on performance. The results are presented in Table 4a, where $f_{negative}$ achieves a 0.7 mAP improvement, achieving 35.8 mAP, while f_{rank} leads to a 0.5 mAP improvement,

Table 4. Ablation Study. We conduct an ablation comparison for all potential choices of the method proposed in this paper.

f_n	f_r	AP	APs	APM	APL
N	N	35.1	18.7	39.5	48.2
Y	N	35.8(+0.7)	18.4	40.5	49.8
N	Y	35.6(+0.5)	18.8	40.1	49.4
Y	Y	36.1(+1.0)	19.4	41.1	50.3

(b) The impact of auxiliary loss functions on model performance. f_n denotes that we proposed $f_{negative}$. f_r means f_{rank}.

k	AP	AP50	AP75	APs	APM	APL
100	36.7	54.7	39.8	18.9	41.7	51.5
150	36.7	54.7	39.9	19.0	41.7	51.1
200	**36.8**	55.0	39.7	18.8	41.6	51.3
ALL	36.5	54.6	40.1	18.5	41.3	50.5

(a) Effect of different number of top-n model performance. ALL indicates that all predictions are used to calculate lo

m	AP	AP50	AP75	APs	APM	APL
0.01	**36.2**	53.8	39.5	19.2	41.3	49.9
0.02	36.0	53.6	39.4	19.4	41.0	50.0
0.03	36.1	53.8	39.5	18.8	41.1	50.5

(d) Effect of different number of top-n model performance. ALL indicates that all predictions are used to calculate loss

Loc	AP	AP50	AP75	APs	APM	APL
1	36.8	54.8	39.8	19.0	41.7	51.0
2	**37.1**	55.2	40.2	18.8	41.9	52.4
N	35.7	53.6	38.6	17.9	40.5	50.0

(c) Efficiency of different locations. Location: 1 decoder, 2 encoder. N presents no stop gard.

resulting in 35.6 mAP. Additionally, the model attains its peak performance, an mAP of 36.1, upon applying both $f_{negative}$ and f_{rank}, marking a 1.0 mAP enhancement.

Top-k Strategy. In step (3), only the top-k samples are utilized for the ultimate prediction. Consequently, the classification loss calculation takes into account merely the top-k samples. This section delves into the influence of varying k values on the model's performance. The findings are depicted in Table 4b. YOLOF, devoid of the top-k strategy, attains a mere 36.5 mAP. The model's performance is further improved by treating all predictions as binary classification problems and training only on the top-k examples. When the k value is set to 200, YOLOF achieves a 0.3 mAP improvement over the model without the top-k strategy, reaching 36.8 mAP.

Hyperparameter m. The parameters m and t play crucial roles in our model. Precisely, m adjusts the score gap, whereas t is employed in the first step to eliminate low-score samples. In most detection models, including YOLOF, a small value is typically assigned to ensure a high recall rate. To minimize the number of hyperparameters, we maintain the value of t constant (0.05). We perform experiments in this section to explore the influence of varying m values on the model's performance. As depicted in Table4c, the model delivers optimal performance when m is set to 0.01, yielding a mAP of 36.2.

Table 5. Comparison with different state-of-the-art NMS-free decectors. All FPS are evaluated on a single TAITAN. To be fair, all networks are evaluated on input images with 800 short edges and 1333 long edges. Sparse R-CNN, DATE-F, DATE-R and OneNet are all evaluated on mmdetection [2]. For DeFCN, we evaluate the obtained on cvpods [15].

Model	FPS	AP	AP50	AP75	AP_S	AP_M	AP_L
Sparse R-CNN [10]	21(+17)	37.9(-0.8)	56.0	40.5	20.7	40.0	53.5
OneNet [9]	22(+16)	35.4(+1.7)	53.3	38.1	19.3	38.6	45.4
DATE-F [4]	22(+16)	37.3(-0.2)	55.3	40.7	21.2	40.3	48.8
DATE-R [4]	23(+15)	37.0(+0.1)	54.9	40.4	20.5	39.8	49.0
DeFCN [13]	20(+18)	37.8(-0.7)	55.6	41.8	22.1	41.3	48.7
YOLOF$_{our}$	38	37.1	55.2	40.2	18.8	41.9	52.4

Stop-Gradient Location. The YOLOF-ono yielded only 31.6 mAP, which is 5.9 mAP lower than the NMS version of YOLOF. As shown in Table 1, using the stop-gradient strategy significantly improves the model's performance, increasing it from 31.6 mAP to 35.1 mAP, resulting in a gain of 4.1 mAP. This section delves into the effects of varying stop-gradient locations on the model's performance. The results are presented in Table 4d. Stopping the gradients at the classification and regression subnetworks yields the poorest model performance, with only 30.1 mAP. Stopping the gradient at the prediction head leads to a model with 36.8 mAP, while stopping the gradient at the encoder achieves the highest model performance of 37.1 mAP.

3.4 Comparison with Other NMS-Free Detectors

Our implementation of the NMS-free version achieves the fastest inference speed within the absolute gap of 1 mAP (Table 5). Sparse R-CNN [9] reaches 37.9 mAP at 21 FPS. Compared to it, our model falls in precision 0.8 mAP, but we achieve a significant advantage in inference speed, up to 17 FPS. Compared to OneNet [8], our model outperforms it by 1.7 mAP and is 16 FPS faster. When compared to DATE [4], our model is 15 FPS faster than DATE-F and 16 FPS faster than DATE-R. DeFCN [12] is an end-to-end detector based on FCOS [12]. DeFCN uses one-to-one matching, auxiliary loss, and 3DMF to eliminate NMS successfully. Compared to DeFCN, our method has a slightly lower model performance by less than 0.7 mAP, but our detector is nearly twice as fast.

4 Conclusion

This article illustrates the limitations of NMS in practical application and proposes a real-time end-to-end model based on YOLOF. To discard NMS, this paper presents three methods, including the gradient termination strategy that trains only a subset of the model parameters and an auxiliary loss function to supervise background samples during training, as well as the semantic anchor optimization strategy to eliminate the prediction of other scales of Anchor at the same position. The NMS-free version of YOLOF implemented in this paper achieves a performance difference of within 1 mAP compared to the original version. In addition, improved YOLOF without NMS increases the detection speed by 1 FPS and can correctly detect objects with high overlap. We hope that the approach presented in this paper can facilitate the practical application of real-time and end-to-end object detection models.

Acknowledgements. This work was also partially supported by Guangdong Artificial Intelligence and Digital Economy Laboratory (Guangzhou).

References

1. Bolya, D., Foley, S., Hays, J., Hoffman, J.: Tide: a general toolbox for identifying object detection errors. In: Computer Vision–ECCV 2020: 16th European Conference, Glasgow, UK, August 23–28, 2020, Proceedings, Part III 16, pp. 558–573. Springer (2020)
2. Chen, K., et al.: MMDetection: Open mmlab detection toolbox and benchmark. arXiv preprint arXiv:1906.07155 (2019)
3. Chen, Q., Wang, Y., Yang, T., Zhang, X., Cheng, J., Sun, J.: You only look one-level feature. In: Proceedings of the IEEE/CVF conference on computer vision and pattern recognition, pp. 13039–13048 (2021)
4. Chen, Y., Chen, Q., Hu, Q., Cheng, J.: Date: dual assignment for end-to-end fully convolutional object detection. arXiv preprint arXiv:2211.13859 (2022)
5. Lin, T.Y., Goyal, P., Girshick, R., He, K., Dollár, P.: Focal loss for dense object detection. In: Proceedings of the IEEE international conference on computer vision, pp. 2980–2988 (2017)
6. Lin, T.Y., et al.: Microsoft coco: Common objects in context. In: Computer Vision– ECCV 2014: 13th European Conference, Zurich, Switzerland, September 6–12, 2014, Proceedings, Part V 13, pp. 740–755. Springer (2014)
7. Rezatofighi, H., et al.: Generalized intersection over union: a metric and a loss for bounding box regression. In: Proceedings of the IEEE/CVF conference on computer vision and pattern recognition, pp. 658–666 (2019)
8. Shao, S., et al.: Crowdhuman: A benchmark for detecting human in a crowd. arXiv preprint arXiv:1805.00123 (2018)
9. Sun, P., et al.: What makes for end-to-end object detection? In: Proceedings of the 38th International Conference on Machine Learning. Proceedings of Machine Learning Research, vol. 139, pp. 9934–9944. PMLR (2021)
10. Sun, P., et al.: Sparse r-cnn: End-to-end object detection with learnable proposals. In: Proceedings of the IEEE/CVF conference on computer vision and pattern recognition, pp. 14454–14463 (2021)
11. Targ, S., Almeida, D., Lyman, K.: Resnet in resnet: Generalizing residual architectures. arXiv preprint arXiv:1603.08029 (2016)
12. 12Tian, Z., Shen, C., Chen, H., He, T.: Fcos: Fully convolutional one-stage object detection. In: Proceedings of the IEEE/CVF international conference on computer vision, pp. 9627–9636 (2019)
13. Wang, J., et al.: End-to-end object detection with fully convolutional network. In: Proceedings of the IEEE/CVF conference on computer vision and pattern recognition, pp. 15849–15858 (2021)

14. Wu, Y., Kirillov, A., Massa, F., Lo, W.Y., Girshick, R.: Detectron2 (2019). https://github.com/facebookresearch/detectron2
15. Zheng, Z., et al.: Enhancing geometric factors in model learning and inference for object detection and instance segmentation (2021)
16. 16Zhou, Q., Yu, C., Shen, C., Wang, Z., Li, H.: Object detection made simpler by eliminating heuristic nms (2021)
17. Zhu*, B., et al.: cvpods: All-in-one toolbox for computer vision research (2020)
18. Bolya, D., Zhou, C., Xiao, F., Lee, Y.J.: Yolact: Real-time instance segmentation. In: Proceedings of the IEEE/CVF international conference on computer vision, pp. 9157–9166 (2019)
19. Zheng, Z., et al.: Distance-iou loss: Faster and better learning for bounding box regression. In: The AAAI Conference on Artificial Intelligence (AAAI) (2020)

BiRGAN: Bi-directional Deep Image Retargeting

Di Sun[1], Yunxiang Wang[1], Tingting Yang[1], Yijing Mei[2], and Gang Pan[2](✉)

[1] College of Artificial Intelligence, Tianjin University of Science and Technology, Tianjin 300222, China
[2] College of Intelligence and Computing, Tianjin University, Tianjin 300350, China
`pangang@tju.edu.cn`

Abstract. Current single retargeting operators perform poorly on diverse images and varying target sizes, rendering them unsuitable for both image reduction and expansion simultaneously. In this paper, we present a deep bi-directional image retargeting network, BiRGAN. The network performs two opposite processes: one training a generator to learn the process of downsizing images, and another learning the upsizing process. The output from the first process is fed into the second, creating a comprehensive closed loop. This network is designed to comprehend the deformation process of retargeted images by employing multiple methodologies and executing retargeting operations within the feature space. Experimental results demonstrate that BiRGAN outperforms previous methods in terms of overall image retargeting results.

Keywords: Image Retargeting · GAN · Bi-directional · IRQA

1 Introduction

Multimedia devices with various screen sizes are becoming increasingly prevalent. Normally, these devices possess diverse aspect ratios and image resolutions, necessitating the adaptation of images to fit the specific target devices. We define the task of adapting an image to best suit a target display device as image retargeting or resizing.

Early content-aware methods [1–8] initially estimate the salient regions of the image and then resize the image while preserving the content of such regions. Since the salient regions are obtained from low-level semantic features, it is common for these methods to result in structural distortion and the creation of artificial artifacts.

In recent years, there are some deep learning measures that implement a complete end-to-end training process [9–16]. However, these approaches rely heavily on calculating importance maps, once the calculation of importance map fails, it usually leads to poor quality of the retargeting results, which significantly limits the generality of these methods.

Moreover, current single retargeting operators may not perform well on multifarious images and various target sizes. Therefore, synthesizing multiple operators is an effective solution. Unlike Multi-operator [3] and Photo Squarization [10], which combine different

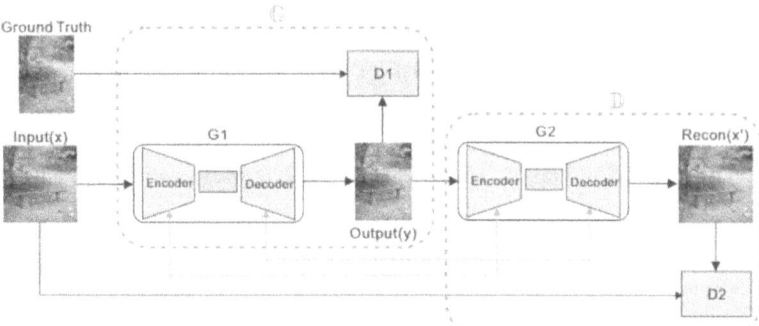

Fig. 1. Overview of the BiRGAN: The model implements a bi-directional retargeting process. It feeds the input image Input(x) into the generator G_1 to generate a width-reduced image Output(y), and then sends y and the corresponding ground truth to the discriminator D_1 for distinguishing. At the same time, y is fed into generator G_1 as input to generate an image Recon(x') with expanded width, after which x' and x are input to the discriminator D_2 together.

operators in an optimal way and then operate directly on the pixel space, we try to start from the retargeting process of different operators. The key idea is put the best performance of retargeting results of different images together, and then learn how to deform the original image into the best through a complete end-to-end training. Finally, retargeting operation is carried out in the feature space, so that the result can be better expressed.

In this paper, we propose a generative adversarial network (GAN) based bi-directional retargeting network (BiRGAN) in this paper. The network needs to complete two reciprocal retargeting processes respectively. One is training a generator to learn the process of resizing images to smaller sizes, and the other is a discriminator that learns the process of resizing images to larger sizes. The output of the first process is fed into the second process as the input over here, causing the network to form a complete closed loop, and the two processes compete with each other in the hope that both can produce preferable results. Our main contributions can be summarized as:

- We offer a new perspective into supervised image retargeting that utilizes data from multiple operators within the feature space. The proposed strategy can circumvent the constraints associated with relying solely on a single calculation method for determining the importance map.
- We propose the BiRGAN network, a bi-directional image retargeting framework. It can achieve visually pleasing results for both image reduction and expansion. Furthermore, it offers a comprehensive framework that accommodates a diverse range of tasks involving reciprocal processes.

2 Related Work

Most of conventional image retargeting approaches are based on content perception. Discrete methods [1–3] usually extract the saliency information of pixels in an image, and then define an operation method to insert or delete pixels to obtain the retargeted image. Continuous methods [5, 6] typically cover a uniform grid on an original image, and assign a different zoom factor to each grid unit. The zoom factor of important areas is larger than other areas. Nevertheless, these traditional content-aware methods normally extract and utilize low-level features, ignoring high-level semantics, so their effects are limited.

Existing image retargeting quality assessment algorithms can be roughly classified into subjective methods and objective methods. Subjective approaches require many participants to vote repeatedly on a large number of retargeted images and then evaluate the retargeted images according to the votes. For example, Castillo et al. use eye tracking to compare image retargeted images by examining gaze fixations and viewing patterns. Objective methods are evaluated based on the analysis of the salient region and structure of image.

Many deep learning based image retargeting approaches have been invented. However, these approaches mainly perform retargeting operation by means of the depth feature maps extracted from the pre-training network, which are not an end-to-end training process. Subsequently, Song et al. [10] present a CNN-based framework to introduce user preference into a multi-operator retargeting algorithm. Cho et al. [11] propose a weakly and self-supervised deep network to learn a shift map from the original image to the retargeting map. Although these methods are end-to-end training, they are essentially dependent on the importance map obtained by calculation, so their results are also limited by the calculation measure of the importance map. After that, Tan et al. [12] develop an unsupervised deep cyclic image retargeting method (CycleIR) that improves the quality of retargeted images by introducing cyclic perception consistency loss. However, all of these methods [9–13, 15–17] directly perform retargeting in the image space but not in the feature space, which can lead to unnatural distortions in results.

Recently, GAN has been applied to image retargeting. For example, Shocher et al. [14] suggest a fully unsupervised image-specific GAN(InGAN) that trains on a single input image and learns its internal distribution of patches. However, InGAN [14] learns a local block in the original image as ground truth. In other words, InGAN [14] mainly considers the texture information of the image, and does not take into account the semantics or scene information of the image. Mei et al. [18] introduce a deep supervised technique into the image retargeting task. This deep model learns a shift map to implement pixel-wise mapping from the source image to the target image in the feature space. But MRGAN only considers retargeting images to smaller sizes.

2.1 Retargeting Dataset

Three public datasets exist for image retargeting, namely MIT RetargetMe, CUHK, and NIRD. Each of these datasets comprises retargeted images generated through various methods, accompanied by corresponding subjective evaluation scores.

MIT RetargetMe Dataset. This dataset contains 37 original images and 296 retargeted results. The retargeted results are generated by eight retargeting algorithms, including CR, SCL, SC, MULTIOP, SM, SNS, SV, and WARP. The retargeting is set to either 50% or 25% of the original image's height or width respectively. Each original image is labeled with six attributes.

CUHK Dataset. The CUHK dataset comprises 57 original images and 171 retargeted results. For each original image, three retargeting operators are randomly selected from ten representative retargeting algorithms, resulting in the generation of corresponding retargeted images.

NRID Dataset. The NRID dataset comprises 35 original images, with five distinct retargeting algorithms applied to generate retargeted images: MO, SCL, SC, SM, and WARP. The original image in NRID dataset also has the same six attributes as MIT RetargetMe dataset.

However, the above three public datasets are currently insufficiently populated to adequately support the training process of the network. Furthermore, most of these datasets are utilized for comparing IRQA methods, which implies that we cannot identify the optimal retargeted image (ground truth). Consequently, a significant impediment to research in image retargeting based on GAN is the absence of benchmark datasets.

TIReD Dataset. Mei et al. introduce a new dataset named TIReD, which consists of 6,576 pairs generated by multiple operators using Image Retargeting Quality Assessment (IRQA) algorithm. Each pair consists of an original image and its corresponding retargeted image, which is selected from results of seven retargeting algorithms using the IRQA algorithm. The retargeted image that corresponds to the original image serves as the ground truth.

3 Retargeting TIReD ++ Dataset

Our goal is to achieve retargeting by learning the target retargeted images using the GAN network. The focal point and challenge in this process, however, lies in the selection of the target image. In the realm of image retargeting, numerous methods have been proposed, however, there exists no stringent standard to assess which type of retargeted image is superior. To solve this problem, we contribute a comprehensive dataset named TIReD ++ for image retargeting. The overview of data generation is shown in Fig. 2. We implement certain representative prior retargeting algorithms, including: uniform scaling (USL), seam-carving (SC) [1], improved seam-carving (ISC) [2], scale-and-stretch (SNS) [22], shift map (SM) [4], Cycle-IR [13], WSSDCNN [12], SAMIR [11]. We employ the eight retargeting operators implemented to perform the identical retargeting on the same original input image. We divide the retargeted image with the same input and this input image (9 images in total) into the same group.

We then adopt the IRQA algorithm, TRASIM [19] as the evaluation criteria, to score the retargeted image based on original input image in each group. We finally consider the retargeted image with the highest score within the group as the best performance (ground truth) and pair it with the original image for training purposes. We consider the ground truth as a reference, and create a pair of input images that correspond with the original image for training purposes. There are 7, 074 image pairs in total. They are with different width scaling ratios, one for the ratio of 0.5 and the other for 0.75. Specifically, each has 3,537 retargeting-image pairs, including the original images and retargeted images (ground truth). The training dataset has 2,800 pairs, and the test dataset has 737

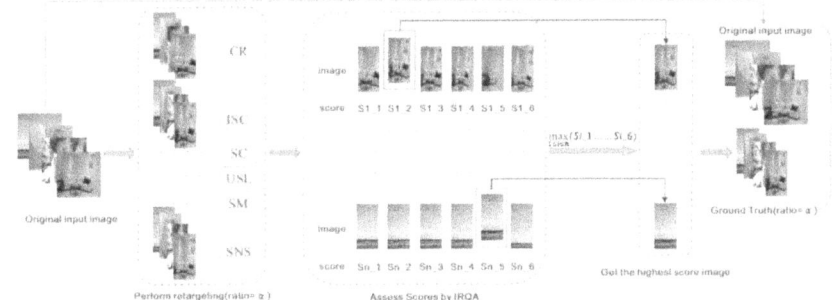

Fig. 2. Overview of Data Collection. We use the collected original image as input. Then we use the IRQA algorithm in [19] to generate the retargeted image as the ground truth.

(a)Input   (b)0.75   (c)0.5   (a)Input   (b)0.75   (c)0.5

Fig. 3. Some example images in the constructed dataset. (a) is the original image; (b) is the ground truth at a width scaling ratio of 0.75; and (c) is the ground truth at a width scaling ratio of 0.50.

pairs. Figure 3 shows some images in our dataset. In each group, we display the selection of the corresponding ground truth for different styles of images.

4 Approach

4.1 BiRGAN Model

In this section, only the width adjustment of the image is described as an example. The overall architecture of BiRGAN is shown in Fig. 1. BiRGAN has two subnetworks, Retargeting Generation (G) and Retargeting Verification (D). G is based on GAN to generate images with reduced width. D uses a structure similar to G to expand the image width. In general, G first generates a width-reduced retargeted image, and then D takes this retargeted image and the original image as input. D reconstructs the original image, and evaluates the similarity of the reconstructed image and the original image, so as to verify whether the result of G completely retains the important features of the original image. That is, G and D form a GAN-like structure. G is similar to the generator of the GAN network, and D is equivalent to the discriminator analogously.

Retargeting Generation (Generator). Retargeting Generation (G), similar to the generator in GAN network, which realizes the retargeting operation of reducing the image width. As shown in Fig. 1. It includes a complete GAN structure with a generator G_1 and a discriminator D_1. It feeds the input image into G_1 to generates a width-reduced image Y. Then it sends y together with the corresponding ground truth to D_1 for discrimination.

For the G_1, we adopt a "U-Net" network as the generator which follows an encoder-decoder structure similar to the one used in [18]. Based on the U-Net structure, we add the Dilated Convolutions and the 1 x 1 Convolution. The encoder part splices a common layer of convolution and the output feature map of the convolution layer into the next layer of convolution to encode, in this way, the features extracted from different receptive fields can be fused to obtain more complete features, which is also beneficial to the redirection at different resolutions, and 1 x 1 convolution can increase the interaction between channels, increase online learning capabilities. For discriminator D_1, it uses the full convolution patch discriminator [20]. Since that the difference between the retargeted image and the original image is relatively small. Patches in patch discriminator has better local characteristics. During the training, the resulting image is fed into D with ground truth, and a matrix of N × N is output, where N is the size of patch, and the value of the matrix is the result of the patch.

Retargeting Verification (Discriminator). The structure of Retargeting Verification module (D) is the same as Retargeting Generation module (G), including a generator G_2 and a discriminator D_2. Therefore, it may be regarded as a discriminator in GAN network formally.

The structure of Retargeting Verification module (D) is the same as Retargeting Generation module (G), including a generator G_2 and a discriminator D_2. Its generator takes the retargeted image from Retargeting Generation module as input, and mainly implements the retargeting of expanding the image width. It then seeds the generated expanded image and original input image into the D_2 for distinguishing. In general, D verifies or discriminates whether the generated image of G completely preserves the important features in the original input image by reconstructing the input image and evaluating the similarity of the reconstructed image and the input image. Therefore, it may be regarded as a discriminator in GAN network formally.

Since that Retargeting Generation and Retargeting Verification are equivalent to a GAN structure, when the G starting point is high, if D' is trained from the beginning, the generator and discriminator function in GAN structure will be out of balance. Affect the effectiveness of the network. Therefore, in order to avoid this effect, the D module is also pre-trained in this paper. Considering that G and D are an interactive and reciprocal process, and when the original image is input into G, this module is based on the ground truth in the retargeting dataset established in the paper.

Therefore, if ground truth is used as input for D, the module should be trained with the original image as the standard. The G_1 and D_1 of Retargeting Generation G are the same as G_2 and D_2 of Retargeting Verification D. However, in the process of pre-training, the generator G_2 takes the ground truth in G as the input, and then generates the generated image with expanded width. Then the retargeted image of G_2 and the original input image in G are fed into the discriminant D_2 for line discrimination.

When both G and D are pre-trained, the G_1 and D_1 of G remain unchanged, while the G_2 and D_2 of D turn to an approximate discriminator during the actual combined training. That is to say, when a retargeted image with a reduced width is generated in the process of G, it needs to be input to the generator G_2 in D to generate the retargeted result with a wider width. At the same time, the ground truth in G needs to be input to G_2 to generate the retargeted image. Not only that, in the pre-training process, the ground truth in G has been used as input, and the original image in G has been used as the standard to adjust the network parameters. In this way, the global training of bi-directional retargeting can be performed with D as the discriminator of G in the form.

4.2 Loss Design

Adversarial Loss. The network of GANs require simultaneous training both the generator and the discriminator. We design the adversarial losses for the two GANs. The equations are as follows:

$$\mathcal{L}_{GAN_1}(G_1, D_1) = \mathbb{E}_{x_{gt} \sim p_{ddta}(x_{gt})}[\log D_1(x_{gt})] \\ + \mathbb{E}_{x \sim p_{data}(x)}[\log(1 - D_1(G_1(x)))], \quad (1)$$

$$\mathcal{L}_{GAN_2}(G_1, G_2, D_2) = \mathbb{E}_{x_{gt} \sim p_{data}(x_{gt})}\left[\log D_2\left(G_2(x_{gt})\right)\right] \\ + \mathbb{E}_{x \sim p_{data}(x)}\left[\log\left(1 - D_2(G_2(G_1(x)))\right)\right], \quad (2)$$

where L_{GAN1} is the adversarial loss for the G, and xgt is the corresponding width reduced image in the dataset of ground truth. L_{GAN2} is the adversarial loss for the D, x is the original input image.

Since that D is used as the discriminator of G, the adversarial loss of BiRGAN is as follows:

$$\mathcal{L}_{BiRHGAN}(G_1, G_2, D_2) = \mathbb{E}_{x_{gt} \sim p_{data}(x_{gt})}\left[\log D_2\left(G_2(x_{gt})\right)\right] \\ + \mathbb{E}_{x \sim p_{data}(x)}\left[\log\left(1 - D_2(G_2(G_1(x)))\right)\right], \quad (3)$$

Other Loss. For training stability, we use L_1 loss [20] to emphasize the matching of each corresponding pixel between the generated image and the real image, encouraging robustness and less fuzziness. They are defined as follows:

$$\mathcal{L}_{G_1 L_1}(G_1) = \|x_{gt} - G_1(x)\|_1, \quad (4)$$

$$\mathcal{L}_{G_2 L_1}(G_1, G_2) = \|x - G_2(x_{gl})\|_1, \quad (5)$$

where $L_{G1!L1}$ is the L_1 loss designed for the network represented by G_1, and $L_{G2!l1}$ is designed for G_2. $\|\cdot\|_1$ is the L_1 norm.

In addition, the ideal retargeting model should generate a retargeted image that is highly consistent with the input image in terms of visual perception, without obvious distortion and artificial artifacts, and can completely preserve important image information. Therefore, we use the reconstruction loss to keep the uniformity of the image before redirection and the mapping after redirection through a reciprocal redirection.

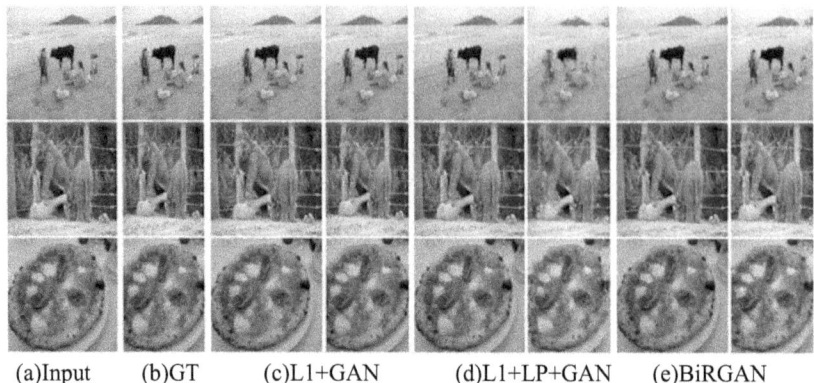

Fig. 4. Ablation Study. (a) and (b) are the original image and ground truth, ((c)-(e)) are results trained with a different loss. For each group, the left shows the image generated by expanding the width in the bi-directional process, and the right side is the result of the width reduced, and the image on the right side is the input for generation process of the left.

This loss is to perform the consistency constraint between pixels between the original reconstructed image and the original input image in G_1 generator after the retargeted image generated by G_1 is passed through G_2 the reconstruction loss not only keeps the structure and content of the two independent redirection processes, but also promotes and restrains each other between the two processes. Lres Loss as Eq. 6:

$$L_{\text{res}}(G_1, G_2) = x - G_2(G_1(x))_1, \qquad (6)$$

Total Loss. After we have defined different losses to evaluate the network, we get the target equation for BiRGAN. Here λ are the set parameters of contribution weight to the total loss, which are obtained according to the experiment. The expression is as follows:

$$\begin{aligned} G^* = & \underset{G_1}{\text{argmin}}\underset{D_1}{\text{max}} L_{GAN_1}(G_1, D_1) + \underset{G_1}{\text{argmin}}\underset{\mathbb{D}}{\text{max}} L_{GAN_2}(G_1, G_2, D_2) \\ & + \lambda_{G_1L_1} L_{G_1L_1}(G_1) + \lambda_{G_2L_2} L_{G_2L_2}(G_1, G_2) + \lambda_{\text{res}} L_{\text{res}}(G_1, G_2), \end{aligned} \qquad (7)$$

5 Experiment

BiRGAN is implemented based on python and tensorflow. In the training, we set the value of λ_{G1L1}, λ_{G2L2} and λres to 1000. We also employ batch normalization [21] in most convolutional blocks to encourage stability of the proposed model. In the experiment, our model performed a complete end-to-end training using the Adam optimizer [22].

The batch size is set to 4. We trained it on NVIDIA Tesla V100 GPU with 32GB GPU memory.

(a) Original image (b) SC (c) IMSC (d) SM (e) SNS (f) USL (g) Cycle-IR (h) WSSDCNN (i) SAMIR (j) Ours

Fig. 5. Visual comparison of our method with representative retargeting approaches. (a) is the original image, (b)-(i) are retargeting images by prevous methods, (j) is our results.

5.1 Ablation Study

In order to train two GANs in our model and improve their stability, in addition to Adversarial Loss, we also use L1 Loss and Reconstruction Loss to assist in it. Here, we conducted an ablation study to verify the importance of these losses.

Figure 4 illustrates their differences in optimizing the BiRGAN with several examples of retargeted images. It can be seen that L_1 loss pays more attention to matching at pixel-level and lacks high-frequency information, so its introduction can improve the visual effect of generated images. Conversely, Reconstruction loss is more concerned with content perception and structural similarity. Therefore, only BiRGAN (which use Adversarial loss, L_1 loss and Reconstruction loss simultaneously) achieves the best results, producing rationally meaningful images and reducing artifacts dramatically.

5.2 Comparison with Previous Methods

Figure 5 shows a visual comparison between BiRGAN and several previous retargeting methods by adjusting the width of the input image to 0.75 of its original width on both TIRED ++ dataset and RetargetMe dataset. Among them, (a) is the original image, and (b)-(k) are the retargeted images by SC [1], IMSC [2], SM [4], SNS [22], USL, Cycle-IR [13], WSSDCNN [12], SAMIR [11] and our method. It can be seen that SC and IMSC may deform important objects when the seam passes through them. SNS pays too much attention to the retention of all information and neglects the retention of important information. When the shift map in SM fails to calculate, the original image will lose or seriously distort important information. USL simply merges adjacent pixels together, resulting in an excessive reduction of significant objects. In addition, Cycle-IR has the same problem as SNS. The retargeted results of the WSSDCNN are often distorted.

InGAN does not consider semantic information because it is not a traditional retargeting algorithm, so it works well on texture images, but not on semantic images such as people. Thanks to the large retargeting dataset TIRED + +, powerful supervised learning, and the effectiveness of bi-directional retargeting processes, BiRGAN can generate high quality target images. Compared with previous methods, it can be seen that our approach can not only avoid image distortion during retargeting, but also keep the lines in the image well without causing the color distortion of the image.

Table 1. Retargeting results in terms of NIQE, BRISQU and NBIQA on the new dataset and RetargetMe(RM).

Method	NIQE	BRISQUE	NBIQA	NIQE(RM)	BRISQUE(RM)	NBIQA(RM)
SC	6.2021	25.306	24.2240	7.2791	29.540	24.9689
IMSC	6.2237	23.5643	23.6607	7.4080	28.668	24.5436
USL	6.0452	22.146	23.7220	7.4080	23.827	23.4995
SM	6.1605	23.398	24.6454	6.8286	25.925	25.9928
SNS	5.7373	20.302	24.7172	5.9054	17.364	20.9607
Cycle-IR	5.8676	22.562	23.2554	6.1286	21.008	20.9531
WSSDCNN	5.9394	22.014	23.4985	6.4185	23.161	23.2155
SAMIR	6.8352	39.7886	42.1039	6.6493	38.7707	41.9513
Ours	5.6302	21.1829	22.9749	5.6985	17.5583	18.1242

5.3 Quantitative Assessment

Table 1 presents the quantitative assessment results using objective evaluation methods on the proposed dataset TIRED ++ and RetargetMe(RM). It can be seen that the BIRGAN model has the best performance in NIQE and NBIQA, although it is not perfect in BRISQUE compared with other advanced methods.

6 Conclusion

In this paper, we have proposed a bi-directional retargeting network based on GAN. It conducts two completely opposite retargeting processes independently, and competes to achieve preferable results. Simultaneously, the retargeting operation is performed in feature space of the image which allows for a reduction in artifacts and distortions through reconstruction of the retargeted image, enhancing its naturalness and authenticity. The proposed network implements two operations that are inverse to each other, so it also provides a unified framework for a variety of different tasks involving reciprocal processes.

Acknowledgments. This work was funded by the Natural Science Foundation of Tianjin Municipality (No. 21JCYBJC00640), 2023 CCF-Baidu Songguo Foundation (Research on Scene Text Recognition Based on PaddlePaddle).

References

1. Avidan, S., Shamir, A.: Seam carving for content-aware image resizing. In: ACM Transactions on Graphics (TOG), vol. 26, p. 10. ACM (2007)
2. Rubinstein, M., Shamir, A., Avidan, S.: Improved seam carving for video retargeting. In: ACM Transactions on Graphics (TOG), vol. 27, p. 16. ACM (2008)
3. Rubinstein, M., Shamir, A., Avidan, S.: Multi-operator media retargeting. ACM Transactions on graphics (TOG) **28**(3), 23 (2009)
4. Pritch, Y., Kav-Venaki, E., Peleg, S.: Shift-map image editing. In: 2009 IEEE 12th International Conference on Computer Vision, pp. 151–158. IEEE (2009)
5. Panozzo, D., Weber, O., Sorkine, O.: Robust image retargeting via axis-aligned deformation. In: Computer Graphics Forum, vol. 31, pp. 229–236. Wiley Online Library (2012)
6. Lin, S.-S., Yeh, I.-C., Lin, C.-H., Lee, T.-Y.: Patch-based image warping for content-aware retargeting. IEEE Trans. Multimedia **15**(2), 359–368 (2012)
7. Chen, R., Freedman, D., Karni, Z., Gotsman, C., Liu, L.: Content-aware image resizing by quadratic programming. In: 2010 IEEE Computer Society Conference on Computer Vision and Pattern Recognition-Workshops, pp. 1–8. IEEE (2010)
8. Shi, M., Yang, L., Peng, G., Xu, D.: A content-aware image resizing method with prominent object size adjusted. In: Proceedings of the 17th ACM Symposium on Virtual Reality Software and Technology, pp. 175–176. ACM (2010)
9. Song, E., Lee, M., Lee, S.: Carvingnet: Content-guided seam carving using deep convolution neural network. IEEE Access **7**, 284–292 (2018)
10. Song, Y., et al.: Photo squarization by deep multi-operator retargeting. In: ACM Multimedia, pp. 1047–1055 (2018)
11. Cho, D., Park, J., Oh, T.-H., Tai, Y.-W., So Kweon, I.: Weakly-and self-supervised learning for content-aware deep image retargeting. In: Proceedings of the IEEE International Conference on Computer Vision, pp. 4558–4567 (2017)
12. Tan, W., Yan, B., Lin, C., Niu, X.: Cycle-ir: Deep cyclic image retargeting. IEEE Trans. Multimedia **22**(7), 1730–1743 (2019)
13. Shocher, A., Bagon, S., Isola, P., Irani, M.: Internal distribution matching for natural image retargeting. arXiv preprint arXiv:1812.00231 (2018)
14. Zhou, Y., Chen, Z., Li, W.: Weakly supervised reinforced multi-operator image retargeting. IEEE Trans. Circuits Syst. Video Technol. **31**(1), 126–139 (2020)
15. Kajiura, N., Kosugi, S., Wang, X., Yamasaki, T.: Self-play reinforcement learning for fast image retargeting. In: Proceedings of the 28th ACM International Conference on Multimedia, pp. 1755–1763 (2020)
16. Tang, Z., Yao, J., Zhang, Q.: Multi-operator image retargeting in compressed domain by preserving aspect ratio of important contents. Multimedia Tools and Applications, 1–22 (2022)
17. Mei, Y., Guo, X., Sun, D., Pan, G., Zhang, J.: Deep supervised image retargeting. In: 2021 IEEE International Conference on Multimedia and Expo (ICME), pp. 1–6. IEEE (2021)
18. Liang, Y., Liu, Y.-J., Gutierrez, D.: Objective quality prediction of image retargeting algorithms. IEEE Trans. Visual Comput. Graphics **23**(2), 1099–1110 (2016)
19. Isola, P., Zhu, J.-Y., Zhou, T., Efros, A.A.: Image-to-image translation with conditional adversarial networks. In: Proceedings of the IEEE Conference on Computer Vision and Pattern Recognition, pp. 1125–1134 (2017)
20. Ioffe, S., Szegedy, C.: Batch normalization: Accelerating deep network training by reducing internal covariate shift. arXiv preprint arXiv:1502.03167 (2015)
21. Kingma, D.P., Ba, J.: Adam: A method for stochastic optimization. arXiv preprint arXiv:1412.6980 (2014)
22. Wang, Y.-S., Tai, C.-L., Sorkine, O., Lee, T.-Y.: Optimized scale-and-stretch for image resizing. In: ACM Transactions on Graphics (TOG), vol. 27, p. 118. ACM (2008)

MulTIR: Deep Multi-Target Image Retargeting

Di Sun[1], Yitong Guo[1], Chaojie Yao[1], Yijing Mei[2], Dufeng Chen[3], and Gang Pan[2]($\boxtimes$)

[1] College of Artificial Intelligence, Tianjin University of Science and Technology, Tianjin 300222, China
[2] College of Intelligence and Computing, Tianjin University, Tianjin 300350, China
pangang@tju.edu.cn
[3] Beijing Geotechnical and Investigation Engineering Insititute, Beijing 100080, China

Abstract. Image retargeting aims to resize images to fit various devices while maintaining good viewing experiences. Normally, multi-operator image retargeting shows better performance than single operator strategy, however, there is still no single method that performs well on all cases. This inspires us to provide a general image retargeting framework that can adaptively learns from multiple methods. We present a multi-target image retargeting model named MulTIR, which learns the deformation process from multiple diverse outputs and automatically pick the optimal target in feature space. We also introduce a Mean-GAN-Min-Task loss to adapt the additional targets in each training example. Experimental results indicate the superiority of MulTIR against representative methods.

Keywords: Image retargeting · Multi-target · GAN · 1-to-M mapping

1 Introduction

The rise of media devices necessitates adjusting images and videos for full-screen display with appropriate aspect ratios and resolutions. Traditional scaling techniques often result in distortions like shrinking, clipping, or stretching. Image retargeting technology addresses this by adjusting aspect ratios while preserving essential information. Recent content-aware methods have seen success by utilizing saliency maps and various importance measures like pixel gradient and color contrast [1–8]. However, these methods are constrained by fixed designs, and a single retargeting operator may not perform well for all scenarios.

In recent years, deep learning has shown its excellent performance in various applications. Recently, some learning based retargeting technologies have been presented [9–15]. Most methods use pre-trained network or improved network to extract deep features to calculate the corresponding importance map, and then directly perform retargeting operation in image space. The first end-to-end learning-based method is WSSDCNN ([13]), which utilizes an encoder-decoder to learn an attention map. Although the great progress has been made, this method has a limit on the sizes of the input images. Tan et al. ([14]) develop Cycle-IR, an unsupervised method that improves the quality of retargeted images by introducing cyclic perception consistency loss, however, it can not handle the situations when the important areas cover high proportion of the whole images. In general, there are little studies that attempt to address image retargeting problem by using supervised methods. This is because the evaluation of retargeted images from the perspective of vision is highly subjective, so it's difficult to construct a dedicated dataset to train the deep retargeting models.

Different from the task with clear objective or evaluation criteria, the image retargeting task is an uncertain problem, that is, the method to produce the desired retargeted result is unfixed, and the way to evaluate retargeted results is subjective. In some work, multiple operator-mixed measures are presented to accommodate the variation on various images and target sizes [2, 12, 16–20]. In general, multi-operator approaches perform better than single operator strategy, but they essentially arrange the order of operators to find the best combination, which is easy to fall into local optimum.

In this paper, we present a multiple target image retargeting method that deals with the aforementioned challenges. Rather than 1-to-1 training with an unavailable ground truth, we provide more than one target for each input image to automatically learn the optimal target in feature space. To our knowledge, this is the first attempt to address image retargeting in a deep multi-target learning manner. To accommodate the research, we construct a 1-to-M image retargeting dataset that consists of multiple diverse target images.

How to model for guiding 1-to-M mapping learning? We design MulTIR, a deep multi-target model based on Generative Adversarial Network(GAN) [21]. MulTIR performs retargeting operations in feature space, this makes it possible to pay attention to the generation of image details while learning the overall deformation of target images, so as to improve the naturalness and authenticity of the image. The last challenge for training such a retargeting generator is to solve the diversity among the target images obtained from multiple retargeting operators for the same input. We design a MeanGAN-Min-Task loss that carefully employs two different aggregate functions to guide the generation from multiple diverse targets encountered during training. Moreover, we provide in-depth experiments and demonstrate that MulTIR achieves superior performance compared with the state-of-the-art algorithms. The major contributions are as below:

- We provide a new solution into deep image retargeting that exploits information from multiple operators within the feature space. To our knowledge, this is the first attempt to address image retargeting in a deep multi-target learning manner.
- We present a deep learning-based image retargeting network that resolves uncertain target images by exploring 1-to-M mapping learning in feature space.

2 Related Work

Image retargeting requires adjusting input images into arbitrary size on the premise of preserving regions of importance. Early attempts usually employ some content-aware approaches to transform image to the target size. They can be generally divided into discrete and continuous methods. A typical discrete method is seam carving(SC) ([1]) which iteratively deletes or inserts pixels that produce the least loss of energy to preserve the visual saliency. Rubinstein et al. ([7]) modify seam carving by removing a seam from the minimum energy change to determine the energy of a pixel. Pritch et al. ([3]) present a Shift-Map (SM) technique to remove or add band regions. Normally, these methods [1–3, 7] resize the image by removing discrete regions, which easily bring visual distortions. In contrast, continuous measures [5, 8] utilize non-uniform grid deformation to preserve important areas. For example, Wang et al. ([8]) iteratively calculate the optimal scaling factor of each local area, and update the image with the help of saliency map. Guo et al. ([5]) construct a saliency-based mesh representation which is consistent with the underlying image structures. In general, these traditional approaches require computing a salience map based on hand-drafted features. The quality of salience map directly affects the performance of these approaches.

More recently, many learning-based retargeting methods have been developed, such as CarvingNet [9], DeepIR [10]. However, above approaches require separate steps to perform retargeting operation, rather than an end-to-end training process. Whereafter, Cho et al. [13] pose a weakly and selfsupervised end-to-end model to learn a shift map from the original image to the retargeting map. Although the methods are end-to-end training, they are essentially dependent on the importance map obtained by calculation, so their results are also limited by the calculation measure of the importance map. Besides, Tan et al. [14] develop an unsupervised deep cyclic image retargeting method (Cycle-IR) that improves the quality with cyclic perception consistency loss, however, it cannot handle images with large areas of visual importance. Shocher et al. [22] pose a fully unsupervised image specific GAN(InGAN). It uses a single input image to learn its internal patch distribution to synthesize a different size output. Therefore, the time cost is intolerable for abundant synthesis task. it does not take into account the semantics or scenes of the image.

As for multi-operator image retargeting, Rubinstein et al. [2] are the earliest to propose multi-operator retargeting by combining several representative operators in an optimal manner. Song et al. [12] present a CNN-based framework that introduces user preference for researching the photo squarization problem in the image retargeting field. Zhou et al. [19] utilize reinforcement learning to perform global optimization. These methods generally arrange the order of operators to find the best combination, and then perform the retargeting operation in image space. They are essentially searching for the optimal operator according to different strategies.

3 Approach

Our aim is to design a deep model which can produce visually pleasing ratargeted images. A key aspect is that each original input corresponds to multiple target images obtained by different methods, as shown in Fig. 1.

3.1 Formulation

We use the power of Generative Adversarial Network (GAN) [21]. It contains a generator G and a discriminator D. The generator takes the input image x, and together with a transformation T (which determines the target size), it maps to a target y. The generator G is designed to produce "real" images, while the discriminator D undergoes adversarial

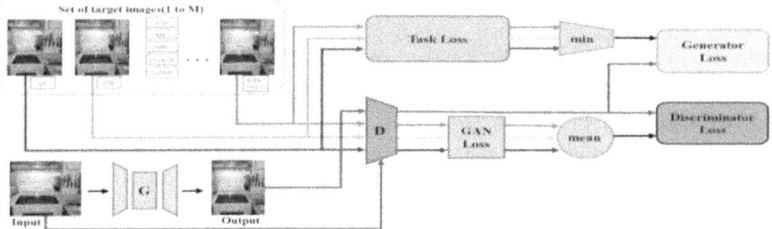

Fig. 1. MulTIR architecture. A generative adversarial network for image retargeting that illustrates multiple different outputs encountered during training.

training to determine whether an image is real or fake. Mathematically, this optimization problem can be written as:

$$G^* = \min_G \max_D L_{gan}(x, y) \tag{1}$$

$$L_{gan}(x, y) = \mathbb{E}_{(y)} \log D(y) + \mathbb{E}_{(x,T)} \log(1 - D(G(x; T))) \tag{2}$$

The L_{gan} encourages the distribution of $G(x; T)$ is matched to that of x. In fact, applying only L_{gan} may cause mode collapse, so the GAN loss is normally combined with a task loss. We follow the common way to include a task loss which aims to avoid mode collapse. The total loss function is summarized as:

$$L_{total}(x, y) = \lambda L_{gan}(x, y) + L_{task}(x, y), \tag{3}$$

However, we have multiple targets $y_i^{(1)}, y_i^{(2)}, \ldots, y_i^{(M_i)}$ for the same input x_i. It's worth emphasizing that the number of M_i may vary for different inputs, so this 1-to-M mapping can be viewed as a regular 1-to-1 mapping problem: $\left(x_1, y_1^{(1)}\right), \ldots, (x_1, y_1^{(M_1)}), \ldots, \left(x_N, y_N^{(1)}\right), \ldots, \left(x_N, y_N^{(M_i)}\right)$. Motivated by [23], our method treats $(x_i^{(1)}, y_i^{(1)}, y_i^{(2)}, \ldots, y_i^{(M_i)})$ as a single training example, and these pairs are randomly fetched to train the network. To fit the additional targets in each training case, we introduce a Mean-GAN-Min-Task loss. The generator G and the discriminator D employ two different aggregate functions, respectively. The final loss is formulated as:

$$L(x_i, y_i^{(1)}, \ldots, y_i^{(M_i)}) = \frac{\lambda}{M_i} \sum_{j=1}^{M_i} L_{gan}(x_i, y_i^{(j)}) + \min_{j \in (1, \ldots, M_i)} L_{task}(x_i, y_i^{(j)}) \tag{4}$$

Here we average over the target images to aggregate the GAN loss. The generator adaptively pick the most suitable target to generate on-the-fly by means of the min aggregate function. The discriminator learns to distinguish the generated ratargeted image from all target images with equal importance by using the mean aggregate function. Hence, the issue of conflicting gradients caused by diverse modalities is effectively alleviated.

3.2 Task Loss

As previously mentioned, we follow the common in GAN to include a task loss. For our retargeting task, the task loss includes L_1, L_{tv} and L_p.

First, we use a per-pixel loss L_1, which is the L1 distance between the generated image and the corresponding target image to enhance the pixel matching. It is defined as below:

$$L_1 = \|y - G(x)\|_1, \tag{5}$$

In order to maintain the object shape and enhance the smoothness in generated images, we also adopt a total variation loss L_{tv} as shown in equation:

$$L_{tv} = \frac{1}{CWH} \|\nabla G(x) - \nabla y\|_1, \tag{6}$$

where C denotes the channel number, ∇ represents the image gradient, and W and H are width and height, respectively.

In addition, we employ a perceptual loss L_P to constrain the feature similarity between the generated image and the corresponding target.

$$L_p = \sum_{l=L-2}^{L-1} \beta_l \cdot \|\Phi_l(y) - \Phi_l(G(x))\|_2, \tag{7}$$

where L represents the number of convolution blocks in the pre-trained $VGG19$. β contributes the weight of each item to the total perceptual loss. Φ_l is used to extract the feature map of the l-th convolution block in $VGG19$. $\|\cdot\|_2$ is the Euclidean norm.

Finally, the combined task loss function is as follows:

$$L_{task}(x, y) = \lambda_1 L_1(x, y) + \lambda_2 L_{tv}(x, y) + \lambda_3 L_p(x, y), \tag{8}$$

here λ_i is the set parameter of contribution weight to the task loss, which is obtained according to the experiment.

3.3 Network Details

The generator G follows the hourglass architecture [24]. Dilated convolutions are utilized to expand the receptive field of the convolutions, so as to preserve global characteristics of the image and enhance the network applicability for different scale images. At the same time, the 1×1 convolution can increase the interaction among 6 channels and increase the network learning ability. The bottleneck uses ResNet module that consists of six residual-blocks. The decoder of G is completely symmetrical with the encoder part. Resize-convolution layer is used as an alternative instead of regular deconvolution, and skip connections are also employed between the mirrored layers of the encoder and decoder part. The network architecture of the generator is shown in Fig. 2.

For discriminator D, we use the patch discriminator with full convolution. Normally, PatchGAN helps to generate nice texture and shape. Because the generator part has taken overall information into account, we focus on local features in the discriminator.

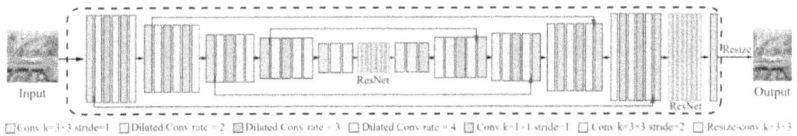

Fig. 2. The architecture of generator G. The red lines demonstrate skip-connections, and k is the kernel size. (Color figure online)

4 Experiments

4.1 Experimental Settings

TIReD Dataset ([25]). TIReD is a deep paired dataset in image retargeting. It composed of 6,576 pair images. Instead of directly using these pair images, we focus on retargeted images obtained by different methods, so we use the original input and its corresponding retargeted results.

Experimental Settings. The experiments are carried out under the configuration of NVIDIA TITAN V GPU with 12GB memory and Intel i7-10700K processor. The proposed network is implemented in PyTorch. We train and update the network parameters by the ADAM optimizer with an initial leaning rate 2×10^{-4}. We train the model on the TIReD which includes 5,000 groups with multiple target images. In training, we set the value of β_{L-1} in L_P to 2 and β_{L-2} to 1. The values of λ is set to 10. And in formula 8, the values of $\lambda 1$, $\lambda 2$ and $\lambda 3$ are 1000, 10 and 0.01, respectively. The activation functions of the encoder and decoder use LReLU and ReLU respectively. We also employ batch normalization in most convolutional blocks to encourage stability of the proposed model. Here the batch size is set to 4.

4.2 Ablation Study

Figure 3 shows the results in ablation study, where column (a) shows the original input, column (b) indicates the result of MulTIR model, and column (c)–(e) are the results without using L_1, L_{tv} and L_p respectively. It can be found that the design of L_1 makes the network more stable and has a more positive effect on the truthiness of the generated image (the first line in Fig. 3). L_{tv} has a great effect on maintaining straight lines and object shapes(see the first and second rows in Fig. 3), the circle of wheels and the boundary of people and animals are maintained better. It makes the model more sensitive to pure edge lines and generate results with more correct contours. L_p makes the semantic information of the retargeted image more correct. It can be observed that the semantic information is better preserved in the two cases in Fig. 3. In addition, as we can see from Table 1, the evaluation achieves the best performance when all the loss functions are included. It is thus proved that each loss function has a definite effect.

4.3 Performance Comparison

We compare MulTIR with the following state-of-the-art image retargeting algorithms, which include SC [1], ISC [7], SM [3], SNS [8], USL, Cycle-IR [14], WSSDCNN [13] and SAMIR [19] on TIReD and RetargetMe.

(a)   (b)   (c)   (d)   (e)

Fig. 3. Ablation study. (a) Original images. (b) Our results. (c)-(e) Results without $\mathcal{L}_1$, $\mathcal{L}_{tv}$ and $\mathcal{L}_P$, respectively.

Table 1. Retargeting results for ablation study. The values in bold indicate the best performances.

Metric	No-$\mathcal{L}_P$	No-$\mathcal{L}_{tv}$	No-$\mathcal{L}_1$	Ours
NIQE	6.3466	5.9318	6.0561	**5.7364**
BRISQU	24.4563	22.3521	23.2343	**20.2025**
NBIQA	25.3482	20.7672	22.8723	**20.3855**

Qualitative Evaluation. Figure 4 provides visual comparisons of our results with other methods. The first three rows depict results on TIReD. While most methods preserve contents with semantic importance, there are deformations of lines and edges. SC and ISC tend to generate shape inconsistencies, SM creates discontinuous artifacts, and SCL excessively reduces important objects by merging adjacent pixels. WSSDCNN exhibits shape deformations on the tower and pencil (Fig. 4(i)). Some semantic content loss is observed in Fig. 4(g), while Cycle-IR experiences similar issues with missing details affecting visual experience (Fig. 4(h)). In contrast, MulTIR performs better, preserving both human and shadow parts well (Fig. 4(j)). The last three rows showcase cases on RetargetMe, where most methods cause varying degrees of shape distortions as highlighted in the red box. In contrast, MulTIR better preserves content and avoids distortions, benefiting from deep supervised learning and semantic information effectiveness. MulTIR's ability to learn from multiple methods enables high-quality retargeted images across various inputs.

Quantitative Evaluation. We numerically compare our algorithm with three image quality evaluation metrics NIQE [26], BRISQU [27] and NBIQA [28]. Among them, NIQE algorithm is closer to the human vision system, which is effective enough to evaluate image quality. BRISQU algorithm needs to calculate the feature vectors based on extracted natural scene statistics, so as to evaluate image quality from the perspective of spatial domain. The NBIQA algorithm mainly considers the feature information from both transform and spatial domain and trains the regression model to predict the image

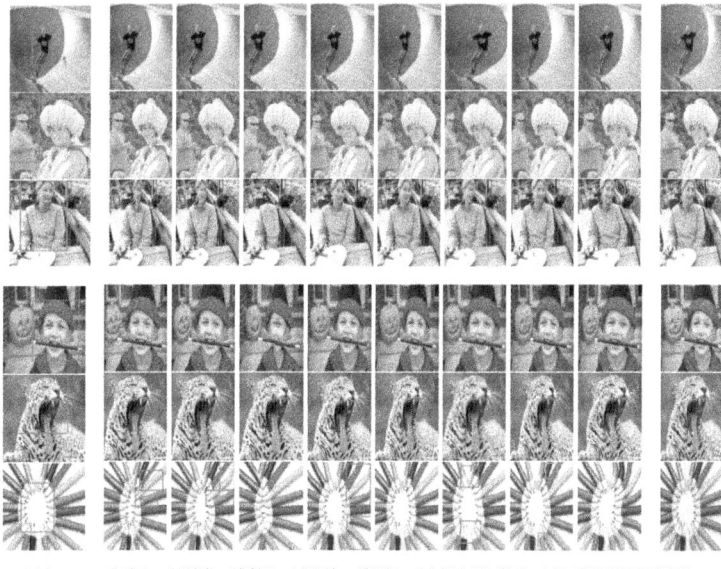

(a) input (b)SC (c)ISC (d)SM (e)SNS (f)USL (g) SAMIR (h)CycleIR (i)WSSDCNN (j)ours

Fig. 4. Visual comparison of our method with representative retargeting approaches on TIReD and RetargetMe dataset.

quality score. Table 2 presents the objective evaluation of the proposed algorithm with 8 representative methods, our model achieves the best or the second best performance.

User Study. We further conduct a user study to evaluate the subjective quality of the proposed method. 20 participants from different backgrounds are recruited (age from 25 to 50, 10 males and 10 females). 30 groups of images are displayed randomly for each participant in turn. The leftmost side of each group is the original image, followed by 9 randomly arranged retargeted images. Each switch from one group to another would rearrange the 9 choices randomly. Each participant chooses two images he likes from the nine image options, without time limit. As shown in Table 3, our work receives the highest number of votes. In addition, considering that the uniform scaling method is a moderate baseline, it is qualitatively meaningful that our method records the most votes.

Table 2. Comparison with recent works on TIReD and RetargetMe. The values in bold and underlined demonstrate the best and the second best performance respectively.

Method	NIQE	BRISQUE	NBIQA	NIQE (RM)	BRISQUE (RM)	NBIQA (RM)
SC	6.1959	25.306	24.085	7.2971	29.540	24.950
ISC	6.2171	23.564	23.508	7.4080	28.668	24.525

(*continued*)

Table 2. (*continued*)

Method	NIQE	BRISQUE	NBIQA	NIQE (RM)	BRISQUE (RM)	NBIQA (RM)
SM	6.1496	23.398	24.441	6.8255	25.925	25.951
SNS	5.7299	**20.302**	24.393	5.9060	**17.364**	20.899
USL	6.0372	22.146	24.007	6.6481	23.827	23.478
SAMIR	6.0672	22.841	24.470	7.0125	25.172	24.346
Cycle-IR	5.8608	22.562	23.211	6.1486	21.008	20.953
WSSDCNN	5.9312	22.214	23.300	6.4185	23.161	23.216
Ours	**5.6912**	22.135	**23.181**	**5.9157**	18.327	**19.851**

Table 3. The voting results of user study for comparing with representative methods. There are 20 participants with 2 votes each, and 1200 votes in the total. Our results have received more votes and more user preferences.

Method	USL	SC	ISC	SM	SNS	SAMIR	Cycle-IR	WSSDCNN	Ours
Votes	125	116	114	116	151	106	143	150	179
Proportion	10.4%	9.5%	9.7%	9.5%	12.6%	8.8%	11.9%	12.5%	14.9%

5 Conclusion

This study provide new insights into supervised image retargeting. For the first time, multiple ground truths learning is exploited to address the uncertain target image problem in image retargeting task. We employ a comprehensive dataset with groups of target images generated by different retargeting methods to ensure data diversity. We then present an effective deep model to implement the proposed MulTIR. Extensive experiments indicate the superior performance of the proposed method.

Acknowledgments. This work was funded by the Natural Science Foundation of Tianjin (No. 21JCYBJC00640), 2023 CCF-Baidu Songguo Foundation Research on Scene Text Recognition Based on PaddlePaddle).

References

1. Avidan, S., Shamir, A.: Seam carving for content-aware image resizing. ToG (2007)
2. Rubinstein, M., Shamir, A., Avidan, S.: Multi-operator media retargeting. ToG **23** (2009)
3. Pritch, Y., Kav-Venaki, E., Peleg, S.: Shift-map image editing. In: ICCV, pp. 151–158. IEEE (2009)
4. Lin, S.-S., Yeh, I.-C., Lin, C.-H., Lee, T.-Y.: Patch-based image warping for content-aware retargeting. TMM **15**(2), 359–368 (2012)

5. Guo, Y., Feng, L., Jian, S., Zhou, Z.H., Gleicher, M.: Image retargeting using mesh parametrization. TMM **11**(5), 856–867 (2009)
6. Asheghi, B., Salehpour, P., Khiavi, A.M., Hashemzadeh, M.: A comprehensive review on content-aware image retargeting: from classical to state-of-the-art methods. Signal Process. **195**, 108496 (2022). https://doi.org/10.1016/j.sigpro.2022.108496
7. Rubinstein, M., Shamir, A., Avidan, S.: Improved seam carving for video retargeting. ToG **27**, 16–1169 (2008)
8. Wang, Y.-S., Tai, C.-L., Sorkine, O., Lee, T.-Y.: Optimized scale-and-stretch for image resizing. In: ToG, p. 118. ACM (2008)
9. Song, E., Lee, M., Lee, S.: CarvingNet: content-guided seam carving using deep convolution neural network. Access, 284–292 (2018)
10. Lin, J., Zhou, T., Chen, Z.: DeepIR: a deep semantics driven framework for image retargeting. arXiv preprint arXiv:1811.07793 (2018)
11. Arar, M., Danon, D., Cohen-Or, D., Shamir, A.: Image resizing by reconstruction from deep features. arXiv preprint arXiv:1904.08475 (2019)
12. Song, Y., Tang, F., Dong, W., Zhang, X., Deussen, O., Lee, T.-Y., et al.: Photo squarization by deep multi-operator retargeting. In: MM, pp. 1047–1055. ACM (2018)
13. Cho, D., Park, J., Oh, T.-H., Tai, Y.-W., So Kweon, I.: Weakly-and self-supervised learning for content-aware deep image retargeting. In: ICCV, pp. 4558–4567. IEEE (2017)
14. Tan, W., Yan, B., Lin, C., Niu, X.: Cycle-IR: deep cyclic image retargeting. TMM **22**(7), 1730–1743 (2020)
15. Imani, H., Islam, M.B., Wong, L.-K.: Saliency-aware stereoscopic video retargeting. In: Proceedings of the IEEE/CVF Conference on Computer Vision and Pattern Recognition (CVPR) Workshops, pp. 1230–1239 (2023)
16. Qiu, Z., Ren, T., Liu, Y., Bei, J., Yang, Y.: Multi-operator image retargeting based on automatic quality assessment. In: ICIG, pp. 428–433 (2013)
17. Qian, Z., Tang, Z., Jiang, H., Kan, C.: Multi-operator image retargeting with preserving aspect ratio of important contents, pp. 306–315 (2017)
18. Wu, L., Yan, C., Jian, M., Liu, S., Dong, W., Chen, C.W.: A fast hybrid retargeting scheme with seam context and content aware strip partition. Neurocomputing **286**, 198–213 (2018)
19. Zhou, Y., Chen, Z., Li, W.: Weakly supervised reinforced multi-operator image retargeting. TCSVT **PP**(99), 1 (2020)
20. Tang, Z., Yao, J., Zhang, Q.: Multi-operator image retargeting in compressed domain by preserving aspect ratio of important contents. Multimedia Tools Appl. **81**, 1–22 (2022)
21. Goodfellow, I., et al.: Generative adversarial nets. In: NeurIPS, pp. 2672–2680 (2014)
22. Shocher, A., Bagon, S., Isola, P., Irani, M.: Internal distribution matching for natural image retargeting. arXiv preprint arXiv:1812.00231 (2018)
23. Li, M., Lin, Z., Mech, R., Yumer, E., Ramanan, D.: Photo-sketching: inferring contour drawings from images. In: WACV, pp. 1403–1412. IEEE (2019)
24. Ronneberger, O., Fischer, P., Brox, T.: U-net: Convolutional networks for biomedical image segmentation. In: Navab, N., Hornegger, J., Wells, W.M., Frangi, A.F. (eds.) MICCAI 2015. LNCS, vol. 9351, pp. 234–241. Springer, Cham (2015). https://doi.org/10.1007/978-3-319-24574-4_28
25. Mei, Y., Guo, X., Sun, D., Pan, G., Zhang, J.: Deep supervised image retargeting. In: ICME, pp. 1–6. IEEE (2021)
26. Mittal, A., Soundararajan, R., Bovik, A.C.: Making a "completely blind" image quality analyzer. SPL **20**, 209–212 (2012)
27. Mittal, A., Moorthy, A.K., Bovik, A.C.: No-reference image quality assessment in the spatial domain. TIP **21**(12), 4695–4708 (2012)
28. Ou, F.-Z., Wang, Y.-G., Zhu, G.: A novel blind image quality assessment method based on refined natural scene statistics. In: ICIP, pp. 1004–1008 (2019)

PAAM (Parameter-free Attentional Aggregation Model)

Xuan-Hao Qi, Min Zhi(✉), Zeng Mi, Wei Hu, Yan-Jun Yin, Yue-Ning Zhang, Wen-Tao Duan, and Zhe Lian

College of Computer Science and Technology, Inner Mongolia Normal University, Hohhot 010022, China
cieczm@imnu.edu.cn

Abstract. The channel attention mechanism and spatial attention mechanism are crucial in enhancing the performance of convolutional neural networks. However, most existing methods focus on developing more intricate attention modules to improve performance, which inevitably increases the number of model parameters. To address the trade-off between performance and parameter count, this paper introduces an efficient Parameter-free Attention Aggregation Model (PAAM) plug-and-play module. The module first creates a Local Feature Enhancement Module (LFEM) using adaptive pooling. Firstly, the local feature enhancement module (LFEM) is constructed through adaptive pooling to enhance the expression of local features; secondly, the local-global feature interaction module (L-GFIM) is used to realize the mutual compensation between local and global features, which effectively extends the coverage of local-global interaction. The experimental results indicate that PAAM outperforms the SOTA model in ImageNet-1K, Cifar-10, and Cifar-100 image classification datasets.

Keywords: Attention Mechanism · Parameter-free · Local-global Feature Mutual Compensation · Computer Vision

1 Introduction

The field of deep learning has led to a significant focus on image recognition using convolutional neural networks [1] (CNNs). In 2012, AlexNet [2] gained recognition for its ability to learn representations, generalize, and maintain translation invariance, leading to its success in the ILSVRC ImageNet competition. Following this, VGGNet [3] achieved second place in 2014 and has since been used as the foundation for further research. In 2014, Ian Goodfellow's team proposed the generative adversarial network [4] (GAN), which achieved great success in image generation and natural language processing (NLP). In 2015, Microsoft Labs proposed the residual network [5] (ResNet), which successfully mitigated the problem of gradient vanishing in deep neural networks by using jump connections. In the same year, Ronneberger's team [6] proposed U-Net, initially for biomedical image segmentation, and later widely used for image semantic segmentation. In 2017, two lightweight network architectures were proposed: MobileNet

[7] and ShuffleNet [8]. DenseNet [9] improved performance through dense connectivity and feature reuse. Currently, the mainstream research trend aims to enhance the feature extraction capability of CNNs and improve their performance by improving the network structure. This is achieved through the design of stacked convolution, residual connectivity, and dense connectivity. This is an important research direction in the current field of computer vision [10].

Another area of research has concentrated on constructing plug-and-play attention modules. The plug-and-play attention modules are designed to be flexible and versatile, allowing for easy integration into various network architectures without significant modifications to the overall structure. They refine the output features within the convolutional layer, enabling the entire network to learn more feature information. Additionally, the attention mechanism assigns different weights to the features, highlighting important ones and suppressing minor ones, ultimately improving network performance. Using SE-Net [11] as an example, the SE module, which is an independent network architecture, can be directly inserted into various networks, such as VGG, ResNet, and ResNeXts [12], to significantly enhance the performance of the baseline model.

Currently, plug-and-play attention modules have limitations. (1) Most attention modules focus on extracting local features independently along the channel or spatial dimension. However, this approach often ignores the correlation between spatial and channel information, resulting in the model losing key information about local features across channels and spaces, which affects its overall performance. (2) Many existing attention modules are connected in series, acquiring only local or global feature information, which limits the model's expressive ability and scope of application by failing to realize the mutual compensation of local-global features. To address these issues, this paper proposes a plug-and-play, lightweight, parameterless attention mechanism.

The main contribution of this paper is specifically 3 points:

1. The LFEM module is inspired by the human attention mechanism. It uses adaptive pooling to dynamically select feature regions of interest, filter out redundant information, and focus on critical local information in the image. This enhances the ability to capture key local features and ultimately improves pixel-level feature extraction.
2. The L-GFIM module utilizes a new local-global feature interaction strategy to combine channel attention, spatial attention, cross-channel, and spatial attention, achieving mutual compensation between local and global features. Additionally, the residual structure is employed to preserve the original image information, preventing information loss caused by network deepening and ensuring the model accurately captures the image's detail information.
3. PAAM has zero parameters and is highly flexible, making it easy to integrate into various deep learning architectures. In comparison to other popular attention models, this algorithm demonstrates significant advantages in terms of accuracy, parameter count, and speed.

2 Related Work

Attention mechanism is an effective method to improve the accuracy of image processing tasks, and its core idea is to mimic the selective perception mechanism of the human visual system, dynamically adjusting the feature weights of the input image, focusing the attention on the most important regions in the image and suppressing the irrelevant parts, so as to improve the performance and accuracy of the computer vision system. In the process of machine learning, the attention mechanism can enhance its ability to discriminate between useful and redundant data information to improve model performance. This technique has been widely used in various fields of deep learning, such as target detection, image super-resolution, and human pose estimation. Currently existing attention mechanisms are mainly categorized into channel attention mechanisms and hybrid channel and spatial attention.

1. Almost all current models of channel attention are based on the composition of the compression and expansion module of SE-Net. This module enhances and suppresses feature information in the channels to obtain the correlation between them, resulting in high-quality feature maps.
2. ECA-Net [13] uses one-dimensional convolution to obtain neighboring channel information, resulting in more accurate channel attention information. This allows high-dimensional channels to interact over a longer range while introducing fewer parameters and minimal computation.
3. GCT [14] combines gating mechanisms and normalization methods to selectively use different channel feature information for modeling.
4. SK-Net [15] uses Selective Kernel convolution instead of ordinary convolution to obtain receptive fields of different sizes by dynamically selecting convolution kernels. This allows for better adaptation to different object shapes and sizes.
5. CG [16] starts with the overall semantics and information of the image and uses a lightweight global context module to capture the image's overall structure and semantic relations. The four types of channel attention can be combined into the form shown in Fig. 1. Channel attention and Channel and spatial mixed attention methods.
6. CBAM [17] extracts refined feature map information sequentially from two dimensions using channel attention and spatial attention to comprehensively capture the long-term dependency relationship between features.
7. BAM [18] uses parallel channel and spatial attention mechanisms to achieve the complementarity of channel and spatial information without losing any information.
8. PSA [19] introduces nonlinear transformations while maintaining high resolution in space and channels by polarizing the self-attention module to output more detailed feature maps.
9. A2-Net [20] collects key features from the entire space into a compact set. The first level of attention selectively collects key features from the entire space, while the second level of attention adaptively distributes the collected key features. (6) to (9) These four types of attention for channel and spatial mixing can be combined in the form of Fig. 1. Channel attention and Channel and spatial mixed attention methods.

Figure 1. Channel attention and Channel and spatial mixed attention methods. Presents methods of channel attention and hybrid channel-spatial attention. While these approaches have achieved excellent performance, each attention model still has limitations, specifically in that they can only capture either channel or spatial feature information separately, failing to establish an information flow between channels and spaces.

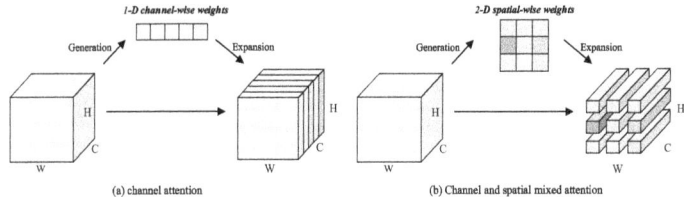

Fig. 1. Channel attention and Channel and spatial mixed attention methods.

This results in insufficient capability of the models to capture contextual semantic information. To address these issues, this paper effectively establishes contextual dependencies through the LFEM and L-GFEM modules. Experiments conducted on the public datasets ImageNet-1K, Cifar-10, and Cifar-100 demonstrate that, without requiring any additional parameters, PAAM outperforms other SOTA models in image classification tasks.

3 Method

This paper proposes a novel attention mechanism that utilizes mutual compensation between local and global features to capture both global context information and local detail features of an image. This approach addresses the issue of relying on single information and eliminates incomplete overall structure of the target, resulting in refined target contours compared to other attention mechanisms. The proposed model effectively integrates rich global and local feature information. The importance of image classification and target detection cannot be overstated.

Figure 2. Overall framework diagram of the network. Illustrates the PAAM network structure, which comprises three main components: the local feature enhancement module (LFEM), the global feature enhancement module (GFEM), and the local-global feature interaction module (L-GFIM). LFEM utilizes adaptive pooling to extract local enhancement features across channels and spaces in adjacent local regions. GFEM adopts the energy function to obtain global features across channels and spaces simultaneously. L-GFIM fuses the parallel extracted global features and local features. The fusion of global and local features compensates for local-global features, allowing the model to better understand and utilize feature information at different scales. The residual structure is used to obtain the original image information, avoiding network deepening that leads to information loss and ensuring that the model accurately captures detail information in the image. Where C, H, and W represent the channel size, height, and width of the image.

3.1 Local Feature Enhancement Module

To address the challenge of obtaining local information on subtle differences in the feature map, we designed a Local Feature Enhancement Module (LFEM) inspired by the BAM model. The LFEM enhances local feature expression by applying it to adjacent local regions. It consists of a parallel attention mechanism, which effectively suppresses

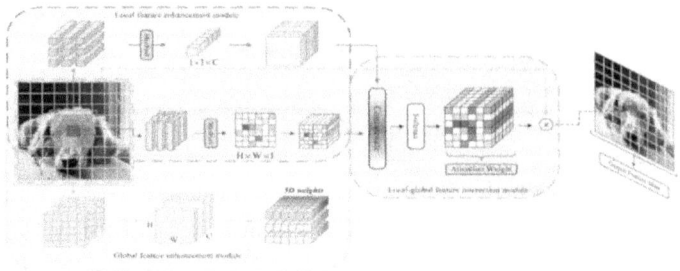

Fig. 2. Overall framework diagram of the network.

various interferences. Please refer to Fig. 1. Channel attention and Channel and spatial mixed attention methods. For a visual representation of the LFEM. Please refer to Fig. 1. Channel attention and Channel and spatial mixed attention methods. For a visual representation of the LFEM. Part 1 is channel attention, which redistributes the channel weights in the feature map through the maximum pooling operation to increase the weights of the relevant channels and reduce the weights of the remaining channels; part 2 is spatial attention, which re-gives the spatial weights more reasonably through the maximum pooling approach to give the potential spatial information in the feature map a higher weight, and reduces the remaining region weights; By adjusting the feature weights of the input image dynamically, attention is focused on the most critical local regions in the image while suppressing irrelevant parts. This effectively improves the performance and accuracy of the model.

Channel Attention. A global maximum pooling operation is performed along the spatial dimensions (i.e., height and width) of the input feature maps to compress the feature maps from $H \times W \times C$ to $1 \times 1 \times C$, thus obtaining a one-dimensional vector as the channel attention map, which is essentially a local representation of the most salient features of each channel in the entire spatial extent, and $y_C \in \mathbb{R}^{H \times W}$ is used as the weight coefficients of each channel, which is computed as shown in Eq. (1):

$$A_{ch}(y_C) = max\left(\frac{1}{H \times W}\sum_{i=1}^{H}\sum_{j=1}^{W}y_C(i,j)\right) \quad (1)$$

The channel attention mechanism selects the most representative feature values in each channel through maximum pooling and calculates channel weights accordingly to emphasize key channels and suppress non-key channels.

Spatial Attention. To achieve focused attention on the most important feature part of the spatial feature map, a global maximum pooling operation is performed along the channel dimensions of the input feature map to compress the feature map from $H \times W \times C$ to $H \times W \times 1$, generating a spatial attention weight map. The weight coefficient $x_{H \times W} \in \mathbb{R}^C$ for each space is calculated as shown in Eq. (2):

$$A_{sp}(x_{H \times W}) = max\left(\frac{1}{C}\sum_{i=1}^{C}x_{H \times W}(i)\right) \quad (2)$$

Spatial attention captures local spatial information across the feature map by calculating the maximum value of each spatial element on each channel and using it as the generated spatial attention weights.

3.2 Global Feature Enhancement Module

The GFEM module addresses the limitation of traditional methods in feature extraction, which only have a single method and struggle to obtain cross-channel and spatial attention information simultaneously. By calculating the linear divisibility between neurons, the module obtains cross-channel and spatial attention information at once. This approach not only overcomes the limitations of traditional methods but also comprehensively understands the feature structure of the data, enabling the refinement of global feature processing. The module defines an energy function for each neuron, as shown in Eq. (3):

$$e_t(\omega_t, b_t, y, x_i) = (y_t - \hat{t})^2 + \frac{1}{M-1}\sum_{i=1}^{M-1}(y_o - \hat{x}_i)^2 \qquad (3)$$

where y_t and y_o represent the outputs of the target neuron and other neurons, respectively. $\hat{t}$ and x_i represent the true values of the target neuron and other neurons, respectively. M is the number of neurons per channel, and i represents the neuron index. Additionally, ω_t and b_t are the neuron weights and biases, respectively.

Secondly, this paper calculates the linear separability between the target neuron and other neurons in the same channel by minimizing the energy function. To simplify the calculation, binary labels of $y_t = 1$ and $y_o = -1$ are used, and a regular term is added to obtain the final energy function, as shown in Eq. (4):

$$e_t(\omega_t, b_t, y, x_i) = \frac{1}{M-1}\sum_{i=1}^{M-1}(-1 - (\omega_t x_i + b_t))^2 + (-1 - (\omega_t x_i + b_t))^2 + \lambda\omega_t^2 \qquad (4)$$

Then, the mean $\mu_t = \frac{1}{M-1}\sum_{i=1}^{M-1} x_i$ and variance $\sigma_t^2 = \frac{1}{M-1}\sum_{i=1}^{M-1}(x_i - \mu_t)^2$ of all neurons on a single channel were used in order to calculate the reduction of the number of model parameters to obtain the minimum energy for each position as shown in Eq. (5):

$$e_t^* = \frac{4(\hat{\sigma}^2 + 2\lambda)}{(t - \mu_t)^2 + 2\sigma_t^2 + 2\lambda} \qquad (5)$$

where the smaller the value of e_t^*, the more separable the target neuron and other neurons of the current feature map are, and the more significant the contribution is, proving that the neuron is more important.

Finally, each neuron weight on the feature map is evaluated using $1/e_t^*$ to obtain the final output feature map $\tilde{X}$ as shown in Eq. (6):

$$\tilde{X} = sigmoid\left(\frac{1}{E}\right) \qquad (6)$$

where E is the set of all neuron e_t^* values for the feature map, and the addition of a sigmoid function limits the values in E from being too large.

The GFEM module demonstrates its unique advantage in the process of feature extraction by fully considering the interaction of information across different channels and spatial locations in the feature map. This allows for simultaneous attention to information across different channels (such as color and texture) and spatial locations in the image. The GFEM module is able to improve target recognition accuracy by considering multiple features in the image, thus avoiding the recognition bias caused by the traditional method that relies on single information acquisition.

3.3 Local-Global Feature Interaction Module (L-GFIM)

The Local-Global Feature Interaction Module (L-GFIM) integrates the features generated by the parallel local feature enhancement module and the global feature enhancement module to realize mutual compensation between the local and global features without losing any important information. The Local-Global Feature Interaction Module (L-GFIM) integrates the features generated by the parallel local feature enhancement module and the global feature enhancement module to realize mutual compensation between the local and global features without losing any important information. L-GFIM comprises the channel attention module $A_{ch} \in \mathbb{R}^{1 \times 1 \times C}$, the spatial attention module $A_{sp} \in \mathbb{R}^{H \times W \times 1}$, and the 3D attention module $A_{3D} \in \mathbb{R}^{H \times W \times C}$.

First, the maximum pooling operation is used to convert channel features and spatial features into local features, which are then used as feature weights. Next, 3D attention constructs an optimized energy function to compute uniform global weights in the feature maps and calculates the linear divisibility between neurons to determine the importance of each neuron. Finally, the channel and spatial attention maps are expanded along the reduced dimension, recombined with the 3D attention map, and the representation of the reorganized attention map is enhanced using the sigmoid gating mechanism. The enhanced attention map is then multiplied with the original input feature map to form the final output feature map. The entire process is shown in Eq. (7):

$$F' = \sigma \left(A_{sp} \otimes A_{ch} \otimes A_{3D} \right) \otimes F \qquad (7)$$

where $\otimes$ denotes the element-by-element multiplication operation, σ is the sigmoid function $\sigma(x) = \frac{1}{1+e^{-x}}$, and F' is used as the output of the PAAM module.

The L-GFIM module has a significant advantage in capturing channel and spatial correlations, which enhances the diversity and expressiveness of features. This is achieved by skillfully fusing the weight distributions of the channel and spatial dimensions, and integrating local and global information to capture complementary features. This design allows the model to concentrate on the most crucial parts of the input feature map, emphasize the most significant feature regions, and effectively suppress various interfering factors. This improves recognition accuracy and provides robust support for complex tasks.

4 Experimental Results

To test the model's effectiveness and generalization ability, this paper conducts numerous experiments on standard public datasets, including ImageNet-1K, CIFAR-10, CIFAR-100, in the field of image classification. The results are compared with those of other similar attention models with representative parametric quantities.

4.1 Experimental Details

This paper utilizes CUDA 11.6 as the computing platform for the deep learning framework, PyTorch 2.0.1, and Python 3.8 to develop the model. The NVIDIA GeForce RTX 3090 high-performance graphics card is used to train the model. Figure 3. Top-1 and Top-5 accuracy curves. Displays the curves of Top-1 and Top-5 accuracy during model training and testing, where the PAAM module is utilized to enhance the ResNet-50 baseline network. The Fig. 3. Top-1 and Top-5 accuracy curves. Shows that the introduction of the PAAM module significantly improves the performance of the baseline model in both the training and testing phases. The PAAM module enhances the recognition accuracy of the model by strengthening the relationship between the channels and spaces of the features. This validates the effectiveness of the parameter-free attention model proposed in this paper for image recognition tasks.

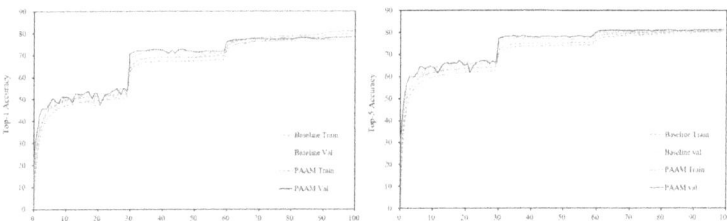

Fig. 3. Top-1 and Top-5 accuracy curves.

4.2 Experiment Comparing Parameter Count

Attention models currently in use employ additional sub-networks to generate attention weights, which increases model complexity compared to PAAM. PAAM, on the other hand, extracts 1D, 2D, and 3D information from input feature maps simultaneously by performing only element-by-element operations. Table 1. Comparison of structural design and parameters of different attention modules.lists the operations and parametric quantities of mainstream attention modules.

Operators are: k and r are the number of filters and the reduction ratio, respectively, and C stands for the number of channels; GAP, CAP, GMP, and CMP refer to spatially averaged pooling, channel averaged pooling, spatially maximal pooling, and channel maximal pooling, respectively; and C2D, C1D, FC, and BN refer to the standard convolution, the channel convolution, the standard fully-connected layer, and the bulk normalisation, respectively.

Table 1. Comparison of structural design and parameters of different attention modules.

Attention Modules	Operators	Parameters	Value
CBAM	GAP, GMP, FC, ReLU, CAP, CMP, BN, C2D, /, +, ⊙	$2C^2/r + 2k^2$	0.09M
SE	GAP, FC, ReLU, /, +, ⊙	$2C^2/r$	0.09M
ECA	GAP, C1D, /, +, ⊙	k	0M
PAAM	GAP, /, +, ⊙	0	0M

4.3 Image Classification Experiments

The ImageNet dataset comprises over 1.2 million color images, each of a specific size, and divided into 1000 categories. The dataset is further divided into a training set of 1.2 million images and a test set of 50,000 images. In this paper, the model is trained on the training set and the Top-1 accuracy of the output is tested on the test set. Top-1 accuracy refers to the accuracy of the first-ranked category that matches the actual results. The training process consists of 100 epochs, with an initial learning rate of 0.1. The learning rate is reduced by a factor of 10 at rounds 30, 60, and 90. For the MobileNet model, the initial learning rate is set to 0.5, and the weight decay rate is 4e-5. The training process for this model consists of 150 epochs. Table 2. ImageNet-1K dataset classification performance comparison. Presents the experimental results of the compared models on the ImageNet dataset. The PAAM model designed in this paper outperforms other existing attention-based models with zero parameters. Specifically, in ResNet-18, the Top1 accuracy is improved by 0.17% compared to CBAM, and better results are also achieved in ResNet-101. Furthermore, PAAM outperforms all other attention-based modules when using ResNet-34, ResNet-50, ResNeXt-50, and MobileNet as baseline models. It can also be added to existing networks without any additional parameters. Table 2. ImageNet-1K dataset classification performance comparison. Shows that SE and ECA have faster inference speeds than CBAM and SRM, and PAAM has even further speed improvements compared to other attention modules.

Table 3. Comparison of results with other methods on the CIFAR-10 and CIFAR-100 datasets. Presents the relevant data. The method proposed in this paper demonstrates significant advantages over several baseline models. When ResNet-20 and PreResNet-20 are used as the baseline models, the method in this paper outperforms other attention models in terms of accuracy and achieves the highest accuracy rate. In the PreResNet-101 network, SimAM achieved the best accuracy on CIFAR-10 (94.90) and CIFAR-100 (76.24), respectively. However, PAAM outperforms SimAM with a Top-1 accuracy of 94.91 compared to 76.57, respectively. Additionally, PAAM is capable of enhancing the performance of the WideResNet-20x10 large-scale network while maintaining its flexibility and versatility as a parameter-free attention module.

Table 2. ImageNet-1K dataset classification performance comparison.

Model	Top-1 Acc.	Top-5 Acc.	Baseline	+ Parameters	# FLOPs	Speed
ResNet-18	70.33%	89.58%	**11.69 M**	0	**1.82 G**	215 FPS
+SE	71.19%	**90.21%**	11.78 M	0.087 M	1.82 G	144 FPS
+CBAM	71.24%	90.04%	11.78 M	0.090 M	1.82 G	78 FPS
+ECA	70.71%	89.85%	11.69 M	36	1.82 G	148 FPS
+SRM	71.09%	89.98%	11.69 M	0.004 M	1.82 G	115 FPS
+PAAM	**71.41%**	89.88%	11.69 M	0	1.82 G	147 FPS
ResNet-34	73.75%	91.60%	**21.80 M**	0	**3.67 G**	119 FPS
+SE	74.32%	91.99%	21.95 M	0.157 M	3.67 G	81 FPS
+CBAM	74.41%	91.85%	21.96 M	0.163 M	3.67 G	38 FPS
+ECA	74.03%	91.73%	21.80 M	74	3.67 G	82 FPS
+SRM	**74.49%**	92.01%	21.81 M	0.008 M	3.67 G	59 FPS
+PAAM	74.47%	**92.04%**	**21.80 M**	0	3.67 G	78 FPS
ResNet-50	76.34%	93.12%	**25.56 M**	0	**4.11 G**	89 FPS
+SE	77.51%	93.74%	28.07 M	2.515 M	4.12 G	64 FPS
+CBAM	**77.63%**	**93.88%**	28.09 M	2.533 M	4.12 G	33 FPS
+ECA	77.17%	93.52%	25.56 M	88	4.12 G	64 FPS
+SRM	77.51%	93.06%	25.59 M	0.030 M	4.11 G	56 FPS
+PAAM	77.47%	93.69%	**25.56 M**	0	4.11 G	64 FPS
ResNet-101	77.82%	93.85%	**44.55 M**	0	**7.83 G**	47 FPS
+SE	78.39%	94.13%	49.29 M	4.743 M	7.85 G	33 FPS
+CBAM	78.57%	**94.18%**	49.33 M	4.781 M	7.85 G	14 FPS
+ECA	78.46%	94.12%	44.55 M	171	7.84 G	33 FPS
+SRM	78.58%	94.15%	44.68 M	0.065 M	7.83 G	25 FPS
+PAAM	**78.70%**	94.12%	**44.55 M**	0	7.83 G	32 FPS
ResNeXt-50	77.47%	93.52%	**25.03 M**	0	4.26 G	70 FPS
+SE	77.96%	93.93%	27.54 M	2.51 M	4.27 G	53 FPS
+CBAM	**78.06%**	**94.07%**	27.56 M	2.53 M	4.27 G	32 FPS
+ECA	77.74%	93.87%	25.03 M	86	4.27 G	54 FPS
+SRM	78.04%	93.91%	25.06 M	0.030 M	4.26 G	46 FPS
+PAAM	78.02%	93.96%	**25.03 M**	0	4.26 G	53 FPS
MobileNet	71.90%	90.51%	**3.50 M**	0	**0.31 G**	99 FPS
+SE	72.46%	**90.85%**	3.53 M	0.028 M	0.31 G	65 FPS

(*continued*)

Table 2. (*continued*)

Model	Top-1 Acc.	Top-5 Acc.	Baseline	+ Parameters	# FLOPs	Speed
+CBAM	**72.49%**	90.78%	3.54 M	0.032 M	0.32 G	35 FPS
+ECA	72.01%	90.46%	3.50 M	59	0.31 G	66 FPS
+SRM	72.32%	90.70%	3.51 M	0.003 M	0.31 G	53 FPS
+PAAM	72.40%	90.72%	**3.50 M**	**0**	**0.31 G**	66 FPS

Table 3. Comparison of results with other methods on the CIFAR-10 and CIFAR-100 datasets.

Attention Method	ResNet-20		ResNet-56		ResNet-101		MobileNetV2	
	C10	C100	C10	C100	C10	C100	C10	C100
Baseline	92.33	68.88	93.58	72.24	94.51	75.54	91.86	71.32
+SE	92.42	69.45	93.69	**72.84**	94.68	**76.56**	91.79	71.54
+CBAM	92.60	69.47	93.82	72.47	**94.83**	76.45	91.88	71.79
+ECA	92.35	68.89	93.68	72.45	94.72	76.33	92.34	71.24
+GC	92.47	69.16	93.58	72.50	94.78	76.21	91.73	71.78
+SimAM	92.73	69.57	93.76	72.82	94.72	76.42	**92.36**	**72.08**
+PAAM	**92.83**	**69.67**	**93.82**	72.73	94.77	76.45	92.35	71.98
Attention Method	PreResNet-20		PreResNet-56		PreResNet-101		WideResNet-20x10	
	C10	C100	C10	C100	C10	C100	C10	C100
Baseline	92.14	68.70	93.71	71.83	94.22	75.95	95.78	81.31
+SE	92.24	68.70	93.57	72.57	94.40	76.57	96.24	81.30
+CBAM	92.19	68.76	93.67	72.16	94.37	76.01	95.98	80.54
+ECA	92.16	68.31	93.78	72.43	94.70	76.11	**96.12**	80.35
+GC	92.19	68.96	93.77	72.44	94.85	75.48	96.12	79.98
+SimAM	92.47	69.13	93.80	72.36	94.90	76.24	96.09	81.51
+PAAM	**93.33**	**71.42**	**93.80**	**74.12**	**94.91**	**76.57**	96.03	**81.46**

5 Conclusion

This paper proposes a LFEM local feature enhancement module and a L-GFIM local-global feature interaction module to address the issue of existing attention mechanism models not fully realizing the complementarity of local and global information, resulting in information flow failure. The combination of the features of two different local attention mechanisms in LFEM effectively promotes information interaction between local windows. The experimental results indicate that the algorithm proposed in this paper outperforms the SOTA model when the number of parameters is zero. This demonstrates that the L-GFIM proposed in this paper achieves information flow between local and global windows through the local-global feature compensation strategy, capturing more semantic information of the feature maps and having a more powerful contextual modeling capability.

Acknowledgments. This work was supported by Natural Science Foundation Program of Inner Mongolia (No. 2023MS06009).

References

1. Chen, Y.: Convolutional neural network for sentence classification. Master's thesis, University of Waterloo (2015)
2. Krizhevsky, A., Sutskever, I., Hinton, G.E.: ImageNet classification with deep convolutional neural networks. Commun. ACM **60**(6), 84–90 (2017)
3. Simonyan, K., Zisserman, A.: Very deep convolutional networks for large-scale image recognition. arXiv preprint arXiv:1409.1556 (2014)
4. Goodfellow, I., et al.: Generative adversarial nets. Adv. Neural Inf. Process. Syst. **27** (2014)
5. He, K., Zhang, X., Ren, S., Sun, J.: Deep residual learning for image recognition. In: Proceedings of the IEEE Conference on Computer Vision and Pattern Recognition, pp. 770–778 (2016)
6. Ronneberger, O., Fischer, P., Brox, T.: U-net: Convolutional networks for biomedical image segmentation. In: Navab, N., Hornegger, J., Wells, W.M., Frangi, A.F. (eds.) MICCAI 2015. LNCS, vol. 9351, pp. 234–241. Springer, Cham (2015). https://doi.org/10.1007/978-3-319-24574-4_28
7. Howard, A.G., et al.: MobileNets: Efficient convolutional neural networks for mobile vision applications. arXiv preprint arXiv:1704.04861 (2017)
8. Zhang, X., Zhou, X., Lin, M., Sun, J.: ShuffleNet: an extremely efficient convolutional neural network for mobile devices. In: Proceedings of the IEEE Conference on Computer Vision and Pattern Recognition, pp. 6848–6856 (2018)
9. Huang, G., Liu, Z., Van Der Maaten, L., Weinberger, K.Q.: Densely connected convolutional networks. In: Proceedings of the IEEE Conference on Computer Vision and Pattern Recognition, pp. 4700–4708 (2017)
10. Yin, Y., et al.: Artificial neural networks for finger vein recognition: a survey. arXiv preprint arXiv:2208.13341 (2022)
11. Hu, J., Shen, L., Sun, G.: Squeeze-and-excitation networks. In: Proceedings of the IEEE Conference on Computer Vision and Pattern Recognition, pp. 7132–7141 (2018)
12. Xie, S., Girshick, R., Doll´ar, P., Tu, Z., He, K.: Aggregated residual transformations for deep neural networks. In: Proceedings of the IEEE Conference on Computer Vision and Pattern Recognition, pp. 1492–1500 (2017)
13. Wang, Q., Wu, B., Zhu, P., Li, P., Zuo, W., Hu, Q.: ECA-Net: efficient channel attention for deep convolutional neural networks. In: Proceedings of the IEEE/CVF Conference on Computer Vision and Pattern Recognition, pp. 11534–11542 (2020)
14. Yang, Z., Zhu, L., Wu, Y., Yang, Y.: Gated channel transformation for visual recognition. In: Proceedings of the IEEE/CVF Conference on Computer Vision and Pattern Recognition, pp. 11794–11803 (2020)
15. Li, X., Wang, W., Hu, X., Yang, J.: Selective kernel networks. In: Proceedings of the IEEE/CVF Conference on Computer Vision and Pattern Recognition, pp. 510–519 (2019)
16. Wu, T., Tang, S., Zhang, R., Cao, J., Zhang, Y.: CGNet: a light-weight context guided network for semantic segmentation. IEEE Trans. Image Process. **30**, 1169–1179 (2020)

17. Woo, S., Park, J., Lee, J.Y., Kweon, I.S.: CBAM: convolutional block attention module. In: Proceedings of the European Conference on Computer Vision (ECCV), pp. 3–19 (2018)
18. Park, J., Woo, S., Lee, J.Y., Kweon, I.S.: BAM: Bottleneck attention module. arXiv preprint arXiv:1807.06514 (2018)
19. Zhao, H., et al.: PSANet: Pointwise spatial attention network for scene parsing. In: Proceedings of the European Conference on Computer Vision (ECCV), pp. 267–283 (2018)
20. Xu, K., Wang, Z., Shi, J., Li, H., Zhang, Q.C.: A2-net: Molecular structure estimation from cryo-EM density volumes. In: Proceedings of the AAAI Conference on Artificial Intelligence, vol. 33, pp. 1230–1237 (2019)

FRFT Domain Watermarking Algorithm Based on GA Adaptive Optimization

Qiaoqiao Du, Yanchen Zhao, Weijie Hao, and Wenyin Zhang(✉)

Linyi University, Lanshan District, Linyi City 276000, China
zhangwenyin@lyu.edu.cn

Abstract. In the field of digital communication and copyright protection, digital watermark technology is extremely critical to ensure the security of secret communications and copyrighted information. This paper proposes an improved hybrid watermark optimization scheme. This scheme takes advantage of the multilevel wavelet transform (MDWT) to embed watermark information in the fractional Fourier transform domain by modifying the singular values of the image. At the same time, a genetic algorithm (GA) is designed to optimize system parameters. Ensure adaptive and efficient embedding of watermarks. To further enhance the security of the watermark, the Arnold transform (AT) is used to process the watermark, adding an extra layer of security to it. In addition, this solution conducts a comprehensive evaluation of watermarks of different sizes, and the experimental results confirm the efficiency of the system: the peak signal-to-noise ratio (PSNR) values are all above 48dB, and the structural similarity (SSIM) and normalized correlation coefficient (NC) are all close to 1. Compared with some existing algorithms, this scheme performs well in resisting common image processing attacks and has strong robustness while maintaining good invisibility and security.

Keywords: MDWT · GA · singular value decomposition (SVD) · fractional Fourier transform (FRFT) · watermark

1 Introduction

The rapid development of the Internet and signal processing technology makes it easier to copy and process data, which undoubtedly increases the demand for copyright data protection. As a cutting-edge copyright protection technology, digital watermarking [1] uses specific algorithms to cleverly embed identification information into the original multimedia content without affecting its value and use. Early digital watermarking algorithms were mainly based on spatial domain methods. Among them, the least significant bit (LSB) [2] method is popular for its simple pixel replacement strategy, but its security and robustness are relatively low. Transform domain algorithms are widely used due to their strong robustness. Liu X L et al. [3] used DWT to embed robust watermarks in YCbCr color space to achieve blind extraction. Ko et al. [4] proposed a robust and transparent watermarking method by modifying the discrete cosine transform (DCT) coefficient difference. Srivastava et al. [5] combined DWT and pixel modification methods to improve system performance. In addition, SVD has also attracted much attention. Zhou et al. [6] combined DWT, All-Phase Discrete Cosine Biorthogonal Transform (APDCBT), and SVD to achieve watermark embedding and recovery. Zhu T et al. [7] proposed an optimized watermarking algorithm based on SVD and integer wavelet transform (IWT), which provides a valuable direction for further improvement and application of watermarking technology. In addition, the integration of multiple technologies is becoming a trend. Nazir H et al. [8] integrated DWT, Heisenberg decomposition (HbD), SVD, and 4D hyperchaotic system, and used an improved fruit fly optimization algorithm to optimize the watermark embedding process, and the experimental results were satisfactory. Gao H et al. [9] combined various technologies such as the Random Sample Consistency (RANSAC) algorithm and improved artificial bee colony to solve the geometric distortion correction and false positive problem (FPP), etc., and made contributions to the development of the watermarking field. To enhance the security of watermarks, Loan N A et al. [10] proposed a method of blind digital image watermarking technology based on chaotic encryption. Garg P et al. [11] combined DWT, SVD, entropy, and pixel position shuffling methods. In addition, Wu J Y et al. [12] used SVD ghost imaging for watermark encryption, which further enhanced the security of the watermark system. Makbol N M et al. [13] designed an image watermarking scheme based on SVD. Su et al. [14] proposed a blind color image watermarking algorithm based on LU decomposition and applied the AT and MD5-based Hash pseudo-random number algorithm to enhance the security and robustness of the watermark. To find a balance between robustness and imperceptibility, researchers have conducted a lot of exploration. Ansari et al. [15] used IWT and SVD combined with the artificial bee colony (ABC) algorithm to optimize watermark performance. Liu J et al. [16] combined DWT, Heisenberg decomposition (HD), and SVD, and used the fruit fly optimization algorithm to optimize and achieve watermark embedding. In addition, some research also focuses on adaptive watermarking methods. Wang B et al. [17] combined SVD and Wang-Landau sampling methods to propose an adaptive image watermarking method by selecting the principal component as the embedding position. In addition, Ernawan F et al. [18] designed an adaptive scaling factor method based on DWT and DCT coefficients. Wang X et al. [19] proposed a parallel multiple watermarking method with adaptive inter-block correlation to improve watermarking capacity. The proposal of these methods provides new ideas and methods for improving the performance and security of watermarking systems. In terms of the computational efficiency of watermark processing, Cao Y et al. [20] optimized the DCT algorithm and data accuracy and used the FPGA cloud platform to accelerate watermark processing, achieving a highly scalable, widely shareable, and more secure digital watermark application. The above research shows that watermark technology has made significant progress in terms of security, robustness, embedding capacity, and computational efficiency, providing a more comprehensive and efficient solution for copyright protection and security of digital media. To better balance the robustness and imperceptibility of the digital watermarking system, this paper proposes an FRFT domain watermarking algorithm based on GA adaptive optimization. This method aims to design a digital watermarking system with better performance to achieve better performance in copyright.

2 Main Related Technologies

2.1 Discrete Wavelet Transform (DWT)

DWT is a mathematical transformation method used in science and engineering. It provides a compact representation of image energy and shows good results in resisting image processing attacks. By applying DWT, four sub-band representations of the original image are obtained, namely LH, HL, HH, and LL sub-bands. Among them, the LL subband contains most of the information of the image and has strong attack resistance, which makes the LL subband the preferred subband for embedding robust watermarks.

2.2 Singular Value Decomposition (SVD)

SVD is a linear algebra tool that is applied to orthogonal matrices and plays an important role in the field of image processing. It has good stability. Even if a slight perturbation is applied to the image, the change of its matrix singular value will not exceed the maximum singular value of the perturbation matrix. In addition, since singular values mainly reflect the brightness characteristics of the image and are not directly related to its visual details, this makes SVD an effective watermark embedding method.

2.3 Fractional Fourier Transform (FRFT)

FRFT is a transform that takes into account both time domain and frequency domain characteristics. Its rotation characteristics and angular continuity make it have broad application prospects in the field of digital watermarking, providing great flexibility for watermarking solutions. When the fractional order transforms from 0 to 1, the time domain information of the image gradually decreases and the frequency domain information gradually increases. In watermark embedding, the flexibility and adaptability of information embedding can be enhanced by selecting an appropriate fractional order.

2.4 Genetic Algorithm (GA)

GA simulates the natural selection and genetic evolution process in nature, allowing individuals in the population to experience natural reproduction, crossover, and mutation. Following the evolutionary principle of "survival of the fittest, survival of the fittest", the algorithm eliminates individuals with poor performance from generation to generation, while retaining and replicating individuals with excellent performance. After successive generations of selection and genetic mechanisms, the best individuals can eventually be gradually cultivated. When mapped into the problem solution space, it is equivalent to finding the best solution through N generations of iterative optimization. This process is not only efficient but also highly adaptable, making GA a powerful tool for solving complex optimization problems.

3 Watermark Scheme

This paper proposes an FRFT domain watermarking algorithm based on GA adaptive optimization to achieve more covert and robust watermark embedding. First, AT is performed on the watermark to disperse the information in the entire frequency domain and reduce the local characteristics of the watermark, thereby encrypting the image. Secondly, by adjusting the order of FRFT, the spatial frequency domain representation of the image is obtained, and information can be selectively embedded into different frequency components according to the characteristics of different images. Use FRFT and GA adaptive optimization to improve the watermarking algorithm to make it more flexible and adaptable. It can adaptively adjust according to different characteristics of the image to obtain optimal parameters. Then certain rules are used to embed the singular values of the watermark into the singular values of the host image to improve the robustness of the watermark system and make it more difficult to detect and delete. Therefore, better embedding and extraction effects can be achieved, allowing the watermarking system to achieve a better balance between invisibility and robustness.

In addition, the design of GA and the watermark embedding process have been optimized to minimize time complexity. GA uses appropriate crossover and mutation operations to increase the convergence speed and reduce the number of iterations. During the watermark embedding process, we select mathematical transformations and parameter settings while considering computational efficiency and time overhead. This paper also conducts experiments on watermarks of different sizes to verify the performance of the proposed watermark scheme. The proposed watermark scheme will be comprehensively discussed below, including watermark embedding and extraction methods and GA-based watermark optimization algorithm.

3.1 Watermark Embedding and Extraction Methods

The watermark embedding algorithm takes the carrier image and grayscale watermark as input and takes the watermarked image as output. The extraction algorithm takes watermarked images as input and uses the extracted watermark as output. The pseudocode representation of embedding and extraction is given below (Algorithm 1, 2).

3.2 GA-Based Digital Watermark Algorithm

This paper uses GA to optimize system parameters to find the optimal watermark embedding strength α and FRFT transformation order a. In the population initialization stage, the optimal value range determined by the experience of PSNR and NC in previous papers is used as the individual value range to solve the problem of gradually slowing down the convergence speed when processing a large amount of data. To avoid falling into local optimality, the elite retention strategy is first adopted. This method can prevent the loss of effective solutions, help improve the convergence speed of the algorithm, and obtain better samples under the guidance of excellent fitness modes. Furthermore, appropriate crossover and mutation operations are introduced to maintain the diversity of the population. The crossover operation should ensure that the search space can be effectively explored when operating on the PSNR and NC of two crossed individuals.

The mutation operation needs to have sufficient randomness, such as random addition and subtraction of PSNR and NC values, to avoid the algorithm falling into the local optimal solution prematurely. In this article, GA is run individually 30 times while maintaining a large population size each time, and when the optimal fitness stagnates, iteration end measures are taken. Finally, through a comprehensive comparison of these running results, the risk of falling into the local optimal solution can be better avoided, thereby improving the global search effect.

Algorithm 1: Watermark Embedding

Input: Original image C, Watermark W   **Output**: Watermarked image C_W
1: C_YUV ← RGB_to_YUV(C)
2: U ← Extract_U(C_YUV)
3: W_arnold ← Arnold(W)
4: a ← Optimize_FRFT_GA(U, W_arnold)
5: α ← Optimize_Embedding_Strength_GA(U, W_arnold)
6: Cf ← FRFT(U, a)
7: Wf ← FRFT(W_arnold, a)
8: R ← Size_Ratio(U, W)
9: Cf_LL ← Multi_Level_DWT(Cf, R)
10: S_c, U_c, V_c ← SVD(Cf_LL)
11: S_w, U_w, V_w ← SVD(Wf)
12: S_cw ← S_c + α * S_w
13: Cu_watermarked ← Reconstruct_U(S_cw, U_c, V_c)
14: Cu_IDWT ← IDWT(Cu_watermarked)
15: Cu_final ← IFRFT(Cu_IDWT, a)
16: C_W_YUV ← Merge_Y_U_V(C_YUV.Y, Cu_final, C_YUV.V)
17: C_W ← YUV_to_RGB(C_W_YUV)
18: Return C_W

Algorithm 2: Watermark Extraction

Input: Watermarked image C_W   **Output**: Extracted watermark W
1: C_YUV ← RGB_to_YUV(C_W)
2: U ← Extract_U(C_YUV)
3: a ← Optimize_FRFT_GA(U)
4: Ef ← FRFT(U, a)
5: R ← Determine_Size_Ratio(U)
6: Ef_LL ← Multi_Level_DWT(Ef, R)
7: S_Cw ← Extract_Singular_Value_Matrix(Ef_LL)
8: α ← Optimal_Embedding_Strength_GA(U)
9: E_Sw ← Extracted_Singular_Value_Matrix(S_Cw, S_c, α)
10: E_W ← Reconstruct_Watermark(E_Sw)
11: E_W ← IFRFT(E_W, a)
12: W ← Arnold(E_W)
13: Return W

$$fitness = \frac{PSNR}{100} + 1.1 \frac{\sum_{i=1}^{n} NCarr[i]}{NCnum} \tag{1}$$

In terms of evaluating the performance of the watermark algorithm, this paper designs a fitness function based on PSNR and NC. The weighted sum of PSNR and NC is shown in Eq. (1). Where $\sum_{i=1}^{n} NCarr[i]$ represents the sum of all elements in the normalized correlation coefficient array, and PSNR is normalized to the range [0,1]. In order to balance transparency and robustness, we need to multiply by a weighting factor to adjust the importance of the normalized correlation coefficient to fully evaluate the performance of the watermarking algorithm. The following is the pseudo code representation of GA (Algorithm 3).

Algorithm 3: Genetic Algorithm for Watermarking Parameters Optimization

Input: popSize, individualSize; **Output**: bestIndividual(optimized watermark parameters);
1: a = rand(); alpha = rand();
2: for each individual in population do
3:   psnr, nc = EmbedWatermark(a, aplha); fitness = CalculateFitness(psnr, nc);
4:   individual = [a, alpha, psnr, nc, fitness]; insertPop(individual);
5: end for
6: While iteration <= maxIterations && stagnationCount < stagnationThreshold do
7:   newPopulation = zeros(populationSize, individualSize);
8:   newPopSize = 0;
9:   While newPopSize < populationSize do
10:    eliteIndividuals = sortedPop(1:eliteSize, :);
11:    for each selected pair of individual do
12:      if rand () <= crossoverProb then
13:        crossOverMethod(eliteIndividuals);
14:      end if
15:      if rand () <= mutationProb then
16:        mutationMethod(eliteIndividuals);
17:      end if
18:      updatePsnrAndNc(individual);
19:      updateFitness(individual);
20:      insertNewPop(individuals);
21:    end for
22: end while
23: if improvement is found then
24:    updateFitness(bestIndividual);
25: end if
26: bestIndividual = population(bestIndividualIndex,:);
27: stagnationCount += 1
28: end while
29: finalBestIndividual = newBestIndividual < bestIndividual ? newBestIndividual:bestIndividual

4 Experimental Results and Performance Analysis

To conduct a fair performance comparison and verify the effectiveness and stability of the proposed scheme, this scheme was tested on 128*128, 64*64, and 32*32 watermarks, and the experimental programming environment was Matlab2023b. Six 512*512 color images are selected as carrier images (shown in Fig. 1, namely Barbara, Monarch, Airplane, Boat, Wall, and Flower), and Pepper grayscale image watermark is used as the watermark image. In addition, the GA-related operating parameter settings are shown in Table 1.

Fig. 1. Carrier picture.

Table 1. GA operating parameters.

Operating parameters	Experience	Experimental parameters
Population size M	20–100	50
Number of iterations T	50–500	50
Crossover probability P1	0.4–1.0	0.8
Mutation probability P2	0.0001–0.1	0.5

4.1 Evaluation Indicators

PSNR and SSIM are used to evaluate the imperceptibility of the algorithm, and their definitions are shown in formulas (2) and (3) respectively. In formula (2), MAX represents the maximum possible value of the signal, and MSE is the mean square error between the original signal and the distorted signal. Generally speaking, when the PSNR is greater than or equal to 30dB, the human eye cannot perceive the embedded watermark information; when it is greater than 40dB, the image quality is considered to be high and very close to the original image. In formula (3), x and y represent the original image and the distorted image respectively, σ_{xy} represents the mean of the image, σ represents the standard deviation of the image, μ represents the covariance between the images x and y, and C_1 and C_2 are constants. Generally, the closer the SSIM is to 1, the stronger the structural similarity between the two images and the better the quality of the image. Compared with PSNR, SSIM pays more attention to the structural information of the image and can better reflect the human eye's perception of image quality.

$$PSNR(dB) = 10 \lg \left[\frac{MAX^2}{MSE} \right] = 10 \lg \left[\frac{255^2}{MSE} \right] \qquad (2)$$

$$SSIM(x, y) = \frac{(2\mu_x\mu_y + C_1)(2\sigma_{xy} + C_2)}{(\mu_x^2\mu_y^2 + C_1)(\sigma_x^2 + \sigma_y^2 + C_2)} \quad (3)$$

$$NC = \frac{\sum_{i=0}^{M-1}\sum_{j=0}^{N-1} w(i,j)v(i,j)}{\sum_{i=0}^{M-1}\sum_{j=0}^{N-1} [w(i,j)]^2} \quad (4)$$

NC is used to evaluate the similarity between the extracted watermark and the original watermark. Its definition is as shown in formula (4), where w is the original watermark, v is the extracted watermark, and the watermark size is recorded as $M * N$.

4.2 Solution Performance Analysis and Comparison

To verify the effectiveness of the proposed scheme, this section conducts two sets of experiments: one uses random embedding parameters, and the other uses GA to find the best parameters. The experimental results of using random embedding parameters when embedding a 128*128 watermark on some carrier images are given below (Table 2). Experimental results optimized by GA (Table 3). Through analysis, it can be found that for different carrier images, embedding larger-sized watermarks will reduce the PSNR of the image, because more information will lead to greater distortion. Therefore, when embedding a 128*128 watermark, the PSNR is relatively low; while when embedding a 32*32 watermark, the PSNR is relatively high. This is due to the smaller amount of watermark information and relatively less distortion. However, no matter what size of the watermark is embedded, the solution optimized by GA shows significant performance improvement. In all experiments, the PSNR of the GA-optimized scheme is higher than 48dB, and both SSIM and NC are close to 1. In contrast, the scheme using random parameters is far inferior to the optimized scheme. Experimental results show that the scheme optimized by GA performs well in terms of PSNR, SSIM, and NC. This shows that this solution has achieved remarkable results in improving the stability and effectiveness of the watermarking system, and has good invisibility and image quality maintenance capabilities.

Table 2. Watermark model performance test (without GA).

Host Image	Parameter 1 = 0.1				Parameter 2 = 0.01			
	Parameter 2	PSNR	SSIM	NC	Parameter 1	PSNR	SSIM	NC
Barbara	0.01	15.2212	0.5857	0.0319	0.1	15.2212	0.5857	0.0319
	0.02	15.2267	0.5862	0.0422	0.2	14.8594	0.5557	0.0080
	0.03	15.2322	0.5866	0.0458	0.3	14.5509	0.5501	0.0369
Monarch	0.01	17.2443	0.7900	0.0250	0.1	17.2443	0.7900	0.0250
	0.02	17.2507	0.7904	0.0294	0.2	16.7130	0.7656	0.0067
	0.03	17.2568	0.7907	0.0317	0.3	16.3748	0.7556	0.0492

(continued)

Table 2. (continued)

Host Image	Parameter 1 = 0.1				Parameter 2 = 0.01			
	Parameter 2	PSNR	SSIM	NC	Parameter 1	PSNR	SSIM	NC
Airplane	0.01	11.3131	0.2068	0.0076	0.1	11.3131	0.2068	0.0076
	0.02	11.3177	0.2076	0.0157	0.2	10.8672	0.1722	0.0038
	0.03	11.3220	0.2083	0.0189	0.3	10.4234	0.1824	0.0012

To further verify the superiority of this algorithm in terms of imperceptibility, this scheme is compared with [3, 8, 9, 11–14, 17, 18] and [20] were compared. According to the data in Table 4, it can be seen that the PSNR of the proposed method is better than that of the comparison scheme, indicating that the scheme can effectively embed watermark information while maintaining image quality, and has good imperceptibility, further proving the effectiveness of this method.

Table 3. Watermark model performance test (with GA).

Host Image		Parameter 1.2(Optimized)		PSNR	SSIM	NC
Barbara	128*128	0.5055	0.0200	48.8587	0.9994	0.9991
Monarch		0.5049	0.0200	48.9544	0.9998	0.9989
Airplane		0.5026	0.0255	48.8129	0.9986	0.9996
Barbara	64*64	0.5186	0.0343	49.6097	0.9991	0.9993
Monarch		0.5206	0.0324	49.8866	0.9999	0.9987
Airplane		0.5051	0.0400	49.8389	0.9998	0.9988
Barbara	32*32	0.5526	0.0400	50.7233	0.9996	0.9991
Monarch		0.5347	0.0400	50.9853	0.9999	0.9974
Airplane		0.5677	0.0400	50.4023	0.9987	0.9995

Table 4. Comparison of imperceptibility with some jobs (PSNR).

128*128			64*64				
[8]	[17]	Propose	[9]	[8]	[20]	[3]	Propose
35.2342	40.4600	**48.8221**	32.5550	41.1389	35.9700	40.8500	**49.6707**
32*32							
-	[18]	[11]	[12]	[14]	[13]	Propose	-
-	47.1120	42.6029	46.2504	39.4164	42.9449	**50.7790**	-

4.3 Attack Experiment

To test the robustness of the scheme, eight different image processing attacks were performed on watermarked images, namely Wiener Filter (WF), Median Filter (MF), Gaussian Low-pass Filter (GLF), and Average Filter (AF), Speckle Noise (SN 0.001), Crop (Cr 2%), JPEG 2000 Compression (J2 CR = 8) and Sharpening (SH 0.8). Taking Barbara and Monarch as carrier images and embedding watermarks of different sizes as examples, the NC values are calculated respectively, as shown in Table 5. Through analysis, it can be seen that after common attack processing, the average value of NC of this watermark system is above 0.96 and close to 1, indicating that the watermark information can still maintain its integrity and stability well after being attacked.

In addition, the changing trends of NC values in watermark images of different sizes are generally similar. For example, filtering attacks such as MF and GLF have little impact on watermarks, and the NC value remains at a high level; while attacks such as J2 and Cr will have a certain impact on watermark extraction, but the watermark still has a relatively high degree of rashness. Great sex. After the watermark image size is reduced, the watermark's robustness decreases, and the NC value under some attack methods decreases, but overall it still maintains a high stability. It shows that this scheme can still maintain a good watermark extraction effect after some attacks and has good robustness.

Finally, we compare the proposed watermarking scheme with some existing methods to evaluate its robustness. The specific comparison results are shown in Table 6–7. For Table 6, we observe that for the 128*28 watermark, most of the NC values after the attack are above 0.96, indicating that the watermark can be extracted relatively completely. After AF and SH attacks, the NC values are 0.9961 and 0.9966 respectively, indicating that the extracted watermark has high quality. For the 64*64 watermark, the NC value after most attacks is above 0.97. Among them, GLF and Cr attacks have less impact on watermarks, and their NC values are 0.9981 and 0.9947 respectively. For the 32*32 watermark, the NC value after most attacks also remains above 0.96. Among them, after AF and Cr attacks, the extracted watermark performs better in terms of integrity, and its NC values are 0.9918 and 0.9917 respectively.

Overall, the NC value of our watermarking scheme under most attacks is higher than that of the contrasting scheme. For Table 7, it can be known that: except for MF attacks, the average NC value of our watermark scheme is significantly higher than other schemes, indicating that this method has high robustness and stability against common image processing attacks. This provides strong support for its reliability in practical applications.

In general, this watermarking scheme can still extract nearly complete watermark information after some common attacks. It shows that the algorithm has good robustness against attacks such as filtering, shearing, sharpening, and noise, which further verifies the effectiveness of the method.

Table 5. Extract watermark from the attacked image and find NC.

Attacks	128*128		64*64		32*32	
	Barbara	Monarch	Barbara	Monarch	Monarch	Monarch
WF	0.9604	0.9645	0.9811	0.9813	0.9629	0.9569
MF	0.9762	0.9805	0.9891	0.9914	0.9760	0.9676
GLF	0.9882	0.9903	0.9958	0.9984	0.9880	0.9838
AF	0.9972	0.9969	0.9910	0.9944	0.9889	0.9890
SN	0.9741	0.9709	0.9927	0.9802	0.9895	0.9922
Cr	0.9797	0.9836	0.9976	0.9941	0.9885	0.9895
J2	0.9753	0.9803	0.9700	0.9867	0.9606	0.9642
SH	0.9977	0.9966	0.9907	0.9942	0.9888	0.9888

Table 6. Comparison of NC-based robustness under some attacks.

Attacks	OurNC128 (ref NC)	Our NC64 (ref NC)	Our NC32 (ref NC)
WF	**0.9641** (0.9880 [16])	**0.9792**	**0.9626**
MF	**0.9754**	**0.9874** (0.9258 [4])	**0.9608** (0.9338 [14], 0.9793 [6])
GLF	**0.9877**	**0.9981** (0.9992[16])	**0.9878** (0.9905 [7])
AF	**0.9960** (0.9539[16])	**0.9943**	**0.9918** (0.9561 [11], 0.9741 [6])
Cr	**0.9846** (0.9785 [16])	**0.9947** (0.9760 [16])	**0.9917**
SH	**0.9967** (0.9842 [17])	**0.9940** (0.9591 [10], 0.9855 [5], 0.9807 [4])	**0.9915**

Table 7. Robustness comparison of the scheme based on average NC under certain attacks.

Attacks	Scheme [8]	Scheme [10]	Scheme [15]	Our NC
MF	0.8474	0.9235	0.9894	**0.9745**
GLF	0.8272	0.9173	-	**0.9912**
AF	0.8269	-	0.9747	**0.9940**
SN	0.9518	-	-	**0.9792**
SH	0.8565	0.9591	0.9485	**0.9941**

5 Conclusion

In this study, we design and verify an innovative hybrid watermark optimization scheme. The watermarking algorithm is improved by integrating MDWT, SVD, and FRFT technology to effectively embed watermark information in the FRFT domain. The GA is designed to adaptively optimize the key parameters of the watermark, which significantly improves the performance of the watermark system. The results show that the proposed scheme is satisfactory in terms of concealment, robustness, and security. In the future, it is planned to combine the current method with neural networks to explore and solve large-capacity and adaptive location embedding problems. At the same time, we will continue to strengthen the security protection of watermarking algorithms, especially against attacks such as encryption analysis and reverse engineering, and continuously improve and strengthen the watermarking scheme to ensure its robustness in the face of various attacks.

Acknowledgments. This study was funded by Natural Science Foundation of Shandong Province (ZR2020MF058).

Disclosure of Interests. The authors have no competing interests to declare that are relevant to the content of this article.

References

1. Cox, I.J., Miller, M.L., Bloom, J.A., et al.: Digital Watermarking. Morgan Kaufmann, San Francisco (2002)
2. Chan, C.K., Cheng, L.M.: Hiding data in images by simple LSB substitution. Pattern Recogn. **37**(3), 469–474 (2004)
3. Liu, X.L., Lin, C.C., Yuan, S.M.: Blind dual watermarking for color images' authentication and copyright protection. IEEE Trans. Circuits Syst. Video Technol. **28**(5), 1047–1055 (2016)
4. Ko, H.-J., et al.: Robust and blind image watermarking in DCT domain using inter-block coefficient correlation. Inf. Sci. **517**, 128–147 (2020)
5. Srivastava, R., et al.: Image watermarking approach using a hybrid domain based on performance parameter analysis. Information **12**(8), 310 (2021)
6. Zhou, X., Zhang, H., Wang, C.: A robust image watermarking technique based on DWT, APDCBT, and SVD. Symmetry **10**(3), 77 (2018)
7. Zhu, T., Qu, W., Cao, W.: An optimized image watermarking algorithm based on SVD and IWT. J. Supercomput. **78**(1), 222–237 (2022)
8. Nazir, H., Bajwa, I.S., Samiullah, M., et al.: Robust secure color image watermarking using 4D hyperchaotic system, DWT, HbD, and SVD based on improved FOA algorithm. Secur. Commun. Netw. **2021**, 1–17 (2021)
9. Gao, H., Chen, Q.: A robust and secure image watermarking scheme using SURF and improved artificial bee colony algorithm in DWT domain. Optik **242**, 166954 (2021)
10. Loan, N.A., Hurrah, N.N., Parah, S.A., et al.: Secure and robust digital image watermarking using coefficient differencing and chaotic encryption. IEEE Access **6**, 19876–19897 (2018)

11. Garg, P., Rama, K.R.: Secured and multi optimized image watermarking using SVD and entropy and prearranged embedding locations in transform domain. J. Discrete Math. Sci. Crypt. **23**(1), 73–82 (2020)
12. Wu, J.Y., Huang, W.L., Wen, R.H., et al.: Hybrid watermarking scheme based on singular value decomposition ghost imaging. Optica Appl. **50**(4) (2020)
13. Makbol, N.M., Khoo, B.E., Rassem, T.H., et al.: A new reliable optimized image watermarking scheme based on the integer wavelet transform and singular value decomposition for copyright protection. Inf. Sci. **417**, 381–400 (2017)
14. Su, Q., et al.: A new algorithm of blind color image watermarking based on LU decomposition. Multidimension. Syst. Signal Process. **29**, 1055–1074 (2018)
15. Ansari, I.A., Pant, M., Ahn, C.W.: Robust and false positive free watermarking in IWT domain using SVD and ABC. Eng. Appl. Artif. Intell. **49**, 114–125 (2016)
16. Liu, J., Huang, J., Luo, Y., et al.: An optimized image watermarking method based on HD and SVD in DWT domain. IEEE Access **7**, 80849–80860 (2019)
17. Wang, B., Zhao, P.: An adaptive image watermarking method combining SVD and Wang-Landau sampling in DWT domain. Mathematics **8**(5), 691 (2020)
18. Ernawan, F., Ariatmanto, D., Firdaus, A.: An improved image watermarking by modifying selected DWT-DCT coefficients. IEEE Access **9**, 45474–45485 (2021)
19. Wang, X., Yuan, X., Li, M., et al.: Parallel multiple watermarking using adaptive Inter-Block correlation. Expert Syst. Appl. **213**, 119011 (2023)
20. Cao, Y., Yu, F., Tang, Y.: A digital watermarking encryption technique based on FPGA cloud accelerator. IEEE Access **8**, 11800–11814 (2020)

Joint Semantic Feature and Optical Flow Learning for Automatic Echocardiography Segmentation

Juan Lyu[1], Jinpeng Meng[2], Yu Zhang[1(✉)], Sai Ho Ling[3], and Lin Sun[1]

[1] College of Artificial Intelligence, Tianjin University of Science and Technology, Tianjin 300457, China
{Lvjuan,Zhangyuai,Sunlin}@tust.edu.cn
[2] College of Light Industry Science and Engineering, Tianjin University of Science and Technology, Tianjin 300457, China
22062212@mail.tust.edu.cn
[3] School of Electrical and Data Engineering, Faculty of Engineering and Information Technology, University of Technology Sydney, Sydney, NSW 2007, Australia
Steve.Ling@uts.edu.au

Abstract. The left ventricle ejection fraction is an important index for assessing cardiac function and diagnosing cardiac diseases. At present, EchoNet-Dynamic dataset is the unique large-scale resource for studying ejection fraction estimation by echocardiography. Through segmentation of the end-systolic and end-diastolic frames, the ejection fraction can be calculated based on the volumes at these phases. However, existing segmentation methods either mostly focus on single-frame segmentation and rarely consider information across consecutive frames, or they fail to effectively exploit temporal information between consecutive frames, resulting in suboptimal segmentation performance. In our study, we constructed a dual-branch spatial-temporal feature extraction model for achieving echocardiogram video segmentation. One branch was dedicated to extracting semantic features of frames under supervision, while the other branch learned the optical flows between frames in an unsupervised manner. Subsequently, we jointly trained these two branches using a temporal consistency mechanism to acquire spatial-temporal features of the frames. This approach enhances both video segmentation performance and the consistency of transition frame segmentation. Experimental results demonstrate that our proposed model achieves promising segmentation performance compared to existing methods.

Keywords: Echocardiography Segmentation · Optical Flow · Joint Learning

1 Introduction

Cardiovascular diseases are the leading cause of death worldwide, accounting for 32% of the total global deaths, of which heart attack and stroke represent 85% of these deaths. It is recommended by World Health Organization (WHO) that early diagnosing is crucial for cardiovascular diseases. For evaluating heart function and structure, echocardiography is a commonly utilized tool in any stage of clinical practice [1]. At present, deep learning has been the most popular way of echocardiography segmentation task and achieved much better performance. Paper [2, 3] utilized U-Net-based networks to segment the ES and ED frames. Li et al. proposed a multi-level and multi-scale dense pyramid and deep supervision network (DPSN) for segmentation of key frames in multi-chamber views [4]. Other approaches [5, 6] integrated convolutional neural network (CNN) models with transformer modules to utilize image patches for segmentation. Some researchers have also incorporated attention techniques such as pyramid local attention [7], bridge attention [6], and attention refinement modules [8] to enhance feature fusion effectiveness for segmentation. However, the above single-image segmentation methods typically overlook the temporal information and inter-frame correlations between video frames, resulting in challenges in accurately delineating the left ventricular region, particularly in intermediate transition frames.

Recently, more studies started to focus on the echocardiographic video segmentation, which located the ES and ED frames based on the volumes obtained by the segmentation of all frames. To introduce temporal information, some of the methods adopted 3D structures to extract the semantic and temporal features at the same time. For example, Wei et al. proposed a co-learning network that trains both at the appearance level and the shape level based on 3D U-Net [9, 10]. Chen et al. proposed a 3D U-Net for echocardiography video segmentation by learning the ED and ES segmentation and motion tracking between the frames at the same time [10]. However, the 3D-based networks cannot be used in single image cases, which has limitations in clinical practice. Other approaches employed the 2D plus time (2D + t) architecture to discover spatial-temporal information, which take videos or image sequences as inputs. Li et al. proposed a multi-view echocardiographic video segmentation network based on long-short term memory (LSTM), named MV-RAN [11]. Although the MV-RAN can model the temporal consistency, the LSTM structure is time-consuming and causes the end frames of the video to perform worse than the beginnings due to the errors accumulated. Sirhani et al. proposed a EchoRCNN model based on the mask region-based CNN (Mask RCNN) [12]. However, the ground truth mask of the first frame of the video should be delineated, which increases the cost of clinical application. Moreover, the proposed EchoRCNN was validated on a small dataset with only 750 videos. Painchaud et al. proposed an enforced temporal consistency post-processing approach to achieve echocardiographic video segmentation [13]. However, its performance improvement is limited. Wu et al. proposed an adaptive spatiotemporal semantic calibration (ASSC) module to utilize the spatio-temporal information between consecutive frames and to overcome the drawback that the optical-flow-based models are sensitive to speckle noise [14]. However, the ASSC module used a series of transformations and imported several learnable transformation metrics for both coordinate warping calibration and channel-wise feature weighting calibration, which made the model more complex and difficult to learn these metrics.

In this research, we introduced a novel dual-branch spatial-temporal joint learning network for echocardiographic video segmentation. The network consists of a 2D image segmentation branch to learn the spatial features of the inputs and to achieve the frames segmentation, and an optical flow learning branch to extract the optical flow between every two frames. Based on the optical flow learned from two consecutive frames, we jointly learned spatial and temporal information using a temporal consistency module between the warped segmentation prediction and the real segmentation prediction at t time. The contributions of this paper are as follows.

- We developed a dual-branch network which consists of a supervised semantic segmentation branch, and an unsupervised optical flow learning branch to learn the consistency between the consecutive frames.
- We jointly trained the two branches using the temporal consistency technique to learn the spatial-temporal features of the videos.
- The proposed model achieved a promising segmentation performance on the EchoNet-Dynamic dataset and demonstrated higher consistency in transition frames than other approaches.

The rest of the paper is organized as follows: Sect. 2 presents the details of the proposed method, the framework workflow, the segmentation learning and optical flow learning processes, and the joint learning mechanism. Section 3 introduces the materials of this paper, including the dataset we used and implementation details. Section 4 shows the experimental results of our proposed algorithm and demonstrates the comparison results with existing approaches. Finally, we conclude the paper in Sect. 5.

2 Methods

In this work, we presented a dual-branch echocardiographic video segmentation approach that uses video clips as inputs. As illustrated in Fig. 1, the proposed network consists of two branches. The segmentation branch was employed to segment the left ventricle area in each frame. The optical flow branch was used to learn the optical flow changes and temporal information between frame pairs. Finally, we jointly trained two branches by the proposed temporal consistency mechanism.

2.1 Overview of Framework Workflow

The architecture of the proposed model is a spatial and temporal combination structure, composed of two branches: the segmentation branch and the optical flow branch. The videos in the EchoNet-Dynamic dataset are typically large, with an average duration of more than 176 frames, while only two frames in each video are labeled. When training the frames in pairs, only two frames can be used to update the segmentation branch, while all frame pairs are used to update the optical flow branch.. In this paper, in the training stage, we set two clips for each video, the ES frame and its former and later two frames as clip one, the ED frame and its former and later two frames as clip two. They are defined as $c1$: $\{I_{ES-1}, I_{ES}, I_{ES+1}\}$ and $c2$: $\{I_{ED-1}, I_{ED}, I_{ED+1}\}$. All clips were used in the training in pairs to learn the semantic segmentation and optical flow parallelly according to the model shown in Fig. 1. In the testing stage, we tested all the frames of each video and output their predicted left ventricle masks only using the segmentation branch.

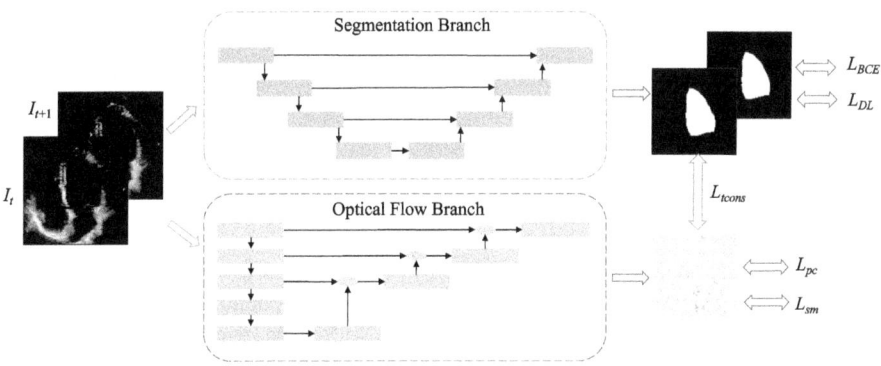

Fig. 1. The architecture of the proposed echocardiography segmentation network. The structure of each branch is presented in corresponding box roughly.

2.2 Segmentation Learning

For the segmentation branch, we adopted a 2D image segmentation network to learn the spatial semantic features of the input echocardiography. The main target of this branch is to distinguish between the region of interest (left ventricle) and the background. Therefore, in this branch, we adopted the baseline model U-Net to focus on spatial semantic feature extraction, more details can be found in paper [15].

As shown in Fig. 2, the input images are trained in pairs between two consecutive frames, denoted as I_t and I_{t+1}. We represented the segmentation branch as $S_g(x)$, where g is its corresponding parameter, and simply referred to it as the S branch for convenience. The corresponding outputs of two input pairs are $S_g(I_t)$ and $S_g(I_{t+1})$, respectively. The S branch was trained using two common semantic segmen-tation loss functions: binary cross−entropy (BCE) loss and dice loss (DL), which are defined as

$$L_{BCE} = -y \log \hat{y} - (1-y) \log(1-\hat{y}), \tag{1}$$

where y and $\hat{y}$ denote semantic region label and the predicted result, respectively.

$$L_{Dice} = 1 - \frac{2|Y \cap G|}{|Y| + |G|}, \tag{2}$$

where we set the predicted segmentation results as Y and its corresponding label as G; the numerator denotes the twice of the overlap area of two sets Y and G, the denominator is the sum of elements in the two sets.

The total loss function of the S branch is defined as

$$L_S = L_{BCE} + L_{Dice}. \tag{3}$$

Notably, the segmentation learning was supervised, with human experts annotating the masks. That is, the segmentation branch can only output their predicted masks for frames without mask labels; they cannot be used to update the weights of the network.

2.3 Optical Flow Learning

For the optical flow branch, we employed a specialized network to learn temporal information between two adjacent frames through the optical flow. Compared to region-based networks, it is more suitable to use a pixel-level algorithm to discover the pixel-scale movement between two consecutive frames. In particular, most of the brightness changes occur at the edge of the heart chambers, which can also help to distinguish the edge from the background.

In this section, we designed a modified FlowNet based on FlowNetSimple [16]. Figure 2 illustrates the architecture of the modified FlowNet, denoted as mFlowNet. The blue component is derived from the original FlowNetSimple, which we customized by importing part of layers. The green section represents our modifications, in which we added more up-sampled layers to ensure that the outputs are of the same size as the inputs. The reason is that we hope to use deconvolutions to learn the up-sampling process, instead of the interpolation during the warping computation. The corresponding hyperparameters for each operation are provided below them in Fig. 2, where f denotes the number of features, k denotes the kernel size of the convolution, s denotes the step size, p denotes the padding size. The number of features of the deconvolution in refine operation is specified below the Refine block. "Up flow" represents the up-sampled operation to predict flow. In mFlowNet, we also adopted the encoder and decoder structures to learn the optical flow between every two frames. In detail, it contains five normal convolution and down-sampling blocks in the encoder. For the decoder, we introduced two additional up-sampling layers and one more feature fusion layer to ensure that the output size matches that of the input.

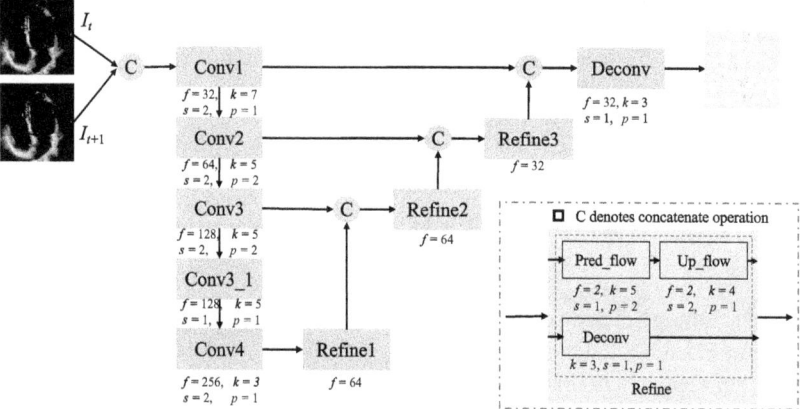

Fig. 2. The architecture of the mFlowNet. The blue rectangles represent the original FlowNet blocks, while the green rectangles represent the modified parts by this work. (Color figure online)

We represented the optical flow branch as $O_p(x)$, where p is its corresponding parameter, and simply named it as O branch. The inputs of the O branch are still in pairs, I_t and I_{t+1}, which are the same as the inputs of the S branch. Two frames of inputs were concatenated in pairs at the channel level, forming a 6-channel input. The output of the mFlowNet is the optical flow between the two input frames, presented as $M_{t \to t+1}$. The mFlowNet was trained in an unsupervised manner and its update was depended on the basic characteristics of optical flow, photometric consistency and motion smoothness.

Photometric consistency loss [16, 18] is to constrain a frame and the warped image from its adjacent frame, which is defined as

$$L_{pc} = \alpha \frac{1 - SSIM(I - I_w)}{2} + (1 - \alpha)||I - I_w||_1, \tag{4}$$

where I_w is the warped image, $SSIM$ is the structural similarity index and α is set to 0.85 accordingly [18]. The purpose of motion smoothness is intended to eliminate erroneous predictions while preserving crisp details, which is defined as

$$L_{sm} = \sum_{x,y} |\nabla M(x, y)| \cdot (e^{-|\nabla I(x,y)|}), \tag{5}$$

where ∇ is the vector differential operator, $|\cdot|$ denotes element-wise absolute value. The total loss function for O branch is presented as

$$L_O = \lambda_1 L_{pc} + \lambda_2 L_{sm}, \tag{6}$$

where λ_1 and λ_2 is the corresponding weights of two losses, respectively.

2.4 Cooperation Mechanism and Joint Learning

For the above two branches, the S branch is to learn the spatial semantic features, and the O branch is to discover the temporal features between the frames. We utilized temporal consistency constraints to fuse the learned features to further improve the segmentation performance. We adopted the temporal consistency module in [19]. They defined the temporal consistency constraint as the function of the encoder output features at time t and the warped features from time $t + 1$. However, in this paper, the temporal consistency constraint is defined as a function of the segmentation output at time t and the warped output from time $t + 1$ using the learnt optical flow from the O branch. The rationale behind this choice is that the edges between the left ventricle and the background tend to be blurred in ultrasound imaging. Therefore, the temporal consistency module that only works on the segmentation output can help filter out the background and noise from non-left ventricle regions. Since the segmentation output is binary, that is, the pixel values of the segmented background are all zero, only the segmented left ventricle region is used for the optical flow warping computation.

Given a pair of input frames I_t and I_{t+1}, we got their semantic segmentation results from branch S, Y_t and Y_{t+1}, respectively, and obtained their predicted optical flow from branch O, $M_{t \to t+1}$. Then we warped Y_{t+1} to Y'_t by optical flow $M_{t \to t+1}$, which is calculated by

$$Y'_t = \text{Warp}(Y_{t+1}, M_{t \to t+1}), \tag{7}$$

where we also used differentiable bilinear interpolation for warping. Since our dataset does not have the occluded issue, the temporal consistency loss is defined as

$$L_{tcons} = \sum_{x,y} ||Y'^{xy} - Y^{xy}||. \tag{8}$$

In this way, we introduced temporal features into spatial space through optical flow and warping. Consequently, we are able to use the temporal O branch to extract features from the unlabeled frames and then enhance the semantic segmentation result through warping. Two branches work together in an end-to-end manner to achieve the video segmentation and improve the performance of the model.

The total loss function of the proposed model is

$$L = L_S + L_O + \lambda_3 L_{tcons} = L_{BCE} + L_{Dice} + \lambda_1 L_{pc} + \lambda_2 L_{sm} + \lambda_3 L_{tcons}, \qquad (9)$$

where the weights of L_S and L_O are set to 1, the weights of L_{tcons} is λ_3.

3 Materials

3.1 Data

EchoNet-Dynamic is a large-scale, publicly available echocardiography video dataset for cardiac function assessment that we employed in this paper. The EchoNet-Dynamic dataset contains 10,030 echocardiographic videos recorded independently by 10,030 people. For each video, the video length, the positions (time points), masks and volumes of ES and ED frames, and the correspondingly calculated EF are provided. The size of all the frames in the dataset is 112 × 112. All the annotations are supplied by experienced experts.

3.2 Implementation Details

The experiments were implemented using the Pytorch library version 1.6.0. The training and testing were done on a machine with an Intel Core i7-9700K CPU processor, 31.2 GB of memory, and a GeForce 2080 Ti 11GB GPU, under the Ubuntu 18.04 operating system.

The dataset was divided into training, validation, and testing sets in the ratios of 75%, 12.5%, and 12.5%, respectively, which is the same as the setting of EchoNet−Dynamic [20]. For fair comparison with parts of other models, we also evaluate the proposed method following their training and testing ratio of 80%:20%. During the training stage, as mentioned previously, we utilized video clips to train the proposed model. Each clip generates four pairs of inputs for every video. In the testing stage, we tested all the frames in each video. We trained the model for 100 epochs with a batch size of one. We used the Adam optimizer to update the model weights with an initial learning rate of 1.6 × 10−5. For the loss function, we experimentally set the λ_1, λ_2, and λ_3 to be 5, 0.2, and 0.4, respectively. In this work, we utilized Dice coefficient score and Hausdorff distance (HD) to evaluate the segmentation performance of the proposed model. Dice score is related to the dice loss and defined as

$$Dice(Y, G) = 1 - L_{Dice}. \qquad (10)$$

HD is used to valuate the maximum distance between the prediction Y and ground truth G, HD is defined as

$$H(Y, G) = \max(h(Y, G), h(G, Y)), \qquad (11)$$

we take direct Hausdorff distance from Y to G as an example, it is presented as

$$h(Y, G) = \max_{y \in Y}(\max_{g \in G}(d(y, g))), \tag{12}$$

where $d(y, g)$ denotes the Euclidean distance between y and g.

4 Experiment

First, we investigated the effectiveness of introducing temporal features into the spatial feature extraction network for left ventricle segmentation of echocardiogram video. Second, we evaluated relations between the performance of the proposed method with the number of samples in the training clips. Third, we validated the advancement of the proposed method by comparing it with the existing networks on the EchoNet-Dynamic dataset.

4.1 Evaluation of Introducing Optical Flow Branch

We evaluated the effectiveness of importing the optical flow branch by comparing it with the spatial semantic network, U-Net. The comparison results are shown in Table 1. It turns out that extracting both spatial and temporal features at the same time is better for video segmentation than extracting only spatial features. The temporal features contain the information between the adjacent frames, thereby the network can provide spatial-temporal information for neighboring frames in the videos.

Table 1. Evaluation of Introducing Optical Flow Branch

Structure	Dice score (%)
U-Net	88.76
U-Net + FlowNetSimple	92.50
U-Net + mFlowNet (this work)	**92.64**

4.2 Affection of Training Sample Numbers

In Table 2, we compared the results of training with different amounts of samples, including 6 (this work), 10, 18, and ES to ED frames.

It can be seen that the segmentation performance decreases as the number of samples increases. This suggests that when more unlabeled data is introduced, the segmentation heavily relies on accurate optical flow estimation. However, since the learning process of the optical flow is unsupervised, it may lead to an accumulation of errors during the warping phase if the training samples are too numerous, resulting in decreased segmentation accuracy. Therefore, the optimal training length for this project is 6 samples.

Table 2. Comparison Results of Using Different Samples for Training

Num of Samples per Video	Dice score (%)
6 (this work)	**92.64**
10	92.44
18	92.12
ES to ED frames	89.44

4.3 Comparison with Existing Methods

We compared the proposed model with existing approaches on the EchoNet-Dynamic dataset to validate its segmentation performance, as shown in Table 3. For the 2D ES and ED frames segmentation methods, we compared several algorithms, including the primary algorithm by Ouyang et al., the **EchoNet-Dynamic** method [20] and three recent models: TransBridge [5] (offering **TransBridge-B** and **TransBridge-L** variants), **PLANet** [7], and **Bi-DCNet** [8]. They were evaluated on the training, testing, and validation sets provided by the EchoNet-Dynamic dataset, with a ratio of 75:12.5:12.5, referred to as ratio-1 for convenience. For echocardiographic video segmentation algorithms, we compared two approaches: **Joint-Net** [21] and a recent network [14] named **BSSF-Net**. Training and testing sets were randomly selected from the EchoNet-Dynamic dataset in an 80:20 ratio, denoted as ratio-2. These methods employed 5-fold cross-validation for evaluation and did not include a separate validation set. For comparison, we evaluated our proposed model and the baseline EchoNet-Dynamic algorithm using both ratios.

Table 3. Comparison Result with Existing Methods

Methods	Year	Train/Val/Test: 75/12.5/12.5		Train/Val/Test:80/-/20	
		Dice Score(%)	HD(mm)	Dice Score (mean ± STD)(%)	HD (mean ± STD)(mm)
EchoNet-Dynamic	2020	91.97	2.32	93.79 ± 0.22	2.27 ± 0.47
Joint-net	2020	-	-	90.91 ± 0.36	3.85 ± 0.92
TransBridge-B	2021	91.39	4.41	-	-
TransBridge-L	2021	91.64	4.19	-	-
PLANet	2021	-	-	91.92 ± 0.34	3.42 ± 0.67
BSSF-Net	2022	-	-	92.87 ± 0.16	2.93 ± 0.72
Bi-DCNet	2023	92.25	-	-	-
Ours	2024	**92.64**	**2.23**	**96.99 ± 0.12**	**1.76 ± 0.47**

In Table 3, our proposed method achieves the best segmentation results in both data ratios. For ratio-1, we achieved a Dice score of 92.64%, which is 0.39% higher than Bi-DCNet. In ratio-2, the proposed model demonstrates outstanding performance with a mean Dice score of 96.99%, surpassing ESSF-Net by 4.12% and EchoNet-Dynamic algorithm by 3.2%. This suggests that our spatial-temporal joint learning model excels in identifying the blurred edges of the left ventricle. Additionally, it indicates that the joint learning of semantic features and optical flows better exploits spatial-temporal information compared to 2D image segmentation methods and strategies proposed by Joint-net and BSSF-Net.

The comparison results were then represented in two different ways. Firstly, we compared the segmentation results of expert-labeled ES and ED frames. As depicted in Fig. 3, it is evident from the orange boxes that the contours segmented by our proposed technique are closer to the labels than those segmented by the EchoNet-Dynamic algorithm, indicating that our method can more accurately segment the left ventricle borders.

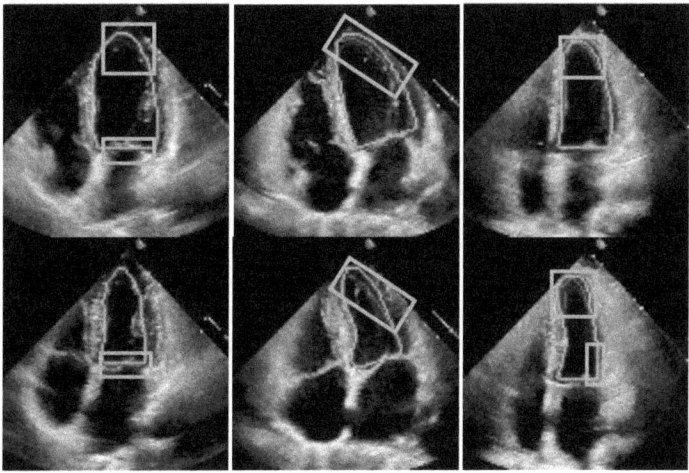

Fig. 3. Comparison results of ES and ED frames. Every column is an example of ES and ED frames in a video. The red circles are the results of this work, the blues are the results of the EchoNet-Dynamic algorithm, and the greens are the labels. (Color figure online)

Second, we exhibited the comparison results of unlabeled transition frames between this work and the EchoNet-Dynamic algorithm in Fig. 4. It can be seen that the EchoNet-Dynamic method was able to roughly segment the targets of ES and ED frames in the orange boxes. However, it is not able to distinguish targets in transition frames correctly, which is supposed to be affected by the imaging quality and noise. It indicates that the proposed method can not only more properly segment the ES and ED frames, but also more stably and reliably segment the transition frames in each video by learning the information between the key frames as well as the transition frames.

To summarize, the proposed method attained superior performance in echocardiography video segmentation by extracting the spatial-temporal properties of the frames. Compared to existing approaches, our method not only surpasses them in segmenting ES and ED frames but also demonstrates more consistent segmentation ability across other transition frames.

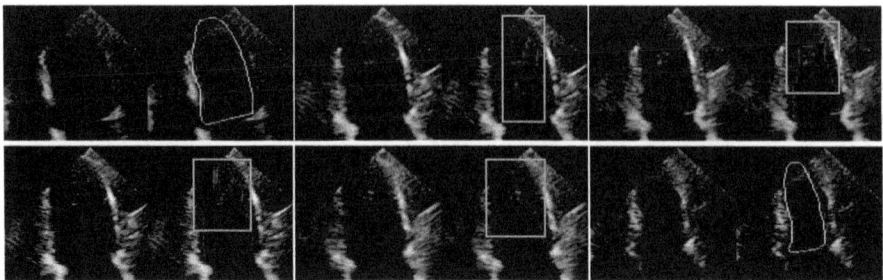

Fig. 4. Comparison results of unlabeled transition frames are depicted in pictures (a) and (b) for two separate videos, respectively. Each picture displays the original image on the left and the corresponding comparison visualization on the right.

5 Conclusion

In this paper, we developed a novel echocardiography video segmentation network on the EchoNet-Dynamic dataset, which consists of a semantic features extraction branch and an optical flow learning branch. The two branches work together to combine the spatial and temporal information of the videos using a temporal consistency module to improve the performance of the left ventricle segmentation. The experimental results reveal that the proposed model achieves a promising performance compared with 2D ES and ED frames segmentation and echocardiographic video segmentation approaches, with a dice score of 92.46%. In the future, we will investigate more advanced temporal feature extraction strategies and the fuse mechanism to improve model segmentation performance.

References

1. Spencer, K.T., Kimura, B.J., Korcarz, C.E., Pellikka, P.A., Rahko, P.S., Siegel, R.J.: Focused cardiac ultrasound: recommendations from the american society of echocardiography. J. Am. Soc. Echocardiogr. **26**(6), 567–581 (2013)
2. Ali, Y., Janabi-Sharifi, F., Beheshti, S.: Echocardiographic image segmentation using deep res-u network. Biomed. Signal Process. Control **64**, 102248 (2021)
3. Puyol-Antón, E., et al.: Ai-enabled assessment of cardiac systolic and diastolic function from echocardiography. arXiv preprint arXiv:2203.11726 (2022)
4. Li, M., et al.: Unified model for interpreting multi-view echocardiographic sequences without temporal information. Appl. Soft Comput. **88**, 106049 (2020)
5. Deng, K., Meng, Y., Gao, D., Bridge, J., Shen, Y., Lip, G., Zhao, Y., Zheng, Y.: TransBridge: a lightweight transformer for left ventricle segmentation in echocardiography. In: Noble, J.A., Aylward, S., Grimwood, A., Min, Z., Lee, S.-L., Hu, Y. (eds.) ASMUS 2021. LNCS, vol. 12967, pp. 63–72. Springer, Cham (2021). https://doi.org/10.1007/978-3-030-87583-1_7
6. Shi, S., Alimu, P., Mahemuti, P., Chen, Q., Wu, H.: The study of echocardiography of left-ventricle segmentation combining transformer and CNN. SSRN 4184447 (2022)
7. Liu, F., Wang, K., Liu, D., Yang, X., Tian, J.: Deep pyramid local attention neural network for cardiac structure segmentation in two-dimensional echocardiography. Med. Image Anal. **67**, 101873 (2021)

8. Ye, Z., Kumar, Y.J., Song, F., Li, G., Zhang, S.: Bi-DCNet: bilateral network with dilated convolutions for left ventricle segmentation. Life **13**(4), 1040 (2023)
9. Wei, H., Cao, H., Cao, Y., Zhou, Y., Xue, W., Ni, D., Li, S.: Temporal-consistent segmentation of echocardiography with co-learning from appearance and shape. In: Martel, A.L., Abolmaesumi, P., Stoyanov, D., Mateus, D., Zuluaga, M.A., Zhou, S.K., Racoceanu, D., Joskowicz, L. (eds.) MICCAI 2020. LNCS, vol. 12262, pp. 623–632. Springer, Cham (2020). https://doi.org/10.1007/978-3-030-59713-9_60
10. Chen, Y., Zhang, X., Haggerty, C.M., Stough, J.V.: Assessing the generalizability of temporally coherent echocardiography video segmentation. In: Medical Imaging 2021: Image Processing, vol. 11596, pp. 463–469. International Society for Optics and Photonics (2021)
11. Li, M., Wang, C., Zhang, H., Yang, G.: MV-RAN: multiview recurrent aggregation network for echocardiographic sequences segmentation and full cardiac cycle analysis. Comput. Biol. Med. **120**, 103728 (2020)
12. Sirjani, N., et al.: Automatic cardiac evaluations using a deep video object segmentation network. Insights Imaging **13**(1), 1–14 (2022)
13. Painchaud, N., Duchateau, N., Bernard, O., Jodoin, P.-M.: Echocardiography segmentation with enforced temporal consistency. IEEE Trans. Med. Imaging **41**(10), 2867–2878 (2022)
14. Wu, H., Liu, J., Xiao, F., Wen, Z., Cheng, L., Qin, J.: Semi-supervised segmentation of echocardiography videos via noise-resilient spatiotemporal semantic calibration and fusion. Med. Image Anal. **78**, 102397 (2022)
15. Ronneberger, O., Fischer, P., Brox, T.: U-net: Convolutional networks for biomedical image segmentation. In: Navab, N., Hornegger, J., Wells, W.M., Frangi, A.F. (eds.) MICCAI 2015. LNCS, vol. 9351, pp. 234–241. Springer, Cham (2015). https://doi.org/10.1007/978-3-319-24574-4_28
16. Dosovitskiy, A., et al.: FlowNet: learning optical flow with convolutional networks. In: Proceedings of the IEEE International Conference on Computer Vision, pp. 2758–2766 (2015)
17. Godard, C., Mac Aodha, O., Brostow, G.J.: Unsupervised monocular depth estimation with left-right consistency. In: Proceedings of the IEEE Conference on Computer Vision and Pattern Recognition, pp. 270–279 (2017)
18. Yin, Z., Shi, J.: GeoNet: unsupervised learning of dense depth, optical flow and camera pose. In: Proceedings of the IEEE Conference on Computer Vision and Pattern Recognition, pp. 1983–1992 (2018)
19. Ding, M., Wang, Z., Zhou, B., Shi, J., Lu, Z., Luo, P.: Every frame counts: joint learning of video segmentation and optical flow. In: Proceedings of the AAAI Conference on Artificial Intelligence, vol. 34, pp. 10713–10720 (2020)
20. Ouyang, D., et al.: Video-based AI for beat-to-beat assessment of cardiac function. Nature **580**(7802), 252–256 (2020)
21. Ta, K., Ahn, S.S., Stendahl, J.C., Sinusas, A.J., Duncan, J.S.: A semi-supervised joint network for simultaneous left ventricular motion tracking and segmentation in 4D echocardiography. In: Martel, A.L., Abolmaesumi, P., Stoyanov, D., Mateus, D., Zuluaga, M.A., Zhou, S.K., Racoceanu, D., Joskowicz, L. (eds.) MICCAI 2020. LNCS, vol. 12266, pp. 468–477. Springer, Cham (2020). https://doi.org/10.1007/978-3-030-59725-2_45

FMUnet: Frequency Feature Enhancement Multi-level U-Net for Low-Dose CT Denoising with a Real Collected LDCT Image Dataset

Yu Zhang[1], Xinqi Yang[1], Guoliang Gong[1(✉)], Xianghong Meng[2], Xiaoliang Wang[2], and Zhongwei Zhang[1]

[1] College of Artificial Intelligence, Tianjin University of Science and Technology, No. 9 Dishisan Dajie, Tianjin 300457, China
gongguoliang@tust.edu.cn
[2] Radiology Department, Tianjin Hospital, No.406 Jiefang South Road, Tianjin 300211, China

Abstract. Accompanying the widespread use of CT systems in medical diagnostics has highlighted concerns about the health risks associated with X-ray radiation exposure. Despite reducing the use of X-rays, low-dose computed tomography (LDCT) as a method to mitigate radiation risk is often plagued by quantum noise due to the scarcity of X-ray photons in low-dose scenarios. This results in image edge discontinuities, smoothing of small target structures, and the emergence of low-contrast visual effects. These manifestations of visual degradation primarily occur within the high-frequency band of the image, this study focuses on enhancing the quality of LDCT images by optimizing the utilization of frequency domain features. Specifically, we adopt a multi-level supervised U-shaped neural network and introduce a novel Frequency Feature Attention (FFA) mechanism. FFA utilizes convolution to diversify frequency features, then modulates them using channel weights to enhance learning of beneficial frequencies. We also introduce frequency domain loss based on fast Fourier transform to supervise the model's learning in the frequency domain. Furthermore, considering that synthetic data might introduce biases or distribution mismatches absent in real data, we established a real LDCT dataset. For each volunteer, one regular-dose CT scan and one low-dose CT scan are conducted respectively, resulting in a total of 4310 pairs of NDCT-LDCT images. Through experiments on the contributed dataset, our method produces superior results and outperforms other methods, significantly improving the quality of low-dose CT images, and providing strong technical support for reducing X-ray radiation risks while ensuring the accuracy of image diagnosis.

Keywords: Low-dose CT · CT denoising · LDCT image dataset · U-net · Frequency Feature Attention

1 Introduction

Computerized Tomography (CT) is a reliable and non-invasive medical imaging modality that aids in detecting pathological abnormalities in the human body, such as tumors, vascular diseases, pulmonary nodules, internal injuries, and fractures, and it has found extensive use in clinical treatment and diagnosis [1, 2] Concerns regarding the heightened exposure to X-ray radiation have emerged as an inevitable challenge for both CT manufacturers and healthcare institutions [3], thus drawing considerable social attention to the problem of low-dose computed tomography (LDCT) due to its potential for reducing X-ray radiation. However, due to the principles of X-ray imaging [4], CT images typically suffer from quantum noise and various artifacts during LDCT acquisition. Among these, quantum noise is embedded in LDCT due to the scarcity of X-ray photons during image acquisition. The scarcity of X-ray photons leads to visual degradation manifestations such as edge discontinuities, smoothing of fine structures, and the formation of low-contrast visual effects, which are visual manifestations of quantum noise. Therefore, enhancing the quality of CT images under low X-ray radiation doses is a highly meaningful research endeavor.

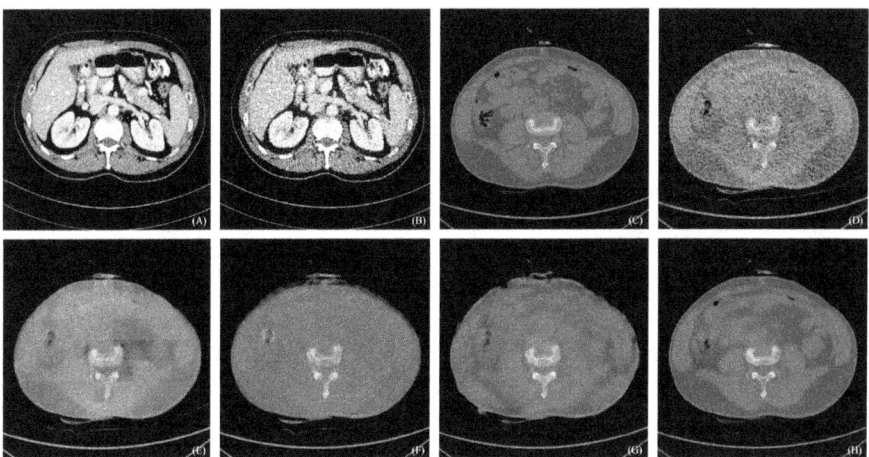

Fig. 1. Comparison between the public dataset and our contributed dataset, as well as comparison between our highlighted model and other LDCT models. (A) Mayo LDCT Challenge's NDCT (B) Mayo LDCT Challenge's LDCT (C) our dataset's NDCT (D) our dataset's LDCT (E) CTformer (F) EDCNN (G) RED-CNN (H) FMUnet

With the emergence of deep learning, it have become the mainstream method for denoising LDCT images [5], but it also has many problems.

Firstly, deep learning, as a data-driven approach, relies heavily on large volumes of supervised data to achieve optimal performance, where the quality of the dataset directly impacts the accuracy and generalization capabilities of the model. However, in existing methods for constructing public datasets, taking AAPM-Mayo Dataset as an example, low-dose computed tomography (LDCT) images are simulated only by adding mixed Poisson-Gaussian distribution (MPGD) noise to normal-dose computed tomography (NDCT) images [6, 7]. As shown in Fig. 1(A) (B), despite the addition of noise, organ boundaries remain clear. However, this approach may not accurately reflect the distribution characteristics of real LDCT images. For instance, in LDCT images, factors such as the shortage of X-ray photons and patient motion can contribute to image blurring [8–10] and streak artifacts [11–14] typically manifest along the long axis of highly absorbing objects. Existing datasets may not simulate these degradation characteristics of LDCT images, making the noise distribution learned by models trained on these public datasets unable to accurately reflect the characteristics of real LDCT images, affecting their generalization ability. Therefore, we organized volunteers and collected complete real LDCT-NDCT image pairs to fill the gap in the lack of real datasets in this field. As shown in Fig. 1(A) (B), our real LDCT images show more blurred organ boundaries and lower contrast, and unlike MPGD noise, real noise has a distribution similar to scattering from the center. This also confirms a clear difference between the distribution of artificial and real noise. The details of collecting the dataset will be covered later.

Secondly, the existing LDCT image deep learning models only consider the features of the image domain, but ignore the more obvious characteristics of CT images in the frequency domain. In LDCT images, noise mainly resides in the high-frequency band, while the low-frequency band of the image primarily contains essential texture information and other useful information. For example, in the field of sparse view CT reconstruction and image reduction or enhancement, many models combine frequency domain and spatial domain information to improve image quality. Arabi et al. [15] combined spatial and transform domain filtering to reduce quantization uncertainty while enhancing image texture. Lee et al. [16] proposed a deep learning model using a fully convolutional network combining sinogram, image spatial domain and hybrid domain and wavelet transform. Lal et al. [17] applied the original image domain based super-resolution reconstruction method to the frequency domain to achieve higher performance. Uetani et al.[18] processed the high frequency and low frequency in the image separately, and performed deep learning reconstruction specifically for the high frequency domain, which effectively reduced the noise in the image. In the above methods, dual-domain or multi-domain is used to improve the image quality in the process of model inference or reconstruction. In recent studies, many advanced results have been achieved by working with convolutional advance frequency features. The study by Park et al. [19] found that the convolution operator has the property of a high-pass filter, which can amplify the high-frequency components in the feature map. Wang et al. [20] also revealed that CNN has the ability to capture high-frequency components of images that are imperceptible to humans and that high-frequency components help explain the generalization of convolutional neural networks. This is also confirmed by Cui's research [21], where his network using convolution to extract frequency features achieves the best performance in several degraded image reduction fields such as image motion blur. Inspired by this observation, we propose a multi-level supervised U-shaped network, called FMUnet, and introduce a Frequency Feature Attention (FFA). This attention mechanism can enhance beneficial frequencies, strengthening the model's learning of LDCT frequency domain features. To address the issue of excessive smoothing in pixel-based loss functions and enhance supervision of frequency domain learning, we introduce a frequency domain loss based on the Fast Fourier Transform, combining it with pixel-based loss functions to supervise model training using dual-domain loss functions. Subsequently, we will retrain and test the proposed model and current well-performing models on our proposed dataset. Objective experiments demonstrate that method produces superior results and outperforms other methods on our contributed dataset. As seen in Fig. 1(E–H), our model exhibits stronger noise suppression capability and boundary texture inpainting capabilities.

In summary, our work makes the following key contributions:

- We first build a real LDCT image dataset. Twice CT scans are executed for each volunteer, once with low-dose and once with high-dose, resulting in 4310 pairs of 0.625mm slice images.
- We proposed a multi-level supervised U-shaped network (FMUnet) tailored to the characteristics of LDCT. Additionally, we designed a Frequency Feature Attention (FFA) mechanism to enhance the model's learning of beneficial frequencies based on the frequency domain characteristics of LDCT. To address the issue of excessive smoothing in pixel-based loss functions and to strengthen frequency domain learning, we introduced a frequency domain loss based on the Fast Fourier Transform.
- We retrained and tested our proposed model on the introduced dataset and compared it with mainstream models. The objective experimental results demonstrate the superior performance of our method on the dataset compared to others. Our approach exhibits stronger noise suppression capabilities and clearer texture restoration effects, resulting in significant improvements both visually and metrically.

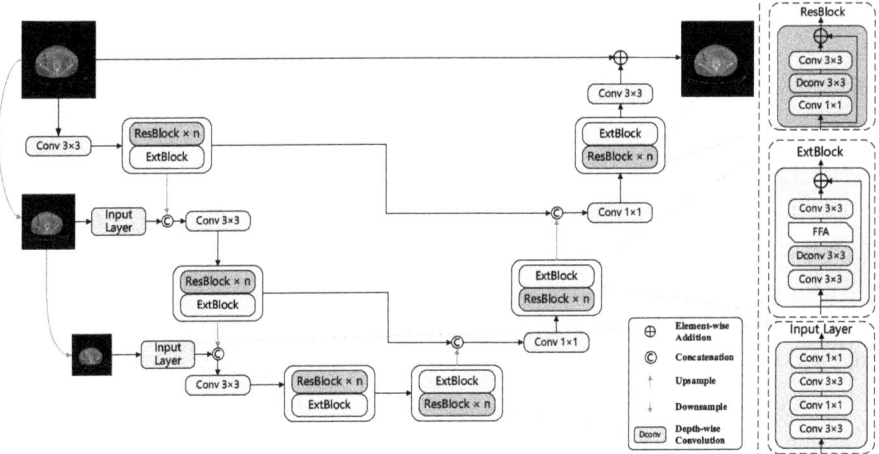

Fig. 2. The structure of the proposed network consists of multiple encoder and decoder architectures for hierarchical feature learning. Both the encoder and decoder are composed of ExtBlock layers and several ResBlock layers, albeit in different sequences.

2 Methods

In this section, we firstly introduce the overall architecture of our prominent network. Subsequently, we provide a detailed description of our highlighted FFA attention module. Finally, we present the design of the loss function.

2.1 FMUnet

Figure 2 illustrates the overall architecture of our proposed framework. Our convolutional neural network adopts an encoder-decoder architecture, where each encoder consists of 12 residual blocks followed by an attention module, and the decoder mirrors this structure but in reverse order. Between the two 3 × 3 convolutional layers within each residual block, we insert a 3 × 3 depth-wise convolutional layer (transposed convolution) to enhance feature learning during the encoding and decoding processes.

Initially, starting from the input LDCT image, a 3 × 3 convolutional layer is used to extract shallow features. Subsequently, the image undergoes three encoding stages. After the first and second encoding layers, the downsampled image is merged into the feature map, followed by a 3 × 3 convolutional layer to fuse features and adjust channel numbers. Upon completion of the final encoder, the network has performed deep and global feature extraction. Subsequently, the image resolution is gradually increased through three decoders. In the decoding process, 1 × 1 convolutional layers are used to reduce channel numbers. Finally, the decoding results are adjusted by a 3 × 3 convolutional layer, and two skip connections are added during the encoding-decoding process, connecting the input image and the predicted image.

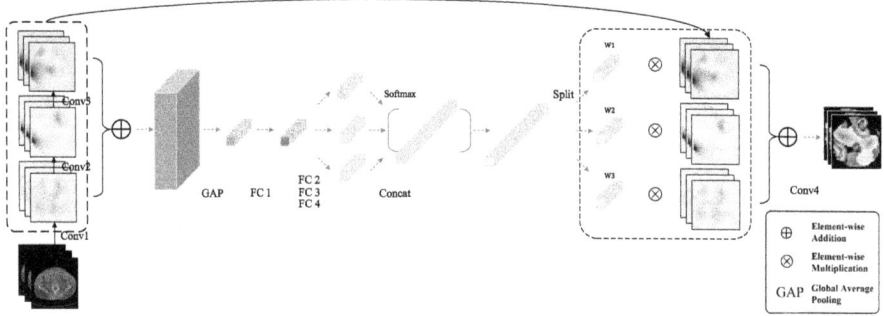

Fig. 3. The FFA (Frequency Feature Attention) extracts and enhances beneficial features in the frequency domain. For clarity, the figure contains only three frequency extraction branches.

2.2 Frequency Feature Attention (FFA)

In addition to the U-shaped backbone network, we propose a frequency-domain channel attention module to enhance the model's learning of LDCT image frequencies (see Fig. 3). Typically, noise primarily resides in the high-frequency bands of LDCT images, and furthermore, the remaining low-frequency bands not only contain the main content of the image but also include weakened image textures, which are noise-free [22]. Under this premise, inspired by [19, 20], we recognize that the convolution operator has the property of a high-pass filter and that high-frequency components help explain the generalization of convolutional neural networks, that is, it is able to amplify the high-frequency components in the feature map. Therefore, we first exploit this property to enhance and amplify the high-frequency feature signal layer-by-layer. Subsequently, we calculate the weights of different frequency channels and modulate them to ultimately improve the model's ability to recover beneficial signals in the frequency domain.

Firstly, for the input feature map $I \in R^{C \times H \times W}$ I, multiple parallel 3×3 convolutional layers are utilized to separate and extract different frequency segment features F_1, F_2 and F_i as follows:

$$F_1 = f_{3\times3}^1(I) \tag{1}$$

$$F_2 = f_{3\times3}^2\left(f_{3\times3}^1(I)\right) \tag{2}$$

$$F_i = f_{3\times3}^i\left(\ldots\left(f_{3\times3}^2\left(f_{3\times3}^1(I)\right)\right)\right) \tag{3}$$

where $f_{3\times3}$ represents a 3×3 convolutional layer. (For simplicity, we only show the case of using three convolutional layers in Fig. 3) After extracting three frequency bands, the weights of the three frequency channels are calculated through global pooling and fully connected layers, as follows:

$$\left| W_i = \text{FC}_i(\text{FC}_0(\text{GAP}(\textstyle\sum_i F_i))), i \in \{1, \ldots, i\} \right| \tag{4}$$

where FC represents a fully connected layer, $W \in R^C$ denotes the initial weights, and GAP represents global average pooling. We process the preliminary weights obtained from the two fully connected layers of the second layer through a Softmax function to obtain the final frequency attention weights:

$$W_i' = \frac{e^{W_i}}{\sum_{j=1}^{i \times C} e^{W_j}} \tag{5}$$

where W_i' represents the final weight of the corresponding channel, i.e., the channel attention weight. After applying the weights, the overall output of FFA is as follows:

$$\hat{I} = f_{1\times1}\left(\sum_i W_i' \cdot F_i\right) \tag{6}$$

2.3 Loss Function

Since previous methods typically used only pixel-level loss (such as mean squared error), this may lead to over-smoothing issues. However, the imaging principle of CT images involves the frequency domain, and the features in our proposed network also utilize the frequency domain. Therefore, in the loss function, in addition to using the spatial domain L_1 loss function, we also add the loss L_F after the fast Fourier transform. This makes the loss function pay more attention to the differences in the frequency content of the image, including the overall structure and texture of the image, rather than just comparing at the pixel level. The formula is as follows:

$$L_1 = \frac{1}{N} \sum_{i=1}^{W} \sum_{j=1}^{H} \left| I(i,j) - \hat{I}(i,j) \right| \tag{7}$$

$$L_{\mathcal{F}} = \frac{1}{N} \sum_{i=1}^{W} \sum_{j=1}^{H} \left| \mathcal{F}(I(i,j)) - \mathcal{F}(\hat{I}(i,j)) \right| \tag{8}$$

where $\mathcal{F}$ is the Fast Fourier Transform, N is the total number of pixels in the image, W and H represent the width and height of the image, respectively. The final loss function is as follows, where λ is empirically set to 0.1:

$$L = L_1 + \lambda L_{\mathcal{F}} \tag{9}$$

3 Experiments

3.1 Datasets

Existing publicly available datasets simulate quarter-dose images by artificially adding noise to NDCT images, but there may be significant differences between the distribution of this artificial noise and the distribution of real noise. Models trained on datasets with artificially added noise may not generalize well in real-world applications. With this in mind, we propose a real LDCT dataset. In our dataset, we obtained NDCT and LDCT images with a slice thickness of 0.625 mm from lung and abdominal CT scans of six anonymous volunteers, totaling 4310 pairs of 512 × 512 images. The tube current settings for the X-ray tube were distributed as 120 kV and 80 kV, with tube currents of 250 ms and 10 ms, respectively. Our dataset is more challenging, with fewer boundary and texture information in the CT images and higher noise levels. Although this setup makes the task more challenging, it can increase the robustness of the trained models and ensure that the models learn the real noise distribution of LDCT images.

3.2 Implementation Details

We divided the proposed dataset into two parts randomly at a ratio of 2:8, with 3448 pairs of 512 × 512 images used for training and the remaining 862 pairs used as the test set. Our network was trained using the Adam optimizer ($\beta_1 = 0.9$, $\beta_2 = 0.999$) with an initial learning rate of $1e^{-4}$, which was decreased to $1e^{-6}$ using cosine annealing. The batch size was set to 4. For data augmentation, we employed horizontal flipping of images with a probability of 0.5. The model was trained on patches of size 256 × 256 and tested on full resolution. Training was conducted for 300 epochs on an NVIDIA GeForce RTX 4090.

3.3 Performance Comparisons

In this session, we compared FMUnet with three advanced methods, and the comparative algorithms are trained for 300 epochs on our real LDCT dataset. A brief introduction of the three algorithms is as follows:

1. CTformer[23]: A Transformer-based model that achieves superior denoising effects by using convolution-free operations and the Token2Token mechanism, thereby improving the model's interpretability.
2. EDCNN[24]: Designed an edge-enhancement module based on trainable Sobel convolutions to enhance edge information extraction, and achieved better denoising effects by introducing the edge-enhancement module and composite loss functions.
3. RED-CNN[25]: Adopted a residual autoencoder structure, combining the advantages of autoencoders and convolutional neural networks, using symmetric convolutional and deconvolutional layers to enhance denoising and structure preservation for low-dose CT images.

Table 1. On the proposed dataset, quantitative evaluations of different models are conducted using PSNR, SSIM, and RMSE.

Method	PSNR↑	SSIM↑	RMSE↓
LDCT	22.27	0.4890	22.01
RED-CNN	29.98	0.8788	8.869
EDCNN	27.57	0.8486	11.58
CTformer	26.66	0.7765	12.67
ours	**36.60**	**0.9325**	**4.2370**

Specific training methods and dataset information are introduced below (Table 1).

Quantitative Analysis. We compared high-performance LDCT methods such as CTformer, EDCNN, and RED-CNN, and retrained these models on our dataset. We employed peak signal-to-noise ratio (PSNR), Structural Similarity Index (SSIM), and Root Mean Square Error (RMSE) evaluation metrics. For image quality evaluation. From the results table, we observe an enhancement in image quality across all three metrics for all the methods evaluated. Specifically, our proposed model achieved a gain of 14.33 dB PSNR relative to LDCT, outperforming previous prominent models. This also indicates that models designed for previous datasets lack sufficient recovery and reconstruction capabilities when faced with strong noise, strong blurring, weak boundaries, and weak contour features in real datasets. Our model not only considers noise suppression but also addresses the reconstruction of various details in LDCT images. This sets a precedent for future models.

Qualitative Analysis. As depicted in Fig. 4, these results were randomly selected from the test set. Compared to Low-Dose CT (LDCT), all methods show effectiveness in denoising, but our proposed FMUnet method approaches the quality of conventional Dose CT (NDCT) more closely. Upon comprehensive analysis of the complete volumetric CT images, we observed that our model outperforms others in edge sharpness and noise suppression, with relatively less noise present in the images. Upon careful examination of the region highlighted by the red box in the first image, we observed that

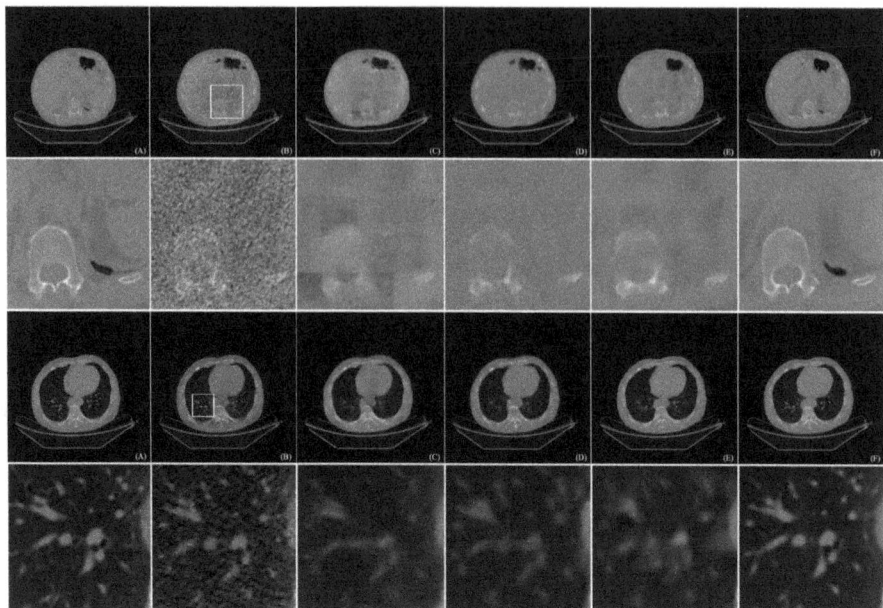

Fig. 4. Visual comparison of various models, the second and fourth rows are the zoomed areas marked by red boxes (A) NDCT, (B)LDCT, (C) CTformer, (D) EDCNN, (E) RED-CNN, (F) FMUnet

our model almost perfectly restored the shape and boundaries of the spine, with contours of dark and light tissues closer to NDCT. While other models achieved some noise suppression, they struggled to restore the contours and shapes of the spine and tissues. In the second image, the white shadow area in the lung region of our model exhibits higher contrast and clearer edges. The over-smoothing issue caused by pixel-wise loss, mentioned in the article, is particularly evident in the comparative models, as they tend to blur the edges of the white shadow in the lungs while reducing noise to some extent. Through comparison, we found that our proposed model demonstrates stronger capabilities in noise suppression, image restoration, and edge preservation. This is attributed to our introduced frequency-domain loss function, which mitigates the over-smoothing issue caused by pixel-wise loss, and our proposed FFA attention model, which strengthens the low-frequency domain's organizational texture information (such as spine edges and lung white shadows) while attenuating noise in the high-frequency domain.

Table 2. Conducting ablation experiments on FMUnet using the proposed dataset.

Method	PSNR	Params(M)
Baseline	35.72	6.89
Baseline + FFA	36.51	8.61
Baseline + FFA + Dconv(Full)	**36.60**	**8.65**

3.4 Ablation Study

We conducted ablation experiments to validate our modules. The dataset used in the ablation experiments remained the one proposed by us. We created a baseline network by eliminating the FFA attention module and deformable convolution (Dconv). The model's parameter variations are on the right side of the table. The results of the channel experiments indicate that our prominent attention mechanism enhances the performance of the model compared to the baseline network. The training method is consistent with the above. The baseline network achieved a PSNR of 35.72 dB on the dataset. By enhancing the frequency signal, our FFA attention yielded a progress gain of 0.79 dB PSNR on the baseline model (see Table 2). Using Dconv can improve by 0.09 dB. The complete network structure integrating FFA and Dconv achieved the highest score. Our results clearly demonstrate the effectiveness of our design (Fig. 5).

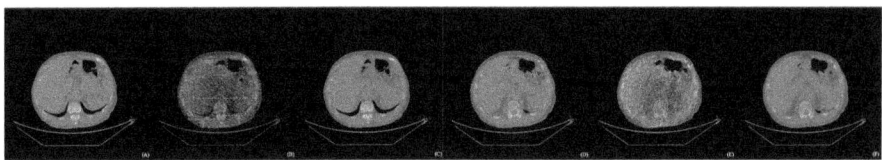

Fig. 5. Robustness of FMUnet for organ migration (A) NDCT-1, (B) LDCT-1, (C) output-1, (D) NDCT-2, (E) LDCT-2, (F) output-2

4 Discussion

In the real LDCT dataset we propose, despite the presence of more realistic noise distribution, image blur, and streak artifacts, these significant degradation characteristics actually enhance the generalization capability and accuracy of deep learning models. However, upon careful analysis of the dataset, we noted an average displacement of 2 to 3 pixels in organ positions between the same set of LDCT and Normal Dose CT (NDCT) images. This displacement is primarily due to minor organ movements caused by the subject's breathing during the two different dose scanning processes, which is unavoidable. Observing the predictions of our model, we found that it not only effectively denoises and reconstructs LDCT images but also demonstrates robustness to organ position displacement caused by breathing. For example, As shown in Fig. 4(A–C), a randomly selected pair of images demonstrates that despite shape changes in the black low-density areas marked by red boxes in the input LDCT images due to breathing, our model can still correct this displacement, making its shape more akin to that of the NDCT images. In Fig. 4(D–F), this corrective effect is more pronounced, with the predicted black contours closely matching those of the NDCT images. To assess the clinical value of this finding, we invited several doctors to review the test results of the model. They generally agreed that the model's predictions are within an acceptable range and can assist doctors in making diagnostic judgments to a certain extent.

5 Conclusion

We established a real LDCT image dataset by recruiting volunteers for image acquisition, addressing the shortcomings of existing publicly available datasets in artificially introducing noise and failing to accurately reflect the degradation characteristics of real LDCT images. Secondly, we proposed a multi-level supervised U-net and designed frequency feature attention to enhance the model's learning of beneficial frequency information. Additionally, to address the issue of excessive smoothing in pixel-based loss functions and to strengthen frequency domain learning, we introduced frequency domain loss based on fast Fourier transform. Finally, through retraining and testing our proposed model and comparing it with baseline models, experiments demonstrated that our model achieved superior performance on our proposed dataset, and we achieve great improvement in both qualitative and quantitative experiments, exhibiting stronger noise suppression capability and clearer organizational edge representation. These achievements provide valuable references and insights for the development of LDCT image denoising.

References

1. Mathews, J.P., Campbell, Q.P., Xu, H., Halleck, P.: A review of the application of X-ray computed tomography to the study of coal. Fuel **209**, 10–24 (2017)
2. Seeram, E.: Computed Tomography: Physical Principles, Clinical Applications, and Quality Control. Elsevier (2015)
3. Brenner, D.J., Hall, E.J.: Computed tomography — an increasing source of radiation exposure. N. Engl. J. Med. **357**, 2277–2284 (2007). https://doi.org/10.1056/NEJMra072149
4. Xu, Q., Yu, H., Mou, X., Zhang, L., Hsieh, J., Wang, G.: Low-dose X-ray CT reconstruction via dictionary learning. IEEE Trans. Med. Imaging **31**, 1682–1697 (2012)
5. Wang, G., Ye, J.C., De Man, B.: Deep learning for tomographic image reconstruction. Nat. Mach. Intell. **2**, 737–748 (2020)
6. McCollough, C.H., et al.: Low-dose CT for the detection and classification of metastatic liver lesions: results of the 2016 low dose CT grand challenge. Med. Phys. **44**, e339–e352 (2017). https://doi.org/10.1002/mp.12345
7. Ding, Q., Long, Y., Zhang, X., Fessler, J.A.: Statistical image reconstruction using mixed Poisson-Gaussian Noise Model for X-Ray CT (2018). http://arxiv.org/abs/1801.09533
8. Du, W., Chen, H., Wu, Z., Sun, H., Liao, P., Zhang, Y.: Stacked competitive networks for noise reduction in low-dose CT. PLoS ONE **12**, e0190069 (2017)
9. Shiri Lord, I.: Ultra-low-dose chest CT imaging of COVID-19 patients using a deep residual neural network (2020)
10. Wu, D., Kim, K., Fakhri, G.E., Li, Q.: A cascaded convolutional neural network for X-ray low-dose CT image denoising (2017). http://arxiv.org/abs/1705.04267
11. Zhong, A., Li, B., Luo, N., Xu, Y., Zhou, L., Zhen, X.: Image restoration for low-dose CT via transfer learning and residual network. IEEE Access **8**, 112078–112091 (2020)
12. Kang, E., Chang, W., Yoo, J., Ye, J.C.: Deep convolutional framelet denosing for low-dose CT via wavelet residual network. IEEE Trans. Med. Imaging **37**, 1358–1369 (2018)
13. Ming, J., Yi, B., Zhang, Y., Li, H.: Low-dose CT image denoising using classification densely connected residual network. KSII Trans. Internet Inf. Syst. TIIS. **14**, 2480–2496 (2020)
14. Yang, L., Shangguan, H., Zhang, X., Wang, A., Han, Z.: High-frequency sensitive generative adversarial network for low-dose CT image denoising. IEEE Access. **8**, 930–943 (2019)

15. Arabi, H., Zaidi, H.: Improvement of image quality in PET using post-reconstruction hybrid spatial-frequency domain filtering. Phys. Med. Biol. **63**, 215010 (2018)
16. Lee, D., Choi, S., Kim, H.: High quality imaging from sparsely sampled computed tomography data with deep learning and wavelet transform in various domains. Med. Phys. **46**, 104–115 (2019). https://doi.org/10.1002/mp.13258
17. Lal, A., et al.: A frequency domain SIM reconstruction algorithm using reduced number of images. IEEE Trans. Image Process. **27**, 4555–4570 (2018)
18. Uetani, H., et al.: A preliminary study of deep learning-based reconstruction specialized for denoising in high-frequency domain: use-fulness in high-resolution three-dimensional magnetic resonance cisternography of the cerebellopontine angle. Neuroradiology **63**, 63–71 (2021). https://doi.org/10.1007/s00234-020-02513-w
19. Park, N., Kim, S.: How do vision transformers work? (2022). http://arxiv.org/abs/2202.06709
20. Wang, H., Wu, X., Huang, Z., Xing, E.P.: High-frequency component helps explain the generalization of convolutional neural networks. In: Proceedings of the 2020 IEEE/CVF Conference on Computer Vision and Pattern Recognition (CVPR), pp. 8681–8691. IEEE, Seattle (2020). https://doi.org/10.1109/CVPR42600.2020.00871
21. Cui, Y., Knoll, A.: Exploring the potential of channel interactions for image restoration. Knowl.-Based Syst. **282**, 111156 (2023). https://doi.org/10.1016/j.knosys.2023.111156
22. Zhang, Z., Yu, L., Liang, X., Zhao, W., Xing, L.: TransCT: dual-path transformer for low dose computed tomography. In: De Bruijne, M., et al. (eds.) Medical Image Computing and Computer Assisted Intervention – MICCAI 2021, pp. 55–64. Springer International Publishing, Cham (2021)
23. Wang, D., Fan, F., Wu, Z., Liu, R., Wang, F., Yu, H.: CTformer: convolution-free Token2Token dilated vision transformer for low-dose CT denoising. Phys. Med. Biol. **68**, 065012 (2023). https://doi.org/10.1088/1361-6560/acc000
24. Liang, T., Jin, Y., Li, Y., Wang, T.: EDCNN: edge enhancement-based densely connected network with compound loss for low-dose CT denoising. In: Proceedings of the 2020 15th IEEE International Conference on Signal Processing (ICSP), pp. 193–198. IEEE, Beijing (2020)
25. Chen, H., et al.: Low-dose CT with a residual encoder-decoder convolutional neural network. IEEE Trans. Med. Imaging **36**, 2524–2535 (2017). https://doi.org/10.1109/TMI.2017.2715284

Research on Intelligent Recognition Algorithm of Container Numbers in Ports Based on Deep Learning

Zhehao Lin, Chen Dong(✉), and Yuxuan Wan

School of Computer Science and Engineering, Tianjin University of Technology, Tianjin 300380, China
dongc@tjut.edu.cn

Abstract. The identification of container number has important application value in the field of logistics and cargo transportation. A new container number recognition algorithm was proposed in this paper to solve the difficult problems such as different illumination conditions, blurred image, loud noise, damaged and polluted container number, zigzag deformation, etc. First, the low-light enhancement algorithm based on Retinex theory was used to process the container number image to deal with the problems of inconsistent port lighting conditions and background noise. The super-resolution reconstruction was used to deal with the problems of container surface contamination and container number damage. The backbone network was replaced by MobileNetv3 by improving the YOLOv5 algorithm. The ECA attention mechanism was added to achieve lightweight model and accurate location of box number area. STN is added before the convolutional layer of the CRNN to correct the image. Public images on Github and official images of Tianjin Port were used to generate samples through DCGAN network, and their data were enhanced. The obtained 6961 container number images were used as data sets to train the improved CRNN model. The mAP of the proposed method in container number location using the improved YOLOv5 reaches 93.7%, the accuracy rate reaches 94.5% in container number identification using the improved CRNN, and the average recognition speed reaches 29.1 frames/s. The method performs well in real-time performance and realizes the lightweight of the model. It can meet the requirements of port real-time and accurate identification of container number.

1 Introduction

With the continuous development of global trade and the rapid growth of logistics industry, container transport, as one of the main modes of cargo transport, has become an important part of the global trade and logistics field. However, in the process of container management and logistics tracking, the accurate location and identification of container number has always been a challenging problem. For different port lighting conditions, container number damage pollution, tortuous deformation, blurred images, loud noise, accurate real-time identification of the box number and other problems, the traditional container number identification method was often difficult to meet the actual needs.

With the development of artificial intelligence technology, algorithms based on deep learning are widely used in the field of object detection [1–4]. For example, Wang Zhenpeng et al. [5] improved Faster-RCNN and added the attention mechanism in the area generation network (RPN) to improve the detection speed of the case number while ensuring the accuracy. However, further improvement and verification were needed for complex environments such as the case number being seriously soiled and low light. Xu Zhengguang et al. [6] used YOLOv3 object detection algorithm and deeplabv3plus semantic segmentation algorithm to locate the character region of the display screen, which has good stability and real-time performance, but was limited to small samples. Zhang Ran et al. [7] adopted the average maximum suppression range (AMSR) algorithm to identify the boundary of the container code region, so as to reduce the interference of container images. This framework could meet the operating requirements in detection accuracy and processing speed, but it did not analyze the specific complex scene of the port.

In the field of character recognition, the application of deep learning has developed rapidly, and the use of neural networks for container number recognition [8–11] could solve some cases that could not be correctly recognized by humans. For example, Li Yanchao et al. [12] proposed an end-to-end box number recognition algorithm by locating regions and detecting characters and classifying them, which could cope with various factors such as uneven illumination, background changes and other image quality degradation factors, and the recognition accuracy has improved compared with other algorithms composed of character classifiers. However, there is no significant optimization for lightweight deployment and real-time recognition of the model. Chao Mi et al. [13] For problems such as container number inclination and deflection, the differential edge detection algorithm was used to binary segment the container number image, improved square method was used to locate the container number, BP neural network was used to identify the container number, and the comprehensive recognition rate was improved compared with traditional methods and yolov3. However, the defacement and character repair of the case number were not fully considered. Yang Dapeng et al. [14] used lightweight network as the trunk and added MRFPN feature extraction module to extract semantic information, which reduced the computational load and could meet the requirements of actual container number code recognition, but did not verify container numbers in various arrangements.

In this paper, a new container number identification method was proposed to address the requirements of accurate and real-time identification of container numbers due to different lighting conditions, blurred images, loud noise, damaged and polluted container numbers, zigzag deformation in ports: First, the low-light enhancement algorithm based on Retinex theory was used to reduce the impact of different port light on image quality, and super-resolution reconstruction was used to solve the problems of damaged, polluted, tortuous and deformed container number. MobileNetv3 was replaced by the backbone network of YOLOv5. In addition, ECA (Efficient Channel Attention) was added to Neck, and the improved YOLOv5 network was used to locate the container number area. DCGAN (Deep Convolutional Generative Adversarial Network) is used to generate the CRNN model after training the container number sample. Before CRNN, the Spatial Transformer Network (STN) was added to correct the container number in the image, and the container number was finally identified. This method achieves a good balance between detection speed and accuracy, and could be applied to real-time detection of container number on embedded devices.

2 Container Number Localization and Recognition Workflow

The workflow of container number location and identification in the complex scenario of the port is shown in Fig. 1. For the task of container number identification, the data collection and processing were carried out first. A rich and diverse training dataset was constructed by using the on-site shooting of the port and the data set provided by the Tianjin Port official, and the expanded sample of the container number generated by DCGAN to train the improved YOLOv5 model and the improved CRNN model. For the image with container number to be processed, the low-light enhancement algorithm based on Retinex theory was first used to enhance the image sharpness and contrast. Then, the improved YOLOv5 algorithm was used to locate the container number area and crop out the valid container number area in the image. Finally, the improved CRNN model was used for text correction and character recognition. After identifying the character information in the container number, the verification code was used to verify the correctness of the recognition. Finally, the accurate recognition result of the container number was obtained.

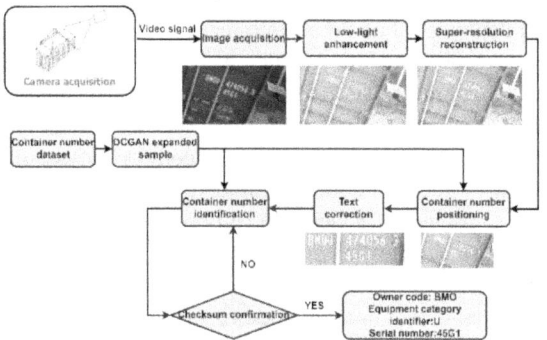

Fig. 1. Container number identification process in complex scenarios.

3 Low-Light Enhancement Method Based on Retinex Theory

In container number recognition, image quality directly affects the recognition accuracy. Under low light conditions, the image quality is poor, the noise is large, the color is distorted, and the recognition accuracy is affected. In this paper, low light enhancement algorithm based on Retinex theory is used to improve image quality. The specific process is shown in Fig. 2.

Initially, the original RGB image was converted into the HSV color space, and the luminance component V was processed using the Multi-Scale Retinex (MSR) algorithm,

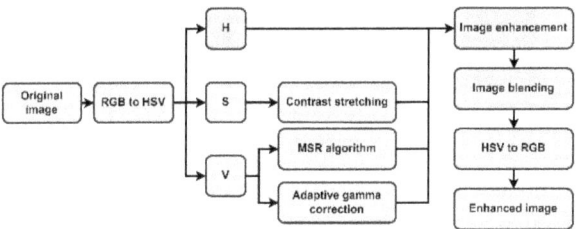

Fig. 2. Low-light enhancement process diagram Based on Retinex theory.

with the Retinex model described by Eqs. (1) and (2). Adaptive gamma correction was then applied to enhance the brightness and contrast of the image. This approach made the details in dark areas clearer, which aided in improving the recognizability of the container number image.

$$I(x, y) = R(x, y) \times L(x, y) \tag{1}$$

In the formula, $I(x,y)$ represents the original image, $R(x,y)$ denotes the object's reflection component, and $L(x,y)$ indicates the object's incident component.

$$V_{out} = GV_{in}^{\beta} \tag{2}$$

In the equation, V_{in} is the input luminance value, V_{out} is the output luminance value, and G is a parameter for Gamma correction.

Subsequently, after converting the saturation component S to the HSV color space, contrast stretching operations were conducted to enhance the vividness and visual impact of the image, with the specific stretching process described by Eq. (3). This aids in highlighting color features within the container number image, making it easier for recognition algorithms to capture key information.

$$S_{out} = (S_{in} - \min)\frac{N_{max} - N_{min}}{\max - \min} + N_{min} \tag{3}$$

In the equation, S_{in} represents the pixel value of the original image, max and min respectively denote the maximum and minimum pixel values of the original image, N_{max} and N_{min} respectively represent the maximum and minimum pixel values of the target image, and S_{out} is the pixel value of the image after contrast stretching treatment.

Finally, the processed HSV image components are fused and converted back to RGB to obtain the enhanced image. The brightness, contrast and clarity of the container number image after low-light enhancement are improved, effectively improving the accuracy of container number positioning and recognition, as shown in Fig. 3.

Fig. 3. Example of container images before and after low-light enhancement.

4 Character Super Resolution Reconstruction

In the identification of port container number, the problems such as ambiguity and distortion caused by damage and fouling affect the identification. The text super-resolution reconstruction technology can improve the clarity and readability of the carton number image, enhance the accuracy and stability of the recognition algorithm, effectively reduce the blur and noise interference, and help to accurately identify and extract the carton number information.

First, the high-resolution and corresponding low-resolution container number images in the dataset were used as training samples. Then, the image was preprocessed, including denoising and contrast enhancement. In the training stage, the SRCNN deep learning model was used. The specific network structure diagram of the model was shown in Fig. 4, where f_1 and f_3 respectively represent the convolution layer sizes corresponding to layers 1 and 3, n_1 and n_2 respectively represent the first and second nonlinear mapping layers.

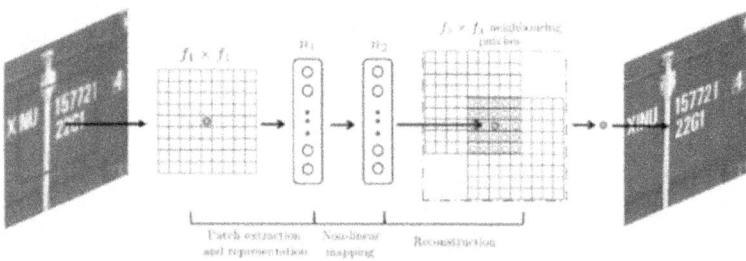

Fig. 4. Network structure of SRCNN

SRCNN model reconstructs high-resolution images by learning the mapping relationship between high-low resolution image pairs. By training and optimizing the model parameters, the model can accurately convert low-resolution images into high-resolution images. Figure 5 shows the comparison effect before and after reconstruction. This scheme significantly improves the clarity and identification accuracy of port container images, and thus improves the speed and accuracy of container number identification.

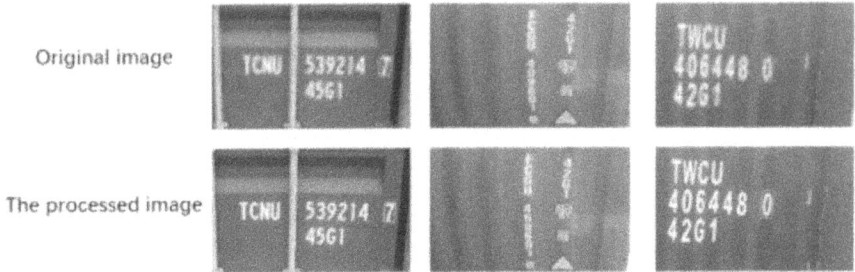

Fig. 5. Sample map of super resolution reconstruction.

5 Container Number Localization Method Based on YOLOv5

5.1 MobileNetv3 Module

MobileNetv3, a lightweight deep learning model, significantly improves its deployment efficiency in resource-constrained environments by adopting Bottleneck layer design (including linear bottleneck and depth-separable convolution) and adaptive activation functions. Its lightweight characteristics make it easier to deploy the model after replacing the YOLOv5 backbone network on mobile devices and embedded facilities in port terminals, meeting the real-time requirements of container number area detection while maintaining high detection accuracy. Global average pooling further reduces the number of parameters, improves model generalization ability, and ensures that both speed and accuracy requirements are met in container number positioning tasks.

5.2 ECA

The structure of the ECA attention mechanism was shown in Fig. 6. Initially, the feature map undergoes Global Average Pooling (GAP) to obtain aggregated features. The size of the one-dimensional convolution kernel was calculated based on the number of channels, followed by a one-dimensional convolution operation. Lastly, the Sigmoid activation function was used to learn the weight of each channel. ECA discarded the method of achieving channel communication through fully connected layers, focusing instead on each channel and its k adjacent channels to facilitate cross-channel information interaction, as shown in Eq. (4). By adding the ECA attention mechanism in the Neck, it is possible to effectively extract more information from the feature maps without significantly affecting the overall model parameters. This also avoided the impact of dimensionality reduction operations, thereby improving the accuracy of the model's detection.

$$K = \psi(C) = \left| \frac{\log_2(C)}{\gamma} + \frac{b}{\gamma} \right|_{odd} \qquad (4)$$

In the equation, γ is set to 2, b is 1, K is the size of the convolutional kernel, C is the number of channels, and $|t|_{odd}$ represents the nearest odd number to t.

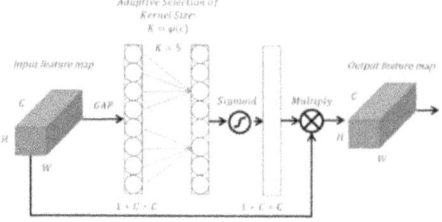

Fig. 6. ECA attention module.

5.3 Improvements to the YOLOv5 Model

YOLOv5 is composed of Backbone, Neck and Head, and is suitable for container number positioning. Backbone uses CSPDarknet53 to extract features, Neck fuses features of different levels through FPN, and Head predicts the position and category of the box number. Aiming at real-time, lightweight and small target detection requirements when deployed to embedded devices, this paper proposes an improved YOLOv5 algorithm, the specific structure of which is shown in Fig. 7.

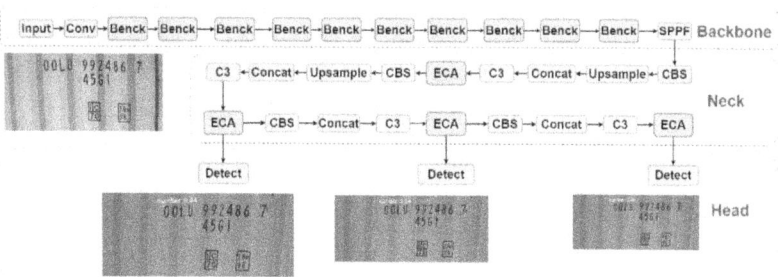

Fig. 7. Improved YOLOv5 network structure.

Firstly, the Backbone of YOLOv5 is replaced by Benck in MobileNetv3. MobileNetv3, as a lightweight network structure, has low parameter number and computational complexity, which was suitable for operation in resource-limited environments of embedded devices. At the same time, less computation was required, which could improve the reasoning speed. Secondly, adding ECA attention mechanism to Neck can effectively capture the dependencies between different channels in the feature map, and improve the model's ability to focus on the container number region and feature representation.

5.4 Generating Samples with DCGAN

DCGAN is an improvement of GAN, introducing convolutional neural network as the main architecture of generator and discriminator, which can capture spatial relationships and features of images and generate more realistic images. DCGAN eliminates the fully connected layer and uses convolution and deconvolution layers to reduce parameters and improve stability and generalization. It also introduces batch normalization and Leaky ReLU activation functions to speed up training, improve image quality, and avoid gradient disappearance. For container number generation, DCGAN can generate samples conforming to the characteristics of the real container number, expand the data set to improve the CRNN model, and improve the robustness and generalization ability of the model. Figure 8 shows a partial sample of the generated container numbers.

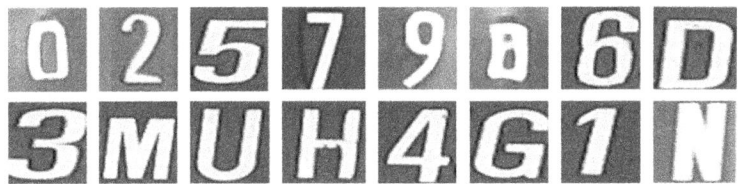

Fig. 8. Examples of sample images generated by DCGAN.

6 Improved CRNN for Container Number Identification

The task of port container number identification faces many challenges, such as fuzzy container number, soiling, surface deformation, etc. The traditional method is difficult to deal with effectively. In contrast, the CRNN model has significant advantages in this area. First, traditional methods require manual design of feature extractors or tedious pre-processing, while CRNN learns features directly from raw images through end-to-end learning, reducing the need for manual intervention. Secondly, CRNN combines the structure of convolutional layer and cyclic layer, which can make full use of spatial information of image and sequence information of text to understand and recognize the box number more comprehensively. In addition, by learning large amounts of data, CRNNs are better able to adapt to different forms and arrangements of box numbers without having to design specific rules or models for different situations. In order to improve the recognition accuracy of the CRNN model for the skewed container number image, this paper introduced the STN module, and the specific improved CRNN process was shown in Fig. 9.

In the CRNN model, feature extraction mainly relied on the convolutional layer, but the character recognition ability for distortion, tilt or Angle deviation was weak, which limited the robustness of the model. By learning the spatial transformation information of the image, STN module could make the model better adapt to the container number image of different scale, rotation and Angle of view. In the whole process, feature extraction and representation learning were firstly carried out through the localization network to capture the key feature points or feature regions in the image, which described the geometric structure and spatial transformation information of the image. Subsequently, the STN network predicted the parameters required to perform the spatial transformation, including rotation Angle, scaling ratio, and displacement, through the learned feature representation. These parameters were applied to the input image to implement geometric

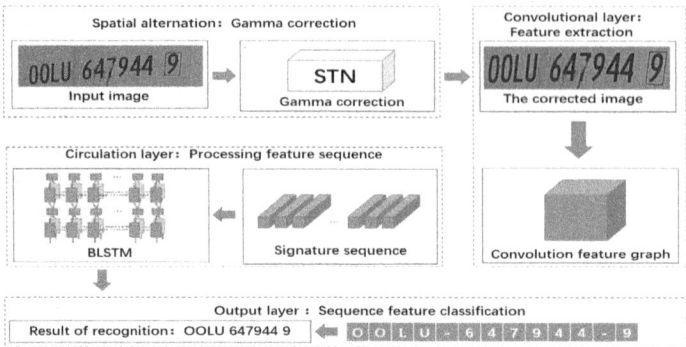

Fig. 9. Improved CRNN flowchart.

transformations of the image, such as rotation, scaling, and translation. Finally, the CRNN model recognizes characters on images transformed by STN space.

7 Experimental Results and Analysis

7.1 Dataset

By using a total of 2851 images with container number provided by Tianjin Port official and open data set on Github [15], data enhancement processing was carried out on them, including blurring, increasing brightness, reducing brightness, adding Gaussian noise, image offset and modifying size. A dataset containing 6961 images of damaged containers was constructed. The constructed dataset contained images of container numbers at multiple ports, under various extreme conditions, which correspond to the Obscure, Dim, Surface bending, Long-range shooting, High light, Dim, Foggy days, Contaminated or Angle skew images of container numbers in eight different environments and three different permutations of container numbers. The data set was divided into training set, verification set and test set according to the ratio of 8:1:1 to ensure that there is enough sample data in the training process, the verification process was effective, and the test evaluation was objective and accurate. The data enhancement legend was shown in Fig. 10.

Fig. 10. Data enhanced image of container number.

7.2 The Improved YOLOv5 Was Used for Experimental Analysis of Container Number Region Positioning

In order to objectively evaluate the effectiveness of the improved YOLOv5 model, the model was evaluated in terms of Precision, Recall and mAP@0.5. After the common target detection algorithm Faster-RCNN YOLOv3, YOLOv4, YOLOv5 algorithm and the improved YOLOv5 model training, the training accuracy and recall rate, the mAP values for such as shown in Table 1.

Table 1. The results of container number location were compared by different target detection algorithm.

Algorithm	Precision	Recall	mAP@0.5
Faster-RCNN	78.9%	79.4%	76.1%
YOLOv3	70.2%	78.5%	72.5%
YOLOv4	83.7%	81.2%	82.1%
YOLOv5	85.2%	82.5%	88.4%
Improved YOLOv5	94.3%	86.2%	93.7%

By comparing the experimental data, it could be found that the detection accuracy of the improved YOLOv5 model is the highest, reaching 93.7%. In terms of detection speed, the original YOLOv5 model was the fastest, while the improved YOLOv5 model was the second fastest, but there was little difference, which met the standard of real-time port detection and met the real-time requirement.

Based on the analysis of three different arrangement of container number images and the detection of container number under eight extreme conditions, the optimized model could be used as a judgment standard for regional positioning of container number. The specific positioning and detection effects were shown in Fig. 11.

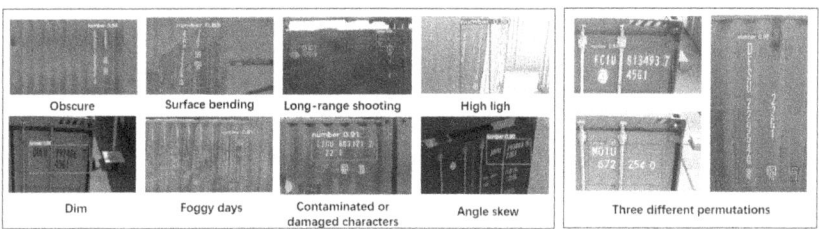

Fig. 11. Locating container numbers in various environments.

7.3 Analysis of the Improved CRNN for Container Number Recognition

In order to verify the effectiveness of lightweight and text recognition accuracy optimization of the proposed model, the proposed model was deployed on the embedded device

Jetson Nano to verify its performance. The deployment and recognition results are shown in Fig. 12. The traditional OCR model, YOLOv5 + CRNN model and the Improved YOLOv5 + Improved CRNN model were compared with the Improved YOLOV5 + Improved CRNN model, and the results were shown in Table 2.

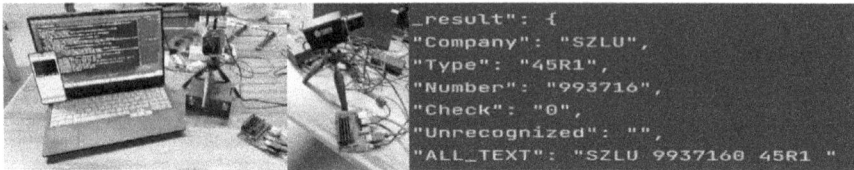

Fig. 12. Container number identification using Jetson Nano.

Table 2. Captions should be placed above the tables.

Algorithm	Model size	Recognition speed/(Frames/s)	mAP@0.5
Traditional OCR	14.5 MB	27.6	88.1%
YOLOv5 + CRNN	15.8 MB	30.4	91.9%
Improved YOLOv5 + Improved CRNN	14.2 MB	29.1	94.5%

By comparing the experimental data, it could be found that the accuracy rate of the improved CRNN model reaches 94.5%, and in terms of detection speed, the average recognition speed was 29.1 frames/s. Compared with the YOLOv5 + CRNN model, the speed of the improved model in this paper has decreased, but there was little difference. Moreover, the identification accuracy rate was improved to a greater extent, and the requirements of real-time container number identification in ports were better met. The specific identification effect deployed on embedded devices was shown in Fig. 13.

Fig. 13. Different arrangement of box number recognition effect.

8 Conclusion and Future Work

In view of the complex scenarios of container number recognition, such as different port lighting conditions, damaged and polluted container number, tortuous deformation, blurred image and loud noise, a new algorithm for container number recognition were proposed in this paper, and satisfactory results were obtained by using various technical means. First, the low light enhancement algorithm based on Retinex was used to process the image, which effectively solved the problems of insufficient light and background noise in the port, and the super-resolution reconstruction was used to deal with the situation of the container surface and the container number. Secondly, the improved YOLOv5 algorithm, by replacing the backbone network to MobileNetv3 and adding ECA attention mechanism to Neck, realized the model lightweight and accurate positioning of the box number region. Finally, the DCGAN network was used to generate samples, together with the public container number images of Github and the official container number images of Tianjin Port, to generate a dataset containing a total of 6961 container number images in three arrangements and eight extreme environments. Using this data set to train the improved CRNN model with STN network, the container number recognition was realized accurately, showing good real-time and recognition accuracy. Experimental verification showed that the improved algorithm could achieve 94.5% accuracy for container number recognition, and the average container number recognition speed is 29.1 frames/s, which was lower than the original YOLOv5 + CRNN model, but still met the real-time recognition requirements, which proved the effectiveness, robustness and generalization ability of the improved algorithm.

There are still some problems in this study. When the container number is damaged or dirty, the identification result is not accurate enough. In the future, the text recognition can be carried out after the text repair of the container number in the image. This is of great significance for the port to achieve automated container number identification and promote the rapid upgrade of port logistics. The current container number positioning model and container number recognition model adopt the strategy of separate training and optimization. In the future, we can consider integrating the two models to realize a new end-to-end method, so that the two can optimize each other during training.

References

1. Wang, A., Ren, C., Zhao, S., Mu, S.: Attention guided multi-level feature aggregation network for camouflaged object detection. Image Vis. Comput. **144**, 104953 (2024)
2. Zhang, J., Tian, M., Yang, Z., Li, J., Zhao, L.: An improved target detection method based on YOLOv5 in natural orchard environments. Comput. Electron. Agric. **219**, 108780 (2024)
3. Zhou, J., Yang, D., Song, T., Ye, Y., Zhang, X., Song, Y.: Improved YOLOv7 models based on modulated deformable convolution and swin transformer for object detection in fisheye images. Image Vis. Comput. **144**, 104966 (2024)
4. Zhu, P.F., Zhu, Q.L., Dong, X., Sun, M.C.: Flying target detection technology based on GNSS multipath signals. Sensors **24**(5), 1706 (2024). https://doi.org/10.3390/s24051706
5. Wang, Z., Wang, Y.: FRCA: High-Efficiency Container Number Detection and Recognition Algorithm with Enhanced Attention (2020)
6. Xu, Z.G., Wang, L., Niu, S., Kan, G.: A method of positioning and recognition of electronic scale characters based on deep learning. J. Phys. Conf. Ser. **1693**(1), 012122 (2020). https://doi.org/10.1088/1742-6596/1693/1/012122
7. Ran, Z., Zhila, B., Teng, W., Zheng, L.: An adaptive deep learning framework for shipping container code localization and recognition. IEEE Trans. Instrum. Meas. **70**, 1–13 (2021). https://doi.org/10.1109/TIM.2020.3016108

8. Capurro, C., Provatorova, V., Kanoulas, E.: Experimenting with training a neural network in transkribus to recognise text in a multilingual and multi-authored manuscript collection. Heritage **6**(12), 7482–7494 (2023)
9. Meng, F., Ghena, B.: Research on text recognition methods based on artificial intelligence and machine learning. Adv. Comput. Commun. **4**(5), 340–344 (2023). https://doi.org/10.26855/acc.2023.10.014
10. Shu, T., Zhu, K.-X., Qin, H.-B., Yang, C.: Dynamic receptive field adaptation for scene text recognition. Pattern Recognit. Lett. **178**, 55–61 (2024). https://doi.org/10.1016/j.patrec.2023.12.005
11. Yu, M.M., Zhang, H., Yin, F., Liu, C.L.: An approach for handwritten Chinese text recognition unifying character segmentation and recognition. Pattern Recognit. **151**, 110373 (2024)
12. Yanchao, L., Hao, L., Guangwei, G.: Towards end-to-end container code recognition. Multimedia Tools Appl. **81**(11), 15901–15918 (2022)
13. Mi, C., Cao, L., Zhang, Z., Feng, Y., Yao, L., Wu, Y.: A port container code recognition algorithm under natural conditions. J. Coastal Res. **103**(sp1), 822–829 (2020)
14. Yang, D., et al.: Lightweight container code recognition based on multi-reuse feature fusion and multi-branch structure merger. J. Real Time Image Process. **20**(6) (2023). https://doi.org/10.1007/s11554-023-01364-x
15. Bofan, L.: ContainerNumber-OCR. https://github.com/lbf4616/ContainerNumber-OCR?tab=readme-ov-file

Dr-SAM: U-Shape Structure Segment Anything Model for Generalizable Medical Image Segmentation

Xiangzuo Huo[1,2], Shengwei Tian[1(✉)], Bingming Zhou[3], Long Yu[1], and Aolun Li[1,2]

[1] School of Computer Science and Technology, Xinjiang University, Ürümqi, China
tianshengwei@163.com
[2] Xinjiang Key Laboratory of Signal Detection and Processing, Xinjiang University, Ürümqi, China
[3] School of Computer Science, Beijing University of Posts and Telecommunications, Beijing, China

Abstract. Medical image segmentation plays a pivotal role in computer-assisted medical diagnosis, contributing to precise diagnostics, treatment strategizing, and disease tracking. However, the availability of annotated data for medical image segmentation remains restricted, and conventional approaches predominantly rely on bespoke models with limited adaptability across diverse tasks. In this research, we introduce DrSAM, a foundation model for universal medical image segmentation. This model possesses two crucial attributes: (i) the retention and utilization of pre-trained SAM model weights, while introducing a minimal number of supplementary parameters and computations; (ii) the incorporation of a trainable U-shaped residual network and a Medical Output Token designed to capture the distinctive features at various levels within medical images and enhance mask granularity. DrSAM, a fine-tuned model with a subset of medical image datasets, surpasses existing state-of-the-art segmentation foundation models. DrSAM holds substantial potentials for automating medical image segmentation. Code is available at https://github.com/huoxiangzuo/Doctor-SAM.

Keywords: Medical Image Segmentation · Segment Anything Model · Fine Tuning · Feature Fusion

1 Introduction

In recent years, large-scale language models trained on massive corpora have demonstrated remarkable performance in both natural language understanding and generation tasks. Similarly, multimodal foundation models trained on vast amounts of text, images, videos, and other data have exhibited outstanding capabilities in visual content comprehension and generation. Leveraging their exceptional generalization capabilities and rich parameterized knowledge, these foundation models can swiftly adapt to new tasks through carefully designed instructions and fine-tuning techniques. Consequently, the utilization of these powerful, generalization-driven foundation models to address specialized problems across various domains has become a focal point of both research and application endeavors.

Medical image segmentation plays a critical role in modern medical diagnostics. By accurately delineating and identifying vital structures and pathologies within medical images, physicians can make more precise diagnoses, plan treatment strategies, and monitor disease progression [1, 2]. However, it is an expensive and time consuming task to obtain large-scale annotated medical image data in the medical domain, leading many existing methods to rely on custom models tailored for specific tasks, which lack generalizability across different tasks [3, 4, 14, 19].

Applying foundation model technology to specific vertical domains still faces challenges. The original foundation models trained on general domain corpora possess abundant common-sense knowledge but lack specialized knowledge in vertical domains. Conversely, vertical domain foundation models to some extent take on the role of domain experts. Exploring how to leverage existing domain knowledge representation methods such as knowledge graphs to enable vertical domain foundation models to learn, utilize, and integrate domain knowledge requires novel solutions. This endeavor aims to construct responsible, controllable, and interpretable domain expert foundation models.

The recent advancements in natural image segmentation have witnessed the emergence of segmentation foundation models [5, 6], showcasing remarkable versatility and performance across various segmentation tasks. However, their application in medical image segmentation has remained challenging due to substantial domain differences [7, 8]. SAM faces two key challenges: 1) coarse mask boundaries, often leading to the neglect of segmenting thin object structures. 2) Incorrect predictions, mask corruption, or significant errors in challenging cases (e.g., retinal vessels, sessile polyps). SAM and its fine-tuned models exhibit notably poorer performance in fully automatic mode for medical image segmentation. Further investigation reveals that the performance degradation is associated with the multiscale information fusion of adverse prompts and mask segmentation. In fully automatic mode, the inevitable presence of adverse prompts (such as points outside the mask or boxes significantly larger than the mask) may severely mislead the generation of masks.

Segment Anything Model (SAM), trained on over 1 billion masks, has demonstrated unprecedented generalization capabilities across various natural images. Some studies have shown promising results when applying SAM to segment certain medical images, indicating the promising utility of pre-trained SAM weights in the segmentation domain. There are two primary approaches to applying SAM to medical image segmentation: 1) Freezing SAM's image encoder and prompt encoder while only fine-tuning the mask decoder typically yields suboptimal results; 2) Utilizing adaptive [20, 21] or visual prompt [22] techniques to train the image encoder has improved the model's performance in specific domains. However, training such models incurs high GPU memory consumption due to the inability to pre-compute image embeddings. Additionally, these fine-tuning methods still require manually provided boxes or points, making fully automated medical image segmentation challenging to achieve.

To address the aforementioned challenges, we propose DrSAM (Doctor SAM) tailored for application in the medical segmentation domain. Specifically, two novel modules are designed and integrated into SAM: the first is the U-shaped fine-tuning fusion module, which establishes hierarchical skip connections between feature extraction and decoder layers in a U-shaped structure. Additionally, it leverages ViT pre-trained weights to retain domain knowledge feature fine-tuning learning under the basic structure of SAM. The second is the Med-Output Token, a learnable token incorporated alongside the Output Token and Prompt into the attention module. Within each attention layer, the Med-Output Token undergoes self-attention integration with other tokens (token to image) to enhance and refine SAM's performance on medical images. This study conducts segmentation and generalization experiments on publicly available datasets including Hyper Kvasir endoscopy dataset, Cell dataset, and Chase retinal vessel dataset. The results demonstrate that compared to the previously state-of-the-art domain generalization method MedSAM, DrSAM achieves a competitive level of performance. Moreover, DrSAM is trainable on personal devices with entry-level GPUs, thus facilitating the application of foundation models in primary healthcare settings.

Single-source domain generalization poses greater challenges considering training data from only one domain and extending it to an unknown domain, as the diversity of the training domain is limited. Hence, the mainstream solution to this problem involves utilizing data augmentation techniques to generate new domain data, thereby enhancing the diversity and information content of the training data. This approach has led to the design of various generation strategies for single-source domain generalization in computer vision tasks. Chen et al. [23] employed random bias fields to enhance data, which are common image artifacts in clinical MRI, or combined style information from randomly selected instances of different domains, along with additional noise and worst-case combinations to expand the domain space. Ouyang et al. [24] proposed a simple causality-inspired data augmentation method, significantly improving the cross-domain robustness of deep models. In contrast to previous methods, DrSAM enhances the generalization capability of deep models without requiring complex data augmentation, making it more competitive in practical applications.

Many studies have applied the SAM model to typical medical image segmentation tasks [27, 28] and other challenging scenarios [25, 26]. For instance, SAM's comprehensive evaluation across various medical images highlights its high-quality segmentation results for targets with diverse boundary features. However, SAM exhibits significant limitations when segmenting typical medical targets with weak boundaries or low contrast. Consistent with these observations, MedSAM [30], a direct fine-tuning of SAM as the foundation model, significantly enhances SAM's segmentation performance on medical images. MedSAM achieves this goal by fine-tuning SAM on a dataset comprising over one million pairs of medical image-mask pairs. The aforementioned work involves fine-tuning both the mask decoder and the image encoder [20, 29, 30]. Compared to these methods, the proposed DrSAM strikes a balance between performance and efficiency, yielding satisfactory results in fully automatic segmentation.

U-Net [9] holds an unassailable position as a classic medical image segmentation model, emphasizing the importance of extracting features at various levels of medical images by merely connecting encoder features with the decoder features through residuals. SAM [5] not only exhibits higher versatility in terms of model capacity but also may benefit from shared underlying architecture and training processes, yielding more consistent results across different tasks. Ma et al. proposed MedSAM [30], directly fine-tuning medical images on the SAM model, achieving favorable results. However, directly fine-tuning SAM's decoder or introducing numerous new decoder modules disrupts SAM's architecture, severely compromising foundation zero-shot segmentation performance [10]. Ke et al. designed the HQ-SAM architecture, featuring a learnable HQ-output token input alongside the original prompts and output tokens into SAM's mask decoder, training only the proposed modules. This transfer learning fine-tuning approach can generate higher-quality masks while preserving zero-shot capabilities.

Motivation. In this study, we were inspired by classic medical segmentation model U-net [9] and foundation model HQ-SAM [10] to propose a versatile foundation model for medical image segmentation, named DrSAM. DrSAM is capable of predicting highly accurate segmentation masks even in exceedingly challenging scenarios without the need for extensive data and computational resources, demonstrating robust zero-shot capabilities and flexible prompt handling. Specifically, we leverage and retain the pre-trained model weights of SAM while introducing minimal additional parameters and computations, thereby enhancing model efficiency. Furthermore, we devised a trainable U-shaped residual network coupled with a Medical Output Token, which effectively captures features at various levels within medical images, thereby further improving the precision of segmentation masks.

To validate the effectiveness of DrSAM, quantitative and qualitative experimental analyses were conducted. The experiments compared SAM, MedSAM, and the proposed DrSAM on three different segmentation datasets. Evaluation results demonstrate that, compared to other foundation models, DrSAM generates higher-quality masks while retaining zero-shot capability.

2 Method

2.1 DrSAM Architecture Design

In order to fully leverage the underlying architecture of the foundation model and its well-trained weights, we made no alterations to the SAM model's structure. And then, we designed the U-shaped structure on top of it to extract and fuse hierarchical encoder features, as depicted in Fig. 1. Shallow features with high frequency play a crucial role in medical image segmentation [15], and accurate segmentation results depend on both the global semantic context of the input image and local boundary details. Within the ViT encoder, we extract features from different stages of the encoder and fuse them into the corresponding scale of the decoder through residual connections, thereby obtaining advanced object semantics and low-level boundary information within the image. DrSAM comprises three main components: the SAM foundation model, the U-shaped fine-tuning fusion structure, and the Med-Output Token.

SAM Foundation Model. The encoder part of DrSAM still employs the pre-trained ViT-B model of SAM, with the image and prompt encoders frozen during training.

DrSAM does not make any adjustments to the image encoder, allowing image embeddings to be pre-computed before the training phase. Therefore, the training process of DrSAM does not require loading the image encoder. This ensures high GPU efficiency for the proposed method.

U-Structure Feature Extraction. Inspired by the U-Net architecture [9], we adopt the classic encoder-decoder structure. Multi-scale features are extracted from the global attention layer of the image encoder to obtain image embeddings. The early layers of the ViT encoder excel at capturing local features that are essential for capturing high-frequency details. Following the global attention block in the ViT encoder (i.e., with a window size of 0), we extract hierarchical features from various stages. Taking ViT-B as an example, we output features from the 2nd, 5th, 8th, and 12th blocks (in total, there are 12 blocks). The original features from these four stages have shapes of 64×64, and as we progress through the stages, they are upsampled successively to 512×512, 256×256, and 128×128. Through shortcut residual connections, these features are concatenated with the corresponding decoder features, and dimensionality reduction is performed using dual convolutions, akin to the upsampling operation in U-Net. It's noteworthy that in the concatenation of the decoder corresponding to stage 2, we include the transposed convolution upsampled features from SAM, aiming to maximize the retention of SAM's original zero-shot capabilities and prevent catastrophic forgetting.

As illustrated in the Fig. 1, the final hierarchical feature, having dimensions of 512×512, is dot product with the Med-Output Token processed through an MLP to obtain the mask results for DrSAM.

Med-Output Token. In SAM's original design, mask prediction is carried out using an output token, which is jointly inputted into the mask decoder along with the prompt, culminating in a dot product with the mask features. As depicted within the red box in the diagram, we introduce a new component called the Med-Output Token (size of 1×256) to enhance and refine SAM's performance on medical images.

The Med-Output Token, in conjunction with the output token and prompt, is fed into the attention module. In each attention layer, the Med-Output Token undergoes self-attention alongside other tokens (token-to-image), and this information is utilized for weight updates. Furthermore, before performing dot product with the U-shaped hierarchical features, we incorporate a new MLP structure to generate dynamic convolutional kernels from the Med-Output Token. This ensures that the model does not overfit to the new dataset, thereby preserving SAM's zero-shot segmentation capability.

2.2 Training of DrSAM

We exclusively train the proposed U-shaped structure, Med-Output Token, and its associated MLP. Unlike SAM, the prompt section employs a hybrid type of prompts. We keep the weights of the SAM section frozen during training. The initial learning rate is set to 0.001, and we utilize the AdamW optimizer [16] with a batch size of 6. The training is conducted for 20 epochs, and fine-tuning can be trained using a single NVIDIA RTX 3090 GPU.

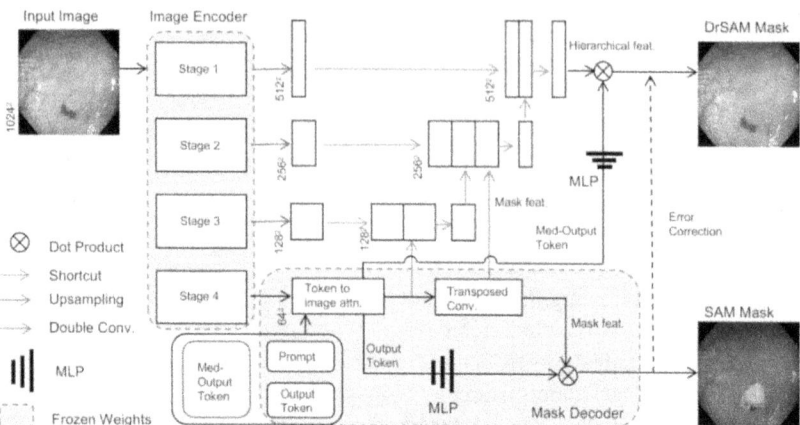

Fig. 1. DrSAM introduces U-structure and Med-Output Token into SAM to achieve high-quality mask prediction more suitable for medical images. In order to maintain the zero-sample capability of SAM, Med-Output Token reuses the mask decoder of SAM, passes through a new MLP layer, and performs dot product with the hierarchical features extracted by U-structure. When training, we fix the model parameters of the pretrained SAM.

For supervising DrSAM's mask predictions, we employ both BCELoss (Binary Cross-Entropy Loss) and Dice Loss, which are two commonly used loss functions in image segmentation tasks. They are typically used in combination to strike a balance between binary classification loss and segmentation accuracy. The formulas are as follows:

$$\text{BCELoss}(y, \hat{y}) = -\frac{1}{N} \sum_{i=1}^{N} [y_i \cdot \log(\hat{y}_i) + (1 - y_i) \cdot \log(1 - \hat{y}_i)] \quad (1)$$

The combined loss function is defined as:

$$\text{Dice Loss}(y, \hat{y}) = 1 - \frac{2 \cdot \sum_{i=1}^{N} y_i \cdot \hat{y}_i}{\sum_{i=1}^{N} y_i^2 + \sum_{i=1}^{N} \hat{y}_i^2} \quad (2)$$

$$\text{Loss}(y, \hat{y}) = \text{BCELoss}(y, \hat{y}) + \text{Dice Loss}(y, \hat{y}) \quad (3)$$

2.3 Inference of DrSAM

DrSAM follows the same inference process as SAM but incorporates mask predictions from the Med-Output Token for medical image mask prediction. During inference, the predicted masks generated by SAM are added to the mask predictions of DrSAM to perform mask correction at a spatial resolution of 512×512. Subsequently, the corrected masks are upsampled to the original resolution of 1024×1024 for output.

2.4 Advantages of DrSAM vs. SAM

The training and inference aspects of SAM and DrSAM are comprehensively compared in Table 1. DrSAM not only yields superior segmentation quality but also demonstrates remarkably fast and cost-effective training, requiring only a single consumer-grade GPU for fine-tuning. Moreover, DrSAM is lightweight and efficient, with negligible increases in model parameters, GPU memory usage, and inference time per image.

2.5 Advantages of DrSAM vs. MedSAM

In comparison to the MedSAM, our DrSAM still exhibits certain advantages in vertical domains. As shown in Table 1, while both MedSAM and DrSAM are compared in terms of training and inference, MedSAM requires substantial computational resources for fine-tuning through extensive medical image data, posing significant challenges for implementation in primary healthcare facilities and educational institutions. Conversely, DrSAM does not necessitate overall fine-tuning of the SAM foundation model; rather, it fine-tunes only the U-shaped multi-scale feature structure. Hence, it boasts lighter training speed and fewer learnable parameters, making it more suitable for deployment in scenarios with limited computational power and data capacity, such as primary healthcare facilities.

3 Experiments

3.1 Datasets

Medical images, as compared with natural images, possess distinct characteristics such as lower quantities and blurry boundaries. To efficiently adapt our model for medical image segmentation, we fine-tuned it on three typical endoscopy, pathology, and corneal vascular datasets: Cell, Chase, and Hyper Kvasir-Seg, which include fine-grained details such as blood vessels and inconspicuous sessile polyps. This significantly enhances the model's robustness in medical image segmentation. We merged the datasets and divided them into a 1/2 training and 1/2 testing split.

Cell Dataset [11]: This dataset originates from the 2018 Data Science Bowl Challenge and is designed for nucleus segmentation in different microscopic images. The challenge in this task lies in handling nucleus segmentation across various environments, including different cell types, magnification levels, and imaging modes. It comprises a total of 670 images. We combined single-cell labeled images to create complete labeled images.

Chase Dataset [12]: This dataset is dedicated to retinal vessel segmentation and includes 28 color retinal images, each of size 999 × 960 pixels, collected from the left and right eyes of 14 children. Every image is annotated by two independent human experts.

Hyper Kvasir-SEG [13]: This dataset consists of 1,000 images, providing both the original images and segmentation masks. In the masks, pixels representing polyp tissue (the region of interest) are indicated by foreground (white mask), while background (black) does not include polyp pixels.

3.2 Performance Comparisons

We compared the baseline foundation segmentation model SAM [5], the improved medical segmentation foundation model MedSAM [30], and our DrSAM. Except for SAM, all these models were trained using the same datasets and training strategies. We evaluated these models on the three datasets using metrics such as mIoU (mean Intersection over Union), mBIoU (mean Background Intersection over Union), and mDice.

As shown in the Table 2, these models, as foundation segmentation models, demonstrate excellent performance in segmenting medical images with clearly defined targets, even SAM without fine-tuning. DrSAM outperforms the other models on all three trained datasets, particularly excelling on the Chase dataset, indicating its superior segmentation capability for narrow objects.

Table 1. Segmentation qualitative performance comparison. *Indicates the performance of the model on the zero-shot dataset.

Method	Learnable Params (M)	GPU	Batch Size	FPS	Mem.
SAM	1191	128	128	5	7.6G
MedSAM	93.8	20	160	5	7.6G
DrSAM(Our)	**33.1**	**1**	**6**	**4.3**	8.2G

Table 2. Segmentation quantitative performance comparison.

Model	Cell			HyperKvasir-SEG			Chase		
	mIoU	mBIoU	mDice	mIoU	mBIoU	mDice	mIoU	mBIoU	mDice
SAM	0.7518	0.7127	0.8571	0.7677	0.5708	0.8686	0.1424	0.1271	0.2493
MedSAM	0.7677	0.7213	0.8686	0.8146	0.6148	0.8807	0.4272	0.421	0.5986
DrSAM	**0.7831**	**0.7709**	**0.8784**	**0.8573**	**0.7105**	**0.9231**	**0.7167**	**0.6911**	**0.7029**

In the qualitative experiments, we observe that while the SAM model is a foundation segmentation model for natural images and can provide good segmentation results for medical images with well-defined cell boundaries without specific training, reaffirming SAM's robust zero-shot capability. However, SAM struggles to accurately segment finer objects (e.g., blood vessels) and objects with blurry boundaries (e.g., sessile polyps) in medical images. After fine-tuning on medical datasets, MedSAM demonstrates improved segmentation performance for fine-grained objects. DrSAM performs well on all three datasets, providing more accurate segmentation for fine-grained objects and object boundaries.

In addition, we also conducted zero-shot experiments on the GlaS [17] and ISIC2018 [18] datasets. As shown in * in Fig. 2, DrSAM also has good zero-shot capabilities, which shows that DrSAM has the capabilities that a foundation model should have. The improvement of the U-shaped structure can enhance the ability to fine-tune the data set and has the potential to generalize to more medical image segmentation tasks.

3.3 Ablation Studies

As shown in the table, we conducted ablation experiments on the Hyper Kvasir-SEG dataset. By adding the trainable Med-Output Token and its corresponding MLP layer, fine-tuning training yields improved results, with mIoU and mDice reaching 0.8161 and 0.8956, respectively. However, it still struggles with the boundaries. The inclusion of the U-shaped structure design results in a relative improvement of 8.2% in mIoU and 3.7% in mDice compared to the baseline. When both components are incorporated, DrSAM achieves the best results (Table 3).

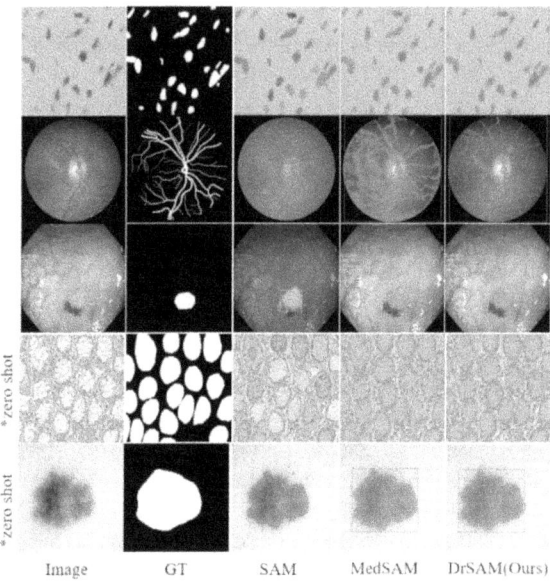

Fig. 2. Segmentation qualitative performance comparison. *Indicates the performance of the model on the zero-shot dataset.

Table 3. DrSAM ablation experiment results on HyperKvasir-SEG dataset.

Component	mIoU	mBIoU	mDice
SAM(baseline)	0.7677	0.5708	0.8686
Add Med-Output Token	0.8161	0.5156	0.8956
Add U-structure	0.8309	0.6158	0.9007
DrSAM(ours)	**0.8573**	**0.7105**	**0.9231**

4 Conclusion

In this paper, we introduce a foundation model, DrSAM, for medical image segmentation that necessitates minimal fine-tuning with only a small amount of data. Our purpose-built U-shaped structure effectively extracts and integrates features across different levels within medical images, while the trainable Med-Output Token refines the mask results. Building upon the foundation of the SAM universal foundation model, we retain its zero-shot capability and foundation segmentation performance. Experimental results demonstrate DrSAM's outstanding versatility in medical segmentation tasks, showcasing substantial potential in the realm of automated medical image segmentation.

Acknowledgements. This work was supported by the National Natural Science Foundation of China under Grant 62162058, and the Tianshan Talent Training Program 2023TSYCLJ0023.

References

1. De Fauw, J., et al.: Clinically applicable deep learning for diagnosis and referral in retinal disease. Nat. Med. **24**(9), 1342–1350 (2018)
2. Ouyang, D., et al.: Video-based AI for beat-to-beat assessment of cardiac function. Nature **580**(7802), 252–256 (2020)
3. Zhao, F., Xie, X.: An overview of interactive medical image segmentation. Ann. BMVA **2013**(7), 1–22 (2013)
4. Huo, X., Sun, G., Tian, S., et al.: HiFuse: hierarchical multi-scale feature fusion network for medical image classification. Biomed. Signal Process. Control **87**, 105534 (2024)
5. Kirillov, A., et al.: Segment Anything (2023). arXiv:2304.02643
6. Zou, X., et al.: Segment Everything Everywhere All at Once (2023). arXiv:2304.06718
7. Mazurowski, M., Dong, H., Gu, H., Yang, J., Konz, N., Zhang, Y.: Segment anything model for medical image analysis: an experimental study. Med. Image Anal. **89**, 102918 (2023)
8. Huang, Y., et al.: Segment Anything Model for Medical Images? (2023). arXiv:2304.14660
9. Ronneberger, O., Fischer, P., Brox, T.: U-net: convolutional networks for biomedical image segmentation. In: Medical Image Computing and Computer-Assisted Intervention – MICCAI 2015: 18th International Conference, Munich, Germany, October 5–9, Proceedings, Part III 18, pp. 234–241 (2015)
10. Ke, L., et al.: Segment Anything in High Quality (2023). arXiv:2306.01567
11. Caicedo, J., et al.: Nucleus segmentation across imaging experiments: the 2018 Data Science Bowl. Nat. Methods **16**(12), 1247–1253 (2019)
12. Fraz, M., et al.: An ensemble classification-based approach applied to retinal blood vessel segmentation. IEEE Trans. Biomed. Eng. **59**(9), 2538–2548 (2012)
13. Borgli, H., et al.: HyperKvasir, a comprehensive multi-class image and video dataset for gastrointestinal endoscopy. Sci. Data **7**(1), 283 (2020)
14. Zhang, C., et al.: A Comprehensive Survey on Segment Anything Model for Vision and Beyond (2023). arXiv:2305.08196
15. Liu, Y., Zhang, S., Chen, J., Yu, Z., Chen, K., Lin, D.: Improving Pixel-Based MIM by Reducing Wasted Modeling Capability (2023). arXiv:2308.00261
16. Loshchilov, I., Hutter, F.: Decoupled weight decay regularization (2017). arXiv:1711.05101
17. Sirinukunwattana, K., et al.: Gland segmentation in colon histology images: The GlaS challenge contest. Med. Image Anal. **35**, 489–502 (2017)

18. Codella, N., et al.: Skin Lesion Analysis Toward Melanoma Detection 2018: A Challenge Hosted by the International Skin Imaging Collaboration (ISIC) (2019). arXiv:1902.03368
19. Huo, X., Tian, S., Yang, Y., Yu, L., Zhang, W., Li, A.: SPA: Self-Peripheral-Attention for central–peripheral interactions in endoscopic image classification and segmentation. Expert Syst. Appl. **245**, 123053 (2024)
20. Wu, J., et al.: Medical SAM Adapter: Adapting Segment Anything Model for Medical Image Segmentation (2023). arXiv:2304.12620
21. Zhang, K., Liu, D.: Customized Segment Anything Model for Medical Image Segmentation (2023). arXiv:2304.13785
22. Chen, T., et al.: SAM fails to segment anything? SAM-Adapter: Adapting SAM in Underperformed Scenes: Camouflage, Shadow, and More (2023). arXiv:2304.09148
23. Chen, C., et al.: Realistic adversarial data augmentation for MR image segmentation. In: MICCAI 2020. LNCS, vol. 12261, pp. 667–677. Springer, Cham (2020). https://doi.org/10.1007/978-3-030-59710-8_65
24. Chen, C., Li, Z., Ouyang, C., Sinclair, M., Bai, W., Rueckert, D.: MaxStyle: adversarial style composition for robust medical image segmentation. In: Wang, L.W., Qi Dou, P., Fletcher, T., Speidel, S., Li, S. (eds.) Medical Image Computing and Computer Assisted Intervention – MICCAI 2022: 25th International Conference, Singapore, September 18–22, 2022, Proceedings, Part V, pp. 151–161. Springer Nature Switzerland, Cham (2022). https://doi.org/10.1007/978-3-031-16443-9_15
25. Chen, J., Bai, X.: Learning to "Segment Anything" in Thermal Infrared Images Through Knowledge Distillation With a Large Scale Dataset SATIR (2023). arXiv:2304.07969
26. Tang, L., Xiao, H., Li, B.: Can SAM Segment Anything? When SAM Meets Camouflaged Object Detection (2023). arXiv:2304.04709
27. Deng, R., et al.: Segment Anything Model (SAM) for Digital Pathology: Assess Zero-Shot Segmentation on Whole Slide Imaging (2023). arXiv:2304.04155
28. Hu, C., Li, X.: When SAM Meets Medical Images: An Investigation of Segment Anything Model (SAM) on Multi-Phase Liver Tumor Segmentation (2023). arXiv:2304.08506
29. Li, Y., Hu, M., Yang, X.: Polyp-SAM: transfer SAM for polyp segmentation. In: Medical Imaging 2024: Computer-Aided Diagnosis, pp. 759–765 (2024)
30. Ma, J., He, Y., Li, F., Han, L., You, C., Wang, B.: Segment anything in medical images. Nat. Commun. **15**(1), 654 (2024)

Aerial Multi-object Tracking via Information Weighting

Pengnian Wu[1], Bangkui Fan[2(✉)], Ruiyu Zhang[3], Yulong Xu[3], and Dong Xue[4(✉)]

[1] School of Software, Northwestern Polytechnical University, Shaanxi, China
[2] Chinese Academy of Engineering, Beijing, China
wpn.ttup@foxmail.com
[3] Intelligent Collaborative Perception and Analytical Cognition Laboratory, Beijing, China
[4] School of Aeronautics, Northwestern Polytechnical University, Shaanxi, China
xuedong@nwpu.edu.cn

Abstract. Multi-object tracking from an aerial perspective often faces typical challenges such as small objects, dual-source motion, and appearance similarity. This often results in low tracking accuracy. In this paper, we propose an Aerial multi-object Tracking method via Information Weighting (ATIW), which comprises four main components: adaptive weighting, distribution feature extraction, prediction box correction, and spatiotemporal feature enhancement. Adaptive weighting involves a dynamic fusion of distribution, motion, and appearance information, tailored to the object's scale and velocity. Distribution feature extraction utilizes the spatial distribution information of objects and their neighbors to facilitate identity association. The purpose of prediction box correction is to mitigate the negative impact of camera rotation on IoU matching. Spatiotemporal feature enhancement aims to fuse corresponding features based on the object's feature similarity in adjacent frames and the object's unique feature differences. The experimental results from the UAVDT dataset demonstrate that the proposed method can effectively improve the performance of aerial multi-object tracking. In particular, the IDF1 metric is improved by 0.5% without retraining the model.

Keywords: Multi-object tracking · Information weighting · Aerial perspective

1 Introduction

Recently, owing to the booming development of the unmanned aerial vehicle (UAV) industry, multi-object tracking technology from an aerial perspective has been gradually gaining widespread use [1]. Compared with the objects captured by common surveillance cameras, those viewed from an aerial perspective are generally small, low-resolution, and feature similar characteristics [2]. Moreover, the motion trajectory of an object in the video is influenced not only by the object itself but also by the motion of the UAV [3]. One of the most representative aerial multi-object tracking datasets is the UAVDT [3]. Existing multi-object tracking methods primarily utilize three types of information: spatial distribution [4], motion [5], and appearance features [6]. In terms of information extraction, ATIW enhances the method of extracting spatial distribution features as outlined in [4]. Additionally, ATIW refines the predicted object bounding box using Kalman filtering [7] and achieves feature enhancement through the method outlined in [8]. Although models based on single-dimensional information can effectively track objects in standard scenarios, their tracking capabilities significantly diminish in complex or dynamic environments. Tracking methods such as those in [5, 9] combine object appearance and motion information. The approach of combining object appearance with distribution information is utilized for tracking in [4, 10].

Fig. 1. Motivation Behind Our ATIW. Images numbered 1 to 4 were captured by a drone during its counterclockwise rotation. The magnified section in the center illustrates the overlapping regions among the four images. These images reveal that the target appears diminutive from the drone's perspective, offering very limited pixel information. Furthermore, while a significant number of targets exhibit similar appearances, their spatial distribution is relatively consistent in the short term. The non-linear nature of the target movement within the frame stems from the drone's own motion.

As shown in Fig. 1, the primary motivation of this research is to optimize the single-dimensional feature extraction method, focusing on the distribution, motion, and appearance characteristics of objects from an aerial perspective. Additionally, from the perspective of multi-level information fusion, this approach comprehensively utilizes the information of numerous objects through dynamic weighting to enhance the accuracy of object tracking. A series of experiments were conducted on the UAVDT dataset [3], demonstrating the efficacy of the proposed ATIW algorithm in enhancing aerial multi-object tracking. The main contributions of this paper are composed of the following four parts:

- Considering the scale and velocity characteristics of the object, we have designed an adaptive weighted fusion scheme that integrates distribution, motion, and appearance information to enhance the tracker.
- To address the challenge posed by small objects with limited information, we have incorporated the object's size and the number of neighbors into the existing distributed feature extraction method.

- To tackle the issue of object identity association failures due to UAV rotation, we propose an object prediction box correction method relying on an enhanced correlation coefficient.
- To address the challenge of similar appearance features, we have further improved the differentiation of appearance features between objects by utilizing the spatio-temporal context information of each object.

2 Introduction

The overall framework of the ATIW is depicted in Fig. 2. The main steps of the ATIW tracker are outlined in Algorithm 1. First, during the pre-processing stage (steps 2 to 8), parameters corresponding to the three types of object features are calculated. Subsequently, in the cost acquisition stage (steps 9 to 11), the identity matching cost for each of the three object feature types is calculated based on the previously determined parameters, culminating in the derivation of a comprehensive cost through adaptive weighting. Finally, during the identity matching stage (steps 12 to 14), the initial matching is conducted using the comprehensive cost, followed by a secondary matching based on the motion cost.

Algorithm 1: The Main Steps of ATIW Tracker

Input: An UAV video sequences $\{I_t\}_{t=1}^{T}$

Output: The tracked bounding box of objects B_t

1 while $t < T$ do
2   Input two adjacent images: I_t, I_{t+1}
3   Calculate the warp matrix according to (13)
4   Correct the prediction box obtained by Kalman filtering according to (14), (15)
5   Calculate the feature enhancement coefficient according to (24), (25)
6   Enhance the appearance feature according to (26)
7   Obtain the distribution feature matrix by R_t according to (8), (9)
8   Update the radius according to (10)
9   Obtain three types of cost matrices according to (19), (23), (27) and (12)
10   Obtain the velocity and size weight matrix according to (3), (6)
11   Adaptive weighting according to (7)
12   Synthesis matching: $matches_1 = Hungarian(C_{Total})$
13   Motion matching for the unmatched tracks and detections:
      $matches_2 = Hungarian(C_{IOU'})$
14   Obtain the tracked bounding box or initialize a new one
15 Return

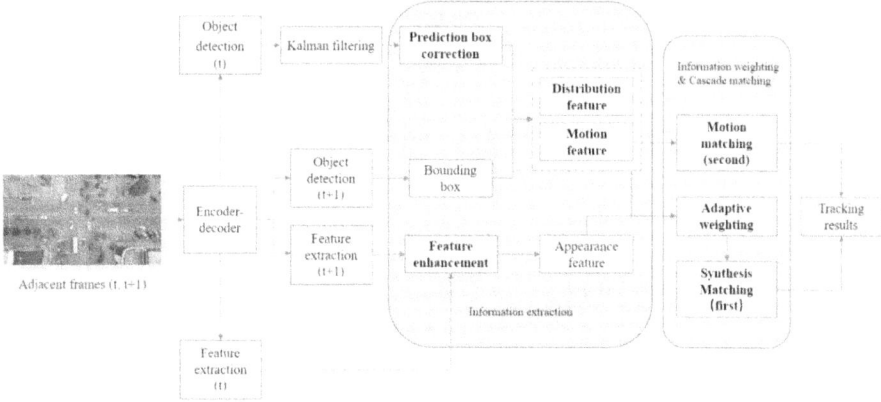

Fig. 2. The framework of our proposed ATIW tracker. The parts marked in bold are our key modules. The ATIW algorithm concentrates on post-processing for tracking by enhancing the model's ability to extract features of three types: distribution, motion, and appearance. It enhances the information fusion and cascade matching mechanism to comprehensively improve the tracking performance of small targets, particularly from the perspective of aerial imagery.

2.1 Adaptive Weighting

Existing methods, including [8, 11], combine object appearance and motion information for multi-object tracking but typically employ a fixed weighting approach. However, the size and velocity of objects vary across different scenes, times, and categories. As demonstrated in formulas (1)–(7), x_i and y_i denote the horizontal and vertical coordinates of the tracking box's center point, respectively. w_j and h_j represent the width and height of the new detection box, respectively. And the values of the parameters α, β, δ, μ are 2.118426, 1.1566297e−06, 0.22828, 0.089536, respectively. W and H denote the width and height of the image containing the newly detected object, respectively. When the object scale is small, resulting in sparse appearance features, the corresponding weight for these features should be reduced, while increasing the weights for the other two types of information. Conversely, when the object's velocity is low, resulting in consistent distribution information in adjacent frames, an increase in the corresponding weight for this information is warranted, while the weight for motion information should be correspondingly reduced.

$$v_i = \sqrt{(x_i - x'_i)^2 + (y_i - y'_i)^2} \tag{1}$$

$$\omega_{ij}^v = e^{-v_i} \tag{2}$$

$$\Omega^v = \begin{pmatrix} \omega_{11}^v & \cdots & \omega_{m1}^v \\ \vdots & \ddots & \vdots \\ \omega_{1n}^v & \cdots & \omega_{mn}^v \end{pmatrix} \tag{3}$$

$$s_j = \sqrt{\frac{w_j \cdot h_j}{W \cdot H}} \tag{4}$$

$$\omega_{ij}^s = \frac{\alpha}{1+\left(\frac{s_j}{\beta}\right)^\delta} - \mu \tag{5}$$

$$\Omega^s = \begin{pmatrix} \omega_{11}^s & \cdots & \omega_{1n}^s \\ \vdots & \ddots & \vdots \\ \omega_{m1}^s & \cdots & \omega_{mn}^s \end{pmatrix} \tag{6}$$

$$C_{Total} = \frac{C_{Feature}+C_{GIOU'}}{2}g(1-\Omega^s)+C_{Distribution}g\Omega^s g\Omega^{v\text{確}}+C_{GIOU'}g\Omega^s g(1-\Omega^v) \tag{7}$$

2.2 Distribution Feature Extraction

The method in [4] neglects the information of other neighbors around the object and the object's own scale information. Furthermore, when the farthest neighbor exceeds the detection range or the nearest neighbor is occluded, applying this method for object identity association may result in significant errors. Therefore, we introduce a method that calculates the distances between the object and its three nearest neighbors, as well as the minimum angle information using the object as a vertex. This method also incorporates the object's scale information and the count of remaining neighbors to construct a unique distribution information vector, thereby enhancing the accuracy of object identity association. Additionally, in identifying neighboring objects, the fixed radius is replaced with a dynamic radius that adjusts automatically based on the number of surrounding neighbors. However, it is crucial that this radius remains consistent when calculating the object's distribution information vector across adjacent frames. The methodology for constructing the object distribution feature vector and the dynamic radius update process are detailed in Formulas (8)–(11). Upon acquiring the object distribution feature vectors for both the previous and current frames, the cosine distance is calculated as per Formula (12) to derive the corresponding distribution cost matrix.

$$d_t' = \left(l_{\min}^t, l_{s\min}^t, l_{t\min}^t, \theta_1^t, \theta_2^t, \theta_3^t, s^t, q^t\right) \tag{8}$$

$$d_{t+1} = \left(l_{\min}^{t+1}, l_{s\min}^{t+1}, l_{t\min}^{t+1}, \theta_1^{t+1}, \theta_2^{t+1}, \theta_3^{t+1}, s^{t+1}, q^{t+1}\right) \tag{9}$$

$$R_{t+1} = \lambda R_t \tag{10}$$

$$\lambda = \begin{cases} \lambda_1 = 0.8, \hat{q}_t > 5 \\ \lambda_2 = 1.2, \hat{q}_t \le 5 \end{cases} \tag{11}$$

$$C_{Distribution} = 1 - \cos\left(D'_{track_t}, D_{det_{t+1}}\right) \tag{12}$$

2.3 Prediction Box Correction

Traditional tracking methods based on the Kalman filter are ineffective in addressing the substantial deviation between the prediction box and the new detection box, a deviation caused by the sudden self-rotation of the UAV in aviation scenarios. Consequently, drawing inspiration from [12, 13], we propose utilizing the enhanced correlation coefficient [14] to adjust the prediction box, thereby minimizing its deviation from the new detection box. The detailed procedure for prediction box correction is delineated in Formulas (13)–(15). First, the coordinates of the other two vertices are calculated based on the top-left and bottom-right vertices of the prediction box. Subsequently, these coordinates, along with those of the initial vertices, are multiplied by the rotation parameters to derive the modified coordinates for all four vertices. Following this, the coordinates for the four vertices of the new prediction box are computed based on the adjusted vertex coordinates. The top-left and bottom-right coordinates of this new box are then determined, culminating in the completion of the prediction box correction. Subsequently, as delineated in Formulas (16)–(22), the GIOU and IOU costs between the corrected prediction box and the new detection box are calculated and then compared to their respective costs prior to correction. In $GIOU'$, post-correction information predominates, whereas in IOU', pre-correction information is more prominent. Ultimately, the motion cost matrix is derived based on Formulas (19) and (23).

$$M_{wrap} = ECC(I_t, I_{t+1}) \tag{13}$$

$$b_w = M_{wrap} \cdot b'_{track_t} \tag{14}$$

$$b''_{tract_t} = \left[\min_y(b_w), \min_x(b_w), \max_y(b_w), \max_x(b_w)\right] \tag{15}$$

$$GIOU_1 = GIOU\left(b'_{track_t}, b_{det_{t+1}}\right) \tag{16}$$

$$GIOU_2 = GIOU\left(b''_{tract_t}, b_{det_{t+1}}\right) \tag{17}$$

$$GIOU'\left(b'_{track_t}, b_{det_{t+1}}\right) = \max(GIOU_1, GIOU_2) \tag{18}$$

$$C_{GIOU'} = 1 - GIOU'\left(B'_{track_t}, B_{det_{t+1}}\right) \tag{19}$$

$$IOU_1 = IOU\left(b'_{track_t}, b_{det_{t+1}}\right) \tag{20}$$

$$IOU_2 = IOU\left(b''_{tract_t}, b_{det_{t+1}}\right) \tag{21}$$

$$IOU'\left(b'_{track_t}, b_{det_{t+1}}\right) = \min(IOU_1, IOU_2) \tag{22}$$

$$C_{IOU'} = 1 - IOU'\left(B'_{track_t}, B_{det_{t+1}}\right) \tag{23}$$

2.4 Spatial-Temporal Feature Enhancement

The image-based ReID method in [8] fails to fully exploit the spatio-temporal distribution characteristics of object appearance information for feature enhancement, thereby limiting improvements in feature similarity for identical objects. Given that prominent object features are crucial for differentiating between objects, we draw on the concept of utilizing spatio-temporal information for feature enhancement from [15]. Consequently, we propose spatio-temporal feature enhancement coefficients, which are derived from object feature similarity in adjacent frames and the object's intrinsic feature variance. Formula (24) illustrates the calculation method for the spatial feature enhancement coefficient, where f^a represents the a-dimensional feature of a specific object post-feature extraction. Formula (25) delineates the calculation method for the time series feature enhancement coefficient, with F_t denoting the feature vector of the specified object in frame t. Salient areas within the object's features are identified through computation, after which these features are amalgamated with their respective weights and superimposed onto the original features, thereby completing the enhancement process. Formula (26) depicts the process of executing feature fusion using the spatio-temporal feature enhancement coefficient, and the appearance cost matrix is finally constructed by Formula (27).

$$\Omega^{f_{spatial}} = \frac{\left(\sum_{a=1}^{A}(f^1-f^a)^2 \ldots \sum_{a=1}^{A}(f^A-f^a)^2\right)}{\max\left(\left(\sum_{a=1}^{A}(f^1-f^a)^2 \ldots \sum_{a=1}^{A}(f^A-f^a)^2\right)\right)} \quad (24)$$

$$\Omega^{f_{temporal}} = \frac{(F_{t+1}-F_t)\cdot(F_{t+1}-F_t)}{\max((F_{t+1}-F_t)\cdot(F_{t+1}-F_t))} \quad (25)$$

$$f'_{t+1} = \left(1-\Omega^{f_{temporal}}\right)\cdot f'_t + \Omega^{f_{temporal}}\cdot\left(f_{t+1}\cdot\left(1+\Omega^{f_{spatial}}\right)\right) \quad (26)$$

$$C_{Feature} = 1 - \cos\left(F'_{track_t}, F_{det_{t+1}}\right) \quad (27)$$

3 Experimental Setup and Results

The UAVDT dataset [3] was selected for model training and testing, with all objects being cars. Performance evaluation indicators were adopted from [17, 18]. The experimental framework is based on FairMOT [8], ensuring consistency in experimental details. The DLA34, pre-trained on the COCO dataset, was utilized as the backbone network, with the number of epochs set to 30. The training and testing platform was configured with a Gold 5218 CPU@2.10GHz × 80 and 2 × (RTX 3090 24G) GPUs.

Table 1 presents the comparison results. The AW module's comprehensive utilization of motion, appearance, and distribution information significantly improves tracking consistency and enhances the IDF1 indicator, as observed in the results. Further, the DFE module enhances the IDF1 metric using target distribution information, and the PBC module improves the model's overall tracking performance by correcting predicted boxes. Additionally, the STFE module, leveraging the capabilities of the preceding modules, employs strengthened features for target identity matching, thereby improving certain non-key tracking metrics. The DFE, PBC, and STFE modules each enhance the model's capacity to extract the three types of information, collectively optimizing tracking performance.

The essence of the proposed algorithm is to enhance target tracking consistency, evidenced by excellent performance in metrics like IDF1 and IDSW, while showing moderate results in the MOTA metric. Hence, Table 2 is dedicated to the comparative analysis of the IDF1 and IDSW metrics. While the new method does not achieve state-of-the-art results in FP and FN metrics, it exhibits improvements over baseline algorithms. In the area marked by a red arrow in Fig. 3, it is evident that in FairMOT's [8] tracking process, there are multiple identity switches in a short period, whereas ATIW maintains consistent object identity throughout. The analysis demonstrates that our proposed method effectively enhances multi-target tracking from an aerial perspective.

Table 1. Ablation study on UAVDT test dataset. Values in bold highlight the best results. The data in the table shows that with the stacking of various modules, the overall tracking performance of the model steadily improves.

Method	IDF1↑	MOTA↑	IDP↑	IDR↑	IDs↓	FP↓	FN↓	FM↓
Baseline	59.1	36.3	71.0	50.7	453	59543	157174	5128
+1	59.4	36.3	71.3	51.0	322	59660	157033	5113
+12	59.6	36.3	71.5	**51.1**	316	59689	**157014**	5130
+123	59.6	36.4	71.5	51.0	321	59487	157099	5103
+1234	**59.6**	**36.4**	**71.5**	51.0	323	**59477**	157107	**5100**

Table 2. Results of different trackers on UAVDT benchmarks. Values in bold highlight the best results. The information of the ignored region is not used. Our method performs well on multiple indicators that reflect tracking performance.

Method	IDF1↑	IDs↓	FP↓	FN↓	FM↓
[16]	23.7	9938	42245	163881	10463
[5]	43.7	2350	**33037**	172628	5787
[5]	58.2	2061	44868	**155290**	6432
[8]	59.1	453	59543	157174	5128
Ours	**59.6**	323	59477	157107	**5100**

Fig. 3. The comparison of tracking performance between FairMOT and ATIW on the UAVDT test dataset. ATIW is still able to continuously track the target during the UAV maneuvering process without undergoing identity switching.

4 Conclusion

This study introduces a novel aerial multi-object tracking algorithm, ATIW, encompassing adaptive weighting, distribution feature extraction, prediction box correction, and spatio-temporal feature enhancement. Experimental results demonstrate that the ATIW algorithm fully leverages the distribution, motion, and appearance information of objects, thereby significantly enhancing aerial multi-object tracking performance. In particular, the IDF1 metric is improved by 0.5% without retraining the model. Future work will concentrate on consistently optimizing the fusion of object distribution, motion, and appearance information, aiming to substantially improve the operational efficiency and robustness of the algorithm on actual UAV platforms.

References

1. Xu, X., et al.: Stn-track: Multiobject tracking of unmanned aerial vehicles by swin transformer neck and new data association method. IEEE Journal of Selected Topics in Applied Earth Observations and Remote Sensing **15**, 8734–8743 (2022)
2. Zhu, P., et al.: Detection and tracking meet drones challenge. IEEE Trans. Pattern Anal. Mach. Intell. **44**(11), 7380–7399 (2021)
3. Du, D., Qi, Y., Yu, H., Yang, Y., Duan, K., Li, G., Zhang, W., Huang, Q., Tian, Q.: The unmanned aerial vehicle benchmark: Object detection and tracking. In: Proceedings of the European conference on computer vision (ECCV). pp. 370–386 (2018)
4. Liu, S., Li, X., Lu, H., He, Y.: Multi-object tracking meets moving uav. In: Proceedings of the IEEE/CVF Conference on Computer Vision and Pattern Recognition. pp. 8876–8885 (2022)
5. Wojke, N., Bewley, A., Paulus, D.: Simple online and realtime tracking with a deep association metric. In: 2017 IEEE international conference on image processing (ICIP). pp. 3645–3649. IEEE (2017)
6. Meinhardt, T., Kirillov, A., Leal-Taixe, L., Feichtenhofer, C.: Trackformer: Multi-object tracking with transformers. In: Proceedings of the IEEE/CVF conference on computer vision and pattern recognition. pp. 8844–8854 (2022)
7. Welch, G., Bishop, G., et al.: An introduction to the kalman filter (1995)
8. Zhang, Y., Wang, C., Wang, X., Zeng, W., Liu, W.: Fairmot: On the fairness of detection and re-identification in multiple object tracking. Int. J. Comput. Vision **129**, 3069–3087 (2021)

9. Yin, J., Wang, W., Meng, Q., Yang, R., Shen, J.: A unified object motion and affinity model for online multi-object tracking. In: Proceedings of the IEEE/CVF Conference on Computer Vision and Pattern Recognition. pp. 6768–6777 (2020)
10. Liang, T., Lan, L., Zhang, X., Peng, X., Luo, Z.: Enhancing the association in multi-object tracking via neighbor graph. Int. J. Intell. Syst. **36**(11), 6713–6730 (2021)
11. Zhang, Y., Sun, P., Jiang, Y., Yu, D., Weng, F., Yuan, Z., Luo, P., Liu, W., Wang, X.: Bytetrack: Multi-object tracking by associating every detection box. In: Computer Vision–ECCV 2022: 17th European Conference, Tel Aviv, Israel, October 23–27, 2022, Proceedings, Part XXII. pp. 1–21. Springer (2022)
12. Yu, H., Li, G., Su, L., Zhong, B., Yao, H., Huang, Q.: Conditional gan based individual and global motion fusion for multiple object tracking in uav videos. Pattern Recogn. Lett. **131**, 219–226 (2020)
13. Yang, J., Ge, H., Su, S., Liu, G.: Transformer-based two-source motion model for multi-object tracking. Applied Intelligence pp. 1–13 (2022)
14. Evangelidis, G.D., Psarakis, E.Z.: Parametric image alignment using enhanced correlation coefficient maximization. IEEE Trans. Pattern Anal. Mach. Intell. **30**(10), 1858–1865 (2008)
15. Fu, Y., Wang, X., Wei, Y., Huang, T.: Sta: Spatial-temporal attention for large scale video-based person re-identification. In: Proceedings of the AAAI conference on artificial intelligence. vol. 33, pp. 8287–8294 (2019)
16. Bochinski, E., Eiselein, V., Sikora, T.: High-speed tracking-by-detection without using image information. In: 2017 14th IEEE international conference on advanced video and signal based surveillance (AVSS). pp. 1–6. IEEE (2017)
17. Milan, A., Leal-Taixé, L., Reid, I., Roth, S., Schindler, K.: Mot16: A benchmark for multi-object tracking. arXiv preprint arXiv:1603.00831 (2016)
18. Ristani, E., Solera, F., Zou, R., Cucchiara, R., Tomasi, C.: Performance measures and a data set for multi-target, multi-camera tracking. In: Computer Vision–ECCV 2016 Workshops: Amsterdam, The Netherlands, October 8–10 and 15–16, 2016, Proceedings, Part II. pp. 17–35. Springer (2016)

Optimization Method for Fractal Image Compression Based on Self-similarity Evaluation and Gradient Bisection Algorithm

Caixu Xu[1], Di Xie[1], Hui Guo[1,2(✉)], Jie He[1,3], and Minglang Chen[1]

[1] Guangxi Key Laboratory of Machine Vision and Intelligent Control, Wuzhou University, Wuzhou 543000, Guangxi, China
3220002921@student.must.edu.mo
[2] Macao University of Science and Technology, Macao 999078, China
[3] College of Computer Science and Electronic Engineering, Hunan University, Changsha 410000, Hunan, China

Abstract. Fractal Image Compression (FIC) is a spatial domain compression technique with high compression ratio and good image quality. It is widely used in the fields of image restoration, denoising and watermarking. However, in terms of coding time, traditional fractal coding takes a certain amount of time for coding due to its need to find the best matching block traversal for sub-blocks. The long coding time is one of the main problems of fractal coding to be solved, which has a certain impact on the efficiency of fractal coding in practical applications. Meanwhile, since fractal coding itself is the application of self-similarity of images, the self-similarity of different categories of images also has a certain impact on the coding effect. To address the above problems, we first designed an algorithm based on SSIM to evaluate the overall self-similarity of images. Secondly, by analyzing the distribution of low-frequency coefficients of the image, we realize the dynamic classification of the sub-blocks to be coded based on the discrete cosine transform (DCT). And an adaptive threshold adjustment mechanism based on gradient bisection is proposed. Through comparative experiments, our optimization method significantly reduced encoding time (i.e., 96.12%) with only a 0.01 dB decrease in PSNR compared to the original FIC. The proposed scheme in this paper increases the usability of fractal coding, and provides a certain reference value for the subsequent fractal coding optimization research.

Keywords: FIC · Self-similarity evaluation · DCT · Dynamic codebook classification

1 Introduction

Fractal image compression method (FIC) [1] uses the self-similarity of the image to remove redundant information, and uses the iterative function system to reconstruct the image. It has the characteristics of high compression ratio, fast decoding speed, and decoding is independent of image resolution. It has been applied to media software such as Microsoft Encarta multimedia encyclopedia and Genuine Fractals plug-in of Photoshop. As a powerful spatial domain compression encoding method, the algorithm principles of FIC are also widely applied in image restoration, image denoising, digital watermarking, and face recognition fields [2–7]. The encoding process of FIC can be understood as a statistical process of similar regions in the image, thus, there is a drawback of long encoding time. Reducing the search range in the coding and matching process is an effective measure to shorten the coding time. Since the low-frequency coefficients after DCT transformation can effectively reflect the energy distribution characteristics of the image, many scholars classify the FIC codebooks based on this and have achieved good optimization results. However, such methods often rely on manually determined classification thresholds, which can impact both the coding efficiency and decoding quality, indicating that there is still room for improvement. Moreover, the effect of FIC essentially depends on the degree of self-similarity of the image, and images with poor structural similarity often exhibit block artifacts during decoding. Therefore, the evaluation of image self-similarity should be studied as a preliminary step in FIC research, enabling individuals to choose the application fields of FIC more accurately. To address these issues, we have refactored the application process of FIC. First, we calculate the self-similarity of the image and then use the calculation results to determine the FIC method to be used. By conducting experiments on two types of datasets, the average coding time of traditional fractal coding is greater than 96 s, while the average coding time of our proposed fractal coding optimization algorithm is only 48.34 s. Our main contributions include (Fig. 1).

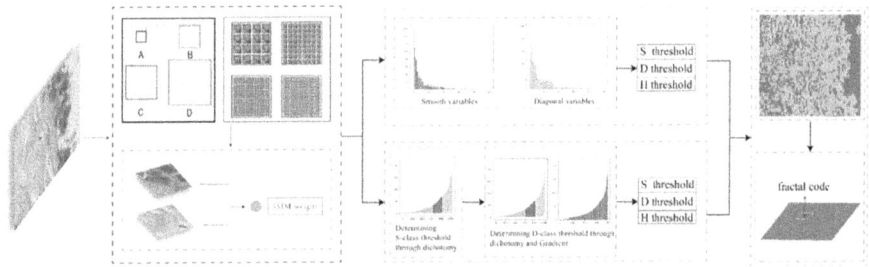

Fig. 1. Overview of the proposed FIC optimization method.

- Introducing the SSIM method to evaluate the self-similarity degree of a single image. We divide the image into various sub-blocks of different scales to cover a wide range of self-similar structures and use SSIM comparison to obtain the similarity relationship between sub-blocks. We also adjust the sub-blocks using downsampling to achieve cross-scale structural similarity comparison of sub-blocks with different sizes.
- Based on the distribution of low-frequency coefficients of multi-class images within the image, we have improved the codebook classification criteria based on DCT low-frequency coefficients to align the codebook clustering with the energy distribution of the image. Furthermore, we have proposed a new coefficient gradient method based on the bisection method on the sorting curve of the low-frequency coefficients. This

method enables the adaptive selection of the classification threshold, resulting in more accurate codebook clustering.
- We improved FIC using the above method and experimentally verified it on random regular images and various microscopic images. Theoretical proof was provided that microscopic images exhibit stronger self-similarity, aligning with human visual perception. Our method significantly enhances coding efficiency while maintaining decoding quality.

2 Related Work

2.1 Evaluation of Image Self-similarity

The degree of self-similarity in an image directly affects the effectiveness of fractal encoding, but there is currently no standard method for evaluating the self-similarity degree of an image. In fact, there have been some mature studies on assessing the similarity between images. Ref. [8] optimize the method for solving the image super-resolution problem using SSIM. The reference [9] optimized the PSNR evaluation method using weighted blur. The above methods are effective for measuring the similarity between images but are unable to directly assess the self-similarity within a single image. In recent years, scholars have quantified some structural properties within a single image using fractal dimension. In reference [10], the analysis of environmental detection images is conducted using fractal dimension. Literature [11] studies the application of fractal dimension in the initialization of recurrent neural networks. Fractal dimension is more suitable for measuring the complexity within an image, with limited effectiveness in expressing the self-similarity of the image. There is still some difference between the degree of self-similarity observed in the human visual system and the fractal dimension. To address this issue, Mu et al. [12] proposed a contrast sub-block selection scheme for the case where the self-similar region has its neighborhood to quantify the self-similarity property of the image. Yuan et al. [13] proposed a self-similarity quantization method for selecting sub-blocks with two-scale comparison. However, literature [12] did not consider the potential self-similarity structure at different scales in different regions, and literature [13] only divided the potential similarity structure into two scales, causing some degree of loss in capturing similarity structures across multiple scales. Therefore, we regard each fractal coding sub-block of a single image as an image, introduce and improve the similarity comparison method between images, and evaluate the self-similarity by combining the structure and brightness of the image in both multi-scale and global aspects.

2.2 DCT-Based Fractal Coding

The internal properties or laws of the image are particularly important for FIC coding rate and decoding quality. The method of neural networks has been widely used in video image compression optimization in recent years [14–16]. In recent years, some scholars have also applied neural network methods to improve fractal coding [17–19]. However, due to the dependence of fractal compression on the self-similarity characteristics of each image, the optimization effect of combining neural networks is relatively limited, and its versatility is poor. In the proposal of local feature-based shape models by [17], it is also mentioned that the annotation process remains a major challenge when neural networks are applied to fractal encoding. Due to the dependence of neural network on image annotation, and different images have different self-similar structures, it is difficult to have a unified and clear target annotation, which leads to its poor performance in fractal coding. DCT transform can better reflect the internal properties of the image, and many scholars have conducted extensive research on the fractal coding optimization scheme based on DCT transform. Among them, Duh et al. proposed a method of classifying the codebook by tripartition according to the low frequency coefficients of the image [20], which can effectively reduce the coding time. However, due to its equal division method for sub-blocks, it may lead to the loss of the optimal matching block in different images due to the different internal properties of the image, so there is still some room for optimization. Rawat et al. also proposed a method combining DCT with fractal encoding [21]. This method compresses color images using DCT to optimize the encoding quality issues caused by blocky artifacts. However, due to the fixed nature of its classification division, it may affect the optimal selection of similar sub-block regions for fractal encoding. Therefore, we choose to optimize the classification method and inter-class threshold dynamic selection based on the [20], aiming to strike a balance between time consumption and decoding quality.

3 Method

3.1 Self-similarity Evaluation Algorithm Based on SSIM

Most natural images exhibit a certain degree of self-similarity in their structure, implying that similar structures may exist at different or the same scales, in close proximity or at a distance. In microscopic images, this property is particularly obvious. As shown in Fig. 2, there may be a large number of cells and microorganisms with the same structure in the same biological microscopic image, which can be directly observed by the human eye.

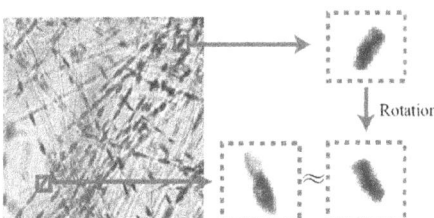

Fig. 2. The self similar structure appearing in bird feather tissue.

Calculating the self-similarity index of an image is the mainstream method for theoretically evaluating the degree of self-similarity. When the original image is segmented into several sub-blocks, each sub-block can be treated as a small-scale image. Therefore, we use SSIM for similarity calculation between sub-blocks, and standardize the scale of sub-blocks through downsampling during the comparison process to capture structural similarities at different scales across regions. Our method operates as shown in Fig. 3, where the image is first divided into a collection of sub-blocks of four different sizes. Define a minimum size block set and create a base block diagram set. Finally, take the coefficients of all the base blocks, and calculate the weighted average based on their global importance proportions to obtain the final self-similarity evaluation coefficient. The SSIM algorithm is as follows:

$$\text{SSIM}(x, y) = l(x, y)^\alpha * c(x, y)^\beta * s(x, y)^\gamma \tag{1}$$

where x and y are two image blocks of the same size. l, c, and s correspond to brightness comparison functions, contrast comparison functions, and structure comparison functions, where α, β, and γ are their weights respectively, all set to l by default in this paper. We calculate the weight of different base blocks by the variance of the gray values of the sub-blocks, and the weight represents the structural complexity ratio of the graph structure in the base block in all the base blocks. The calculation method is as follows:

$$W_n = \frac{V_n - V_{min}}{V_{max} - V_{min}}. \tag{2}$$

V_{max} is the maximum variance, V_{min} is the minimum variance, and V_n is the variance of the NTH basis block. After weighting the basis block in the weight of the image itself, the final self-similarity evaluation coefficient of the image is obtained by accumulating the coefficients of all basis blocks. We refer to this method as self-similarity evaluation based on Cross-scale SSIM (SECS) method, and the specific algorithm as Algorithm 1.

Algorithm 1 Image self-similarity evaluation coefficient algorithm.

Input: Image = [[11, 12,..., 1N], ..., [N1, N2, N3, ..., NN]], B_1 = Subblock set 1, B_2 = Subblock set 2, B_3 = Subblock set 3, B_4 = Subblock set 4.
Output: Self-similarity evaluation coefficient R.
1: for $b = B_{1,...,}2,1$ do
2: Perform SSIM calculations on b separately with B_1, B_2, B_3, and B_4.
3: Calculate the weighting coefficients of each base block.
4: Calculate the top 8 maximum coefficients in each set.
5: C_b = The product of the weighted coefficients of block b and the ssim coefficients.
6: end for
7: for b=$B_{1,...,}$ 2,1 do
8: R = R+ C_b.
9: if b == 1 then
10:   R = mean(R).
11:   return Self-similarity evaluation coefficient R.
12: end if
13: end for

3.2 Codebook Classification Based on Low-Frequency Coefficient Statistics

The energy of the image is mainly concentrated in the low-frequency region. By comparing the low-frequency coefficients of sub-blocks, it is possible to determine whether they

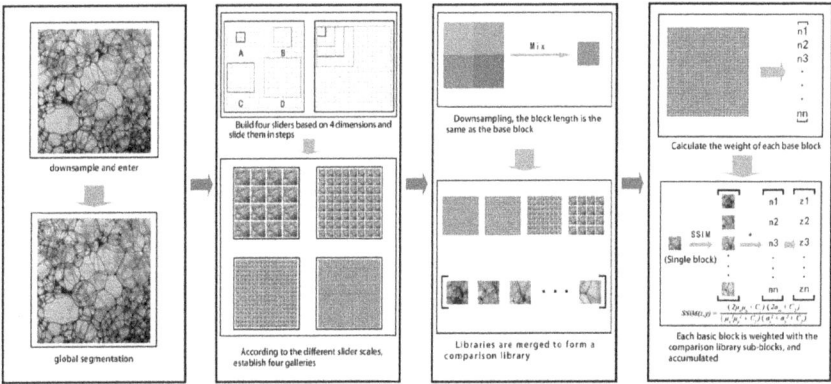

Fig. 3. Self-similarity Evaluation Method Process.

have similar texture distribution characteristics. The Discrete Cosine Transform (DCT) [22], with its excellent performance in aggregating frequency domain energy, has played a significant role in the field of digital image processing. After the image block undergoes DCT transformation, its low-frequency component mainly concentrates in the top-left coefficients of the transformed matrix, which can roughly reflect the energy distribution of the image block. Duh et al. [20] utilized this characteristic of DCT transformation to classify codebooks from the perspective of energy distribution, narrowing down the matching range between R blocks and D blocks. This not only shortens the encoding time but also ensures good decoding quality. Although this method has a clear classification strategy, it does not propose a calculation scheme for the classification threshold. Instead, it directly adopts a trisection method, which inevitably leads to inaccurate classification of some code blocks, affecting the quality of image reconstruction.

$$F(m, n) = \frac{2}{N} C_m C_n \sum_{i=0}^{N-1} \sum_{i=0}^{N-1} f(i, j) \cos\left(\frac{(2i + 1)m\pi}{2N}\right) \times \cos\left(\frac{(2j + 1)m\pi}{2N}\right). \quad (3)$$

In fact, since each image is different, inter-class thresholds should not be fixed and should be able to dynamically adapt to the texture distribution of each image. Therefore, based on the literature [20], we propose a statistical-based threshold dynamic adjustment method. Firstly, the image sub-block is transformed by DCT according to Eq. (3), and Fig. 4 is the low frequency coefficient matrix after transformation, where $F(0, 1)$ reflects the change of energy concentration in the vertical direction, and $F(1, 0)$ reflects the change of energy concentration in the horizontal direction. Therefore, according to $F(0, 1)$ and $F(1, 0)$ divides the image sub-blocks into three categories: smooth, diagonal/sub-diagonal, and horizontal/vertical.

Where N is the length of the image edge. $m, n = 0, 1, 2 \ldots, N - 1, C_k = \begin{cases} \frac{1}{\sqrt{2}}, & \text{if } k = 0 \\ 1, & \text{else} \end{cases}$.

When both $F(0, 1)$ and $F(1, 0)$ are smaller than the smooth threshold T_s, it indicates that the energy concentration changes in both the vertical and horizontal directions of

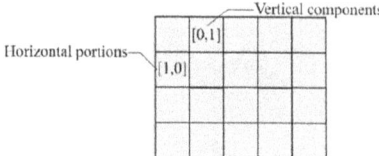

Fig. 4. Horizontal component and vertical component after DCT transformation.

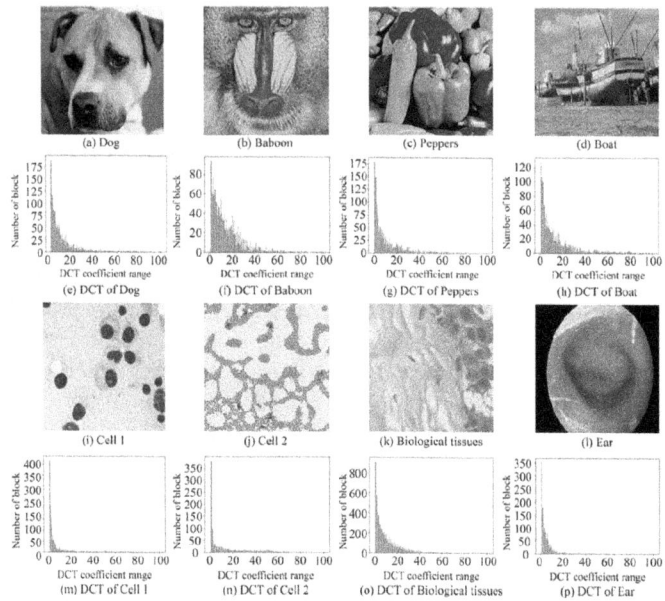

Fig. 5. Distribution of category parameters for images of different categories.

the block are relatively small. This suggests that the sub-block has uniform texture and is a smooth block, classified as the S category. When the absolute value of the difference between $F(0, 1)$ and $F(1, 0)$ is less than the diagonal threshold Td, it indicates that the difference between the vertical and horizontal energy changes and is small. At this time, the energy trend of the sub-block is diagonal or sub-diagonal distribution, and the sub-block belongs to the diagonal/sub-diagonal class, that is, the class D. The energy trend of the remaining domain blocks can be visualized as a horizontal or vertical distribution, belonging to Class H, namely the horizontal/vertical class. The thresholds Ts and Td are key to category classification. After dividing sub-blocks of different types of images, we calculate and sort their DCT horizontal coefficients, vertical coefficients, and their differences. As shown in Fig. 5, the majority of sub-blocks are concentrated in the range of smaller DCT coefficients.

We refer to this method as Fractal encoding based on Statistical histogram of low-frequency coefficients (FSHLC), the specific algorithm as Algorithm 2.

Algorithm 2 A fractal coding algorithm based on a statistical histogram of low-frequency coefficients.

Input: Image = [[11, 12,..., 1N], ..., [N1, N2, N3, ..., NN]], R_s, D_s.
Output: Fractal image encoding C.
1: D_{-list} = Generate Domain Atlas Based on D_s.
2: R_{-list} = Generate Range Atlas Based on R_s.
3: T_s, T_d = Calculate the target position after calculating the low-frequency distribution for the D_{-list}.
4: **for** $r - num = R_{-list}$ **do**
5:     Determine the category of R blocks based on T_s and T_d.
6:     **for** $d_{-num} = D_{-list-s} / D_{-list-d} / D_{-list-h}$ **do**
7:         C_{r-num} = Obtain the best matching block based on affine transformation.
8:     **end for**
9:     **if** $r - num = len(R_{-list})$ **then**
10:         **return** Fractal compression coding C.
11:     **end if**
12: **end for**

3.3 Adaptive Adjustment Methods for Inter-class Thresholds

For some cases where the image structure is not obvious, the threshold selection of the FSHLC method is completely based on statistical observation, which may still lead to the problem of inaccurate division, resulting in too many sub-blocks identified as smooth classes. Therefore, we further propose a dynamic adaptive classification algorithm combining the bisection method and the gradient difference method. For class S the threshold value is determined using the binary method. The DCT transformation is applied to each sub-block first, and $Max(F(0,1), F(1,0))$ is taken as the smoothness coefficient, F_S where F_{sn} for the nth D block is:

$$F_{sn} = \begin{cases} |F_n[1,0]|, & \text{if } (|F_n[1,0]| > |F_n[0,1]|) \\ |F_n[0,1]|, & \text{else} \end{cases} \quad (4)$$

Then sort $F_{S0} - F_{S(m-1)}$ in ascending order, where m represents the total number of sub-blocks. The sorted sequence of F_S is denoted as F_{sl}. For the sorted sequence, calculate the median based on the maximum and minimum values of the smoothness coefficients, and the resulting median value at this point is the initial position, and its corresponding smoothing coefficient is the initial threshold value. Count the number of sub-blocks that are less than this median value and the number of sub-blocks that are greater than this median value, i.e., let $a = \min(F_{sl})$, $b = \max(F_{sl})$, $N_s(a, b)$ be the number of D blocks when F_s takes values in the range from a to b. Iterate the calculation of $S_n(a, b)$ to select the final binary interval, where:

$$S_n(a, b) = \begin{cases} b = \frac{a+b}{2}, & \text{if } N_s\left(a, \frac{a+b}{2}\right) > N_s\left(\frac{a+b}{2}, b\right) \\ a = \frac{a+b}{2}, & \text{else} \end{cases} \quad (5)$$

When the difference between the two is less than 1/10 of the total number of sub-blocks, the median can be considered as the smoother position of the curve, which satisfies the convergence condition. At this point, a small number of extreme values are separated from a large number of small values. The smoothness coefficient at this median position is considered as the smooth class threshold T_S. Otherwise, an iterative operation is performed, i.e., the side with the smaller number of dichotomies is removed, and the judgment is continued by the method for the remaining portion until it stops when the difference between the two sides judgment condition is satisfied. When meet $\left| N_S\left(a, \frac{a+b}{2}\right) - N_S\left(\frac{a+b}{2}, b\right) \right| < \left(\frac{m}{10}\right)$ is met, take $F_{sl\left(\frac{a+b}{2}\right)}$ for S threshold T_s, less than D block as S class of T_s. Figure 6 shows the process of using binary partition method four times continuously on the codebook of dog.

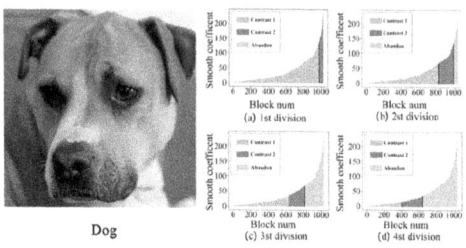

Fig. 6. The binary process of sub blocks.

For the remaining sub-blocks that have not been classified as S class, calculate their diagonal/secondary diagonal class coefficient as F_d, where the F_{dn} of the nth D block is:

$$F_{dn} = ||F_n[1,0]| - |F_n[0,1]||. \tag{6}$$

The same as T_s method, the dichotomy threshold T_{D1} of class D is determined by the dichotomy method. Since the sub-blocks corresponding to the coefficient interval of class S inevitably contain a part of the potential sub-blocks of class D, the parameter selection interval of the diagonal threshold will be narrowed and error will be caused. To address this issue, we construct a gradient map for each pair of adjacent coefficients after the binary process of the S class. Then, we select the position of the D class gradient threshold to minimize the error in the diagonal threshold caused by the missing D class sub-blocks. We set the gradient threshold as T_{D2}. When the number of S class blocks is s, we sort $F_{d(0)}$ to $F_{d(m-s-1)}$ in descending order and calculate the difference between each pair of adjacent coefficients, forming a gradient sequence F_{dl}. The gradient sequence has a total of m-s-1 elements, with the nth element denoted as $F_{dl(n)}$, where:

$$F_{dl(n)} = F_{d(n)} - F_{d(n+1)}. \tag{7}$$

Take the mean of the smallest 50% of elements to calculate the filtering value of the differences. Then, reassign each element in F_{dl} by subtracting the filtering value from the original value at that point in order to filter out a significant number of relatively low-gradient coefficients, where:

$$F_{dl(n)} = F_{d(n)} - F_{d(n+1)} - \frac{\sum_{v=\frac{m-s-1}{2}}^{m-s-1} \left(F_{d(v-1)} - F_{d(v)}\right)}{\frac{m-s-1}{2}}. \tag{8}$$

To reduce some noise, divide the sequence into intervals and reassign each element within each interval to the minimum value within that interval. When dividing into l interval every h elements, the elements within the l-th interval are assigned the value M_l. Among them, $lH = lh, lh+1, lh+2, \ldots, lh+9$.

$$M_l = min(F_{dl(lH)}), \qquad (9)$$

Subsequently, iterate over F_{dl} from smallest to largest, select the corresponding F_d at the position of the first nonzero value as the gradient threshold T_{D2}. Take the average of the binary threshold T_{D1} and the gradient threshold T_{D2} as the final diagonal threshold T_D. Among them, $T_D = \frac{T_{D1}+T_{D2}}{2}$.

Then divide the sub-blocks with F_d less than T_D into class D, and define the remaining sub-blocks as class H. We refer to this method as the Fractal encoding based on Gradient dichotomy of low-frequency coefficients (FGDLC) method, the specific algorithm is as follows:

Algorithm 3 A fractal coding algorithm based on the gradient dichotomy of low-frequency coefficients.

Input: Image = $[[11, 12, \ldots, 1N], \ldots, [N1, N2, N3, \ldots, NN]]$, R_s, D_s.
Output: Fractal image encoding C.
1: D_{-list} = Generate Domain Atlas Based on D_s.
2: R_{-list} = Generate Range Atlas Based on R_s.
3: T_s, T_d = Calculate the target position using gradient bisection method for the D_{-list}.
4: **for** $r\_num = R_{-list}$ **do**
5:    Determine the category of R blocks based on T_s and T_d.
6:    **for** $d\_num = D_{-list-s}/ D_{-list-d}/ D_{-list-h}$ **do**
7:      C_{r-num}= Obtain the best matching block based on affine transformation.
8:    **end for**
9:    **if** $r\_num = len(R_{-list})$ **then**
10:      **return** Fractal compression coding C.
11:    **end if**
12: **end for**

Taking the codebook partition process of image with dog as an example, when the number of remaining D blocks is 100, the list of difference coefficients is built according to the difference between two adjacent coefficients. Then, the mean value of the first 50% difference is taken as the filter value, and the coefficient is subtracted from all the differences to eliminate the coefficient of the less volatile part. And take the minimum value from every h differences as their new value to eliminate individual spiky areas. Then, the position of the first non-zero value on the horizontal axis coordinates is used as the gradient threshold for the D class.

In Fig. 7(a), the horizontal axis represents the sequence number of D blocks after removing the S class, and the vertical axis represents the diagonal coefficient. In Fig. 7(b) and (c), the horizontal axis represents the difference index of sub-blocks, where n indicates comparing the nth sub-block with the (n+1)th sub-block. The vertical axis represents the difference between the two sub-blocks. The third image shows the difference coefficients after the above operation. A non-zero value appears close to 400. When

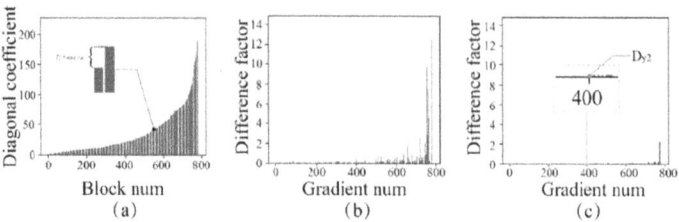

Fig. 7. Gradient selection process.

the non-zero value corresponds to a horizontal coordinate of m, the coefficient of the sub-block with a horizontal coordinate of m in the first image is taken as the gradient threshold. The final D class threshold is calculated as the average of the gradient threshold and the binary threshold. Sub-blocks in Fig. 7(a) with a vertical coordinate less than this threshold are defined as D class. The remaining D blocks are directly defined as H class. During the traversal process of R blocks, if a coefficient is greater than both the S class coefficient and the D class coefficient, it is searched in the H class.

4 Experiment

4.1 Data Sets and Evaluation Criteria

In order to verify whether our self-similarity evaluation method is consistent with human eye observations, and the effectiveness and generalizability of our proposed optimization method for codebook classification, two types of datasets are used in our experiments. The VOC dataset from PASCAL VOC Challenge, and the biomicroscopy dataset from Weakly Supervised Cell Segmentation in Multi-modality High-Resolution Microscopy Images, respectively. In the VOC dataset, different categories of images such as vehicles, portraits, landscapes, etc. are included. And in the biomicrography dataset, multiple categories of biomicrography images with different tissues, locations, and staining methods are included. Meanwhile, in order to avoid the influence of different image sizes or number of channels between different images on the experiments, this paper downsamples all the image sizes used in the experiments to 256 × 256 and converts them to grayscale images for the experiments.

In our proposed codebook classification optimization experiments for fractal coding, the above dataset is used to verify the effectiveness and universality of the coding scheme for different categories of images. In the self-similarity evaluation experiments, in order to verify the consistency of the self-similarity evaluation results proposed in this paper with the evaluation results derived from the human eye vision system, we similarly conduct comparison experiments by using the above VOC dataset, which contains images of a larger number of categories, with the biomicrographic dataset, which is self-similar to a larger number of images under the human eye vision system.

In the fractal coding experiments, we chose Peak Signal-to-Noise Ratio (PSNR) to verify the coding and decoding quality of different algorithms. PSNR is a common image quality evaluation method, which is often used to calculate the similarity of different images before and after coding, and the larger the PSNR is, the more similar the pictures are before and after decoding, and the better the quality of decoding is. The larger PSNR is, the more similar the images are before and after decoding, and the better the decoding quality is.

Where MAX^2 is the maximum pixel gray value and MSE is the mean square error. Generally, we think that the decoding quality is better when the PSNR is greater than or equal to 30 dB.

4.2 Results of Self-similarity Evaluation

Using SECS for calculation, the self similarity coefficient curves of 500 pieces each in these two types of datasets are shown in Fig. 8. Thereinto, the VOC dataset has the largest range of self-similarity evaluation coefficients, with a mean self-similarity of 0.1529. The dataset composed of biological microscopic images shows an overall improvement compared to regular images, with a higher self-similarity coefficient in a large number of images. The average self-similarity evaluation coefficient is 0.1867. As can be seen from Fig. 9, the biomicroscope image has more distribution in the region with larger coefficients than the ordinary image, indicating that the biomicroscope image has higher self-similarity. In addition, the overall span, extreme value and mean value of the self-similarity coefficient of the two types of data sets are shown in Table 1, and it can be found that the coefficient value of the biological microscopic image has smaller fluctuation and larger mean value. The above comparison results show that our method is consistent with the perception results of the human visual system, and can effectively verify the self-similarity of images.

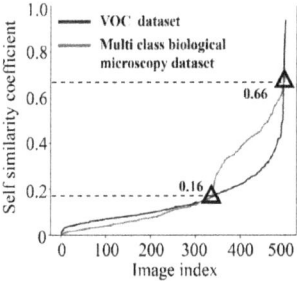
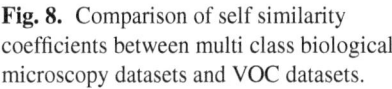
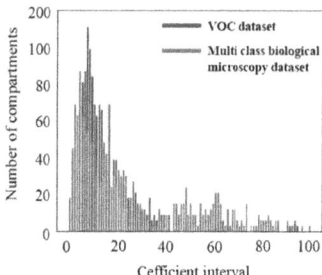

Fig. 8. Comparison of self similarity coefficients between multi class biological microscopy datasets and VOC datasets.

Fig. 9. Self-similarity coefficient distribution of three types of atlases.

4.3 Compression Performance Experiments

Figure 10 shows the visualization results of codebook classification using FSHLC and FGDLC methods. It can be observed that the FGDLC algorithm is more sensitive to the grayscale distribution of images and provides more accurate delineation of different categories.

Table 1. Extreme values, range, and mean of self-similarity evaluation for the three datasets after experimentation.

Correlation coefficient	Global maximum value	Global minimum value	Mean	Span
VOC	0.9325	0.0087	0.1529	0.9238
Microscopic images of multiple types of organisms	0.7140	0.0024	0.1867	0.7116

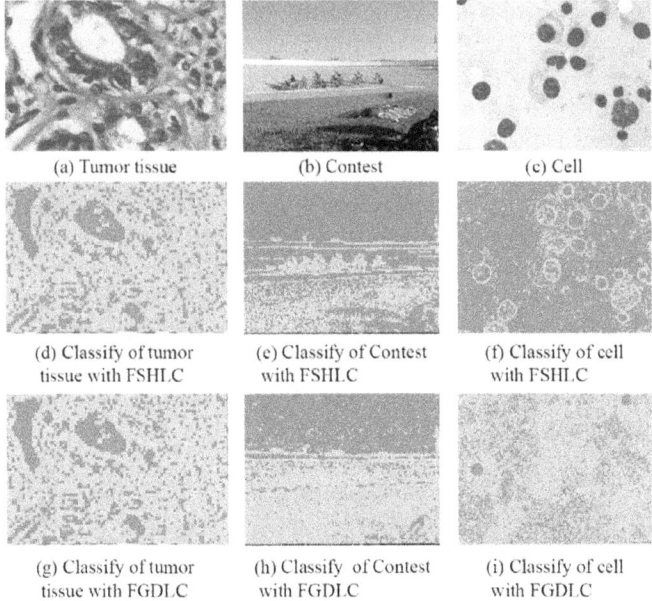

Fig. 10. Visualization of category division using FSHLC and FGDLC algorithms.

Figure 11 shows the overall encoding time curve for the VOC dataset under three algorithms. We used the original FIC as well as FGDLC and FSHLC to encode and decode two types of datasets. The average encoding time and average decoding quality obtained by different algorithms are shown in Table 2. From the table, it can be seen that compared to the original fractal coding, FGDLC optimizes the encoding time without a significant decrease in PSNR. The average encoding time for the VOC dataset decreased to 40.22 s, a speed improvement of 58.39%. For the multi-class biological microscopic dataset, the average encoding time decreased to 40.45 s, a speed improvement of 58.37%. We can also observe that although the FGDLC algorithm shows a minor improvement in decoding quality for the VOC dataset and the multi-class biological microscopic dataset, overall, it does not provide a significant optimization in terms of encoding time.

Therefore, we also conducted a statistical analysis of the minimum encoding time for each category, as shown in Table 3. Although the advantages of the FGDLC algorithm

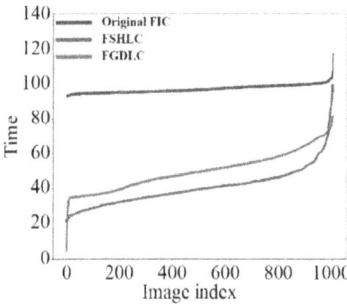

Fig. 11. The encoding time of the VOC dataset by the three types of algorithms.

Table 2. The average peak signal-to-noise ratio and average encoding time after fractal coding for three datasets.

Method	VOC		Microscopic images of multiple types of organisms	
	PSNR (dB)	Time (s)	PSNR (dB)	Time (s)
Original FIC	29.69	96.65	32.11	97.16
FSHLC	26.98(↓0.71)	40.22(↑58.39%)	31.32(↓0.79)	40.45(↑58.37%)
FGDLC	27.50(↓0.19)	49.60(↑48.68%)	31.83(↓0.28)	47.07(↑51.55%)

Table 3. Minimum time for three types of datasets after three types of fractal encoding, along with the corresponding peak signal-to-noise ratio (PSNR) for the image with the minimum time.

Method	VOC		Microscopic images of multiple types of organisms	
	PSNR (dB)	Minimal time (s)	PSNR (dB)	Minimal time (s)
Original FIC	20.41	92.75	33.00	93.66
FSHLC	24.88	20.95	27.75	17.42
FGDLC	37.93	3.88	43.19	6.51

are not significant in Table 2, it can be seen in Table 3, that the FGDLC algorithm only requires a minimum encoding time of 3.88 s for image encoding, while the same image requires 100.03 s for encoding using the original fractal encoding under the same hardware conditions. After decoding, the codebook encoded by the FGDLC algorithm achieves a PSNR of 37.93 dB, only 0.01 dB lower than FIC. This indicates that the FGDLC algorithm provides a very high acceleration ratio for certain images.

5 Conclusion

FIC is a compression method that can ignore the decoding image resolution, but fractal encoding inherently has issues with image adaptability, as well as time consumption problems due to the extensive traversal process during encoding. In our method, we first identify the self-similarity structure of different scales in the image, calculate the self-similarity coefficient of the image to analyze the degree of self-similarity in the image, in order to determine whether the image is suitable for fractal coding. Then, by observing the distribution pattern of low-frequency regions in the image, we improved the classification process of fractal codebooks based on DCT. Furthermore, we achieved dynamic adaptive sub-block classification through the binary gradient method, significantly enhancing the encoding speed. Additionally, by partitioning the codebook using dynamic thresholds, we also ensured a high decoding quality. We validated the effectiveness and universality of the above method on microscopic images and other datasets. We also consider introducing the idea of sparsity into the process of codebook classification to improved compression efficiency. Meanwhile, since our proposed algorithm is mainly based on the low-frequency distribution of the image itself, the algorithm will continue to be further attempted to be applied in some, e.g., video intra-frame data loss problems.

Acknowledgments. This work was supported by the National Natural Science Foundation of China under Grants (61961036), in part by the Natural Science Foundation of Guangxi, China under Grants (20GXNSFAA297259), the National Natural Science Foundation of China under Grants (62162054), in part by the Basic Ability Improvement Project for Young and Middle-aged Teachers in Guangxi, China (2024KY0694), and the Key Research Project of Wuzhou University (2023B001).

Disclosure of Interests. The authors have no competing interests to declare that are relevant to the content of this article.

References

1. Jacquin, A.E.: Image coding based on a fractal theory of iterated contractive image transformations. IEEE Trans. Image Process. **1**(1), 18–30 (1992)
2. Pi, M.H., Li, H.: Fractal indexing with the joint statistical properties and its application in texture image retrieval. IET Image Process. **2**, 218–230 (2008)
3. Zhuang, Z., Lei, N., Raj, A.N.J., Qiu, S.: Application of fractal theory and fuzzy enhancement in ultrasound image segmentation. Med. Biol. Eng. Comput. **57**(3), 623–632 (2019)
4. Cheul, Y.C., Shin, H.J.: A novel fast fractal super resolution technique. IEEE Trans. Consum. Electron. **56**(3), 1537–1541 (2010)
5. Ghazel, M., Freeman, G.H., Vrscay, E.R.: Fractal-wavelet image denoising revisited. IEEE Trans. Image Process. **15**(9), 2669–2675 (2006)
6. Pi, H., Li, H., Li, H.: A novel fractal image watermarking. IEEE Trans. Multimedia **8**(3), 488–499 (2006)
7. Tan, T., Yan, H.: The fractal neighbor distance measure. Pattern Recognit. **35**(6), 1371–1387 (2002)

8. Wang, C.Y., Li, J., Wu, J., Liu, J.: SSIM-based sparse image superresolution with rotation strategy and nonlocal regularization. In: 2022 China Automation Congress (CAC), pp. 2482–2486 (2022)
9. Jamali, M., Karimi, N., Samavi, S.: Weighted fuzzy-based PSNR for watermark visual quality evaluation. In: 2021 29th Iranian Conference on Electrical Engineering (ICEE), pp. 488–492 (2021)
10. Auccahuasi, W., Linares, O., Urbano, K., Sobrino-Mesias, J., Campos-Sobrino, M., Quispe-Peña, H.: Methodology for monitoring lagoon dimensions by means of fractal dimension analysis. In: 2024 2nd International Conference on Intelligent Data Communication Technologies and Internet of Things (IDCIoT), pp. 1722–1726 (2024)
11. Mayer, N.M., Obst, O.: Analyzing echo-state networks using fractal dimension. In: 2022 International Joint Conference on Neural Networks (IJCNN), pp. 1–8 (2022)
12. Mu, Z.C.W.X.M., Yang, Q.: Self-similarity studies of images. J. Zhengzhou Univ. Sci. Ed. **2**, 67–69 (2005)
13. Yuan, F.Z.: Research on image coding technology based on fractals (2009)
14. Lei, F., Ding, Y., Wang, Z.R., Tang, F.F.: Mixed distorted image restoration based on residual double deep Q network. In: 2023 42nd Chinese Control Conference (CCC), pp. 7918–7923 (2023)
15. Afro, P.-A., Strus, L., Bonnaud, L., Caplier, A., Robin, F.: Multi-QP rate distortion optimized quantization using deep learning. In: 2023 IEEE International Conference on Visual Communications and Image Processing (VCIP), pp. 1–5 (2023)
16. Usha Bhanu, N., Saravanakumar, C.: Investigations of machine learning algorithms for high efficiency video coding (HEVC). In: 2023 International Conference on Signal Processing, Computation, Electronics, Power and Telecommunication (IConSCEPT), pp. 1–5 (2023)
17. Xu, H.T., Yan, J.C., Persson, N., Lin, W.Y., Zha, H.Y.: Fractal dimension invariant filtering and its CNN-based implementation. In: 2017 IEEE Conference on Computer Vision and Pattern Recognition (CVPR), pp. 3825–3833 (2017)
18. Maha Lakshmi, G.V.: Implementation of image compression using fractal image compression and neural networks for MRI images. In: 2016 International Conference on Information Science (ICIS), pp. 60–64 (2016)
19. Guo, J.W., Sun, J.G.: An image compression method of fractal based on GSOFM network. In: 2008 Congress on Image and Signal Processing, vol. 1, pp. 421–425 (2008)
20. Duh, D.J., Jeng, J.H., Chen, S.Y.: DCT based simple classification scheme for fractal image compression. Image Vis. Comput. **23**(13), 1115–1121 (2005). https://doi.org/10.1016/j.imavis.2005.05.013
21. Wei Liu, et al.: SSD: single shot multibox detector. In: Computer Vision – ECCV 2016: 14th European Conference, Amsterdam, The Netherlands, October 11–14, 2016, Proceedings, Part I 14, pp. 21–37. Springer (2016)
22. Ahmed, N., Natarajan, T., Rao, K.R.: Discrete cosine transform. IEEE Trans. Comput. **C–23**(1), 90–93 (1974). https://doi.org/10.1109/T-C.1974.223784

DiffGIC: Diffusion Prior Based Null-Space Correction for High Resolution Grayscale Image Colorization

Yachao Li[1,2], Yutian Fu[3], Feng Dong[3], and Dong Liang[1,2(✉)]

[1] College of Computer Science and Technology, Nanjing University of Aeronautics and Astronautics, Nanjing, China
{liyachao,liangdong}@nuaa.edu.cn
[2] Shenzhen Research Institute, Nanjing University of Aeronautics and Astronautics, Nanjing, China
[3] Shanghai Institute of Technical Physics, Chinese Academy of Sciences, Beijing, China
{yutianfu,dongfeng}@mail.sitp.ac.cn

Abstract. Diffusion models have demonstrated exceptional abilities in colorizing grayscale images. To colorize high-resolution images, current methods use a strategy that combines super-resolution with hierarchical image processing (SR-HIPS). This approach involves shrinking the input images for the diffusion model to reduce computational resources. However, this can lead to the loss of detailed information in high-resolution grayscale images. To overcome this limitation, this paper introduces DiffGIC, a novel method leveraging color image decomposition via range-null space decomposition. DiffGIC takes color from low-resolution color images and details from high-resolution grayscale images. By adjusting the color using a pre-trained diffusion model and combining it with detailed grayscale information, our method produces high-quality, high-resolution colored images. Moreover, DiffGIC improves upon the SR-HIPS strategies by adding detailed grayscale details into the colorization process, marking a notable advancement over previous methods.

Keywords: Image Colorization · Diffusion Model · Super-Resolution

1 Introduction

Image colorization, transforming grayscale images into full color, is a thriving research topic within the field of low-level computer vision. Initially, this domain was dominated by studies that concentrated on employing specialized, small-scale datasets to train neural networks to achieve direct conversion from grayscale to color images [1]. However, these methods were constrained by the limited scale of the training datasets, which posed challenges in adapting these techniques to the diverse real-world scenarios. Recently, the focus has shifted towards leveraging the generative capabilities of pre-trained generators [2], known for their outstanding performance. Particularly, text-to-image generative models trained on large-scale datasets stand out for their extensive prior knowledge [3]. Leveraging this knowledge can markedly improve the accuracy and visual quality of image colorization.

(a) High-resolution Grayscale Image (b) SR-HIPS-based method (c) Ours DiffGIC

Fig. 1. (a) The high-resolution (HR) grayscale image. (b) The HR color image generated by SR-HIPS-based method. (c) The HR color image generated by our DiffGIC.

Although diffusion models [4] offer considerable benefits for low-level tasks, the need for GPU memory grows with the size of the image. This poses a challenge when processing high-resolution images. Hierarchical image processing strategy (HIPS) [5], which utilizes super-resolution (SR) techniques, is widely used in practical situations to produce high-resolution color images on limited computational resources. It works by first reducing the resolution of images processed by diffusion models, producing low-resolution color images. These images are then upscaled to higher resolutions through super-resolution models powered by generative adversarial networks [6–9] or diffusion models [10, 11]. This approach often overlooks the finer details in high-resolution grayscale images. As a result, it may not accurately reproduce the nuances of the original high-resolution grayscale images.

In this paper, we introduce a novel diffusion-based method called DiffGIC, which leverages color image decomposition via range-null space decomposition [12] for HIPS-based image colorization. It extracts color from the low-resolution color images and details from the high-resolution grayscale images. Then, it adjusts the color using a pre-trained diffusion model and combines it with extracted details to produce high-resolution colored images. During the color adjustment, a patch-based noise prediction method is adopted to ensure small computational resources. Additionally, our method can be easily applied to SR-HIPS-based methods by adding detailed grayscale details into the colorization process. Experiments show that DiffGIC can produce high-quality, high-resolution color images using small computational resources. Figure 1 illustrates a comparison between DiffGIC and an SR-HIPS-based method. DiffGIC has significant advantages in retaining detailed information in high-resolution grayscale images.

The main contributions of this work are summarized as follows:

- We propose DiffGIC, a novel hierarchical diffusion-based high-resolution grayscale image colorization method that uses small computational resources to produce high-quality, high-resolution color images. Additionally, it can be easily applied to SR-HIPS-based methods to improve performance.
- We introduce a color image decomposition method based on range-null space decomposition. By extracting details from high-resolution grayscale images, we solve the problem of inconsistent details between high-resolution color results and grayscale images. In addition, we introduce a pre-trained diffusion model to adjust the color information in the low-resolution color results to resolve the difference from the expected color information.

- Experiments show that our method has significant advantages over SR-HIPS-based methods in terms of detail consistency with high-resolution grayscale images. At the same time, the proposed method can also be integrated with SR-HIPS-based methods to improve their upper performance bound.

2 Related Work

2.1 Grayscale Image Colorization

Grayscale image colorization aims to enhance grayscale images by adding vibrant colors, resulting in more visually appealing outputs. In recent years, deep learning-based image processing methods have proven very effective in many low-level color-related tasks [13]. Automatic colorization methods [14] focus on estimating the missing color channels in grayscale images to generate realistic color images without relying on text guidance. Although significant progress has been made in these works, automatic colorization still faces the challenge of uncertainty when dealing with real-world problems. Text-driven image colorization methods leverage the rich semantic information in text descriptions to drive colorization and reduce uncertainty. Recently, significant progress in text-to-image diffusion models [3] provides powerful tools for such methods. Some works, such as ControlNet [2], can produce colorization results that are highly consistent with text descriptions by fine-tuning these models.

2.2 Text-Driven Diffusion-Based Grayscale Image Colorization

Diffusion Models [4] learn the image generation process through iterative denoising steps initiated from an initial random noise. They have demonstrated superior performance in many low-level tasks, such as super-resolution [11], image despeckling [15], etc. For text-driven grayscale image coloring, ControlNet [2] colorizes images by introducing grayscale images as conditions to control the image generation process. DiffColor [16] inverses grayscale images into latent features for image generation and fine-tunes the diffusion model to align text descriptions and image colors.

Although these methods have superior performance, they require extensive computational resources, which limits their application in high-resolution grayscale image colorization. Hierarchical image processing strategy (HIPS) [5], which utilizes super-resolution (SR) techniques, is widely used in practical situations to produce high-resolution color images on limited computational resources.

2.3 Image Super-Resolution

Image super-resolution (SR) aims to recover high-resolution (HR) images from degraded low-resolution (LR) observations. ESRGAN [8] and SwinIR-GAN [9] assumed predefined degradation processes, such as bicubic downsampling and blurring using known parameters. BSRGAN [6] and Real-ESRGAN+ [7] propose using a combination of multiple degradation methods to synthesize LR-HR image pairs that mimic real-world data for the real-world blind SR task. Recent diffusion-based works, such as DiffBIR [10] and StableSR [11], have also shown competitive performance in real-world image

SR. However, the lack of utilization of the high-resolution grayscale images during the super-resolution process can result in inconsistencies between the details of color results and the high-resolution grayscale images.

In contrast to the high-resolution image hierarchical colorization based on SR, our approach focuses on leveraging the details in high-resolution grayscale images to address the issue of insufficient details in low-resolution color results. Additionally, it focuses on eliminating the differences between the color information in low-resolution color results and the color information in expected high-resolution color results.

3 DiffGIC

3.1 Preliminaries: Range-Null Space Decomposition

For image colorization and image super-resolution tasks, the degradation process is generally defined as:

$$y = \mathbf{A}x \tag{1}$$

where y denotes the degraded image and x represents the original image. $\mathbf{A}$ represents the degrade operator. To make it easy to understand, we use two operators, $\mathbf{A}_C$ and $\mathbf{A}_{SR}$, to denote the degrade operator for image colorization and image super-resolution. The operator $\mathbf{A}_C$ can be represented as a matrix $[\frac{1}{3}, \frac{1}{3}, \frac{1}{3}]$ that converts each RGB channel pixel $[r, g, b]^T$ to a grayscale value $[\frac{r}{3} + \frac{g}{3} + \frac{b}{3}]$. The operator $\mathbf{A}_{SR}$ can be designed as the average pooling downsampling. We can easily find their pseudo-inverse operators that $\mathbf{A}_C^\dagger$ is represented by the matrix $[1,1,1]$, while $\mathbf{A}_{SR}^\dagger$ is represented by the mean upsampling. Both degrade operators satisfy the equations $\mathbf{A}\mathbf{A}^\dagger \mathbf{A}x \equiv \mathbf{A}x$ and $\mathbf{A}(\mathbf{I} - \mathbf{A}^\dagger \mathbf{A})x \equiv 0$.

According to $\mathbf{A}\mathbf{A}^\dagger \mathbf{A}x \equiv \mathbf{A}x$, $\mathbf{A}^\dagger \mathbf{A}x$ can be seen as projecting x to the range-space of $\mathbf{A}$. In contrast, according to $\mathbf{A}(\mathbf{I} - \mathbf{A}^\dagger \mathbf{A})x \equiv 0$, $(\mathbf{I} - \mathbf{A}^\dagger \mathbf{A})x$ can be seen as projecting x to the null-space of $\mathbf{A}$. Any original image x can be decomposed into these two parts that satisfying:

$$x = \mathbf{A}^\dagger \mathbf{A}x + (\mathbf{I} - \mathbf{A}^\dagger \mathbf{A})x \tag{2}$$

Taking the image coloring task as an example, $\mathbf{A}_C^\dagger \mathbf{A}_C x$ can be regarded as the grayscale detailed information contained in x and $(\mathbf{I} - \mathbf{A}_C^\dagger \mathbf{A}_C)x$ can be seen as the color information contained in x.

3.2 Color Image Decomposition for Hierarchical Image Colorization

For high-resolution (HR) grayscale image colorization, current methods adopt the hierarchical image processing strategy (HIPS) to decrease the computational resource requirements. These HIPS-based methods first decrease the processed image size for text-to-image models and generate the low-resolution (LR) color image x_{lr}. Then, they utilize the super-resolution (SR) models to generate high-resolution image x based on $x_{lr} = \mathbf{A}_{SR}x$. The SR process neglects the detailed information in the HR grayscale image. Based on range-null space decomposition, we can solve this problem by converting the SR process to a new type of process. We generate the HR color image x by fusing the color information in x_{lr} and the detailed information in the HR grayscale image y. Specifically, according to Eq. 2, the color information, denoted as CI, can be extracted from x_{lr} as follows:

$$CI = \left(\mathbf{I} - \mathbf{A}_C^\dagger \mathbf{A}_C\right) x_{lr} \qquad (3)$$

According to Eq. 1 and Eq. 2, the detailed information, denoted as DI, can be extracted from y as follows:

$$DI = \mathbf{A}_C^\dagger \mathbf{A}_C x = \mathbf{A}_C^\dagger y \qquad (4)$$

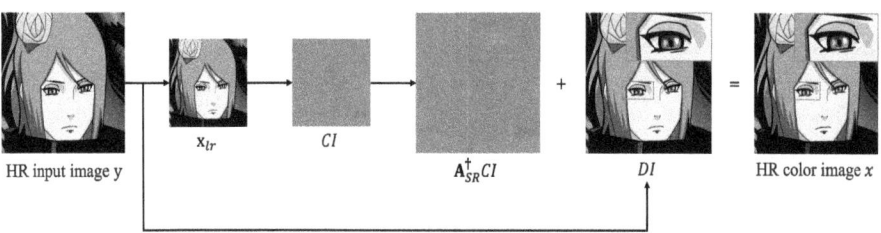

Fig. 2. Hierarchical grayscale image colorization based on range-null space decomposition. From the enlarged area, we can observe that the HR color image x retains the detailed information in HR input image y.

According to Eq. 2 and Eq. 3, we can find that CI is not the corresponding color information in x. So directly adding DI and CI can not generate the HR color image x. To obtain the corresponding color information in x, we first need to analyze the relationship between CI and x. According to $x_{lr} = \mathbf{A}_{SR} x$, we can deduce $CI = \left(\mathbf{I} - \mathbf{A}_C^\dagger \mathbf{A}_C\right) \mathbf{A}_{SR} x = \mathbf{A}_{SR} x - \mathbf{A}_C^\dagger \mathbf{A}_C \mathbf{A}_{SR} x$. According to the designs of $\mathbf{A}_C^\dagger$, $\mathbf{A}_C$ and $\mathbf{A}_{SR}$, we can deduce $\mathbf{A}_C^\dagger \mathbf{A}_C \mathbf{A}_{SR} x = \mathbf{A}_{SR} \mathbf{A}_C^\dagger \mathbf{A}_C x$, where $\mathbf{A}_C^\dagger \mathbf{A}_C x$ can be represented by DI. So the relationship between CI and x can be defined as follows:

$$CI = \mathbf{A}_{SR} x - \mathbf{A}_{SR} DI \qquad (5)$$

Now, let us assume that, which means that $\mathbf{A}_{SR}^\dagger \mathbf{A}_{SR} x = x$ does not lose any information during the downsampling and upsampling processes. The final HR color image can be obtained by:

$$x = DI + \mathbf{A}_{SR}^\dagger CI \qquad (6)$$

As shown in Fig. 2, the HR color image x generated by this new type of process maintains the color information in x_{lr} and the detailed information in the HR grayscale image y. However, since $\mathbf{A}_{SR}^\dagger \mathbf{A}_{SR} x = x$ does not hold in practice, there are some differences in details between the generated result and the original color HR image corresponding to y. According to Eq. 6, we can observe that these differences originate from

$\mathbf{A}_{SR}^{\dagger} CI \neq \left(\mathbf{I} - \mathbf{A}_C^{\dagger}\mathbf{A}_C\right)x$. As shown in Fig. 3, these differences appear as color distortion, which becomes increasingly obvious as the upsampling factor increases. Inspired by DDNM [17], we leverage the prior knowledge of a pre-trained diffusion model to eliminate these differences.

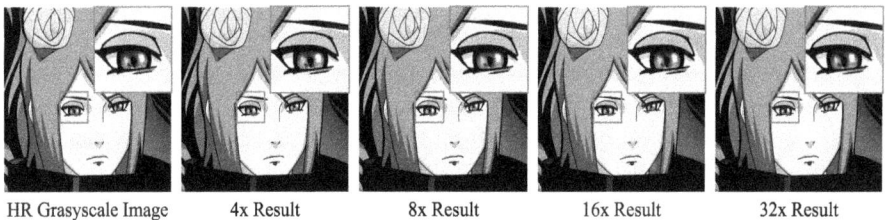

Fig. 3. Hierarchical grayscale image colorization based on range-null space decomposition with different upsampling factors.

3.3 Null-Space Diffusion Prior for Color Information Correction

Diffusion models generate images through T-step iteratively denoising. The generation starts by sampling a noise x_T from an i.i.d. Gaussian distribution and finishes by generating a clean image x_0. Prior knowledge of the diffusion model is included in every image generated during the denoising process. To use the prior knowledge for color correction, we adopt a pre-trained pixel-level diffusion model, allowing us to control the process explicitly. Specifically, we can get a predicted clean image $x_{0|t}$ from noisy image x_t at each timestep t. This operation can be simply represented as follows:

$$x_{0|t} = \tfrac{1}{\alpha_t}(x_t - \sigma_t \epsilon_\theta) \qquad (7)$$

where α_t and σ_t are predefined scale factors, $t \sim \{0, ..., T\}$. To ensure small computation resources, ϵ_θ is defined as the noise fused by weighting noises predicted by the diffusion model in a patch-based manner as described in Mixture of Diffusers [18].

To eliminate the differences originating from $\mathbf{A}_{SR}^{\dagger} CI \neq \left(\mathbf{I} - \mathbf{A}_C^{\dagger}\mathbf{A}_C\right)x$, we extract the color information in $x_{0|t}$ and use it to correct $\mathbf{A}_{SR}^{\dagger} CI$ through the null-space of $\mathbf{A}_{SR}$. Similar to Eq. 3, the color information in $x_{0|t}$ can be defined as $CI_{x|t} = \left(\mathbf{I} - \mathbf{A}_C^{\dagger}\mathbf{A}_C\right)x_{0|t}$. According to Eq. 2, the corrected color information $\widehat{CI}$ can be defined as follows:

$$\widehat{CI} = \mathbf{A}_{SR}^{\dagger} CI + \left(\mathbf{I} - \mathbf{A}_{SR}^{\dagger}\mathbf{A}_{SR}\right) CI_{x|t} \qquad (8)$$

Now, we can replace $\mathbf{A}_{SR}^{\dagger} CI$ in Eq. 6 with $\widehat{CI}$ to obtain the HR color image $\bar{x}_{0|t}$. This process can be defined as follows:

$$\bar{x}_{0|t} = DI + \widehat{CI} \qquad (9)$$

Then, we follow the denoising process of the diffusion model to add noise to $\bar{x}_{0|t}$. To boost the speed, we adopt the fast sampler DDIM [19] and define this process as follows:

$$x_{t-1} = \alpha_{t-1}\bar{x}_{0|t} + \sigma_{t-1}\left(\eta_t \epsilon + \sqrt{1-\eta_t^2}\epsilon_\theta\right), \epsilon \sim N(0, \mathbf{I}) \tag{10}$$

where η_t is a factor that controls the ratio of the newly introduced noise ϵ.

By iteratively controlling the generation process of the diffusion model in the above way, we can obtain the final HR color image x_0. Compared with the results obtained by Eq. 6, x_0 contains color information from x_{lr} and color information corrected by the diffusion model. We name this method as DiffGIC.

4 Experiments

4.1 Implementation Details

We adopted the pre-trained diffusion model provided by [20]. It is trained on the ImageNet [21] dataset with a size of 512 × 512. To reduce the computational resources, we used the patch-based noise prediction and fusion method proposed by Mixture of Diffusers [18] during the inference process. We chose 512 × 512 as the patch size and left the smallest possible overlapping area when dividing patches to reduce the number of patches and minimize the time cost caused by the patch-based noise prediction. During the inference process, we used DDIM as the accelerated sampling algorithm. We set $\eta_t = 1.0$ and adopted 4 DDIM denoising steps for testing.

4.2 Experiment Setup

Dataset. We evaluate our method on real-world datasets. For real-world datasets, we choose the DIV2K [22] validation set and the Real40 dataset we collected from the Internet. Real40 contains 40 images with a 2K resolution covering various real-world scenes, such as faces, streets, buildings, etc. During the evaluation phase, we downsample all images by 4x to simulate LR color results. For DiffGIC, we degrade all images into grayscale images and use them with LR color results as input for HR color image generation. For the SR-HIPS-based methods, we directly take the LR color results as input for 4x SR.

Compared Methods. To verify the effectiveness of our method, we compared our DiffGIC with SR-HIPS-based methods using several most commonly adopted SR methods, i.e., BSRGAN [6], ESRGAN [8], Real-ESRGAN+ [7], SwinIR-GAN [9], StableSR [11] and DiffBIR [10]. To ensure the fairness of the comparison, we also apply the introduced color image decomposition for these SR-HIPS-based methods by replacing the detailed information in the HR color results with the information in the HR grayscale image. For all methods, we use official code and models for testing. For both StableSR and DiffBIR, we adopt the same settings as DiffGIC to reduce their demand on computational resources and set 50 denoising steps for fair comparison.

4.3 Comparing with SR-HIPS-Based Methods

Quantitative Comparisons. We first show the quantitative comparison on the DIV2K [22] validation set and the Real40 dataset. As shown in Table 1 and Table 2, all SR-HIPS-based methods achieve significant improvements in all metrics by utilizing the introduced color image decomposition. Compared with these improved SR-HIPS-based methods, our method achieves the best results on all consistency metrics. Specifically, on the DIV2K validation set, compared with the results of the best improved SR-HIPS-based method, our DiffGIC outperforms 4.23 and 0.0122 on PSNR and SSIM metrics and exhibits a reduction of 0.0232 and 2.51 in LPIPS and FID metrics. On the Real40 dataset, compared with the results of the best improved SR-HIPS-based method, our DiffGIC outperforms 3.63 and 0.013 on PSNR and SSIM metrics and exhibits a reduction of 0.0222 and 1.94 in LPIPS and FID metrics. This demonstrates the superiority of DiffGIC in retaining detailed information of the HR grayscale image.

Qualitative Comparisons. To demonstrate the effectiveness of our method, we present visual results on the DIV2K [22] validation set and Real40 dataset in Fig. 4 and Fig. 5. We can observe that DiffGIC outperforms all SR-HIPS-based methods regarding colorization quality and detail consistency with the HR grayscale image. Specifically, DiffGIC can generate the HR color image with detailed information that is highly consistent with the HR grayscale image, as shown in Fig. 4. The results generated by the SR-HIPS-based methods are not only different from the LR image in terms of color information but also different from the HR grayscale image in terms of detailed information. Furthermore, as shown in Fig. 5, DiffGIC can maintain a high degree of consistency with the HR grayscale image on facial images, while SR-HIPS-based methods generate results that are inconsistent with the details in HR grayscale image.

Table 1. Quantitative comparison with the most commonly used SR-HIPS-based methods on DIV2K [45] validation set. bold and italic represent the best and second best performance, respectively. *: results of the HIPS-based methods improved by the introduced color image decomposition.

Method	PSNR↑	SSIM↑	LPIPS↓	FID↓
BSRGAN [6]	24.92	0.7027	0.3498	36.11
ESRGAN [8]	21.64	0.5728	0.3178	39.80
Real-ESRGAN+ [7]	24.47	0.7021	0.3324	35.36
SwinIR-GAN [9]	24.69	0.7165	0.3187	30.91
DiffBIR [10]	24.00	0.6351	0.3660	31.76
StableSR [11]	21.73	0.5482	0.4071	34.70
BSRGAN*	34.37	0.9648	0.0868	6.82
ESRGAN*	**36.15**	0.9586	**0.0479**	**3.67**
Real-ESRGAN+ *	35.53	**0.9706**	0.0774	5.62
SwinIR-GAN*	34.60	0.9668	0.0785	7.26
DiffBIR*	35.20	0.9616	0.0921	4.28
StableSR*	32.89	0.9407	0.1131	6.02
DiffGIC	*40.38*	*0.9828*	*0.0247*	*1.16*

Table 2. Quantitative comparison with the most used SR-HIPS-based methods on the Real40 dataset. bold and italic represent the best and second best performance, respectively. *: results of the HIPS-based methods improved by the introduced color image decomposition.

Method	PSNR↑	SSIM↑	LPIPS↓	FID↓
BSRGAN [6]	26.88	0.7738	0.3392	40.08
ESRGAN [8]	24.67	0.6866	0.2877	31.90
Real-ESRGAN+ [7]	26.17	0.7748	0.3188	37.36
SwinIR-GAN [9]	26.62	0.7905	0.3024	33.17
DiffBIR [10]	25.11	0.6648	0.4070	27.71
StableSR [11]	23.37	0.6067	0.4122	40.32
BSRGAN*	35.46	0.9651	0.0932	7.94
ESRGAN*	**38.15**	0.9674	**0.0478**	**2.75**
Real-ESRGAN+ *	36.34	**0.9704**	0.0844	5.17
SwinIR-GAN*	35.71	0.9676	0.0855	6.73
DiffBIR*	35.19	0.9473	0.1262	4.15
StableSR*	34.18	0.9376	0.1282	5.02
DiffGIC	*41.78*	*0.9834*	*0.0256*	*0.81*

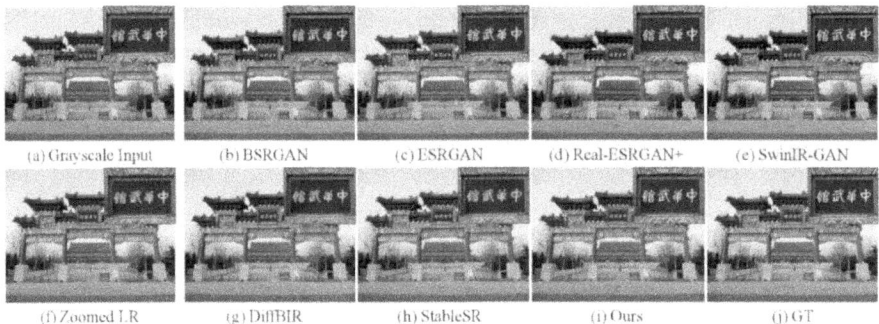

Fig. 4. Qualitative comparisons on the DIV2K [22] validation set. (Zoom in for details)

4.4 Comparison of Computational Resource Requirements

To evaluate the computational resource advantages of DiffGIC, we conducted a comparative analysis using ControlNet [2] based on Stable Diffusion 1.5 [23] as the baseline. Our measurements focused on the maximum GPU memory usage during the coloring process of 100 grayscale images, each sized 2048 × 2048 pixels. To begin, we downscaled all images to a resolution of 512 × 512 pixels and recorded the maximum GPU memory requirements using ControlNet. Subsequently, we measured the maximum GPU memory requirements of all HIPS-based methods for upscaling these low-resolution color results back to 2048 × 2048 pixels. Table 3 shows that using ControlNet to directly colorize grayscale images at high-resolution requires extensive computing resources. Adopting the HIPS-based methods reduces the required computing resources. Furthermore,

Table 3. Computational resource requirements comparison on 100 high-resolution grayscale images, each sized 2048 × 2048 pixels.

Method	Image Size	GPU Memory (GB)
ControlNet [2]	512 × 512	3.34
ControlNet [2]	2048 × 2048	15.5
ControlNet [2] + BSRGAN [6]	2048 × 2048	3.38
ControlNet [2] + ESRGAN [8]	2048 × 2048	3.38
ControlNet [2] + Real-ESRGAN + [7]	2048 × 2048	3.90
ControlNet [2] + SwinIR-GAN [9]	2048 × 2048	3.66
ControlNet [2] + DiffBIR [10]	2048 × 2048	11.76
ControlNet [2] + StableSR [11]	2048 × 2048	12.12
ControlNet [2] + DiffGIC	2048 × 2048	3.66

compared with the diffusion-based methods, our DiffGIC has significant advantages in reducing computing resources.

Table 4. Ablation studies of information sources on DIV2K [22] and Real40 dataset.

Datasets	LR Color Image x_{lr}	Grayscale Image y	Diffusion Prior	PSNR↑	SSIM↑	LPIPS↓	FID↓
DIV2K	✓	✓	✓	26.48	0.7494	0.3843	28.08
	✓	✓		38.94	0.9784	0.0296	1.59
	✓			40.38	0.9828	0.0247	1.16
Real40	✓	✓	✓	26.48	0.7494	0.3843	28.08
	✓	✓		40.48	0.9791	0.0318	1.22
	✓			41.78	0.9834	0.0256	0.81

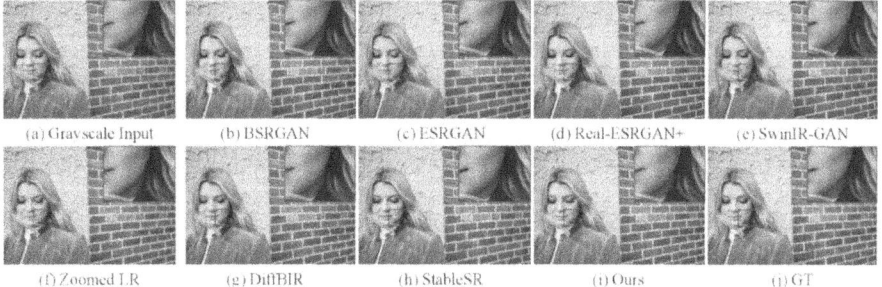

Fig. 5. Qualitative comparisons on real-world images in the Real40 dataset. (Zoom in for details)

4.5 Ablation Study

Our DiffGIC utilizes three sources of information for hierarchical HR grayscale image colorization: the HR grayscale image y, the LR color image x_{lr}, and the diffusion prior of the pre-trained diffusion model. To verify the impact of different information sources on the results, we construct experiments on the DIV2K [22] validation set and Real40 dataset. For hierarchical image colorization, x_{lr} contains the necessary color information and is retained in all settings. As shown in Table 4, removing y results in significantly worse metrics. By introducing diffusion prior knowledge for color information correction, all metrics can be optimized. This demonstrates the importance of detailed information in HR grayscale images for hierarchical image colorization and the effectiveness of using diffusion prior for color information correction.

5 Conclusions

Motivated by the development of text-to-image models and their widespread application in image colorization tasks, this work discusses a common but underexplored problem, namely, how to use the information in HR grayscale images for HIPS-based image colorization. In this paper, we introduce the color image decomposition method based on range-null space decomposition and propose a diffusion-based color information correction method called DiffGIC. Compared with SR-HIPS-based methods, DiffGIC can generate HR color images that are highly consistent in details with the HR grayscale images at a low computational cost. Additionally, the introduced color image decomposition method can be easily applied to SR-HIPS-based methods, improving the consistency between the results and the HR grayscale images.

Acknowledgments. This work is supported in part by the National Natural Science Foundation of China under grant 62272229, the Natural Science Foundation of Jiangsu Province under grant BK20222012, and Shenzhen Science and Technology Program JCYJ20230807142001004.

References

1. Lee, J., Kim, E., Lee, Y., Kim, D., Chang, J., Choo, J.: Reference-based sketch image colorization using augmented-self reference and dense semantic correspondence. In: Proceedings of the IEEE/CVF Conference on Computer Vision and Pattern Recognition, pp. 5801–5810 (2020)
2. Zhang, L., Rao, A., Agrawala, M.: Adding conditional control to text-to-image diffusion models. In: Proceedings of the IEEE/CVF International Conference on Computer Vision, pp. 3836–3847 (2023)
3. Rombach, R., Blattmann, A., Lorenz, D., Esser, P., Ommer, B.: High-resolution image synthesis with latent diffusion models. In: Proceedings of the IEEE/CVF Conference on Computer Vision and Pattern Recognition, pp. 10684–10695 (2022)
4. Song, Y., Sohl-Dickstein, J., Kingma, D.P., Kumar, A., Ermon, S., Poole, B.: Score-based generative modeling through stochastic differential equations. In: International Conference on Learning Representations (2021)

5. Ho, J., Saharia, C., Chan, W., Fleet, D.J., Norouzi, M., Salimans, T.: Cascaded diffusion models for high fidelity image generation. J. Mach. Learn. Res. **23**(47), 1–33 (2022)
6. Zhang, K., Liang, J., Van Gool, L., Timofte, R.: Designing a practical degradation model for deep blind image super-resolution. In: Proceedings of the IEEE/CVF International Conference on Computer Vision, pp. 4791–4800 (2021)
7. Wang, X., Xie, L., Dong, C., Shan, Y.: Real-Esrgan: training real-world blind super-resolution with pure synthetic data. In: Proceedings of the IEEE/CVF International Conference on Computer Vision, pp. 1905–1914 (2021)
8. Wang, X., et al.: ESRGAN: enhanced super-resolution generative adversarial networks. In: Proceedings of the European Conference on Computer Vision Workshops, p. 0 (2018)
9. Liang, J., Cao, J., Sun, G., Zhang, K., Van Gool, L., Timofte, R.: SwinIR: image restoration using Swin transformer. In: Proceedings of the IEEE/CVF International Conference on Computer Vision, pp. 1833–1844 (2021)
10. Lin, X., et al.: DiffBIR: towards blind image restoration with generative diffusion prior. arXiv preprint arXiv:2308.15070 (2023)
11. Wang, J., Yue, Z., Zhou, S., Chan, K.C., Loy, C.C.: Exploiting diffusion prior for real-world image super-resolution. arXiv preprint arXiv:2305.07015 (2023)
12. Wang, Y., Hu, Y., Yu, J., Zhang, J.: GAN prior based null-space learning for consistent super-resolution. In: Proceedings of the AAAI Conference on Artificial Intelligence, vol. 37, pp. 2724–2732 (2023)
13. Li, L., Liang, D., Gao, Y., Huang, S.J., Chen, S.: ALL-E: aesthetics-guided low-light image enhancement. arXiv preprint arXiv:2304.14610 (2023)
14. Wang, Yi., Menghan Xia, Lu., Qi, J.S., Qiao, Yu.: PalGAN: Image Colorization with Palette Generative Adversarial Networks. In: Avidan, S., Brostow, G., Cissé, M., Farinella, G.M., Hassner, T. (eds.) Computer Vision – ECCV 2022: 17th European Conference, Tel Aviv, Israel, October 23–27, 2022, Proceedings, Part XV, pp. 271–288. Springer Nature Switzerland, Cham (2022). https://doi.org/10.1007/978-3-031-19784-0_16
15. Li, S., Higashita, R., Fu, H., Li, H., Niu, J., Liu, J.: Content-preserving diffusion model for unsupervised AS-OCT image Despeckling. In: Greenspan, H., et al. International Conference on Medical Image Computing and Computer-Assisted Intervention, vol. 14226, pp. 660–670. Springer (2023). https://doi.org/10.1007/978-3-031-43990-2_62
16. Lin, J., Xiao, P., Wang, Y., Zhang, R., Zeng, X.: Diffcolor: toward high fidelity text-guided image colorization with diffusion models. arXiv preprint arXiv:2308.01655 (2023)
17. Wang, Y., Yu, J., Zhang, J.: Zero-shot image restoration using denoising diffusion null-space model. In: The Eleventh International Conference on Learning Representations (2023). https://openreview.net/forum?id=mRieQgMtNTQ
18. Jiménez, Á.B.: Mixture of diffusers for scene composition and high resolution image generation. arXiv preprint arXiv:2302.02412 (2023)
19. Song, J., Meng, C., Ermon, S.: Denoising diffusion implicit models. arXiv preprint arXiv:2010.02502 (2020)
20. Dhariwal, P., Nichol, A.: Diffusion models beat GANs on image synthesis. Adv. Neural. Inf. Process. Syst. **34**, 8780–8794 (2021)
21. Russakovsky, O., et al.: ImageNet large scale visual recognition challenge. Int. J. Comput. Vision **115**, 211–252 (2015)
22. Agustsson, E., Timofte, R.: Ntire 2017 challenge on single image super-resolution: dataset and study. In: Proceedings of the IEEE/CVF Conference on Computer Vision and Pattern Recognition workshops, pp. 126–135 (2017)
23. Ramesh, A., Dhariwal, P., Nichol, A., Chu, C., Chen, M.: Hierarchical text-conditional image generation with clip latents. arXiv preprint arXiv:2204.06125 (2022)

Chinese Character Image Inpainting with Skeleton Extraction and Adversarial Learning

Di Sun[1], Tingting Yang[1], Xiangyu Pan[2], Jiahao Wang[2], and Gang Pan[2(✉)]

[1] College of Artificial Intelligence, Tianjin University of Science and Technology, Tianjin 300222, China
[2] College of Intelligence and Computing, Tianjin University, Tianjin 300350, China
pangang@tju.edu.cn

Abstract. Chinese character image inpainting aims to restore the missing textual regions with realistic contents. Existing algorithms for text image inpainting are primarily designed for English characters, however, their performance is suboptimal when applied to Chinese characters. The primary challenge in Chinese character image inpainting lies in the scarcity of open-source datasets for this task. Additionally, conventional image inpainting algorithms fail to account for the guiding significance of the stroke topology structure inherent in Chinese characters during the inpainting process. In this paper, we propose a skeleton extraction algorithm based on line thinning, and contribute a dataset of Chinese character images and their skeleton images accordingly. In particular, we propose a skeleton extraction guided generative framework skeletonGAN for Chinese character inpainting, where the skeleton of Chinese characters is used as prior knowledge to guide the inpainting process. The whole framework comprises two parts: an SE network for skeleton-based Chinese character skeleton extraction and inpainting, and an SR network dedicated to Chinese character image inpainting. Experimental results demonstrate that the proposed method successfully fills the missing character information and achieves significant image inpainting results.

Keywords: Adversarial learning · Chinese character image inpainting · skeleton extraction

1 Introduction

The task of natural image inpainting has been extensively studied, but there are still few researches on Chinese character image inpainting. As a kind of ideographic characters, Chinese characters have a huge number and styles compared with English letters, and each character has a different and complex structure, which makes the task of Chinese image inpainting more difficult.

Due to the unique topological structure of Chinese characters, some methods treat this task as a line extraction and restoration problem [1, 2]. These methods are effective when the stroke has a clear structure, but they cannot handle multiple intersections when dealing with complex structures. In order to generate more realistic results, some studies [3] utilize generative adversarial networks (GANs) to restore Chinese character images. While these methods can yield smoother strokes, the lack of morphological constraints limits their effectiveness in repairing larger defect areas. As the field of image style transfer continues to evolve, some alternative methods [4–6] are presented for Chinese character font generation based on pairwise datasets. However, the creation of paired training datasets often requires significant human resources. Because the Chinese character image dataset is scarce, how to create a Chinese character image dataset with sufficient data quantity and rich data content is a problem.

Inspired by the idea image inpainting technology based on prior knowledge and text style transfer technology based on skeleton extraction, this paper aims to propose a Chinese character image inpainting method based on text skeleton extraction, which better combines the structural features of the text itself to complete the task of Chinese character image inpainting.

One challenge is shared with all the supervised methods: the training process needs paired data as ground truth. But the Chinese character image dataset is scarce, collecting a large scale Chinese character image dataset needs a lot of efforts. In addition, it has two unique scientific challenges: (i) The data set needs to provide a text skeleton image corresponding to the Chinese character image, and (ii) How to better use the structural information provided by the text skeleton image to guide the inpainting process, to ensure that the repaired Chinese character image has a better consistency in strokes.

We address the above challenges by contributing a large scale dataset and developing a deep supervised approach for Chinese character image inpainting. For the dataset, we introduce line thinning to generate datasets of Chinese character images and their skeleton images. For the network, we propose a two-branch image inpainting network inspired by GANs, called skeletonGAN. SkeletonGAN divides the inpainting process of Chinese character images into two stages. The first stage, known as the Character Skeleton Extraction Network (SE), aims to extract the skeleton information from the input defective image of Chinese characters, ultimately obtaining a completed text skeleton. SE employs the concept of text image style transfer to extract structural information from the input defective image of Chinese characters, eliminating stroke style characteristics such as stroke thickness and writing strength, and repairing the extracted defective skeleton structure. The second stage is referred to as the Chinese Characters Image Inpainting Network Based on Text Skeleton (SR). The purpose is to use the complete text skeleton information obtained in the previous stage as a prior knowledge to guide the inpainting of Chinese character images. This process can also be regarded as assign the style of the input Chinese character image to the text skeleton style transfer task.

In summary, the main contributions of this paper are summarized as follows:

- We offer a new perspective into Chinese character inpainting. The combination of adversarial training with skeleton extraction strengthens the perception of structural areas, allowing the model to synthesize the accurate contents.
- We design a skeleton extraction algorithm model based on line thinning, and contribute a Chinese character image dataset with corresponding skeleton images.

- We propose a Chinese character image inpainting framework (skeletonGAN) based on skeleton extraction and adversarial learning, which consists of an adversarial learning-based text skeleton extraction and restoration network SE and a Chinese character image inpainting network SR based on the text skeleton image.

2 Related Work

2.1 Chinese Character Inpainting

Compared with general image inpainting, Chinese characters have complex structures and styles, which make the work of Chinese character image inpainting very attractive and challenging. Recent years, there have also been some works on Chinese character inpainting. For example, CGAN [7] has been used to remove grids from images to recover Chinese characters. Li et al. [8] propose an improved architecture of GoogLeNet, extracting directional Gabor features as prior knowledge and incorporating the obtained feature maps into both the input layer and the original image. Ge et al. [9] pose an occlusion offline handwritten Chinese character inpainting method using a self-attention mechanism. This mechanism effectively addresses this problem, which can use the information of the whole image by using clues from all feature locations. Wang et al. [10] introduce a framework for the generation of semantically enhanced Chinese character inpainting, incorporating a Global Semantic Supervision Module to regulate context semantics. Li et al. [11] propose a prototype-feature-based structure guided generation framework, which is not only capable of adapting to multiple font styles, but also can comprehensively recover the font structures and strokes without the need for masking information through inference on the representations of styles. Zhao et al. [12] dish a character autoencoder based on the branch convolutional channel attention module, which replaces the traditional down-sampling module with BCCAM, gives different weights to repair occluded and unoccluded areas. Zheng et al. [13] put forward the EA-GAN network, which can accurately restore text structure when the damage area is large by introducing the attention mechanism of example texts, for repairing damaged texts in ancient Chinese books. Li et al. [14] develop a diffusion model based method DiffACR to automate the inpainting of eroded ancient Chinese characters. The method simulates erosionfication as a form of cold diffusion and uses a prior mask extracted directly from the damaged image to guide the inpainting process.

2.2 Character Image Style Transfer

Text image style transfer task is a branch of image style transfer task research, which aims to change the stylistic attributes of text while preserving its text content. In recent years, there has been a gradual emergence of research specifically focusing on image style migration for Chinese characters. Tian et al. [15] utilize the pix2pix model [16] by the paired training data to address the issue of image style migration in Chinese character font generation. Chang et al. [17] innovatively adapt the CycleGAN model, to migrate the stylistic feature patterns of images to Chinese font generation using unpaired training data. However, this method may encounter the pattern collapse problem due to the

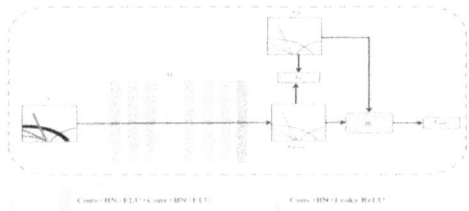

Fig. 1. The skeleton extraction architecture for dataset manufacture. It consists of a generator G and a discriminator D. The generator is based on constant size long convolution follows the ConvBatchNorm-ReLU architecture.

presence of Chinese characters with numerous highly similar strokes [18], which significantly reduces the diversity and quality of the generated results. Zeng et al. [19] pose the StrokeGAN model, which incorporates stroke coding to capture the pattern information of Chinese characters, thereby alleviating the pattern collapse problem of CycleGAN and enhancing the stylistic diversity of its generated characters. Subsequently, Gao et al. [20] present ChiroGAN, a multi-style Chinese character image style migration model based on skeleton transformation and stroke drawing. While these methodologies offer versatile approaches to the Chinese character inpainting task, they fail to yield the anticipated outcomes, indicating that significant challenges persist in our Chinese character inpainting endeavors.

3 Datasets

At present, there is no publicly available dataset specifically for Chinese character inpainting. To address this limitation, we design a skeleton extraction network to extract the skeleton structure from the input image and generate a dataset of Chinese character skeleton images.

Because the Chinese character image and the line image have a similar pair of line structure, inspired by the related research on line vectorization, we use randomly generated lines with different thicknesses and corresponding uniform line images as the training set, and train a line thinning network through adversarial training. Then the model after training is applied to the Chinese character image to generate the corresponding skeleton image, as shown in Fig. 1. The skeleton extraction architecture for dataset manufacture. It consists of a generator G and a discriminator D. The generator is based on constant size long convolution follows the ConvBatchNorm-ReLU architecture. We posit that the skeleton image corresponding to a Chinese character image can effectively remove calligraphic style attributes, such as aspect ratio, radical interval, and stroke density, while preserving skeletal structure elements like thickness, inclination, writing intensity, and the initial and final shape. These skeleton structures can offer prior knowledge during inpainting, thereby facilitating the generation of correctly structured Chinese character images.

We utilize this random masked image to process the Chinese character skeleton images used in the Chinese character image pairs, thereby providing data support for training. The dataset encompasses 3755 commonly used Chinese characters as per the first-level national standard of Chinese characters, and contains a variety of font styles including printed, handwritten, and stylised images of Chinese characters to adapt actual usage. Figure 3 shows some example images in the dataset. The first row depicts the images of Chinese characters paired with their respective text skeletons, while the second rows display the corresponding masked ones shows some images in our dataset.

4 Method

skeletonGAN has two subnetworks, Skeleton Extraction (SE) and Character Restoration (SR). The overview of the network is depicted in Fig. 2.

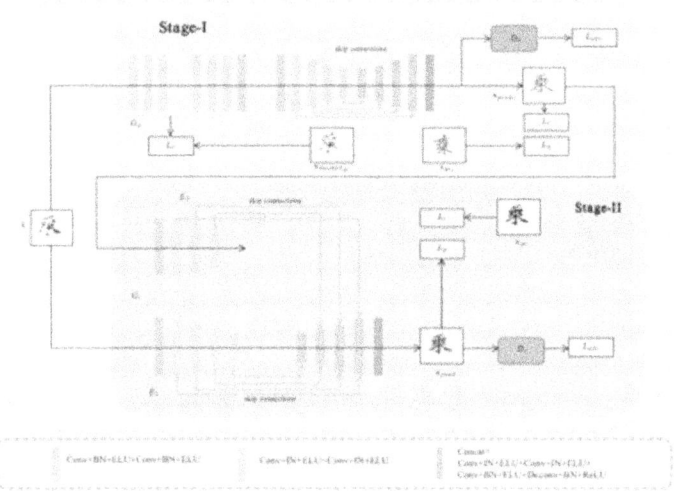

Fig. 2. The overview of skeletonGAN network, SE is used to extract the text skeleton image, in the second stage, SR uses the repaired text skeleton image as a prior knowledge to guide the inpainting process.

Fig. 3. Some example images in the dataset. The first row depicts the images of Chinese characters paired with their respective text skeletons, while the second rows display the corresponding masked ones.

4.1 Generator

The initial stage SE entails the extraction of incomplete features of Chinese character skeletons from defective images. Subsequently, the restored text skeleton images serve as prior knowledge to direct the restoration process in the next stage. The generator Ge extracts skeleton features and synthesizes incomplete Chinese character skeleton images, which are bifurcated into two distinct parts. This method improves the quality of the synthesis results, especially for the connection details of the Chinese character skeleton image. The first segment of Ge employs a long convolution structure, primarily refining the input image, eliminating stroke style information, and yielding an incomplete feature of the Chinese character skeleton image. Conversely, the second segment of Gr utilizes an encoder-decoder framework to synthesize a comprehensive skeleton image of Chinese characters. To preserve more intricate details, a skip connection structure is incorporated between the encoder and decoder. Instead of employing pooling operations, we adopt convolution with 3×3 pixel strides for downsampling, ensuring greater spatial support for masked region generation. The skeleton information can well retain the structure and arrangement information of the character strokes and at the same time eliminate all the stroke style information. We believe that the use of text skeleton images to guide the process of Chinese character images inpainting can be regarded as giving the calligraphy style to the character skeleton. So in the second stage SR, the generator Gr employs two encoders, E_1 and E_2, to extract features of incomplete Chinese character images and character skeleton images respectively. A decoder is then used to amalgamate and decode these two encoded features. The function of encoder E_1 is to extract features from input images as the primary encoder, while encoder E_2 extracts features from Chinese character skeleton images. The input image can provide calligraphy style features, and using Chinese character skeleton images as prior knowledge to guide the process of Chinese character image repair can be viewed as assigning the style of the input image to the Chinese character skeleton image.

4.2 Discriminator

To further promote the generation of more realistic results, we introduce a discriminator D as a binary classifier to distinguish real images from fake ones in both stages. The discriminator in the first stage functions to enhance the quality of the output Chinese skeleton image, ensuring that the stroke structure closely aligns with the actual Chinese image. The discriminator in the second stage is designed to encourage the generator to effectively integrate the structural information from the Chinese skeleton image, resulting in smoother and clearer outcomes.

4.3 Loss Function

The input masked Chinese character images of the network are represented as $\tilde{x}$ and the target output images of the network are represented as x_{gt}, the final output of the generator is expressed as x_{pred}. We first introduce a per-pixel reconstruction loss L_r to the generator, which is the L_2 between the generated Chinese character image and the ground truth image x_{gt}.

$$L_r = \|x_{gt} - \tilde{x}\|_2^2 \tag{1}$$

In order to make the generated image have a high structural similarity with x_{gt}, we then adopt a perceptual loss L_{p_e} to enhance the detailed features. L_{p_e} solves the problem of the influence of multiple fonts, which is the L_1 distance between the output image and the ground truth image, the formula for L_{p_e} can be expressed as:

$$L_{p_e} = \sum_{l=L-2}^{L-1} \beta_l \|\phi_l(x_{gt}) - \phi_l(x_{pred})\|_1 \tag{2}$$

when the mean square error loss function is used, the output image will be relatively smooth, the details are not real enough, and part of the high-frequency information is lost, the formula for L_{p_r} can be expressed as:

$$L_{p_r} = \sum_{l=L-2}^{L-1} \beta_l \|\phi_l(x_{gt}) - \phi_l(x_{pred})\|_2^2 \tag{3}$$

We further employ the adversarial loss. The adversarial loss judges the ability of discriminator to predict whether the character image is real or not. We use x_{pred} and x_{gt} as inputs, where the generator G is trained to minimize this objective against the adversarial D that tries to maximize it. The adversarial losses of SR and SE are expressed by the formulae respectively as

$$L_{adv_e}(G_e, D_e) = E_{(x_{gt})} \log(D_e(x_{gt})) + E_{(x_{pred})} \log(1 - D_e(x_{pred})) \tag{4}$$

$$L_{adv_r}(G_r, D_r) = E_{(x_{gt})} \log(D_r(x_{gt})) + E_{(\tilde{x})} \log(1 - D_r(x_{pred})) \tag{5}$$

The overall loss is defined as follow:

$$L_{skeletonGAN} = L_{SE} + L_{SR} \tag{6}$$

where the loss metric of LSE is denoted as:

$$L_{SE} = \lambda_r L_r + \lambda_{p_e} L_{p_e} + \lambda_{adv} L_{adv_e} \tag{7}$$

where the loss metric of LSR is denoted as:

$$L_{SR} = \lambda_r L_r + \lambda_{p_r} L_{p_r} + \lambda_{adv} L_{adv_r} \tag{8}$$

5 Experimental Results

SkeletonGAN is implemented based on python and pytorch. In training, we set the value of λ_r, λ_{p_e}, λ_{p_r} and λ_{adv} to 1.2, 0.5, 1 and 0.1. We also employ batch normalization in most convolutional blocks to encourage stability of the proposed model. In the experiment, our model perform a complete end-to-end training using the Adam optimizer. The batch size is set to 128. We train it on NVIDIA GeForce RTX 2080Ti GPU with 12GB GPU memory.

5.1 Quantitative Analysis

Figure 4 shows Chinese character inpainting results on the proposed dataset. It can be seen that the proposed algorithm yields satisfactory results, both at the level of text skeleton images and in the final restoration outcomes. Particularly when the style of Chinese character images is strong and the strokes are thicker, it can still generate relatively correct restoration results for Chinese character images. This is because at the first stage, the stroke style features in the input Chinese character images have been eliminated, which can simplify the restoration process of text skeleton images. This part can also be regarded as a restoration task similar to fine-line text images. The complete text skeleton image is used as a priori knowledge, combined with the tasks of image restoration and text style transfer, to ultimately obtain a complete Chinese character image. From the resultant image, it can be clearly seen that the direction of strokes and overall structure in the final restored Chinese character image are consistent with those in the text skeleton image. This also indirectly confirms the correctness of the skeletonGAN.

5.2 Qualitative Results

We compare the inpainting performance with the classic methods: the Examplar-Based Image Inpainting (EBII) [21], and HAN [3]. As illustrated in Fig. 5, the traditional method EBII synthesizes unrecognizable characters due to the large mask. HAN uses hierarchical discriminator to make the characters clear but it is easy to generate wrong characters. Our method can accurately capture visual information, the stroke lines are more smooth. Furthermore, a comparison of the inpainting results for the "Luo" character reveals that the proposed method is superior in preserving the stroke style of Chinese characters, with the stroke style being reapplied to the text skeleton image during the repair process.

5.3 Ablation Study

We show the influence of different factors of the proposed network by removing corresponding loss functions. The quantitative results are illustrated in Table 1. We find that these loss functions can all improve the effect of the model, but the action direction is slightly different. For example, L_{adv} is a crucial part by allowing the generator to avoid strange strokes and make the results semantically correct. Style consistency loss L_p reduces the artificial appearance, such as blurring, making the resulting image sharper overall.

Fig. 4. Visual comparison with the classic methods: (a) ground truth images, (b) original input images, (c)–(e) are results from EBII, HAN, and our method, respectively.

Fig. 5. Chinese character inpainting results on the proposed dataset. In each row from top to down: ground truth images, original input images, target skeleton images and our inpainting results.

Table 1. Inpainting results in terms of PSNR, SSIM, and OCR for ablation study. The values in bold means the best performances.

Methods	no-L_p	no-L_r	no-L_{adv}	skeletonGAN	Groundtruth
PSNR	24.803	23.5209	23.4820	**25.0472**	–
SSIM	0.7980	0.7148	0.7093	**0.8986**	–
OCR	0.7874	0.7642	0.6219	0.8384	**0.8510**

6 Conclusion

This paper demonstrates the effectiveness of introducing skeleton extraction into Chinese character image inpainting. Initially, we utilize paired line images to train a text skeleton extraction network based on line refinement. This effectively addresses the scarcity of skeleton image datasets for Chinese character images, leading to the creation of a new dataset comprising both image and skeleton images of Chinese characters, which are annotated with textual information. The dataset generation process is highly adaptable and can be modified and expanded according to specific requirements. Subsequently, we propose a skeleton extraction guided inpainting scheme that separates the structural characteristics of character images from stroke style attributes and employs the character skeleton as a foundational knowledge source to guide the inpainting process. The experimental results demonstrate that the proposed method outperformed compared models in subjective and objective comparisons.

Acknowledgments. This work was funded by the Natural Science Foundation of Tianjin (No. 21JCYBJC00640), 2023 CCF-Baidu Songguo Foundation (Research on Scene Text Recognition Based on PaddlePaddle).

References

1. Nazeri, K., Ng, E., Joseph, T., Qureshi, F.Z., Ebrahimi, M.: Edgeconnect: Generative image inpainting with adversarial edge learning (2019). arXiv:1901.00212
2. Sasaki, K., Iizuka, S., Simo-Serra, E., Ishikawa, H.: Joint gap detection and inpainting of line drawings. In: Proceedings of the IEEE Conference on Computer Vision and Pattern Recognition, pp. 5725–5733 (2017)
3. Chang, J., Gu, Y., Zhang, Y., Wang, Y.-F., Innovation, C.: Chinese handwriting imitation with hierarchical generative adversarial network. In: BMVC, p. 290 (2018)
4. Chang, J., Gu, Y.: Chinese typography transfer (2017). arXiv:1707.04904
5. Jiang, Y., Lian, Z., Tang, Y., Xiao, J.: DCFont: an end-to-end deep Chinese font generation system. In: SIGGRAPH Asia 2017 Technical Briefs, pp. 1–4 (2017)
6. Wu, S.-J., Yang, C.-Y., Hsu, J.Y.-J.: CalliGAN: style and structure-aware Chinese calligraphy character generator (2020). arXiv:2005.12500
7. Zhong, Z., Yin, F., Zhang, X.-Y., Liu, C.-L.: Handwritten Chinese character blind inpainting with conditional generative adversarial nets. In: 2017 4th IAPR Asian Conference on Pattern Recognition (ACPR), pp. 804–809 (2017). IEEE
8. Li, J., Song, G., Zhang, M.: Occluded offline handwritten Chinese character recognition using deep convolutional generative adversarial network and improved GoogleNet. Neural Comput. Appl. **32**, 4805–4819 (2020)
9. Song, G., Li, J., Wang, Z.: Occluded offline handwritten Chinese character inpainting via generative adversarial network and self-attention mechanism. Neurocomputing **415**, 146–156 (2020)
10. Wang, J., Pan, G., Sun, D., Zhang, J.: Chinese character inpainting with contextual semantic constraints. In: Proceedings of the 29th ACM International Conference on Multimedia, pp. 1829–1837 (2021)
11. Li, H., et al.: Generative character inpainting guided by structural information. Vis. Comput. **37**, 2895–2906 (2021)
12. Zhao, L., Yuan, Z., Lou, Y., Xu, Q., Qiao, X.: An auto-encoder of inscription character inpainting based on branch convolutional channel attention module (2023)
13. Wenjun, Z., Benpeng, S., Ruiqi, F., Xihua, P., Shanxiong, C.: EA-GAN: restoration of text in ancient Chinese books based on an example attention generative adversarial network. Herit. Sci. **11**(1), 42 (2023)

14. Li, H., Du, C., Jiang, Z., Zhang, Y., Ma, J., Ye, C.: Towards automated Chinese ancient character restoration: a diffusion-based method with a new dataset. In: Proceedings of the AAAI Conference on Artificial Intelligence, vol. 38, pp. 3073–3081 (2024)
15. Chen, J., Ji, Y., Chen, H., Xu, X.: Learning one-to-many stylised Chinese character transformation and generation by generative adversarial networks. IET Image Proc. **13**(14), 2680–2686 (2019)
16. Isola, P., Zhu, J.-Y., Zhou, T., Efros, A.A.: Image-to-image translation with conditional adversarial networks. In: Proceedings of the IEEE Conference on Computer Vision and Pattern Recognition, pp. 1125–1134 (2017)
17. Chang, B., Zhang, Q., Pan, S., Meng, L.: Generating handwritten Chinese characters using CycleGAN. In: 2018 IEEE Winter Conference on Applications of Computer Vision (WACV), pp. 199–207 (2018). IEEE
18. Goodfellow, I., et al.: Generative adversarial nets. Adv. Neural Inf. Process. Syst. **27** (2014)
19. Zeng, J., Chen, Q., Liu, Y., Wang, M., Yao, Y.: StrokeGAN: Reducing mode collapse in Chinese font generation via stroke encoding. In: Proceedings of the AAAI Conference on Artificial Intelligence, vol. 35, pp. 3270–3277 (2021)
20. Gao, Y., Wu, J.: GAN-based unpaired Chinese character image translation via skeleton transformation and stroke rendering. In: Proceedings of the AAAI Conference on Artificial Intelligence, vol. 34, pp. 646–653 (2020)
21. Criminisi, A., Perez, P., Toyama, K.: Region filling and object removal by exemplar-based image inpainting. IEEE Trans. Image Process. **13**(9), 1200–1212 (2004). https://doi.org/10.1109/TIP.2004.833105

The Weakly Supervised Network of Hierarchical Attention Mechanism for Fine-Grained Classification

Qian Long[1], Gaihua Wang[1,2(✉)], Hongwei Qu[3(✉)], Jingxuan Yao[1], and Bolun Zhu[1]

[1] College of Artificial Intelligence, Tianjin University of Science and Technology, Tianjin 300457, China
{longqian,wanggh}@tust.edu.cn
[2] Hubei Key Laboratory of Optical Information and Pattern Recognition, Wuhan Institute of Technology, Wuhan 430205, China
[3] Wuhan Electronic Information Institute, Wuhan 430019, China
394139525@qq.com

Abstract. Fine-grained classification is challenging task to discriminate subtle and local differences from sub-categories. Many works improve the accuracy by relying heavily upon the use of the object or part annotations of images whose label are costly. In the paper, a weakly supervised network is proposed for fine-grained image classification without using expensive annotations. Firstly, it learns object detector by hierarchical attention mechanism automatically and localizes the objects or its parts to extract salient feature. Then, based on the theory of prototypical networks, it learns a metric loss function by computing distances to prototype representations of each class which is unsupervised clustering methods. Both are jointed to remove useless information or noise patches and retain discriminative features. Finally, we apply the proposed method to complete the classification of disaster-scene images. Compared with other methods, experimental results demonstrate our method is generalized and robust to different datasets.

Keywords: Fine-grained Classification · Hierarchical Attention Mechanism · Salient Feature · Metric Loss Function · Disaster-scene

1 Introduction

Fine-grained classification aims to recognize subordinate classes within basic-level categories, such as species of birds [1], flowers [2], animals [3], and models of cars [4]. Unlike general methods, the localization of objects and their parts is crucial for fine-grained image classification [5, 6]. It should be capable of localizing and representing the marginal differences within subordinate categories, which makes fine-grained recognition a challenging task.

Early works generally adopt a two-stage learning framework: firstly, they localize the discriminative regions of objects and extract discriminative features, then encode the discriminative features for training classifiers. These methods provide a way of encoding the salient features for distinguishing sub-categories. However, they also have some limitations: (1) the number of parts used is highly empirical, which limits flexibility and makes generalization to other datasets difficult. (2) They heavily rely on labor-consuming labeling, making them applicable only in domains where such annotations are difficult or expensive to obtain.

To address these problems, some researchers have begun to focus on recognizing sub-categories via weakly supervised part detection instead of using expensive annotations. Lin et al. [7] introduce bilinear pooling as the outer product of features, which can capture localized feature interactions from two CNNs. And it has been shown to achieve impressive performance on a wide range of visual tasks. However, bilinear features have high dimensionality, which makes them impractical for subsequent analysis. The compact bilinear representation [8] is derived through a novel kernelized analysis of bilinear pooling, providing insights into the discriminative power of bilinear pooling but with only a few dimensions. Dubey et al. [9] propose concepts from pairwise learning and label confusion, taking a step towards solving the problems of overfitting. Weakly Supervised Spatial Group Attention Network (WSSGA-Net) [10] highlights the correct semantic feature regions for more accurate classification by establishing a semantic enhancement mechanism. PHPQ [11] captures and retains fine-grained semantic information in multi-level features. GCA [12] uses clustering to divide the data into small clusters, and then aggregates them to get fine-grained information.

Object localization is very important for fine-grained image classification. To remove the influence of background noise and obtain meaningful global features, this paper proposes a hierarchical attention framework to localize subtle differences among different subcategories for fine-grained image classification.

2 The Proposed Method

The proposed method consists of four parts: plain CNN including Base conv-net and Conv Block, Attention Block including Attention Map and Max K Response Block, Interaction Model and total loss function. Figure 1 is the structure of network.

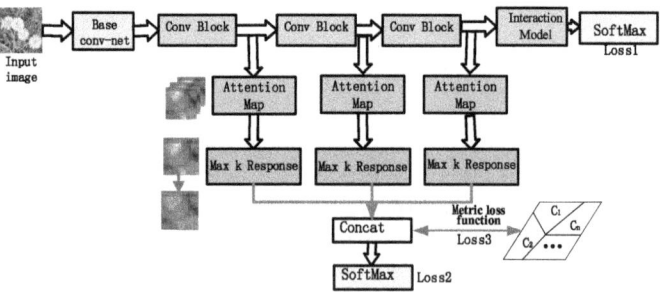

Fig. 1. The structure of network

2.1 Plain CNN

Given an image I, which is resized with $H \times W \times C$, H is the height of image, W is the width of image, C is the channel of image. Firstly, the input image I is passed by a plain CNN. CNN model is fine-tuned from the pre-trained CNN on ImageNet. In our experiments, our plain CNN models include VGG-16 and ResNet-18. Conv Blocks are composed of the conv3, conv4 and conv5 in VGG-16. For Resnet-18, Conv Blocks are con3_x, con4_x and con5_x. The original VGG-16 and Resnet-18 have 1000-class outputs. In this work, CNN model is fine-tuned on ImageNet. Then we get layers from conv1 to conv5 to train our datasets. The last fully-connected layer is reduced to related classes of datasets.

2.2 Attention Block

The whole framework generates a saliency map for input image from a hierarchical attention model. In hierarchical attention model, we extract attention features, which can filter out noisy patches and select the relevant objects. Given feature maps F from Conv Blocks. The outputs F of Conv Blocks are processed by attention mechanism $Mask_c(x, y)$. We define $f_c(x, y)$ at spatial location (x, y) of channel c. The saliency map of is expressed by

$$Mask_c(x, y) = sigmoid(f_c(x, y)) \qquad (1)$$

The output of Attention Map in each layer is computed by

$$M = F(1 + Mask_c) \qquad (2)$$

Multi-scale features are extracted by hierarchy layers. The output of saliency map can indicate the representative regions.

When get saliency feature from attention map, it is that some irrelevant region should be filter out and useful information should be retained. To complete the task, we add the Max K Response Block to find main objects or relevant region. The outputs of attention map are resized to column vector. Then we choose salient feature from the main objects. The max K saliency values are selected by Max K Response Block (Fig. 1). Given the output M of attention map. We select max k values from the M_i (i = 1,2,3). S is the concatenated vector from max k values. It can be expressed by

$$S = topk(M_1, M_2, M_3) \qquad (3)$$

2.3 The Total Loss Functions

Based on attention block, we get some salient features. In the training stage, each prototype C_k is the mean vector of the extracted salient features belonging to its class. N_k is the number of the kth class. Each epoch, When the input belongs to the kth class, we compute a distance between the output S of attention block and C_k. The distance is defined as the metric loss function. It is expressed by

$$Loss3 = MSELoss(S_k, C_k) \qquad (4)$$

After updating the gradient, we update the prototype C_k by

$$C_k = \frac{1}{N_k} \sum_{k}^{S} \qquad (5)$$

The total loss function has three parts. The first part is the loss of whole framework. It is loss1 in Fig. 1. The second part is the loss of the attention Block. It is the loss2 in Fig. 1. The third part is the metric loss function.

3 Experiments

All experiments are performed by PyTorch on NVIDIA GeForce RTX 2060 GPUs. The proposed approach is compared with different methods to verify its effectiveness. Accuracy is adopted as the evaluation metric to evaluate the classification performances. No extra annotation or object bounding box is used in the whole experiments.

3.1 Datasets and Baselines

Datasets. The CUB-200-2011 dataset comprises 11,788 images categorized into 200 subcategories, making it one of the most used datasets for fine-grained image classification. The Stanford Dogs dataset, constructed from images and annotations sourced from ImageNet, serves the purpose of fine-grained image classification tasks. It encompasses 20,580 images representing 120 breeds of dogs from diverse regions worldwide. The Oxford-Flower-17 dataset, on the other hand, contains 17 types of flowers, with each type consisting of 80 images.

Training deep neural networks directly on fine-grained datasets is often impractical, necessitating data preprocessing. In experiments, data augmentation techniques are commonly employed to augment the training image count, including random cropping, translation, and scaling. During training, images are typically randomly cropped to 224 × 224 patches to mitigate overfitting, with multiple patches extracted from the entire image for training purposes.

Baselines. We split state-of-the-art methods into two groups by the basic CNNs used in these methods: VGG-16 and ResNet-18, both of which achieved state-of-the-art performance on ImageNet. We initialize both network with the pre-trained network on the ImageNet and use a weight decay of 0.0001 with a momentum of 0.9 and set the initial learning rate to 0.1. The learning rate is divided by 10 every 20 iterations.

3.2 Comparison with All Kinds of Methods

We compare the proposed method with original BCNN, CBP and HBP. BCNN is a method which replaces the fully connected layers with bilinear pooling. CBP is a compact bilinear pooling method. In original paper of CBP, the features of CBP uses RM and TS projections. In our experiments, it uses TS projections. HBP is hierarchical bilinear pooling method which can integrate multiple cross-layer bilinear features to enhance their representation capability. We define the hierarchical attention model as HA model. We also test the performance of HA model. The model combining the hierarchical attention with prototypical networks is called as WSHA model.

The WSHA model is added on BCNN network, which is called as WSHA-BCNN. The WSHA model is added on CBP network, which is called as WSHA-CBP. The baseline is VGG-16 for BCNN and CBP. We add the proposed model on HBP network, which is called as WSHA-HBP. The baseline is ResNet-18 for WSHA -HBP.

Experiments on CUB-200-2011. Tables 1 and 2 show the comparison results on CUB-200-2011 dataset at the aspect of classification accuracy with 448 × 448 patches and 224 × 224 patches of images. CBP is a compact bilinear pooling method. We add the proposed method to CBP. WSHA-CBP offers the best accuracy that is 77.65%. We add the proposed HA model on HBP network which is called as HAHBP. The baseline is ResNet-18 for HAHBP. The accuracy is 74.82 higher than HBP network. We also test the accuracy of some recent methods, such as PHPQ [11], GCA [12]. PHPQ captures and retains fine-grained semantic information in multi-level features. GCA use cluster to divides the data into small clusters, and then aggregates them. In comparison, the WSHA-CBP achieves the highest classification accuracy among all methods without object and parts annotations.

We also resize original images. The training images are randomly cropped 224 × 224 patches. The test images are center cropped 224 × 224. The results are showed in Table 2. The accuracy also can be improved by using proposed model. If we use the VGG-16 to extract feature, the baseline method is higher than others baseline methods on CBP. Neither object nor parts annotations are used in these approaches, which leads fine-grained image classification to practical application. For different methods, it has an impressive boost when adding our attention model.

Table 1. Table shows the comparison results on CUB-200-2011 dataset with 448 × 448 patches.

Method	Base Model	Accuracy (%)
BCNN	VGG-16	70.34
PHPQ	Resnet-18	74.13
GCA	Vit-B/16	73.40
CBP	VGG-16	72.75
HACBP	VGG-16	73.50
WSHA-CBP	VGG-16	**77.65**
HBP	VGG-16	70.18
	Resnet-18	69.69
HAHBP	Resnet-18	74.82

Table 2. Table shows the comparison results on CUB-200-2011 dataset with 224 × 224 patches.

Method	Base Model	Accuracy (%)
BCNN	VGG-16	72.01
CBP	VGG-16	76.04
HACBP	VGG-16	**77.12**
HBP	VGG-16	72.71
	Resnet-18	72.95
The proposed model on HBP	Resnet-18	73.92

Experiments on Stanford Dogs. The classification accuracy on Stanford dogs is summarized in Table 3. The training images are randomly cropped 224 × 224 patches. The test images are center cropped 224 × 224. We can observe significant improvement for the proposed model compared with others methods. The proposed model on CBP has 80.03% accuracy. We add the HA model on HBP network. The accuracy of the proposed HA model is 78.26 higher than HBP network.

Table 3. Table shows the comparison results on Stanford dogs dataset.

Method	Base Model	Accuracy (%)
BCNN	VGG-16	60.29
PHPQ[19]	Resnet-18	79.83
CBP	VGG-16	78.71
HACBP	VGG-16	78.74
WSHA-CBP	VGG-16	**80.03**
HBP	VGG-16	74.65
	Resnet-18	77.55
HAHBP	Resnet-18	78.26

Experiments on Oxford-Flower-17. Table 4 shows the comparison results on Oxford-Flower-17 dataset. The training images are also randomly cropped 224 × 224 patches. The test images are center cropped 224 × 224. CBP has 89.12% accuracy. The performance of accuracy is 90.88% When adding the proposed model to CBP.

Table 4. Table shows the comparison results on Oxford-Flower-17 dataset.

Method	Base Model	Accuracy (%)
BCNN	VGG-16	84.71
CBP	VGG-16	89.12
HACBP	VGG-16	89.56
WSHA-CBP	VGG-16	**90.88**
HBP	VGG-16	87.52
	Resnet-18	88.09
HAHBP	Resnet-18	90.15

3.3 Applications

Disaster scenes include earthquakes, tsunamis and tornadoes are applied in ours experiments. The database contains approximately 1,757 color images, which have three different disaster types: 760 images are earthquake images; 556 images are tsunami images and the rest 441 images are tornado images. The earthquake data were from the Haitian earthquake in 2010 and the earthquake in Christchurch, New Zealand in 2011; the tsunami data came from the 2004 Tohoku tsunami in Japan and the 2004 Indonesian tsunami; and the tornado data was taken after the Moore tornado in Oklahoma, USA in 2013 [13]. We divide the dataset into different damage-level: DL1, DL2, DL3, which stands for no damage, mild damage, severe damage.

Sample images are cropped 224 × 224. When disaster-scenes are classified by three different disaster types. The experimental results are shown in Table 5. When the dataset is divided into different damage-level. There are three level of each disaster types. The results are shown in Table 6.

Table 5. The prediction of different disaster-scene

Method	Base Model	Type Accuracy (%)
CBP	VGG-16	86.58
HACBP	VGG-16	86.89
WSHA-CBP	VGG-16	**87.10**

In Table 5, we can see that HACBP is better than CBP. When combined HA model with metric loss function. The accuracy has a 1% boost. In Table 6, the first column is the prediction of Tornado level. The second column is the prediction of Earthquake level. The third column is the prediction of Tsunami level.

For Table 6, the prediction of Tornado level is best. The original CBP has 84.10% accuracy. The HACBP is 87.12%. WSHA-CBP has 88.23% accuracy. For the prediction of Earthquake and Tsunami, the accuracies are 61.58% and 59.12 respectively.

Table 6. The prediction of damage level in different disaster

Method	Level Accuracy (%) of Tornado	Level Accuracy (%) of Earthquake	Level Accuracy (%) of Tsunami
CBP	84.10	59.26	54.38
HACBP	87.12	60.52	57.66
WSHACBP	**88.23**	**61.58**	**59.12**

We also give some sample transformation with different stage in the Fig. 2. The first column is the original disaster-scene images. The second column is the images after data augmentation. The third column is the output of attention map. The fourth column is the region of selected features. From the Fig. 2, the salient features are extracted effectively and useless information are filtered out.

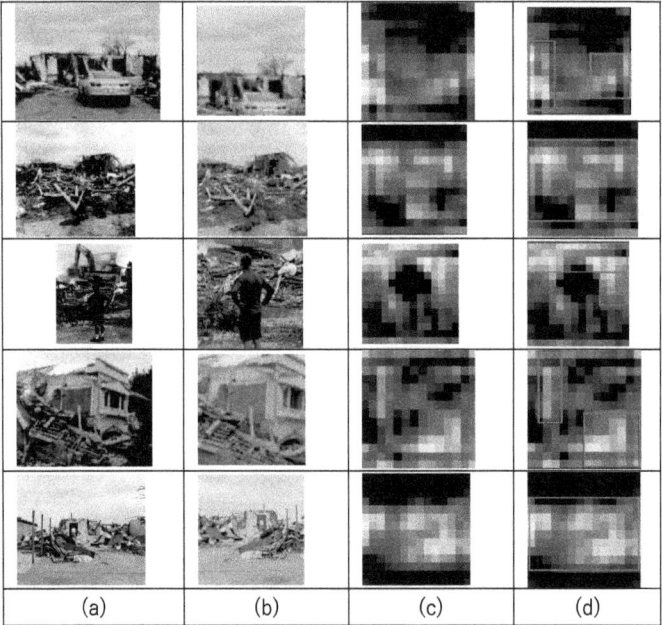

Fig. 2. Sample transformation with different stage: (a) Original images (b) images After the data augmentation (c) the output of attention map (d) The region of the selected feature

4 Conclusions

In this paper, the hierarchy attention model has been proposed for weakly supervised fine-grained image classification, which jointly integrates three level attention models. The hierarchy attentions jointly improve the multi-scale feature learning and have a progressive promotion. The metric loss function is based on clustering method which is unsupervised learning. The proposed approach is demonstrated to perform well on fine-grained image classification without requiring bounding box/part annotations. it should be beneficial to a wide variety of neural network models for applications.

Acknowledgments. This work is supported by the Open Foundation Project of Hubei Key Laboratory of Optical Information and Pattern Recognition, Wuhan Institute of Technology (Grant No. 202306).

References

1. Wah, C., et al.: The Caltech-UCSD Birds-200–2011 Dataset. Computation and Neural Systems Technical Report (2011)
2. OxFord Flowers 17. http://www.robots.ox.ac.uk/~vgg/data/bicos/
3. Khosla, A., et al.: Novel dataset for Fine-Grained Image Categorization. In: IEEE Conference on Computer Vision and Pattern Recognition (CVPR) (2011)
4. Krause, J., et al.: 3D object representations for fine-grained categorization. In: 4th IEEE Workshop on 3D Representation and Recognition, at ICCV 2013 (2013)
5. Wang, Y., Wang, Z.: A survey of recent work on fine-grained image classification techniques. J. Visual Commun. Image Represent. **59**, 210–214 (2019)
6. Cai, D., et al.: Convolutional low-resolution fine-grained classification. Pattern Recogn. Lett. **119**, 166–171 (2019)
7. Lin, T., Aruni, R., Maji, S.: Bilinear CNNs for Fine-Grained Visual Recognition (2017). arXiv:1504.07889v5
8. Gao, Y., et al.: Compact Bilinear Pooling (2016). arXiv:1511.06062v2
9. Dubey, A., et al.: Pairwise confusion for fine-grained visual classification. In: Computer Vision and Pattern Recognition (2018)
10. Xie, J.J., Zhong, Y.J., Zhang, J.G., et al.: A weakly supervised spatial group attention network for fine-grained visual recognition. Appl. Intell. **53**(20), 23301–23315 (2023). https://doi.org/10.1007/s10489-023-04627-z
11. Zeng, Z.Y., Wang, J.P., Chen, B., et al.: Pyramid hybrid pooling quantization for efficient fine-grained image retrieval. Pattern Recogn. Lett. **178**, 106–114 (2024). https://doi.org/10.1016/j.patrec.2023.12.022
12. Otholt, J., Meinel, C., Yang, H.J.: Guided cluster aggregation: a hierarchical approach to generalized category discovery. In: Proceedings of the IEEE/CVF Winter Conference on Applications of Computer Vision (WACV), pp. 2618–2627 (2024). https://openaccess.thecvf.com/content/WACV2024
13. Tang, S., Chen, Z.: Machine understanding of disaster-scene mechanics. IEEE J. Sel. Top. Appl. Earth Observ. Remote Sens. 21 (2019)

CS-KD: Confused Sample Knowledge Distillation for Semantic Segmentation of Aerial Imagery

Yue Sun[1,2], Lingfeng Huang[3], Qi Zhu[1,2], and Dong Liang[1,2(✉)]

[1] College of Computer Science and Technology, Nanjing University of Aeronautics and Astronautics, Nanjing, China
{sun.yue,zhuqi,liangdong}@nuaa.edu.cn
[2] Shenzhen Research Institute, Nanjing University of Aeronautics and Astronautics, Nanjing, China
[3] Shanghai Institute of Technical Physics, Chinese Academy of Sciences, Shanghai, China
huanglingfeng@mail.sitp.ac.cn

Abstract. Currently, semantic segmentation methods based on knowledge distillation (KD) mainly focus on transferring various structured knowledge to the student network and designing corresponding optimization goals to encourage the student network to imitate the output of the teacher network. However, these methods do not consider the impact of sample quality on model training. Especially for aerial images of complex scenes, problems such as object occlusion and boundary blur caused by factors such as illumination and imaging angle will introduce many confused samples. These confused samples can lead to labeling bias or incorrect predictions. Therefore, we propose a confused sample knowledge distillation method (CS-KD) and design an adaptive sample screening strategy. During the training process, CS-KD makes full use of the prediction capabilities of the teacher and student networks at all stages to screen confused samples pixel by pixel and adjust the importance of different training samples. Experiment results verify that, based on the Potsdam and Vaihingen benchmarks, CS-KD can achieve competitive performance compared with other state-of-the art KD methods. Additionally, our research showcases that CS-KD can integrate with existing KD methods to improve their upper performance bound.

Keywords: Semantic Segmentation · Knowledge Distillation · Sample Weighting · Confused Samples

1 Introduction

Semantic segmentation is one of the basic tasks of aerial remote sensing images, and its purpose is to classify each pixel in aerial images. It solves various practical problems through deep neural networks and is widely used in hazard assessment [1], urban planning [2], farmland detection [3], natural disaster detection [4] and other fields. It has important practical significance and application value.

The current deep neural networks, e.g., DeepLab [5, 6], PSPNet [7], HRNet [8], have achieved remarkable success and are widely used in semantic segmentation. However, these methods usually require a large number of pixel-level annotations to achieve good generalization performance, which incurs high storage and training costs. For devices with limited resources, there are significant challenges in deploying these models with high computational complexity and many model parameters. Therefore, model compression has become an important research topic. Model quantization [9] and pruning [10] help reduce inference costs. In contrast, knowledge distillation (KD) [11, 12] transplants the segmentation performance of cumbersome networks into lightweight networks, which is a simple but effective technique.

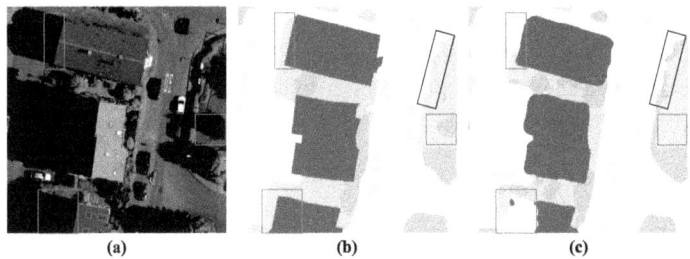

Fig. 1. The confused examples of problems existing from the Vaihingen datasets: (a) Image, (b) Ground Truth (GT), (c) Prediction.

Although semantic segmentation methods based on KD have been successful to a certain extent, there are still some limitations for large-scale aerial images of complex scenes. First, various interference factors may affect the aerial image, such as weather, occlusion, illumination and imaging angle changes. These factors may lead to reduced image quality and the appearance of many confused samples, thereby introducing labeling bias. The model's performance degrades due to learning this incorrect annotation information. As shown in Fig. 1, in the two red boxes on the left, the shadows of tall buildings (blue) block low vegetation (cyan). In the red box on the right, the shadows of tall trees (green) block low vegetation (cyan). This makes occluded vegetation invisible on aerial remote sensing images, causing labeling bias or model prediction errors. In addition, aerial remote sensing scenes have complex and special characteristics. Although there are differences between different types of objects, pixel features can easily be confused in complex backgrounds or situations where objects are intertwined. As shown in the black box in Fig. 1, the pixel features of trees (green) and low vegetation (cyan) are similar, so it is easy to confuse the pixel features, leading to incorrect category classification. These factors increase the challenge of semantic segmentation of aerial imagery.

To cope with the challenge of confused samples in complex aerial scenes and fully employ KD's advantages, we propose a new confused sample knowledge distillation (CS-KD) method. Specifically, in the CS-KD method, we design an adaptive sample screening strategy to measure the quality of samples through the weighting mechanism of teacher and student networks. This collaborative approach provides accurate sample quality assessment to identify confused samples. Then, CS-KD adopts the method of allocating low weights to alleviate the negative impact of confused samples on the student network, thereby improving its segmentation performance. In addition, as an independent KD training strategy, CS-KD can also be combined with existing KD methods to improve the model's upper performance bound.

The main contributions of this work can be summarized as follows:

- We propose a confused sample knowledge distillation (CS-KD) method. At the same time, the proposed CS-KD can also be integrated with existing KD methods to improve their upper performance bound.
- We propose an adaptive sample screening strategy to evaluate the samples' quality and allocate low weights to reduce the negative impact of confused samples on the student network, which is more conducive to stable training of the model in complex scenes.
- The proposed CS-KD can achieve effective segmentation performance in complex aerial remote sensing scenes, providing a reliable and efficient solution for aerial image segmentation tasks.

2 Related Work

2.1 Semantic Segmentation

Fully convolutional network (FCN) [13] was the cornerstone of deep learning technology applied to semantic segmentation problems. SegNet [14] utilized the Maxpooling indices to enhance location information and improve efficiency. PSPNet [7] employed the pyramid pooling module to integrate context and enhance the ability to obtain global information. DeepLabv3 [5] captured multi-scale context information using multiple parallel atrous rates of different proportions. Most efforts have focused on designing inexpensive, lightweight networks to solve this problem. Enet [15] utilized an asymmetric encoder-decoder structure to reduce parameters in a network. ICNet [16] utilized low-resolution semantic information and details of high-resolution images to recover and refine segmentation predictions with low computational cost progressively. BiSeNet [17] balanced speed and accuracy by designing spatial paths with small steps and a contextual path with fast downsampling.

2.2 Knowledge Distillation for Semantic Segmentation

Hinton et al. [18] first introduced the concept of knowledge distillation (KD). Most previous studies on KD, such as [19, 20], focused on image classification. However, image-level KD does not take the locally structured information for semantic segmentation into account, so it is with natural defects for pixel-level semantic segmentation. Most efforts have focused on defining the knowledge for the segmentation task to solve this problem. Liu et al. [12] extracted structured knowledge from teacher network to student network by using two structured distillation schemes. Wang et al. [21] put forward a new intra-class feature variation distillation (IFVD), which transformed the cumbersome teacher model into a compact student model. Shu et al. [22] introduced a new channel-wise KD method that minimized differences between teacher and student networks by utilizing asymmetric KL divergence. Feng et al. [23] improved the classification accuracy of existing compact networks by capturing similar knowledge in the pixel and category dimensions respectively. To solve the problem that the previous techniques ignore the global semantic relationship between pixels in different images, Yang et al. [11] attempted to model pixel–pixel and pixel–region comparison relationships in semantic segmentation tasks as knowledge and transfer global pixel correlation from teachers to students for semantic segmentation.

3 Proposed Method

3.1 Objective of Confused Sample Knowledge Distillation

Semantic segmentation is a dense pixel-level prediction task that assigns a specific class to each pixel in an image. Given an input image I with dimensions $W \times H \times 3$, the feature extractor of a segmenter first extracts a feature map F, where H and W represent the height and width of the input image and feature map, respectively. The categorical logit map Z is generated from feature map F by applying a classifier. Optimization is then performed using a cross-entropy loss:

$$L_{task} = \frac{1}{H \times W} \sum_{h=1}^{H} \sum_{w=1}^{W} CE\left(\sigma\left(Z_{h,w}\right), y_{h,w}\right) \tag{1}$$

where $y_{h,w}$ denotes the ground-truth label for the (h, w)-th pixel, and $Z_{h,w}$ denotes the output logits for the (h, w)-th pixel. The softmax function σ generates the category probability, and CE is the cross-entropy loss to measure the difference between the ground truth and category probability.

The existing KD methods usually use a pixel-wise alignment among class probabilities between a cumbersome teacher network t and a lightweight student network s to obtain a distillation loss, which can be formulated as

$$L_{kd} = \frac{1}{H \times W} \sum_{h=1}^{H} \sum_{w=1}^{W} KL\left[\sigma\left(\frac{Z_{h,w}^{s}}{T}\right) || \sigma\left(\frac{Z_{h,w}^{t}}{T}\right)\right] \tag{2}$$

where $Z_{h,w}^{s}$ and $Z_{h,w}^{t}$ represent the output logits for the (h, w)-th pixel produced from the student and the teacher network, respectively. σ function calculates the category probability of the (h, w)-th pixel generated by the student and teacher networks, respectively. KL denotes the Kullback-Leibler divergence, which measures the difference between two probability distributions. The parameter T represents the temperature taken by distillation and reflects the label's softening degree. For a fair comparison with previous works [11, 12], we set $T = 1$ in our experiments.

To solve the problem of existing KD methods not considering sample quality in complex aerial remote sensing scenes, we propose an adaptive sample screening strategy based on sample quality assessment. This strategy is employed to generate quality scores for the samples. We utilize the quality score of each pixel as a weight to determine the contribution of each pixel. We use Eq. (3) to introduce the weight W_{cskd} into the loss function. The process of generating weight W_{cskd} will be described below.

$$L_{CSKD} = W_{cskd} \cdot L_{task} + L_{kd} \tag{3}$$

3.2 Confused Sample Knowledge Distillation (CS-KD)

In this section, we propose an adaptive sample screening strategy based on KD, and Fig. 2 shows the process of this strategy.

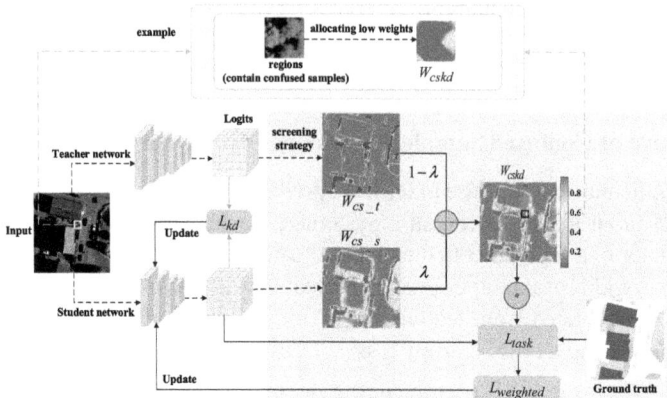

Fig. 2. The proposed distillation method. An illustrative example of allocating low weights to confused samples is provided above the method diagram.

Screening of confused samples requires measuring the sample quality score as a starting point. The original idea is to use the cross-entropy loss of the network as a criterion to evaluate the sample quality. After introducing KD, the most straightforward method is to use the cross-entropy loss of the teacher model as an evaluation criterion of sample quality. However, relying on the teacher to assess sample quality does not consider the student's needs and is inconsistent with the student's cognitive processes. Based on this motivation, we propose a teacher-student cooperation method to evaluate sample quality and dynamically adjust the collaboration weights between the teacher and student networks as the student network's cognitive levels increase. The sample quality score is calculated by a weighted combination of teacher and student networks. For each pixel in the image, first obtain the cross-entropy loss of the teacher and student networks respectively:

$$W_{cs\_s} = CE\left(\sigma\left(Z^s_{h,w}\right), y_{h,w}\right) \tag{4}$$

$$W_{cs\_t} = CE\left(\sigma\left(Z^t_{h,w}\right), y_{h,w}\right) \tag{5}$$

Then, utilize the CE loss weighting of the teacher and student networks to obtain the sample quality score of each pixel:

$$W_{cs} = \lambda \cdot W_{cs\_s} + (1 - \lambda) \cdot W_{cs\_t} \tag{6}$$

where λ is the parameter used to adjust the weight of the student and teacher networks. In the early stages of model training, relying on the student network to judge sample quality may transmit and amplify errors, posing challenges to correcting the student network. In contrast, the supervisory information provided by the teacher network is more accurate and reliable. Therefore, we introduce a warm-up strategy to ensure the stability and reliability of the weights. In practice, we set the initial value of λ to 0. After a warm-up period, the student network can generate more accurate pseudo-labels and calculate sample weights, and the value of λ gradually increases to 0.5. Then, after obtaining the W_{cs} of each pixel, normalize it within the [0, 1] range to obtain each pixel's relative weight W_{cskd}. The calculation formula is as follows:

$$W_{cskd} = \exp\{-W_{cs}\} \tag{7}$$

The value of W_{cskd} reflects the confusing degree of each pixel, with smaller values indicating that the pixel is more likely to be confused. These confused samples may cause the network to learn incorrect annotation information, thus affecting the network's performance. We allocate low weights to mitigate the negative impact of confused samples on the student network's performance, and apply the weight W_{cskd} to the loss function L_{task} of the semantic segmentation task:

$$L_{weighted} = W_{cskd} \cdot L_{task} \tag{8}$$

Finally, we use the CS-KD strategy to calculate the weighted segmentation loss $L_{weighted}$ for each pixel, and the student network updates the network's parameters by minimizing the L_{CSKD}:

$$L_{CSKD} = L_{weighted} + L_{kd} = W_{cskd} \cdot L_{task} + L_{kd} \tag{9}$$

3.3 Integrating with Other Approaches

Since CS-KD only affects L_{task} loss, it can be integrated with other KD methods without introducing additional optimization goals. In experiments, we integrate CS-KD with AT [19], CWD [22], DSD [23] and CIRKD [11] methods. Taking the CIRKD [11] methods as an example, we will demonstrate how to integrate CS-KD into CIRKD and derive the corresponding distillation loss formula.

The total loss defined by CIRKD [11]:

$$L_{CIRKD} = L_{task} + L_{kd} + \alpha L_{batch\_p2p} + \beta L_{memory\_p2p} + \gamma L_{memory\_p2r} \tag{10}$$

where L_{batch_p2p} represents distillation loss of mini-batch-based pixel-to-pixel, L_{memory_p2p} denotes distillation loss of memory-based pixel-to-pixel, L_{memory_p2r} denotes distillation loss of memory-based pixel-to-region. α, β and γ are the weight balance parameters. The further calculation details of L_{batch_p2p}, L_{memory_p2p} and L_{memory_p2r} are described in [11].

The distillation loss of CS-KD:

$$L_{CSKD} = W_{cskd} \cdot L_{task} + L_{kd} \tag{11}$$

After integrating CS-KD, the modified distillation loss of the CIRKD method is derived as follows:

$$L_{CIRKD\_CSKD} = W_{cskd} \cdot L_{task} + L_{kd} + \alpha L_{batch\_p2p} + \beta L_{memory\_p2p} + \gamma L_{memory\_p2r} \tag{12}$$

In this new loss term, we follow the default parameter settings in CIRKD [11], setting the weighting parameter α to 1, β to 0.1, and γ to 0.1. Moreover, CS-KD can seamlessly integrate with other semantic segmentation methods based on KD. This integration allows us to enhance the performance of the student network further from existing approaches.

4 Experiments and Results Analysis

4.1 Experimental Set

This paper carried out experiments on the two image sets of the ISPRS [26] 2D Semantic Labeling Challenge to validate the proposed method. We use DeepLabV3 [5] with ResNet-101 backbone [27] as the cumbersome teacher network for all experiments. For student networks, we use various segmentation architectures to verify the effectiveness of distillation methods. Specifically, DeepLabV3 and PSPNet [7] with different backbones of ResNet-18 and MobileNetV2 [28] are adopted. The networks are trained using mini-batch stochastic gradient descent (SGD) with a momentum of 0.9 and weight decay of 0.0005. We set the number of iterations to 40,000. The learning rate is initialized at 0.02 and is multiplied by $\left(1 - \frac{iter}{iter_{total}}\right)^{0.9}$ during training. In our experiments, we use a 512 × 512 patch size, which fits our memory budget. Normal data augmentation techniques such as random flipping and scaling in the [0.5, 2] range are applied during training. The temperature T is set to be 1. All experiments are conducted on two 3090 GPUs using mixed-precision training.

4.2 Comparing with Existing KD Methods

To verify the performance of CS-KD, we compare it with recent semantic segmentation methods based on KD, including AT [19], CWD [22], DSD [23] and CIRKD [11] on the above two representative datasets. The experimental results are shown in Tables 1 and 2. In experiments, we adopt DeepLabV3 with ResNet-101 backbone as the teacher network, denoted as "Teacher", and DeepLabV3 with ResNet-18 backbone as the student network, denoted as "Student".

The experimental results on the Potsdam dataset are shown in Table 1. All structured KD methods improve the segmentation performance of the student network compared to training without KD. Our CS-KD outperforms other KD methods regarding mIoU, mF_1, and OA, with significant advantages. The highest IoU were obtained by identifying four categories except Car. In addition, the qualitative results are shown in Fig. 3. The validity of our proposed approach is intuitively demonstrated, and the semantic labels produced by CS-KD are more consistent with the ground truth. In order to further verify the effectiveness of our network, we conducted experiments on the Vaihingen dataset, and the experimental results are shown in Table 2. The highest IoU were obtained in identifying the three categories of low vegetation, trees, and cars. The qualitative results are shown in Fig. 4.

Table 1. Experimental results on the Postdam dataset.

Method	IoU					mIoU (%)	mF_1 (%)	OA (%)
	Imp.Surf	Building	Low veg	Tree	Car			
Teacher	84.46	92.56	75.47	74.83	81.64	81.79	84.83	96.16
Student	81.16	89.97	72.69	73.25	76.12	78.62	81.95	95.53
+KD [18]	81.83	89.77	73.51	74.26	75.85	79.05	82.67	95.64
+AT [19]	82.73	90.69	74.20	74.40	78.01	80.01	83.40	95.85
+CWD [22]	83.55	91.06	73.79	72.85	78.71	79.99	83.84	95.81
+DSD [23]	83.44	91.13	73.59	73.42	**79.10**	80.14	83.65	95.82
+CIRKD [11]	83.40	91.48	74.22	74.20	78.74	80.41	83.91	95.91
+Ours	**83.97**	**91.55**	**75.14**	74.76	79.08	**80.90**	**84.14**	**96.02**

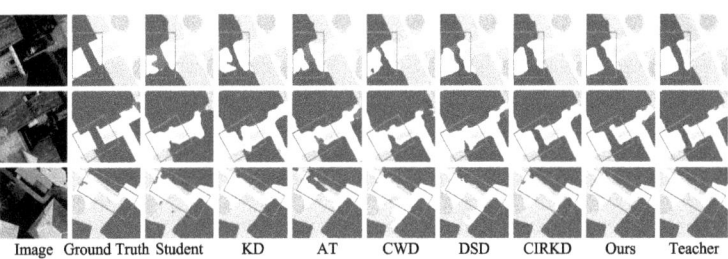

Image Ground Truth Student KD AT CWD DSD CIRKD Ours Teacher

Fig. 3. Examples of segmentation results on the Potsdam dataset. Legend—white: impervious surfaces, blue: buildings, cyan: low vegetation, green: trees, yellow: cars, red: clutter/background (best viewed in color) (color figure online).

4.3 Ablation Study

Ablation Study About the Different Student Networks. To verify the effectiveness and robustness of our CS-KD, we evaluated different student networks on the Potsdam dataset. The experimental results are shown in Table 3. It can be observed from the experimental results that CS-KD achieved considerable results in all student networks, proving the robustness of CS-KD to changes in student network architecture. When using

Table 2. Experimental results on the Postdam dataset.

Method	IoU					mIoU (%)	mF_1 (%)	OA (%)
	Imp.Surf	Building	Low veg	Tree	Car			
Teacher	84.16	88.62	68.12	77.05	69.13	77.42	83.73	95.61
Student	82.58	85.82	64.91	76.04	63.95	74.66	81.56	95.10
+KD [18]	82.84	87.11	67.30	76.05	63.38	75.34	82.11	95.24
+AT [19]	82.80	**87.58**	66.47	75.99	64.64	75.50	82.14	95.27
+CWD [22]	82.81	86.48	66.62	75.70	64.81	75.28	82.04	95.20
+DSD [23]	82.79	86.79	66.28	76.30	65.04	75.44	82.08	95.21
+CIRKD [11]	**83.00**	86.70	66.72	76.07	65.24	75.55	82.34	95.26
+Ours	82.92	87.25	**67.70**	**76.35**	**66.22**	**76.09**	**82.95**	**95.36**

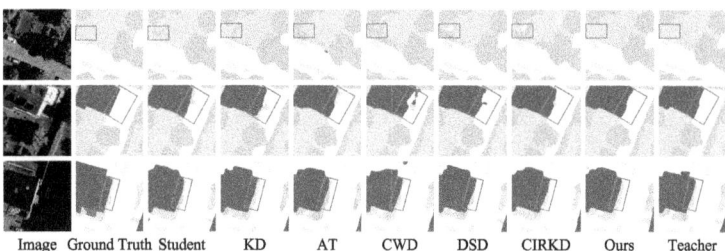

Image   Ground Truth   Student   KD   AT   CWD   DSD   CIRKD   Ours   Teacher

Fig. 4. Examples of segmentation results on the Vaihingen dataset.

a more robust backbone network, the accuracy is improved and is closer to the performance of the teacher network. It should be noted that we use lightweight MobileNetV2 as the backbone network, aiming to verify the performance of CS-KD on lightweight networks to explore the possibility of deploying our method on mobile devices.

Ablation Study About the Effect of λ. We conducted ablation experiments on λ to explore its impact on CS-KD. λ is a parameter used to adjust the weight ratio of student and teacher networks. In Table 4, "[0,0]" means that the value of λ is 0, and only the weight of the teacher network participates in the calculation of loss; "[1,1]" means that only the weight of the student network participates in the loss calculation; "[0.5,0.5]" means that the value of λ is always 0.5, and the weights of the teacher and student networks participate in the calculation of loss in the same proportion; "[0,0.5]" means that the value of λ changes from 0 gradually rises to 0.5, and the weight of the student network gradually participates in the calculation; "[0,1]" means that the value of λ gradually increases from 0 to 1; "[0,0,0.5]" is the method used by CS-KD. A warm-up

Table 3. Ablation study about backbone. * denotes that we do not initialize the backbone with ImageNet [29] pre-trained weights.

Method	mIoU (%)	mF_1 (%)	OA (%)
T: DeepLabV3-Res101	81.79	84.83	96.16
S: DeepLabV3-Res18	78.62	81.95	95.53
+CS-KD	80.90	84.14	96.02
S: DeepLabV3-Res18*	76.76	80.95	95.18
+CS-KD	77.65	81.79	95.36
S: DeepLabV3-MBV2	78.68	82.83	95.59
+CS-KD	79.73	83.35	95.84
S: PSPNet-Res18	79.27	82.83	95.78
+CS-KD	80.18	83.51	95.94

Table 4. Ablation study about the effect of λ in our CS-KD method.

λ	[0,0]	[1,1]	[0.5,0.5]	[0,0.5]	[0,1]	[0,0,0.5]
mIoU (%)	80.44	80.41	80.56	80.64	80.50	**80.90**

phase accounting for 10% of the total iterations is added. The experimental results are shown in Table 4. It can be observed that under the setting of "[0,0,0.5]", the mIoU of the network reaches the highest. The analysis shows that the sample weights provided entirely by the teacher network do not consider the needs of the student network, and the sample weights wholly provided by the immature student network easily transmit and amplify errors, which brings challenges to the correction of the student network. Therefore, the two methods' mIoU is the worst result among these sets of experiments. On the contrary, first giving the model a warm-up stage, the supervision information from the teacher network in the early stage of training is more conducive to the convergence of the student network. The student network acquires judgment ability as the training phase develops and gradually increases the proportion of sample weights provided by the student network to 0.5, reaching the highest mIoU.

4.4 Integrating with Existing KD Methods

We evaluate the performance impact of integrating CS-KD into existing KD methods on the Postdam dataset. We use DeepLabV3-Res18 as the student network and explore the effectiveness of CS-KD in the simplest integrated way under the experimental settings of the original method without changing any hyperparameters. The experimental results are shown in Table 5. Among the five baseline methods, CS-KD effectively improves the performance of all methods and further narrows the performance gap between the student and teacher networks.

Table 5. Integrating with existing KD methods.

Method	mIoU (%)	mF_1 (%)	OA (%)
T: DeepLabV3-Res101	81.79	84.83	96.16
S: DeepLabV3-Res18	78.62	81.95	95.53
+AT [19]	80.01	83.40	95.85
+AT [19]+CS-KD	80.34	83.69	95.87
+CWD [22]	79.99	83.84	95.81
+CWD [22]+CS-KD	80.40	83.88	95.91
+DSD [23]	80.12	83.65	95.82
+DSD [23]+CS-KD	80.36	83.81	95.89
+CIRKD [11]	80.41	83.91	95.91
+CIRKD [11]+CS-KD	80.86	84.21	96.01
+KD [18]	79.04	82.67	95.64
+KD [18]+CS-KD	80.90	84.14	96.02

5 Conclusions

We propose the CS-KD method for complex aerial image semantic segmentation tasks. Unlike previous feature-based and response-based distillation methods, we utilize weight scores that measure the degree of confusion of samples as knowledge to transfer from the teacher network to the student network and adjust the learning process accordingly, effectively improving the overall performance of the student network. CS-KD is easily integrated with existing distillation methods. Experimental results show that CS-KD outperforms existing KD methods. In future research, we will further explore the effectiveness of CS-KD in more complex scenes or other segmentation tasks.

Acknowledgments. This work is supported in part by the National Natural Science Foundation of China under grant 62272229, the Natural Science Foundation of Jiangsu Province under grant BK20222012, and Shenzhen Science and Technology Program JCYJ20230807142001004. The authors would like to thank all the anonymous reviewers for their constructive comments.

References

1. Pham, H.N., et al.: A new deep learning approach based on bilateral semantic segmentation models for sustainable estuarine wetland ecosystem management. Sci. Total Environ. **838**, 155826 (2022)
2. Trenčanová, B., Proença, V., Bernardino, A.: Development of semantic maps of vegetation cover from UAV images to support planning and management in finegrained fire-prone landscapes. Remote Sens. **14**(5), 1262 (2022)
3. Sheng, H., Chen, X., Su, J., Rajagopal, R., Ng, A.: Effective data fusion with generalized vegetation index: evidence from land cover segmentation in agriculture. In: Proceedings of the IEEE/CVF Conference on Computer Vision and Pattern Recognition Workshops, pp. 60–61 (2020)

4. Ji, C., Zhou, W., Lei, J., Ye, L.: Infrared and visible image fusion via multiscale receptive field amplification fusion network. IEEE Signal Process. Lett. (2023)
5. Chen, L.C., Papandreou, G., Schroff, F., Adam, H.: Rethinking atrous convolution for semantic image segmentation (2017). arXiv:1706.05587
6. Chen, L.C., Zhu, Y., Papandreou, G., Schroff, F., Adam, H.: Encoder-decoder with atrous separable convolution for semantic image segmentation. In: ECCV (2018)
7. Zhao, H., Shi, J., Qi, X., Wang, X., Jia, J.: Pyramid scene parsing network. In: Proceedings of the IEEE/CVF Conference on Computer Vision and Pattern Recognition (2017)
8. Wang, J., et al.: Deep high-resolution representation learning for visual recognition. TPAMI **43**(10), 3349–3364 (2020)
9. Wu, J., Leng, C., Wang, Y., Hu, Q., Cheng, J.: Quantized convolutional neural networks for mobile devices. In: Proceedings of the IEEE/CVF Conference on Computer Vision and Pattern Recognition, pp. 4820–4828 (2016)
10. He, W., Wu, M., Liang, M., Lam, S.K.: CAP: context-aware pruning for semantic segmentation. In: Proceedings of the IEEE/CVF Winter Conference on Applications of Computer Vision, pp. 960–969 (2021)
11. Yang, C., Zhou, H., An, Z., Jiang, X., Xu, Y., Zhang, Q.: Cross-image relational knowledge distillation for semantic segmentation. In: Proceedings of the IEEE/CVF Conference on Computer Vision and Pattern Recognition (2022)
12. Liu, Y., Chen, K., Liu, C., Qin, Z., Luo, Z., Wang, J.: Structured knowledge distillation for semantic segmentation. In: Proceedings of the IEEE/CVF Conference on Computer Vision and Pattern Recognition (2019)
13. Long, J., Shelhamer, E., Darrell, T.: Fully convolutional networks for semantic segmentation. In: Proceedings of the IEEE Conference on Computer Vision and Pattern Recognition, pp. 3431–3440 (2015)
14. Badrinarayanan, V., Kendall, A., Cipolla, R.: SegNet: a deep convolutional encoder-decoder architecture for image segmentation. IEEE Trans. Pattern Anal. Mach. Intell. **39**(12), 2481–2495 (2017)
15. Paszke, A., Chaurasia, A., Kim, S., Culurciello, E.: ENet: a deep neural network architecture for real-time semantic segmentation (2016). arXiv:1606.02147
16. Zhao, H., Qi, X., Shen, X., Shi, J., Jia, J.: ICNet for real-time semantic segmentation on high-resolution images. In: ECCV (2018)
17. Yu, C., Wang, J., Peng, C., Gao, C., Yu, G., Sang, N.: BiSeNet: Bilateral segmentation network for real-time semantic segmentation. In: ECCV (2018)
18. Hinton, G., Vinyals, O., Dean, J.: Distilling the knowledge in a neural network. In: NeurIPS (2015)
19. Zagoruyko, S., Komodakis, N.: Paying more attention to attention: improving the performance of convolutional neural networks via attention transfer. In: ICLR (2017)
20. Peng, B., et al.: Correlation congruence for knowledge distillation. In: ICCV (2019)
21. Wang, Y., Zhou, W., Jiang, T., Bai, X., Xu, Y.: Intra-class feature variation distillation for semantic segmentation. In: ECCV (2020)
22. Shu, C., Liu, Y., Gao, J., Yan, Z., Shen, C.: Channel-wise knowledge distillation for dense prediction. In: ICCV (2021)
23. Feng, Y., Sun, X., Diao, W., Li, J., Gao, X.: Double similarity distillation for semantic image segmentation. TIP **30**, 5363–5376 (2021)
24. Yu, T., Kumar, S., Gupta, A., Levine, S., Hausman, K., Finn, C.: Gradient surgery for multi-task learning. Adv. Neural. Inf. Process. Syst. **33**, 5824–5836 (2020)
25. Kendall, A., Gal, Y.: What uncertainties do we need in Bayesian deep learning for computer vision? NeurIPS **30** (2017)
26. Rottensteiner, F., Sohn, G., Gerke, M., Wegner, J.D.: ISPRS Semantic Labeling Contest. ISPRS, Leopoldshöhe, Germany **1**(4), 4 (2014)

27. He, K., Zhang, X., Ren, S., Sun, J.: Deep residual learning for image recognition. In: Proceedings of the IEEE/CVF Conference on Computer Vision and Pattern Recognition (2016)
28. Sandler, M., Howard, A., Zhu, M., Zhmoginov, A., Chen, L.C.: MobileNetV2: Inverted residuals and linear bottlenecks. In: Proceedings of the IEEE/CVF Conference on Computer Vision and Pattern Recognition, pp. 4510–4520 (2018)
29. Russakovsky, O., et al.: ImageNet large scale visual recognition challenge. Int. J. Comput. Vis. **115**, 211–252 (2015)

CD-Font: One-Shot Font Generation via Conditional Diffusion Model with Disentangled Guidance

Siyi Chen, Zhenhua Li(✉), and Dong Liang

School of Computer Science and Technology, MIIT Key Laboratory of Pattern Analysis and Machine Intelligence, Nanjing University of Aeronautics and Astronautics, Nanjing, China
{csy624,zhenhua.li,liangdong}@nuaa.edu.cn

Abstract. One-shot font generation aims to create a new font library by extracting style information from the reference font. Most existing font generation methods rely on GAN-based image-to-image translation frameworks, which still suffer from unstable training and imprecise character structure generation due to the nature of adversarial training. In this paper, we propose a one-shot font generation framework named CD-Font, based on a conditional diffusion model with style-content disentangled guidance. Unlike existing methods, we use two different encoders to separate the representations for styles and contents and fuse them as conditions of the diffusion model. Specifically, we concatenate the content image with the noisy image throughout all denoising steps to improve the integrity of character structures. During inference, we present a disentangled guidance sampling strategy to enable the generated font images to exhibit strong correlations with both the reference image and the target character. Extensive experiments and user studies demonstrate that our CD-Font outperforms current methods in one-shot font generation. Furthermore, we apply our method to cross-lingual font generation, showing its promising cross-lingual capability.

Keywords: Automatic Font Generation · Diffusion Model · One-Shot Image Generation

1 Introduction

Automatic font generation is a challenging task that has gained great attention recently [1–3]. Its objective is to generate stylized images of various characters based on the style of reference samples. This approach can significantly save time and effort for expert designers when creating new font libraries, as they only need to manually design a few reference images. This is particularly useful for languages with complex character sets, such as Chinese, Korean, and Japanese. Font generation has a wide range of applications in real world scenarios. It empowers designers, advertisers, and publishers to create unique and visually captivating fonts, enhancing brand identities, print materials, and digital media. Moreover, it aids in preserving and studying ancient writing systems, contributing to academic research and cultural preservation.

With the advancements in deep neural networks, the quality of generated images has been dramatically improved [2–4]. In the early days, most font generation methods were based on Generative Adversarial Networks (GANs) [5]. Zi2zi [6] is the first to employ GANs for Chinese font generation. However, it can only handle fonts that appear in the training set and requires a substantial amount of paired data for supervised training. Numerous few-shot font generation (FFG) methods have been proposed to address these limitations. FFG approaches require only a few (few-shot) or even a single (one-shot) style image as a reference to generate font images. Meanwhile, many GAN-based FFG works [7, 1, 2] have verified that style-content disentanglement can efficiently combine the style features extracted from the reference images with the content features of the content images to generate unseen contents of the target font. Although GAN-based font generation methods have achieved impressive visual quality, their adversarial training nature often results in unstable training and less diversity in generation. Recently, diffusion models have gained great popularity, and many works [8, 9] have witnessed its powerful generative ability. Diff-Font [10] first employs a diffusion model to generate fonts by using predefined tokens to represent the content and extracting the font style from a reference sample. It incorporates strokes as a finer-grained condition to improve the integrity of the generated characters. However, Diff-Font [10] has limitations in its ability to handle unseen characters during inference. To generate a complete font library, it requires incorporating all characters into the training set which significantly impairs the model's generalization ability.

Reference   Imitation results generated by our method

Fig. 1. An ancient poem generated by our method, with each line representing a different font style. The font images in the first column serves as a reference for each style.

The limitations mentioned above highlight the need for further research and development in the field of font generation. Therefore, we propose a diffusion model-based framework for one-shot font generation. As shown in Fig. 1, our method can generate font images of the corresponding style only given one reference image. To achieve this, we use a pre-trained content encoder and a pre-trained style encoder to extract content features and style features, respectively. We also inject the content image into the denoising network to strengthen the control of the character structures. Once the model is trained, it can generate unseen styles with unseen contents, offering greater flexibility and efficiency in font generation task.

In summary, the main contributions of this paper are as follows:

- We propose a one-shot font generation framework based on the conditional diffusion model, which can preserve the structural integrity of the output images without using additional component data.
- During the sampling procedure, we introduce disentangled classifier-free guidance to effectively align the style and character of the generated image with the reference image and target content. It ensures a strong correlation between the input conditions and the output font images.
- Extensive experiments demonstrate competitive performance of our method compared to existing methods, further validating the efficacy of the proposed framework. Moreover, we apply our model to cross-lingual font generation, showing its generalization ability.

2 Related Work

2.1 Few-Shot Font Generation

Few-shot font generation aims to generate a new font library with only a few reference images. Most existing methods in this field adopt the style-content disentanglement paradigm to generate images with various style-content combinations. Based on the representation of style features, existing methods can be broadly categorized into two groups: global style representations and component-based feature representations. Methods using global representations [11, 12] typically model font styles as global statistic features extracted from reference images. On the other hand, component-based font generation approaches [13, 14] usually decompose the whole image into multiple parts or components to extract style information from local regions.

To reduce the dependency on components, MX-Font [7] uses multi-head encoders to implicitly extract different local concepts in a weakly-supervised manner. CG-GAN [15] employs a component-level discriminator to provide fine-grained supervision to the generator. However, these two methods still require component-level labels. FS-Font [16] learns the spatial correspondence between the content and reference glyphs and extracts fine-grained local styles from the references. However, the approach requires carefully selecting reference sets to cover as many specific components as possible. DG-Font [1] uses deformable convolutional networks (DCN) [17] instead of conventional convolutional networks to learn the spatial transformations from the source font to the target font, but suffer from artifacts and incomplete style transfer. CF-Font [2] introduces a content fusion module that uses fused content features to reduce the gap between the source and target domains.

Most of the mentioned methods are based on GANs, which can suffer from training instability issues. To further improve the quality of image generation, Diff-Font [10] introduces diffusion models to one-shot font generation. It treats different characters as different tokens, limiting its ability to generate unseen characters. In addition, Diff-Font uses a stroke dataset that costs human resources to label. These are extremely inconvenient in the few-shot font generation task.

3 Proposed Approach

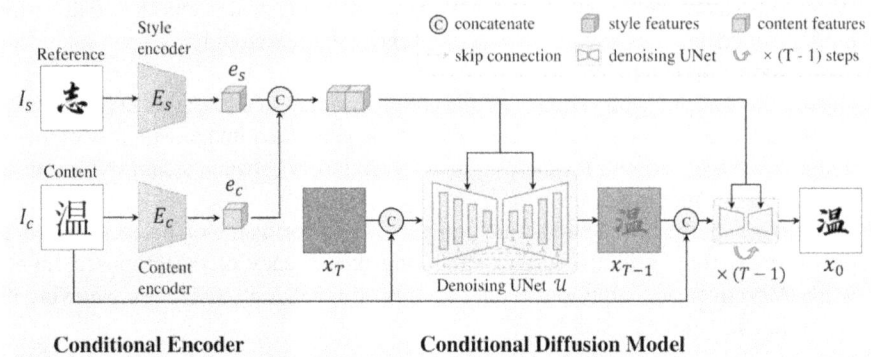

Fig. 2. Framework of our proposed method.

Overall Framework. Figure 2 presents an overview of the proposed approach, which consists of a conditional encoder module and a conditional diffusion module. The goal of our method is to train a conditional diffusion model $p_\theta(x|I_s, I_c)$ given a reference image I_s and a content image I_c. The trained diffusion model can generate a final result x that not only meets the character content matching requirement but also preserves the distinctive style of the reference image.

The denoising network $\mathcal{U}$ in our method adopts the architecture of UNet [18], comprising an encoder and a decoder. The style encoder E_s captures the style patterns of the reference image I_s, while the content encoder E_c extracts the content features from the content image I_c. By incorporating the concatenated features, the denoising network $\mathcal{U}$ effectively preserves crucial style information and structural details throughout the image generation process. To ensure precise control over unseen contents, we further concatenate the content image and the noisy image at each denoising step. This enables us to maintain the desired structure of the character and enhance the generation quality of font images.

3.1 Conditional Encoder

As shown in Fig. 2, the conditional encoder module consists of a style encoder E_s and a content encoder E_c. Both of the encoders are pre-trained and frozen during the training process of the conditional diffusion model. The pre-trained style encoder E_s and content encoder E_c are responsible for encoding the reference image I_s to style condition e_s and the content image I_c to content condition e_c, respectively. Specifically, e_s represents the unique style pattern of the reference image. e_c indicates the character structure of the input content image.

Style Condition. We use a pre-trained style encoder to extract style features. The style encoder is trained following DG-Font [1], which adopts the convolutional neural network architecture of VGG. The output of the convolutional layer is then flattened into a vector using the flatten operation. Subsequently, the flattened vector is passed through a linear layer, which produces the style features e_s. The extraction process can be summarized by the equation:

$$e_s = Proj(flatten(E_s(I_s))) \tag{1}$$

where E_s is the pre-trained style extractor, *flatten* represents unwrapping the multi-dimensional input data into a one-dimensional vector. A linear projection layer *Proj* is applied to unify the dimensionality with other conditions.

Content Condition. In contrast to Diff-Font [10], which uses predefined tokens to represent different characters and cannot handle font generation for unseen contents, we pre-train a content encoder with contrastive learning to encode content condition. Specifically, we feed an image as an anchor and select images with the same content but different styles as positive samples, while choosing images with different contents but same style as negative samples. This approach encourages the encoder to focus more on the content of the image and disregard the variations in font styles. As a result, the extracted features can better represent the structural information of characters. The training of the content encoder is guided by a Triplet Margin Loss, defined as follows:

$$L_{triplet} = max(d(a, p) - d(a, n) + margin, 0) \tag{2}$$

Here, a represents the latent features of the anchor, p represents the latent features of the positive sample, and n represents the latent features of the negative sample. The term $d(a, p)$ represents the distance between the anchor and the positive sample, and $d(a, n)$ represents the distance between the anchor and the negative sample. *margin* is a predefined value that controls the margin between positive and negative samples.

Similarly, we use the trained content encoder to extract features as the extraction process of style condition described above, which is formulated as:

$$e_c = Proj(flatten(E_c(I_c))) \tag{3}$$

where E_c is the trained content encoder, *flatten* represents the flatten operation, and *Proj* is a linear projection layer.

We concatenate the style condition and content condition at the channel level, and then add it with the time embedding of diffusion model to guide the generation process.

3.2 Conditional Diffusion Model

In conditional diffusion models, the forward process remains the same as that of the unconditional model. We adopt the diffusion model proposed in DDPM [19], which defines a Markov chain of diffusion steps to add gradually random noise to the data and then learn to reverse the diffusion process to construct desired data samples. The forward process is a Markovian process with the following conditional distribution:

$$q(x_t|x_{t-1}) = \mathcal{N}(x_t; \sqrt{1 - \beta_t}x_{t-1}, \beta_t \mathbf{I}) \tag{4}$$

where $t \sim [1, T]$ represents the time step, and $\beta_t \in (0, 1)\}_{t=1}^{T}$ is a fixed variance schedule. When $T \to \infty$, x_T becomes equivalent to an isotropic Gaussian distribution. Let $\alpha_t = 1 - \beta_t$ and $\overline{\alpha}_t = \prod_{i=1}^{t} \alpha_i$. We can sample x_t at any arbitrary time step t in a closed form:

$$x_t = \sqrt{\overline{\alpha}_t} x_0 + \sqrt{1 - \overline{\alpha}_t} \epsilon, \epsilon \sim \mathcal{N}(0, \mathbf{I}) \tag{5}$$

During the reverse process, we use a deep neural network p_θ to approximate the true posterior distribution $q(x_{t-1}|x_t)$. In our conditional diffusion model, we take the encoded style features e_s and content features e_c as conditions and input them into the diffusion model to guide the generation of target font images. To enhance control over the character structure in the generation process, we concatenate the noisy image x_t with the content image I_c in the channel-wise dimension. The concatenated image $x'_t = concat(x_t, I_c)$ is then passed through the denoising network $\mathcal{U}$, as illustrated in Fig. 2. The content image I_c will guide the denoising process and ensure that both the intermediate noise representations and the final image align with the given character. Hence, the denoising model is denoted as $p_\theta(x_t, t, e_s, e_c, I_c)$, and the reverse process can be formulated as:

$$\begin{aligned} p_\theta(x_{t-1}|x_t, e_s, e_c, I_c) &= \mathcal{N}(x_{t-1}; \mu_\theta(x_t, t, e_s, e_c, I_c), \beta_t \mathbf{I}) \\ &= \mathcal{N}(x_{t-1}; \mu_\theta(x'_t, t, e_s, e_c), \beta_t \mathbf{I}) \end{aligned} \tag{6}$$

For optimizing the parameters of the network θ, we use the simplified training objective of DDPM [20]. Specifically, we produce a noisy sample x_t corresponding to a time step t by adding Gaussian noise ϵ to x_0 and then predict the added noise according to the style features e_s and the content features e_c. We update the model parameters with a mean square error (MSE) loss, and our training objective can be defined as:

$$L_{mse} = E_{t \sim [1,T], \epsilon \sim \mathcal{N}(0,I)} \left[\| \epsilon - \epsilon_\theta(x'_t, t, e_s, e_c) \|^2 \right] \tag{7}$$

3.3 Disentangled Guidance Sampling Strategy

After the diffusion model learns the conditional distribution, the inference process involves producing a random Gaussian noise $x_T \sim \mathcal{N}(0, I)$ and then sampling from $p_\theta(x_{t-1}|x'_t, e_s, e_c)$ iteratively from $t = T$ to $t = 1$. Although the generated images using the vanilla sampling technique appear acceptable, they often lack strong correlation with the conditional reference image I_s and content image I_c.

To enhance the influence of the conditioning signal e_s and e_c in the sampled images, we adapt the classifier-free guidance technique [9] into our disentangled guidance sampling procedure. We find that to sample images that not only meet the style requirement but also align perfectly with the target character requires disentangled guidance for both style and content. To perform this disentangled guidance, we employ the following equation:

$$\epsilon_{dis} = \epsilon_{uncond} + w_s \epsilon_{style} + w_c \epsilon_{content} \tag{8}$$

where $\epsilon_{uncond} = \epsilon_\theta(x'_t, t, \emptyset, \emptyset)$ is the unconditional prediction of the model. Here, $x'_t = concat(x_t, I_c)$ as mentioned in Sect. 3.2, and $\emptyset$ represents all-zeros tensor. The style-guided prediction and the content-guided prediction are represented by $\epsilon_{style} = \epsilon_\theta(x'_t, t, e_s, \emptyset) - \epsilon_{uncond}$ and $\epsilon_{content} = \epsilon_\theta(x'_t, t, \emptyset, e_c) - \epsilon_{uncond}$, respectively. w_s and w_c are guidance scales corresponding to style and content. In practice, we set the conditions e_s and e_c to $\emptyset$ with a probability of $\eta\%$ independently to get conditional and unconditional models during training.

By leveraging disentangled guidance, we can independently control and emphasize the effect of style and content during sampling. This approach enables us to generate images that not only exhibit the desired style but also maintain precise alignment with the target character, resulting in more faithful outputs.

4 Experiment

4.1 Experimental Setup

Datasets. To verify our one-shot font generation method, we collected a dataset consisting of 280 Chinese fonts. Each font in the dataset contains 1600 commonly used Chinese characters, and all images are resized to 80 × 80 pixels. In the training set, we randomly select 240 fonts, with each font containing 800 characters. The test set contains the remaining 40 unseen fonts with 800 unseen characters. We refer to this test set as the UFUC (Unseen Fonts Unseen Contents) dataset. We choose the *Song* font as our source font to generate content images.

Evaluation Metrics. To quantitatively compare the performance of different methods, we employ five commonly used evaluation metrics in font generation. These metrics can be categorized into pixel-wise metrics and perceptual metrics. Pixel-wise metrics include L1 distance, root mean square error (RMSE), and structural similarity index measure (SSIM). These metrics focus on calculating the pixel-level differences between the generated images and the ground truth. For the Perceptual metrics, we use FID [20] and LPIPS [21] which measure the similarity of features and align more closely with human vision.

Implementation Details. Our model has been trained with $T = 1000$ noising steps and a linear noise schedule. We use the AdamW optimizer with $\beta_1 = 0.9$, $\beta_2 = 0.999$, and a learning rate of $1e-4$. We train our model with 300,000 iterations, a batch size of 24, and a dropout rate of 0.1. To stabilize the model during training, we employ an exponential moving average rate of 0.9999. During inference, we adopt the DDIM [22] sampling strategy with only 15 steps to speed up sampling.

4.2 Experimental Results

Comparison Methods. We compare CD-Font with five state-of-the-art methods: FUNIT [23], MX-Font [7], DG-Font [1], CF-Font [2] and NTF-Loc [3]. For a fair comparison, we retrain all methods with our dataset based on their official codes. During inference, the same reference image of each font is employed for the one-shot setting.

Table 1. Quantitative comparison results on the UFUC dataset. The bold and underlined numbers denote the best and the second best, respectively.

Methods	Unseen Fonts Unseen Contents					User%
	L1 ↓	RMSE ↓	SSIM ↑	LPIPS ↓	FID ↓	
FUNIT [23]	0.0853	0.2408	0.6625	0.1911	48.7913	2.3
MX-Font [7]	0.0793	**0.2262**	0.6896	0.1632	51.1419	5.1
DG-Font [1]	0.0766	0.2425	0.6805	0.1281	42.3230	7.9
CF-Font [2]	0.0761	0.2406	0.6873	0.1277	42.8433	10.5
NTF-Loc [3]	0.0785	0.2332	0.6880	0.1389	40.3823	11.8
Ours	**0.0751**	0.2353	**0.6951**	**0.1266**	**31.0962**	**62.4**

Table 2. Quantitative comparison results on the UFSC dataset. The bold and underlined numbers denote the best and the second best, respectively.

Methods	Unseen Fonts Seen Contents				
	L1 ↓	RMSE ↓	SSIM ↑	LPIPS ↓	FID ↓
FUNIT [23]	0.0835	0.2380	0.6681	0.1877	49.5963
MX-Font [7]	0.0762	**0.2230**	0.6956	0.1605	51.6885
DG-Font [1]	0.0744	0.2388	0.6871	0.1263	44.3547
CF-Font [2]	0.0745	0.2381	0.6916	0.1265	43.7647
NTF-Loc [3]	0.0759	0.2286	0.6960	0.1357	41.3937
Diff-Font [10]	0.0768	0.2375	0.6910	0.1269	37.2524
Ours	**0.0722**	0.2298	**0.7044**	**0.1250**	**31.6030**

Quantitative Comparison. As shown in Table 1, our method outperforms the other compared methods. Although MX-Font [7] achieves the best RMSE on unseen fonts, it suffers a performance drop at the perceptual level. It is noted that RMSE focuses on pixel-wise differences between the generated image and the ground truth while ignores the feature similarity which is more closely related to human perception. We can observe that our method achieves state-of-the-art performance in perceptual-level metrics, i.e., FID [20] and LPIPS [21]. Since Diff-Font [10] cannot handle unseen contents, we also conduct comparative experiments on the testing fonts with seen contents. We refer to unseen fonts with seen contents as UFSC. The quantitative results are presented in Table 2, and our method also outperforms Diff-Font [10] by a margin.

Qualitative Comparison. Figure 3 provides a qualitative comparison of the results. We evaluate the generalization capability of all competitors by selecting five different fonts, including handwriting fonts, artistic fonts, and typewriter fonts. Our method generates characters with high quality in terms of style consistency and structural correctness.

However, FUNIT [23], MX-Font [7], and NTF-Loc [3] often produce results with structural errors, such as missing strokes and incomplete characters. FUNIT is originally an image-to-image translation framework for natural images, it may not perform well with font images. DG-Font [1] and CF-Font [2] tend to lose local details, especially when faced with large style differences between the source and the target fonts.

Fig. 3. Comparisons with the state-of-the-art methods for font generation on the UFUC dataset. We mark structural errors with red boxes, and mismatch styles with blue boxes (color figure online).

4.3 Ablation Study

Effectiveness of Each Module. Table 3 illustrates the effectiveness of different modules. The baseline uses a content encoder and a style encoder to extract content features and style features, respectively. These features are then concatenated and used as conditions for the diffusion model. This configuration is labeled as 'exp1' in Table 3. Then, we concatenate the content image with the noisy image as input to the diffusion model. This is denoted as 'exp2'. As shown in Fig. 4, 'exp2' is capable of generating characters with complete structures compared to 'exp1'. While the images generated using the vanilla sampling technique appear not bad, they often lack a strong correlation with the given content image and target style. To enhance this correlation, we introduce disentangled guidance sampling. As observed in Fig. 4, our model can generate images that preserve more local details of the target font.

Effectiveness of Guidance Scales. We further discuss the influence of the guidance scales w_s and w_c during inference. We gradually change w_s and w_c from 1 to 3 to perform ablation experiments on the UFUC dataset. As shown in Table 4, the setting $w_s = 3$, $w_c = 3$ achieves the best performance in our disentangled guidance sampling strategy. Therefore, we set the guidance scales w_s and w_c to 3 by default for other experiments of our method.

Table 3. Ablation study of different modules on the UFUC dataset. C and D represent concatenate operation and disentangled guidance in our proposed model. The bold and underlined numbers denote the best and the second best, respectively.

Methods	Settings		Unseen Fonts Unseen Contents				
	C	D	L1 ↓	RMSE ↓	SSIM ↑	LPIPS ↓	FID ↓
exp1	✗	✗	0.0770	0.2385	0.6913	0.1303	36.7729
exp2	✓	✗	0.0763	0.2367	0.6932	**0.1263**	32.2503
Ours	✓	✓	**0.0751**	**0.2353**	**0.6951**	0.1266	**31.0962**

Fig. 4. Qualitative ablation results on the UFUC dataset. We mark structural errors with red boxes and mismatched styles with blue boxes (color figure online).

Table 4. Ablation study on the guidance scales.

Guidance Scales	Unseen Fonts Unseen Contents				
	L1 ↓	RMSE ↓	SSIM ↑	LPIPS ↓	FID ↓
$w_s = 1, w_c = 1$	0.0769	0.2387	0.6902	0.1311	29.1867
$w_s = 1, w_c = 3$	0.0752	**0.2353**	0.6950	0.1267	31.0977
$w_s = 3, w_c = 1$	0.0769	0.2386	0.6902	0.1312	**29.0889**
$w_s = 3, w_c = 3$	**0.0751**	**0.2353**	**0.6951**	**0.1266**	31.0962

4.4 Cross-Lingual Font Generation

CD-Font demonstrates the capability to decouple style and content and is able to effectively transfer styles to unknown content. To further validate the generalization of our model, we apply it to cross-lingual font generation. As depicted in Fig. 5, our model successfully generates Korean and Japanese characters without additional training, highlighting its impressive potential in the field of cross-lingual font generation.

Fig. 5. Cross-lingual font generation (Chinese to Korean and Japanese).

5 Conclusion

In this paper, we propose a one-shot font generation framework based on the conditional diffusion model. We follow the style-content disentanglement paradigm, using two different encoders to extract style and content features for generating arbitrary combinations of style and content. To ensure precise control over the characters, we concatenate the content image with the noisy image as input to the model in each denoising step. During inference, we propose disentangled guidance sampling to enable the font images that exhibit strong correlations with both the reference image and the target character. Extensive experiments show the effectiveness of our approach.

Acknowledgments. This work was supported by the National Natural Science Foundation of China (NSFC) under Grants 62102178.

References

1. Xie, Y., Chen, X., Sun, L., Lu, Y.: DG-Font: deformable generative networks for unsupervised font generation. In: Proceedings of the IEEE/CVF Conference on Computer Vision and Pattern Recognition, pp. 5130–5140 (2021)
2. Wang, C., Zhou, M., Ge, T., Jiang, Y., Bao, H., Xu, W.: CF-Font: content fusion for few-shot font generation. In: Proceedings of the IEEE/CVF Conference on Computer Vision and Pattern Recognition, pp. 1858–1867 (2023)
3. Fu, B., He, J., Wang, J., Qiao, Y.: Neural transformation fields for arbitrary-styled font generation. In: Proceedings of the IEEE/CVF Conference on Computer Vision and Pattern Recognition, pp. 22438–22447 (2023)

4. Liang, D., et al.: Semantically contrastive learning for low-light image enhancement. Proc. AAAI Conf. Artif. Intell. **36**(2), 1555–1563 (2022)
5. Goodfellow, I., et al.: Generative adversarial nets. Adv. Neural Inf. Process. Syst. **27** (2014)
6. Tian, Y.: zi2zi: Master Chinese calligraphy with conditional adversarial networks (2017). https://github.com/kaonashi-tyc/zi2zi
7. Park, S., Chun, S., Cha, J., Lee, B., Shim, H.: Multiple heads are better than one: few-shot font generation with multiple localized experts. In: Proceedings of the IEEE/CVF International Conference on Computer Vision, pp. 13900–13909 (2021)
8. Dhariwal, P., Nichol, A.: Diffusion models beat GANs on image synthesis. Adv. Neural. Inf. Process. Syst. **34**, 8780–8794 (2021)
9. Ho, J., Salimans, T.: Classifier-free diffusion guidance. In: NeurIPS 2021 Workshop on Deep Generative Models and Downstream Applications (2021)
10. He, H., et al.: Diff-Font: diffusion model for robust one-shot font generation (2022). arXiv: 2212.05895
11. Zhang, Y., Zhang, Y., Cai, W.: Separating style and content for generalized style transfer. In: Proceedings of the IEEE Conference on Computer Vision and Pattern Recognition, pp. 8447–8455 (2018)
12. Gao, Y., Guo, Y., Lian, Z., Tang, Y., Xiao, J.: Artistic glyph image synthesis via one-stage few-shot learning. ACM Trans. Graph. **38**(6), 1–12 (2019)
13. Wu, S.J., Yang, C.Y., Hsu, J.Y.J.: CalliGAN: style and structure-aware Chinese calligraphy character generator (2020). arXiv:2005.12500
14. Cha, J., Chun, S., Lee, G., Lee, B., Kim, S., Lee, H.: Few-shot compositional font generation with dual memory. In: Vedaldi, A., Bischof, H., Brox, T., Frahm, J.-M. (eds.) ECCV 2020. LNCS, vol. 12364, pp. 735–751. Springer, Cham (2020). https://doi.org/10.1007/978-3-030-58529-7_43
15. Kong, Y., et al.: Look closer to supervise better: one-shot font generation via component-based discriminator. In: Proceedings of the IEEE/CVF Conference on Computer Vision and Pattern Recognition, pp. 13482–13491 (2022)
16. Tang, L., et al.: Few-shot font generation by learning fine-grained local styles. In: Proceedings of the IEEE/CVF Conference on Computer Vision and Pattern Recognition, pp. 7895–7904 (2022)
17. Dai, J., et al.: Deformable convolutional networks. In: Proceedings of the IEEE International Conference on Computer Vision (2017)
18. Ronneberger, O., Fischer, P., Brox, T.: U-Net: Convolutional networks for biomedical image segmentation. In: Medical Image Computing and Computer-Assisted Intervention, pp. 234–241 (2015)
19. Ho, J., Jain, A., Abbeel, P.: Denoising diffusion probabilistic models. Adv. Neural. Inf. Process. Syst. **33**, 6840–6851 (2020)
20. Heusel, M., Ramsauer, H., Unterthiner, T., Nessler, B., Hochreiter, S.: GANs trained by a two time-scale update rule converge to a local Nash equilibrium. Adv. Neural Inf. Process. Syst. **30** (2017)
21. Zhang, R., Isola, P., Efros, A.A., Shechtman, E., Wang, O.: The unreasonable effectiveness of deep features as a perceptual metric. In: Proceedings of the IEEE Conference on Computer Vision and Pattern Recognition, pp. 586–595 (2018)
22. Song, J., Meng, C., Ermon, S.: Denoising diffusion implicit models. In: International Conference on Learning Representations (2020)
23. Liu, M.Y., et al.: Few-shot unsupervised image-to-image translation. In: Proceedings of the IEEE/CVF International Conference on Computer Vision, pp. 10551–10560 (2019)

Image Super-Resolution Reconstruction Based on Dual-Branch Channel Attention

Jinyu Shi[✉], Zhanjun Si, Yingxue Zhang[✉], and Xinbin Yang

Tianjin University of Science and Technology, Tianjin 300457, China
{szj,yxzhang}@tust.edu.cn

Abstract. Image super-resolution reconstruction is an important technique for converting low resolution images into high-resolution images. High resolution images can provide more information and are crucial for advanced visual tasks. However, traditional methods cannot restore image details, resulting in blurring and not meeting practical requirements. In response to this, this paper proposes a dual-branch channel attention residual network (DCARN) for image super-resolution reconstruction, which focuses on the problem of multi-frequency information fusion. The proposed method first improve multi-spectral channel attention by adopting group convolution and discrete cosine transform to adapt to images of different sizes. In order to fully utilize channel and multi-spectral channel attention, a dual-branch channel attention residual block (DCARB) is further designed. Experiments on multiple public datasets show that the proposed method achieves improved performance and performs well on image reconstruction in terms of both subjective and objective quality, with richer stripe texture details.

Keyword: Image super-resolution · multi-spectral channel attention · Discrete cosine transform · Group convolution

1 Introduction

The rich emotional content and fine detail information conveyed by images make communication more vivid. However, images are subject to various influences during their passage, such as equipment limitations and processing methods, which can result in issues such as blurriness, color distortion, and low resolution. In recent years, the internet has been inundated with a profusion of low-resolution images that pose great challenges in terms of efficient utilization, especially in domains like medical imaging, satellite imaging, facial recognition, and surveillance. Therefore, there exists an acute demand for a rapid and effective means to enhance the resolution of such imagery. It is against this backdrop that the technology of image super-resolution reconstruction has emerged. Image super-resolution reconstruction is characterized as the employment of methodologies from disciplines such as signal processing and image processing, aimed at transforming low-resolution images into their high-resolution analogues. This approach serves to fulfill the objective of significantly improving the visual quality of these images.

Image super-resolution technology has undergone multiple stages of development. Early research predominantly relied on interpolation and filtering techniques, which, despite making some strides, often led to blurred and distorted images unsuitable for practical applications. The advent of machine learning and deep learning ushered ISR technology into a new era, with researchers beginning to explore the use of deep neural networks (DNNs) for image up-sampling. Dong et al. [1] marked a groundbreaking milestone by introducing the first convolutional neural network (CNN)-based ISR approach. Their SRCNN model employed a deep CNN to directly generate high-resolution images, pioneering the application of CNNs in ISR tasks. Shi et al. [2] proposed the end-to-end ESPCNN method, which introduced sub-pixel convolutions. This novel technique confined computational operations to the low-resolution domain throughout the network, only utilizing sub-pixel convolutions at the final stage to upscale feature maps into high-resolution images. Subsequently, researchers started incorporating attention mechanisms into visual problems to enhance existing ISR methods. In 2018, Jie et al. [3] introduced the SENet, a network featuring a two-stage mechanism to bolster the performance of crucial channels. Today, DNN-based super-resolution reconstruction has become the prevailing approach, unlocking immense potential in areas such as medical image processing, video surveillance, and smartphone photography.

Although image super-resolution method based on deep learning has been widely used in many fields, it still faces many challenges, such as computational complexity and image distortion. Therefore, it is of great significance to constantly explore new algorithms and improve the efficiency and reconstruction quality of image super-resolution methods. Therefore, this paper proposes an improved image super-resolution method based on improved multi-spectral channel attention mechanism and dual-branch design. The main contributions include:

1) To better incorporate multi-frequency domain information, we propose an improved Multi-Spectral Channel Attention (MSCA) mechanism.
2) To fully harness the advantages of both channel attention and multi-spectral channel attention in enhancing the quality of the high-resolution images, we propose a novel Dual-Branch Channel Attention Residual Block (DCARB).

2 Proposed Method

2.1 Overall Network Structure

In this paper, a dual-branch channel attention residual network (DCARN) is proposed for image super-resolution reconstruction by combining the dual-branch structure and improved multi-spectral channel attention mechanism. The overall structure is shown in Fig. 1.

The FEP is used to initially extract feature maps, which can provide support for the subsequent extraction of deep features. This part includes a convolutional layer and a ReLU activation layer, with a convolutional kernel size of 3 × 3, kernel number of C, a stride of 1, and padding of 1. The purpose of doing this is to ensure consistency in the size of the input and output. The process of preliminary feature extraction can be represented by the following formula:

$$F_{SF} = ReLU(Conv(L_{LR})) \qquad (1)$$

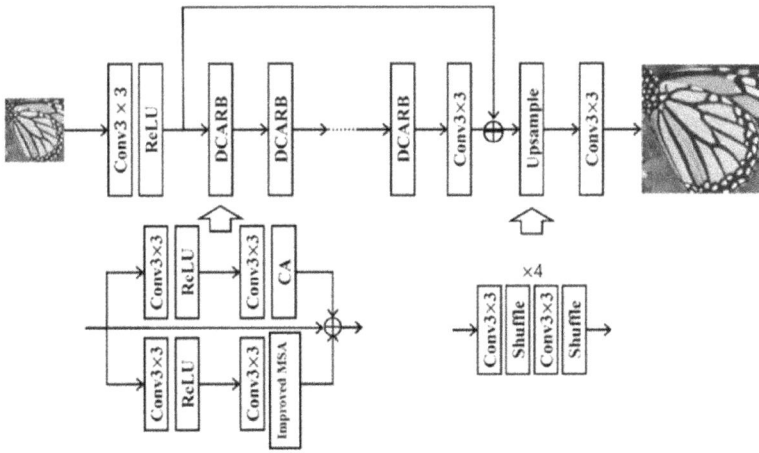

Fig. 1. Dual-branch Channel Attention Residual Network

The NFMP part is used to extract deep features. With the output of the FEP part as the input, more deep and abstract features are extracted for image reconstruction. This part is composed of N Dual-branch Channel Attention Residual Block (DCARB) modules and a convolution layer. The feature extraction process can be expressed by the following formula:

$$F_i = H_i(F_{i-1}) \tag{2}$$

$$F_{NF} = Conv(F_N) + F_{SF} \tag{3}$$

The RP part of this method uses sub-pixel layer for up-sampling, and then reduces the channel dimension to three channels through a convolution layer to obtain the reconstructed super-resolution image. The number of sub-pixel layers will be different when different scales of magnification are used. As mentioned earlier, using the sub-pixel layer can make the whole feature extraction and nonlinear feature extraction part be carried out in the low-resolution space, and at the same time, smaller convolution kernel size is used, which greatly reduces the computational complexity.

2.2 Improved Design of Multi-spectral Channel Attention

Previous implementations of the multi-spectral channel attention mechanism typically employed the Discrete Cosine Transform (DCT) [4] to compress channel information. A set of fixed-width and -height convolutions are constructed while using DCT for channel compression, leading to the limitation that this mechanism is effective in extracting rich information from channels only when the input size is known beforehand. However, the input sizes in image super-resolution reconstruction tasks are inherently variable, making the direct application of multi-spectral channel attention in such scenarios less applicable. This paper, therefore, sets out to improve the multi-spectral channel attention mechanism, adapting it for use in image super-resolution tasks where input dimensions are subject to variation.

This paper associates the principle of group convolution. Its advantage is that it does not need to know the size of the input data, it can more flexibly adapt to tasks with variable input size. For the task of image super-resolution reconstruction, the method of group convolution can make full use of the attention mechanism of multi spectral channels to incorporate more frequency domain information without worrying about the problem of input size. In addition, the use of group convolution also further accelerates the computation. Figure 2 demonstrates the improved multi-spectral channel attention mechanism in this paper.

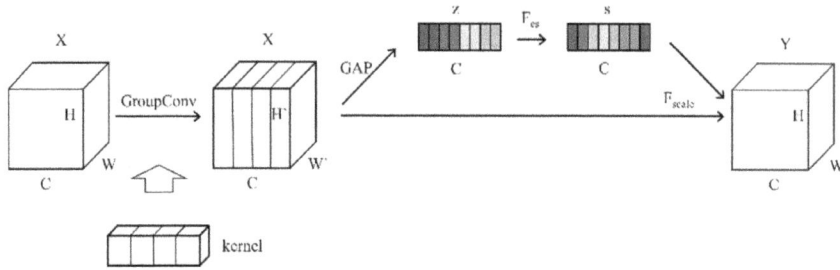

Fig. 2. Improved multi-spectral channel attention

2.3 Dual-Branch Channel Attention Mechanism

Branch structure is a very useful technique when designing deep learning networks. The classical deep learning networks ResNeXt [5], RepVGG [6] all use branch structure to improve the network performance, which enhances the representation ability of the model.

In this regard, this paper adopts the dual-branch structure to integrate the channel attention with the improved multi-spectral channel attention, and innovatively proposes the Dual-branch Channel Attention Residual Block (DCARB), whose structure is shown in Fig. 3. Specifically, considering the advantages of the idea of dual-branch attention in ResNeXt network, this paper also tries to design two branches in this module, each of which has a similar structure. The channel attention branch is responsible for compressing the low-frequency information in the channel to provide the global information of the feature map and generate the low-frequency attention feature map. The multi-spectral channel attention branch utilizes the proposed improved multi-spectral channel attention module, which is responsible for integrating information in other frequency domains into the channel compression process to provide details and edge information in the feature map and generate high-frequency attention feature map.

2.4 Loss Function

In image super-resolution reconstruction, the commonly used loss functions are l_1 and l_2 loss functions. l_1 loss function has better convergence performance, as shown in Fig. 4.

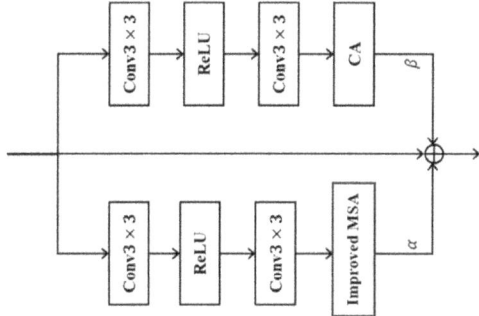

Fig. 3. Dual-branch Channel Attention Residual Block

Through comparison, it can be seen from the figure that in the initial and later stages of training, the loss value of training with l_1 loss function decreases faster and has better convergence performance. Therefore, this paper uses l_1 as the loss function.

The l_1 loss function can be expressed by the following formula:

$$L(\theta) = \frac{1}{N} \sum_{i=1}^{N} |y_i - \widehat{y_i}| \qquad (4)$$

Among them, θ represents the parameters in the network. The goal of training the network is to adjust the network parameters θ to make the loss value as small as possible. $\widehat{y_l}$ represents the number of images in each batch of training samples. Represent high-resolution image; y_i represents the reconstructed image.

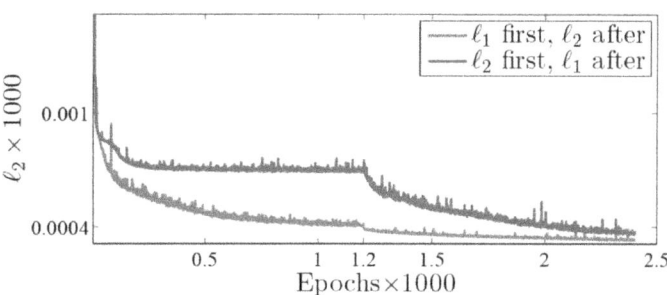

Fig. 4. Comparison of l_1 and l_2 loss function

3 Experiments

3.1 Experimental Setup

In order to fully verify the performance and generalization ability of the algorithm, DIV2K dataset [7], Set5 [8], Set14 [9], Urban100 [10] and Manga109 [11] are used for validation, where the training subset of DIV2K dataset is used as the training set of the network, and the others are used for testing.

3.2 Comparison with Existing Methods

The experiment in this section evaluates the performance from both subjective and objective aspects. Traditional super-resolution reconstruction algorithm Bicubic and four mainstream super-resolution networks SRCNN [12], SRResNet [13], DMCN [14], EDSR [15] are compared. A scaling factor of 4 is selected for validation.

Table 1 shows the performance in terms of PSNR and SSIM indicators of the five methods on four test datasets.

Table 1. Objective comparison with existing methods

Models	Set5 PSNR/SSIM	Set14 PSNR/SSIM	Urban100 PSNR/SSIM	Manga109 PSNR/SSIM
Bicubic	28.42/0.8104	26.00/0.7027	23.14/0.6577	24.89/0.7866
SRCNN	29.97/0.8556	27.20/0.7454	24.11/0.7091	26.63/0.8365
SRResNet	32.09/0.8973	28.55/0.7812	25.99/0.7829	30.31/0.9070
DMCN	32.33/0.8950	28.70/0.7845	26.31/0.7938	/
EDSR	32.46/0.8968	**28.80/0.7876**	**26.64/0.8033**	31.02/0.9148
Ours	**32.51/0.8993**	28.79/0.7870	26.61/0.8014	**31.06/0.9157**

3.3 Visualization of Reconstructed Images

This paper also compares the subjective quality of the reconstructed images. The following four representative images are presented to demonstrate the visual quality.

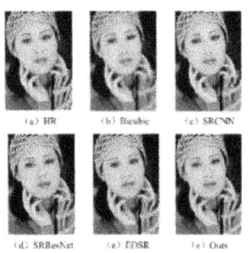

Fig. 5. Comparison of "woman" in Set5 dataset at 4 × SR

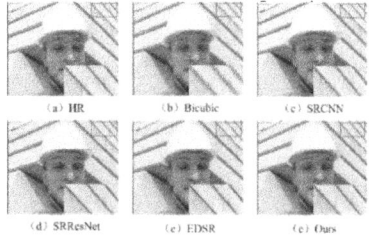

Fig. 6. Comparison of "foreman" in Set14 dataset at 4 × SR

3.4 Ablation Study

In order to verify the effectiveness of the proposed module, this paper compared and analyzed the effectiveness of the dual branch channel attention module. The experimental results are shown in Table 2.

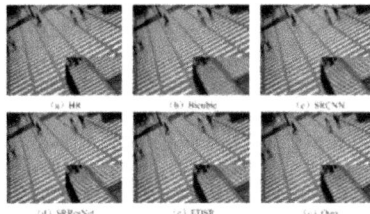

Fig. 7. Comparison of "img_093" in Urban100 dataset at 4 × SR

Fig. 8. Comparison of "DollGun" in Manga109 dataset at 4 × SR

Table 2. Objective evaluation index comparison

Dataset	Metric	Baseline	Baseline + CA	Baseline + MSA	Baseline + DCA
Set5	PSNR/dB	32.02	32.07	32.07	32.20
	SSIM	0.8936	0.8937	0.8941	0.8956
Set14	PSNR/dB	28.47	28.51	28.49	28.56
	SSIM	0.78	0.7804	0.7806	0.7818
Urban100	PSNR/dB	25.88	25.93	25.92	26.08
	SSIM	0.7796	0.7805	0.7807	0.7862
Manga109	PSNR/dB	30.22	30.25	30.27	30.46
	SSIM	0.9046	0.9051	0.9051	0.9081

From the experimental results, it can be seen that the addition of DCA can make the super division network obtain better reconstruction quality, and CA and MSA can also improve the reconstruction effect to varying degrees. From the characteristics of datasets, it can be found that Set14 and Urban100 data sets have more urban buildings and natural scenes than Set5 and Manga109 data sets, which indicates that CA and MSA will focus on different scenes, which on the other hand confirms that the proposed integration of CA and MSA can bring better generalization to the model to improve the network performance.

This paper designed a set of experiments to compare the effects of different attention levels on reconstruction performance. The experimental results are shown in Table 3, and it can be seen that different attention ratios do indeed affect the reconstruction effect, with C5M5 achieving a more balanced effect.

Table 3. Comparison of different combination strategies of the two channel attention

Dataset	Metric	C8M2	C5M5	C2M8
Set5	PSNR/dB	30.3727	**30.4045**	30.3816
	SSIM	0.8612	**0.8615**	0.8612
Set14	PSNR/dB	27.4364	**27.4473**	27.4379
	SSIM	0.7527	**0.7528**	0.7525
Urban100	PSNR/dB	24.3363	**24.3442**	24.3394
	SSIM	0.7175	**0.7177**	0.7174
Manga109	PSNR/dB	27.1716	27.1856	**27.1868**
	SSIM	0.8465	0.8463	**0.8466**

4 Conclusions

This paper proposes a dual-branch channel attention residual network (DCARN) for image super-resolution reconstruction task. By analyzing the characteristics of discrete cosine transform and group convolution, an improved multi-spectral channel attention is designed, solving the limitation of fixed image size. Based on the improvement of multi-spectral channel attention, a dual-branch structure is further proposed to fully integrating the advantages of multi-spectral channel attention and the traditional channel attention. The proposed method is able to take into account the various frequency domain features, helping the network build more rich details in the process of image reconstruction. Thorough experiments are designed to verify the effectiveness of the proposed method from both subjective and objective aspects. Considering the limitations, the downsampling method for low resolution images uses a simple bicubic interpolation method. In practical life, the generation of low resolution images is more complex, and when faced with noise, compression artifacts, or other image degradation, this can lead to a decrease in the performance of the network model in dealing with complex scenes. In the future, we will consider further optimizing the network structure, and continue to improve the robustness and generalization application capability.

References

1. Dong, C., Loy, C. C., He, et al. (2014). Learning a deep convolutional network for image super-resolution. European Conference on Computer Vision
2. Shi, W., Caballero, J., Huszár, F., et al. (2016). Real-time single image and video super-resolution using an efficient sub-pixel convolutional neural network. IEEE Conference on Computer Vision and Pattern Recognition
3. Shocher, A., Cohen, N., & Irani, M. (2018). "zero-shot" super-resolution using deep internal learning. IEEE Conference on Computer Vision and Pattern Recognition
4. Ahmed, N., Natarajan, T., Rao, K.R.: Discrete cosine transform. IEEE Trans. Comput. **100**(1), 90–93 (1974)
5. Yang, C. Y., Ma, C., & Yang, M. H. (2014). Single-image super-resolution: A benchmark. European Conference on Computer Vision

6. Chen, W., Rao, K.R.: Handbook of DCT-Based Audio Coding: Algorithms and Applications. Springer, Cham (2019)
7. Agustsson, E, & Timofte, R. (2017). NTIRE 2017 Challenge on Single Image Super-Resolution: Dataset and Study. IEEE Conference on Computer Vision and Pattern Recognition Workshops
8. Bevilacqua, M., Roumy, A., Guillemot, C., et al. (2012). Low-complexity single-image super-resolution based on nonnegative neighbor embedding. British Machine Vision Conference
9. Yang, J., Wright, J., Huang, T.S., et al.: Image super-resolution via sparse representation. IEEE Trans. Image Process. **19**(11), 2861–2873 (2010)
10. Huang, J. B., Singh, A., & Ahuja, N. (2015). Single image super-resolution from transformed self-exemplars. IEEE Conference on Computer Vision and Pattern Recognition, 5197–5206
11. Matsui, Y., Ito, K., Aramaki, Y., et al.: Sketch-based manga retrieval using manga109 dataset. Multimedia tools and applications **76**, 21811–21838 (2017)
12. Dong, C., Loy, C.C., He, K., et al.: Image super-resolution using deep convolutional networks. IEEE Trans. Pattern Anal. Mach. Intell. **38**(2), 295–307 (2015)
13. Ledig, C, Theis, L, Huszar, F., et al. (2016). Photo-realistic single image super-resolution using a generative adversarial network. IEEE Conference on Computer Vision and Pattern Recognition
14. Wang, X, Wang, C, Wang, C, et al.(2020).Dual-channel Multi-perception Convolutional Network for Image Super-Resolution. Journal of Northeastern University, 41(11), 1564–1576
15. Lim, B, Son, S. Kim, H. et al. (2017). Enhanced deep residual networks for single image super-resolution. IEEE Conference on Computer Vision and Pattern Recognition Workshops

A Flipped Reversible Information Hiding Method Based on AMP

Yaowen Fu, Haoshan Shi, Tianyang Qi(✉), Xueyan Gao, and Yifei Zou

College of Cyberspace Security, University of International Relations, Beijing 100091, China
qitianyang@uir.edu.cn

Abstract. Adaptive MSB Prediction is an effective technique to achieve Reversible Data Hiding in Encrypted Images(RDHEI). Specifically, the image is divided into 2×2 pixels blocks and encrypted to preserve pixel correlation, the shared MSB of pix-els in the block is extracted, only one of the four identical MSBs is saved, and the positions of the three vacated MSBs are embedded with data. However, the pixel blocks with poor correlation cannot embed data, in addition, the scheme has some blocks with very close pixel values but cannot embed data, which limits the embedding capacity. A new MSB prediction-based RDHEI framework is proposed, supporting an adaptive strategy. Flipping strategy makes some unavailable blocks available, enhancing embedding capacity. Experimental results show improved prediction accuracy and embedding capacity while ensuring reversibility.

Keywords: Reversible Data Hiding · Image Encryption · Adaptive Most Significant Bit Prediction · Image Encryption · Multimedia Security

1 Introduction

Reversible Data Hiding in Encrypted Images (RDHEI) is an emerging technique to achieve data hiding into cover image while protecting confidentiality of the content from being leaked [1–10]. Because of reversibility, the original image is able to be fully recovered once the embedded data is extracted. However, the implementation of such a property usually comes at the cost of reducing effective embedding capacity. How to improve capacity in this scenario is becoming a big challenge, which is crucial to the development of this technique.

Most Significant Bit (MSB) prediction is one of the most effective means to achieve RDHEI [11–14]. Even though effective, the existing MSB prediction schemes suffer from the problem of data extraction error [12], the reason is that proposed prediction formula is inaccurate. To deal with this limitation, Wang et al. [14] proposed Adaptive MSB Prediction (AMP), in which a flag with three bits is utilized to record the longest length of common MSBs. As a result, the reversibility can be achieved regardless of the value of length. Obviously, such kind of MSB prediction based RDHEI relies on the consistency of pixels within a selected block, which means once the consistency is not strong enough, the embedding capacity is restrained as a result. In particular, once the associate value of the flag is 0 or 1, which means the longest length of common MSBs is only 0 or 1, the corresponding block is considered to be an unavailable one.

Therefore, in this paper we are going to tackle how to improve the effective embedding capacity of AMP based RDHEI by introducing a flipping strategy with reversibility guaranteed. To the best of our knowledge, our scheme is the first to well improve the capacity of MSB prediction based RDHEI. For unavailable blocks in AMP scheme, we introduce flipping strategy to make most of them available again. The main contributions of this paper are summarized as the following three aspects:

(1) We propose a MSB prediction based RDHEI framework, which supports the proposed adaptive strategy. Specially, available blocks with $md > 1$ are employed to embed data using AMP scheme, while unavailable blocks with $md < 2$ using the proposed FAMP scheme. Moreover, a new 2×2 pixels structure as well as new location maps are also supported as preparations to construct the proposed flipping strategy.

(2) A flipping strategy as well as the novel location maps are introduced to improve the existing MSB prediction based RDHEI. Specially, because of the flipping strategy utilized, some of the unavailable blocks are turned to be available ones through flipping some of the pixels inside. The positions of corresponding pixels are recorded in the newly constructed location maps.

(3) We take experiments to compare the performance of proposed scheme with other schemes. Experimental results show that the proposed scheme is able to achieve better prediction accuracy and greater embedding capacity with reversibility guaranteed.

2 Proposed Scheme

2.1 Framework

Figure 1 depicts the FAMP scheme framework comprising three main modules: image encryption module, secret data embedding module, extraction and recovery module. The image encryption module encrypts and scrambles the original image for confidentiality. Next, the secret data embedding module utilizes the AMP algorithm for initial block selection and rearrangement. Unavailable blocks, indicated by green texture, undergo a second round of selection and rearrangement. Eligible blocks are converted into available ones using the FAMP strategy, while those failing predetermined conditions are placed at the image's end in reverse order. This strategy typically results in the first blocks being embeddable, while the last ones remain unavailable. To maintain reversibility, compressed location maps are generated after each round of block selection, recording the availability of original and flipped blocks. Blocks embedded with the AMP scheme are marked in blue, while those using FAMP are marked in orange.

After secret data embedding, the embedded image is sent to the receiver in the extraction and recovery module. This process is divided into three cases based on the key distribution state, each detailed in Fig. 6.

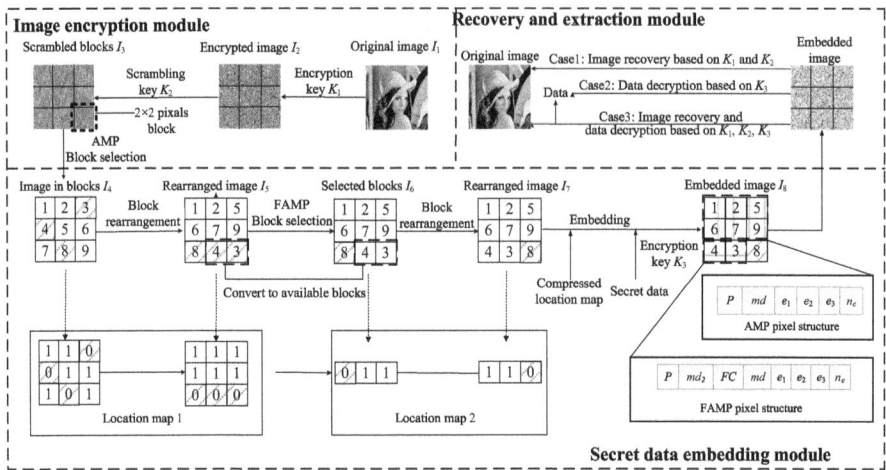

Fig. 1. Propose framework

2.2 Image Encryption

To ensure the security of image transmission, the original image I1 is protected before being transmitted by the image owner, using encryption key K1 and a scrambling key K2. Block-level encryption of the image after stream cipher encryption cannot resist complexity analysis. Attackers can perform complexity analysis on the image en-crypted with stream cipher to obtain partial original images. To enhance security, it is necessary to scramble the image after stream cipher encryption. The encryption method employed in this paper is the same as that described in References [14]. Block-level stream encryption: The process of block-level stream encryption is de-scribed as follows.

Fig. 2. The structure of 2 × 2 pixels block

Step 1: Image Segmentation. $M \times N$-sized original image is divided into pixel blocks of size 2 × 2. The number of pixel blocks is

$$n = \left\lfloor \frac{M}{2} \right\rfloor \times \left\lfloor \frac{N}{2} \right\rfloor \quad (1)$$

Step 2: Pixel decomposition. All pixels within each block are decomposed into 8 bits, denoted as

$$b_m^k(i,j) = \left\lfloor \frac{p_m(i,j)}{2^k} \right\rfloor \bmod 2, k = 0, 1, 2, \cdots, 7. \quad (2)$$

where $P_m(i, j)$ represents the m-th pixel located in the i-th row and j-th column within the block, and $b_m^k(i, j)$ denotes the k-th bit of $P_m(i, j)$.

Step 3: Encrypting Block Pixels. Utilize an encryption key K_1 (e.g.RC4), along with the image I_1 to generate a pseudo-random matrix of size $\lfloor \frac{M}{2} \rfloor \times \lfloor \frac{N}{2} \rfloor$. Subsequently, decompose all values in the generated matrix into binary. Then, encrypt all original pixels in bit level using the formula (3)

$$e_m^k(i, j) = b_m^k(i, j) \oplus r^k(i, j), k = 0, 1, 2, \cdots, 7. \qquad (3)$$

where $r^k(i, j)$ represents the k-th bit of the element located in the i-th row and j-th column of the pseudo-random matrix, and $e_m^k(i, j)$ represents the k-th bit of the m-th pixel within the block situated in the i-th row and j-th column. Finally, obtain the m-th encrypted pixel within the block located in the i-th row and j-th column as

$$E_m(i, j) = \sum_{k=0}^{7} 2^k \times e_m^k(i, j). \qquad (4)$$

Step 4: Scramble Encryption. The encrypted images are once again divided into pixel blocks of size 2×2 by using the encryption key K_1. Subsequently, the scrambling key K_2 is employed to scramble the pixel blocks, altering the arrangement order and producing the final encrypted image. The purpose of scramble encryption is to prevent attackers from conducting complexity analysis to recover parts of the original image.

2.3 Generating Location Map Information

Figure 3 shows the process of location map generation. In scrambled image I_4, available and unavailable blocks are distinguished according to the value of *md*. Blank blocks with *md* > 1 are available and texture ones with *md* < 2 are unavailable. In block rearrangement, the third, fourth, and eighth blocks of image I_4 are arranged in reverse order to the end of the image I_5. The first location map is obtained from I_4 and I_5, in which available blocks are recorded as 0 and unavailable blocks as 1.

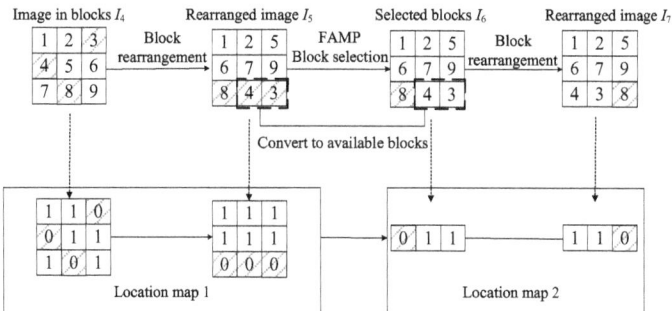

Fig. 3. The process of location map generation

Then, for I_5, FAMP block selection is performed to determine whether unavailable blocks could be turned to available ones according to whether md_2 is greater than 2. Specifically, the 3rd, 4th pixel blocks of I_5 are converted from unavailable blocks to available blocks in image I_6, the 8th pixel block is still an unavailable one. Then, blocks of I_6 are rearranged to generate I_7. In particular, the 8th pixel block of I_6 is arranged in reverse order to the end of I_7. The second location map is obtained from I_4 and I_5, in which available blocks are recorded as 0 and unavailable blocks as 1. The length of this location map just equals to the total number of pixel blocks with $md = 0$ and $md = 1$.

2.4 Flipping Based Adaptive MSB Prediction Scheme

In AMP scheme [14], pixel blocks with $md < 2$ cannot embed data, leading to the problem of low efficiency in pixels utilization. To solve this problem, we introduce FAMP scheme in this part. According to our design, for pixel blocks with $md > 1$, AMP scheme is utilized in data embedding. While for pixel blocks with $md < 2$, the FAMP is introduced to selected bits within corresponding pixel blocks. With the help of FAMP scheme, the number of common MSBs in most blocks is increased as a result, thus creating more space for data embedding. In this section, the detail of the proposed FAMP scheme is outlined.

As shown in Fig. 2, the encrypted image blocks are first divided into available blocks and unavailable blocks. Specifically, use formula (5) to calculate the longest different LSB bits for two pixels,

$$d_i = dif(P, C_i), i = 1, 2, 3. \tag{5}$$

and formula (6) to calculate the common MSB bits md for pixel blocks.

$$md = 8 - max(d_1, d_2, d_3) \tag{6}$$

Blocks with $md > 1$ are available blocks, otherwise they are unavailable blocks. For example, for pixels $P = 171$ and $C_1 = 180$, writing them in binary form yields $P = 171 = (10101011)_2$, $C_1 = 180 = (10110100)_2$. The 5th LSB of P and C_1 is different, indicating that $d_1 = dif(171,180) = 5$, which means that the longest different LSB digit between 171 and 180 pixels is 5. Similarly, using P, C_2 and C_3, calculate d_2 and d_3. Then, calculate the common number of MSB bits md using formula (6).

In this paper, the formula (7) is used to flip pixels C_i with $md < 2$ to obtain a new pixel block, where the first pixel P remains unchanged and C_i is updated as

$$C_i = \begin{cases} F(C_i, max(d_i)), & \text{if } d_i = max(d_1, d_2, d_3) \\ C_i, & \text{other} \end{cases}. \quad i = 1, 2, 3. \tag{7}$$

$F(C_i, max(d_i))$ indicates that the pixel bits corresponding to the maximum of d_1, d_2 and d_3 are flipped. Specifically, the 0 bit is flipped to 1 bit and the 1 bit is flipped to 0, leaving the unflipped pixel bits unchanged. For example, $F(191,7) = (1011\ 1111, 7) = (1100\ 0000)$. In this case $d_1 = 7$ means that the 7th LSB to the 1st LSB of $191 = (1011\ 1111)$ is flipped, 0111111 is flipped to 1000000. After forming the new pixel block, formula (8) calculates the Di between the first pixel P and the other three pixels (C_1, C_2, C_3).

$$D_i = \begin{cases} dif(P, C_i), & if\ d_i = max(d_1, d_2, d_3) \\ d_i, & other \end{cases}. \quad i = 1, 2, 3. \tag{8}$$

D_i represents the position of the first differing MSB between two pixels, where $D_i = dif(P, C_i)$ returns the maximum index of LSB that pixel P does not share with pixel C_i. For example, we have $dif(171, 180) = dif(10101011, 10110100) = 5$, the fifth LSB of 171 and 180 is different. At this time, a new 2×2 pixels block is formed after flipping, md_2 use formula (9) to calculate by using the D_i of the new pixel block.

$$md_2 = 8 - max(D_1, D_2, D_3). \tag{9}$$

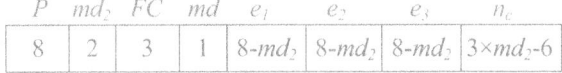

Fig. 4. The proposed 32 bits pixel

The proposed method flips the pixels, and the 32-bit structure of the pixel block is changed. The proposed 32-bit pixel structure is shown in Fig. 4, where pixel P length is 8 bits, the length of md_2 is 2 bits, the length of FC is 3 bits, and e_1, e_2 and e_3 are all ($8-md_2$) bits. Specifically, P is the first pixel of the original pixel blocks, the value range of md_2 calculate to range from 1 to 8, the available block range is from 3 to 8. After statistics, the number of pixel blocks is very small when $md_2 = 7$ and $md_2 = 8$. If length of md_2 use 3 bits to represent the 6 values of md_2, this will reduce the embedding capacity of the image. In order to improve the embedding capacity, $md_2 = 6$ is used to calculate the embedding capacity of pixel blocks with $md = 7$ and $md_2 = 8$ in this paper. The md_2 block has 4 values from 3 to 6, which are represented by only two bits in binary, effectively saving one bit per pixel block.

Table 1. Binary of md_2 value and embedding capacity

	$md = 1$	$md = 2$	$md = 3$	$md = 4$	$md = 5$	$md = 6,7,8$
md_2	-	-	00	01	10	11
n_c (bit)	-	-	3	6	9	12

Specifically, $md_2 = 3$ is represented by binary 00, $md_2 = 4$ is represented by binary 01, $md_2 = 5$ is represented by binary 10, and $md_2 = 6, 7$ and 8 is represented by binary 11. The length of FC is 3 bits, the 3-bit data from left to right indicates whether pixel C_1, C_2, and C_3 is flipped. If the pixel is flipped, the corresponding bit is denoted as 1, or it is denoted as 0. For example, $FC = 101$ represent that pixels C_1 and C_3 are flipped but pixel C_2 is not flipped. The length of md field is 1 bit which represents the md value of the original pixel block. If $md = 0$ before the original pixel block is flipped, it is recorded as 0 md field. If $md = 1$ before the original pixel block is flipped, it is recorded as 1 md field. This 1-bit data md is used when recovering the pixel block. e_1, e_2 and e_3 are the MSBs in the new pixel block that P does not share with C_1, C_2 and C_3. e_i has a length of (8-md_2) bits. The length of Nc is 32 bits minus the length of P, md_2, FC, md, e_1, e_2 and e_3:

$$n_c = 3 \times md_2 - 6 \tag{10}$$

where n_c represents the embedding capacity of the flipped available pixel block and the Table 1 shows the binary representation of md_2 and its embedding capacity.

2.5 Data Embedding

For blocks with $md > 1$, we use AMP scheme to embed data. For blocks with $md < 2$, we utilize the FAMP scheme instead. The corresponding pseudocode is shown in Table 2.

Step 1: **Image encryption.** FAMP scheme adopts encryption key K_1 and scrambling key K_2 to achieve image encryption according to the process in Sect. 3.2.

Step 2: **Block selection using AMP.** Firstly, select pixel blocks with $md > 1$ as available ones to embed secret data. To ensure reversibility, generate a binary matrix of size $\lfloor \frac{M}{2} \rfloor \times \lfloor \frac{N}{2} \rfloor$ as Location Map 1. In particular, bit 1 in the map indicates an available block, and bit 0 an unavailable one.

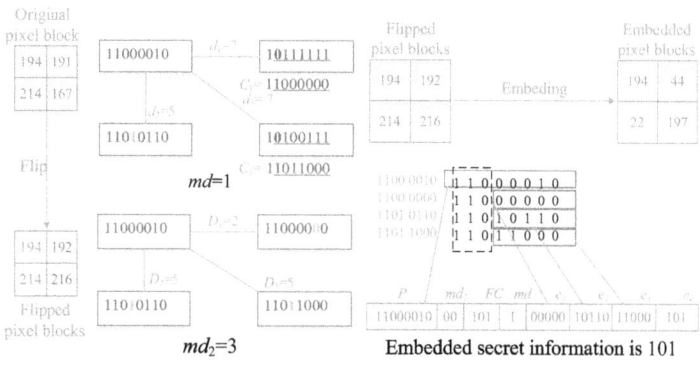

(a) Forming flipped pixel blocks   (b) embedded data

Fig. 5. Four different flipped types of flips when $md = 1$

Step 3: **Rearranging blocks in AMP.** Arrange available blocks with $md > 1$ to first positions of the image, and unavailable ones to the end. Subsequently, compress Location Map 1 before embedding it into available blocks.

Step 4: **Block selection in FAMP.** Flipping the corresponding pixels in unavailable blocks to change their availability. Calculating the corresponding values of md_2, and blocks with $md_2 > 2$ are considered to be available blocks, while those with $md_2 < 3$

are unavailable ones. In Location Map 2, blocks with $md_2 < 3$ are recorded as 0, and blocks with $md_2 \geq 3$ are recorded as 1. The length of Location Map 2 just equals to the number chunks satisfies $md < 2$.

Step 5: **Rearranging blocks in FAMP.** Arrange blocks with $md_2 > 2$ for data embedding towards front position of the image, and reversing the order of the blocks with $md_2 < 3$ towards the back of the image.

Step 6: **Encryption of Embedded Information.** To prevent malicious access to the embedded confidential information, this paper employs classical symmetric encryption algorithms such as RC4 and AES. The embedded confidential information is encrypted using the data encryption key K_3.

Step 7: **Data Embedding.** To ensure reversibility, the lengths of Location Map 1 (lm_1), Location Map 1 (LM_1), the length of Location Map 2 (lm_2), and Location Map 2 (LM_2) are compressed and embedded into the available blocks towards the front of the image. Arithmetic coding is employed in this paper to compress the positional map information. Subsequently, the encrypted confidential data and the end marker are embedded into the remaining available blocks.

Figure 5 shows an example of using FAMP to embed data in a block with $md = 1$. As shown in the Fig. 5(a), this block is composed of pixels $P = 194 = (1100\ 0010)_2$, $C_1 = 191 = (1011\ 1111)_2$, $C_2 = 214 = (1101\ 0110)_2$, $C_3 = 167 = (1010\ 0111)_2$. This block is calculated to obtain $d_1 = 7, d_2 = 5, d_3 = 7$ and $md = 1$ and using the formula (5) and formula (6).

Figure 5(a) flip the pixel corresponding to the maximum value of d_i. In this case, $d_1 = 7, d_2 = 5, d_3 = 7$. Pixels C_1 and C_3 correspond to d_1 and d_3, because maximum value of d_i is 7. Therefore, flipping 7 bits LSB of pixels C_1 and C_3 by using the formula (7). The flipping rule is such that bit 1 is flipped to bit 0, and bit 0 is flipped to bit 1. The 7-bit LSB in pixel C_1 is the red part, 0111111 is flipped to 1000000, resulting in the pixel $C_1 = 192 = (1100\ 0000)_2$. Similarly, the 7-bit LSB in pixel C_3 is the red part, 0100100 is flipped to 1011000, resulting in the pixel $C_3 = 219 = (1101\ 1000)_2$. According to the formula (8), calculating $D_1 = 2$ for pixel C_1 and $D_3 = 5$ for pixel C_3. The new pixel block is composed of $P = 194$, $C_1 = 192$, $C_2 = 214$ and $C_3 = 219$.

Figure 5 (b) shows embedded data, C_1 and C_3 are flipped in Fig. 5 (a), so the FC field is 101. In this flipped pixel block, $md_2 = 3$ is an available block and record in binary as 00 in md_2 field, pixel block of $md_2 = 3$ shares 3 MSB with pixel P. e_1, e_2 and e_3 respectively record the MSBs not shared by C_1, C_2 and C_3 with P. e_1 represents the $(8-md_2)$ bits LSB of $C_1 = 192$, e_1 is 00000. e_2 represents the $(8-md_2)$ bits LSB of $C_2 = 214$, e_2 is 10110. e_3 represents the $(8-md_2)$ bits LSB of $C_3 = 219$, e_3 is 11011. The length of the embedded data n_c is $(3 \times md_2 - 6)$ bits. For the flipped block with $md_2 = 3$, the length of n_c is also 3 bits. In other words, 3 bits data can represent any binary number. In this example, $n_c = 101$. Combining P, md_2, FC, md, e_1, e_2, e_3 and n_c fields forms the pixel block after embedding the data is $P = 194 = (1100\ 0010)_2$, $C_1 = 44 = (0010\ 1100)_2$, $C_2 = 64 = (0101\ 0110)_2$, $C_3 = 167 = (1101\ 1101)_2$.

2.6 Data Extraction and Image Recovery

Depending on the availability of the image encryption key K_1, the scrambling key K_2, and the data encryption key K_3 held by the receiver, three types can be distin-guished:

Case1: For receivers with only keys K_1 and K_2, the original image and the secret information in encrypted form can be obtained.

Step1: Retrieve the position map and identify the embedding boundaries. Divide the embedded image into non-overlapping 2×2 pixels blocks, and extract lm_1, lm_2, LM_1, and LM_2 sequentially. The extracted LM_1 and LM_2 are decompressed to obtain the distribution of usable blocks for AMP and FAMP, along with the embedding boundaries.

Step2: For secret information extraction and pixel block restoration, the AMP-compressed blocks are first restored based on LM_1. The format of AMP blocks is shown in Fig. 2. Sequentially extract P and md, followed by e_1, e_2, and e_3, along with the secret information n_c, and restore the pixels according to the following formula (11).

$$C_i = Trunc(P, md) + e_i, i = 1, 2, 3. \quad (11)$$

Subsequently, restoring the FAMP-compressed pixel blocks based on LM_2. Sequentially extract P, md_2, FC, and md, then extract e_1, e_2, e_3, and the secret information n_c, and restoring the pixels according to the following formula (12).

$$C_i = \begin{cases} Trunc(P, md_2), & \text{if } C_i \text{ unchange} \\ C_i, & \text{if } C_i \text{ flip} \end{cases} . \, i = 1, 2, 3. \quad (12)$$

where $Trunc(P, md_2)$ represents the md_2 MSB of pixel P. "+" denotes the concatenation of the left and right operands, the $F(Trunc(P, md_2) + e_i, md)$ represents the (8-md) LSB of the reversal pixel $Trunc(P, md_2) + e_i$, with the remaining md MSB unchanged. Figure 8 shows an example of FAMP method for recovering pixels. It is known from the location map that this pixel block is embedded data using the FAMP method. Through the position map information, it is known that this pixel block is embedded data using the FAMP method, with pixels $P = 194$, $C_1 = 44$, $C_2 = 22$ and $C_3 = 197$. The four pixels are represented as a 32-bit pixel structure.

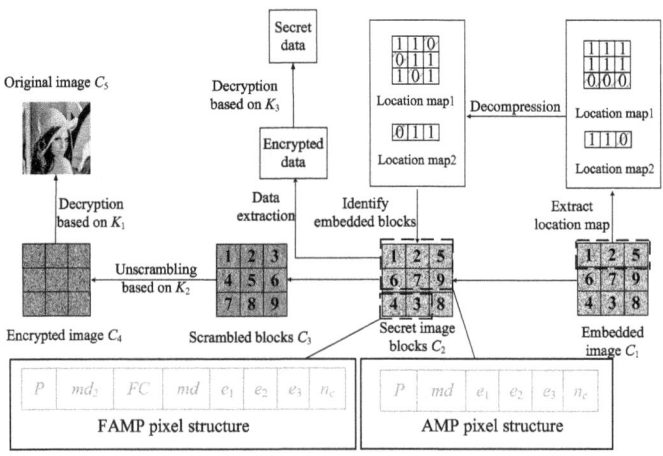

Fig. 6. Data extraction and image recovery

In Fig. 7, the receiver determines from $md_2 = 00 = 3$ that the first 3 bits of C_1, C_2, and C_3 match P, and identifies that e_1, e_2, and e_3 each occupy 5 bits. Thus, $C_1 = Trunc(P, md_2) + e_1 = 110 + 00000 = 11000000$, $C_2 = Trunc(P, md_2) + e_2 = 110 + 10110 = 11010110$, $C_3 = Trunc(P, md_2) + e_3 = 110 + 11000 = 11011000$. Subsequently, with $FC = 101$, it's noted that C_1 and C_3 were flipped while C_2 remained unchanged. Also, given $md = 1$, it is inferred that the 7 LSBs of C_1 and C_3 were flipped. Therefore, $C_1 = F(C_1, 1) = 10111111 = 191$, $C_2 = C_2 = 214$, and $C_3 = F(C_3, 1) = 10100111 = 167$.

Step3: To decrypt the recovered encrypted pixel blocks, decryption is performed sequentially using the scrambling key K_2 and the image encryption key K_1 to restore the original image.

Case2: For receivers with only the key K_3, they can only obtain the plaintext form of the secret information. Repeat Step 1 and Step 2 from Case 1, and decrypt the extracted secret information using the data encryption key K_3.

Case3: For recipients with keys K_1, K_2, and K_3, they can obtain the plaintext forms of both the original image and the secret information. Simply execute Case 1 and Case 2.

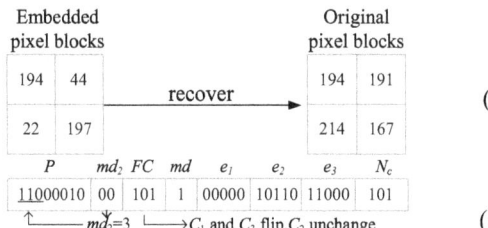

Fig. 7. Recovery of FAMP

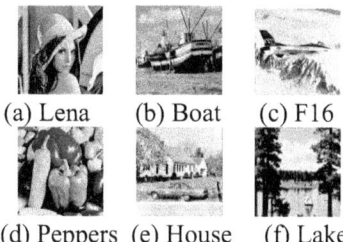

Fig. 8. Test images

3 Experiment Result and Analysis

In this section, we compare the performance of the proposed FAMP scheme with AMP scheme [14] in terms of the number of available blocks and the overall embedding capacity. We perform experiments on six test images selected from the USC-SIPI image database [15], each of which is shown in Fig. 8 (a), (b), (c), (d), (e), and (f) respectively.

As is shown in Fig. 9, the number of available blocks obtained in our scheme is obviously more than that in AMP scheme, proportion of available blocks is 94.5%, 94.8%, 93.3%, 97%, 97.1% and 92.1% in six test images, each of which is greater than 81.8%, 80.6%, 82.3%, 83.8%, 76% and 72.4% in AMP scheme. This is because that once flipping strategy is introduced, the correlation of pixels within previously unavailable blocks turns to be stronger. Taking Lena for example, the proportion of available blocks is 94.5% in the proposed scheme, comparing with 81.8% in AMP scheme. The difference is even more obvious for textural images such as Lake and House, since textural images have more unavailable in AMP compared with smooth images.

We flip blocks of pixels with $md = 0$ and $md = 1$ so that the number of available blocs increases and the embedding capacity increases accordingly. The embedding capacity of a flipped block is related to the pixels within the block, and the embedding capacity usually depends on the smoothness of the image. The smoother the selected pixels are, the larger the embedding capacity is.

The overall embedding capacities are compared in Fig. 10. It is clear from the figure that the proposed scheme is better than its counterpart. In particular, the improvement in embedding capacity is 43,458, 27,252, 25,118, 34,884, 37,522 and 31,740 bits respectively, among which the average improvement value is 30,073 bits. We can find that in House and Lake the texture image, the embedding capacity increases significantly. Therefore, the proposed method is more effective for embedding capacity enhancement in texture images. But in Boat, F16 etc. the embedding capacity is also increased in smooth images. The reason is that smooth images have less overhead of location map information, so proposed scheme can improve embedding capacity for smooth images.

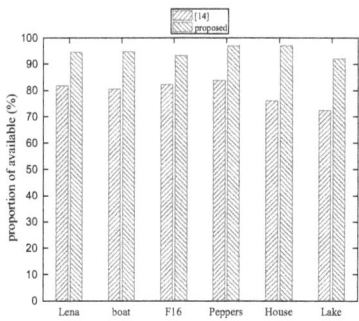

Fig. 9. Proportion of available blocks

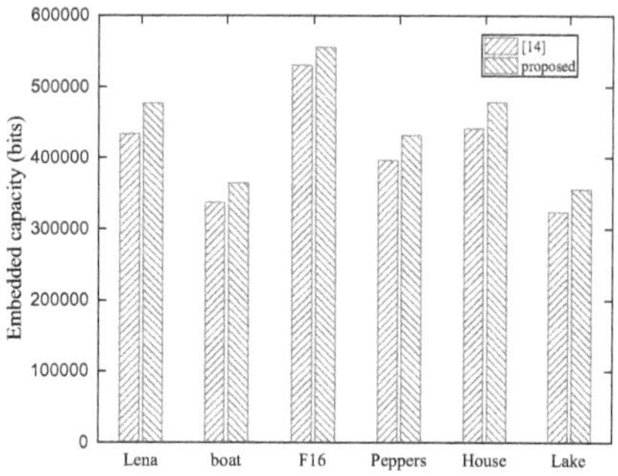

Fig. 10. Embedded capacity

4 Conclusion

This paper proposes a novel scheme base Adaptive MSB prediction in RDHEI. We improve embedding capacity while maintaining reversibility, which is crucial for the development of RDHEI techniques. we introduce FAMP scheme to make previously unavailable blocks available for data embedding. This is achieved by flipping pixels within the block, recording the positions of flipped pixels, and utilizing a new 2 × 2 pixels structure and novel location maps to support the proposed flipping strategy. Experimental results demonstrate the effectiveness of our proposed scheme compared to state-of-the-art techniques. The proposed approach achieves better prediction accuracy and greater embedding capacity while ensuring reversibility.

Acknowledgments. Supported by Student Academic Research Training Project of University of International Relations (No.3262024SWA01).

References

1. Tang, X., Zhou, L., Tang, G., et al.: Reversible data hiding based on improved block selection strategy and pixel value ordering. In: Proceedings of the 19th IEEE International Symposium on Dependable, pp. 619–627. Autonomic and Secure Computing, Canada (2021)
2. Tang, X., Zhou, Y., Cheng, Y., et al.: Weighted average-based complexity calculation in block selection oriented reversible data hiding. Secur. Commun. Netw., 1–15 (2022)
3. Tang, X., Zhou, L., Liu, D., et al.: Reversible data hiding based on improved rhombus predictor and prediction error expansion. In: Proceedings of IEEE 19th International Conference on Trust, pp. 13–21. Security and Privacy in Computing and Communications, China (2020)
4. Tang, X., Zhou, L., Tang, G., et al.: Improved fluctuation derived block selection strategy in pixel value ordering based reversible data hiding. In: Proceedings of the 20th International Workshop on Digital-forensics and Watermarking, pp. 163–177. China (2021)
5. Abdul Karim, M.S., Wong, K.: Universal data embedding in encrypted domain. Signal Process. **94**, 174–182 (2014)
6. Zhang, X.: Neversible data hiding in encrypted image. IEEE Signal Process. Lett. **18**(4), 255–258 (2011)
7. Hong, W., Chen, T.-S., Wu, H.-Y.: An improved reversible data hiding in encrypted images using side match. IEEE Signal Process. Lett. **19**(4), 199–202 (2012)
8. Liao, X., Shu, C.: Reversible data hiding in encrypted images based on absolute mean difference of multiple neighboring pixels. J. Vis. Commun. Image Represent. **28**, 21–27 (2015)
9. Khanam, F.-T.-Z., Song, K.-Y., Kim, S.: A modified reversible data hiding in encrypted image using enhanced measurement functions. In: 2016 Eighth International Conference on Ubiquitous & Future Networks, pp. 869–872 (2016)
10. Rupali, B., Aggarwal, A.: An improved block based joint reversible data hiding in encrypted images by symmetric cryptosystem. Pattern Recogn. Lett. **139**, 60–68 (2018)
11. Wu, X., Sun, W.: High-capacity reversible data hiding in encrypted images by prediction error. Signal Process. **104**, 387–400 (2014)
12. Puteaux, P., Puech, W.: An efficient MSB prediction-based method for high-capacity reversible data hiding in encrypted images. IEEE Trans. Inf. Forensics Secur. **13**(7), 1670–1681 (2018)
13. Wang, Y., Cai, Z., He, W.: High capacity reversible data hiding in encrypted image based on intra-block lossless compression. IEEE Trans. Multimedia **23**, 1466–1473 (2021)
14. Wang, Y., He, W.: High capacity reversible data hiding in encrypted image based on adaptive MSB prediction. IEEE Trans. Multimedia **24**, 1288–1298 (2022)
15. Image database of sipi. [EB/OL]. http://sipi.usc.edu/database/. Accessed Apr 2018

Decoupling Control in Text-to-Image Diffusion Models

Shitong Cao, Xuejie Zhang, Jin Wang, and Xiaobing Zhou(✉)

School of Information Science and Engineering,
Yunnan University, Kunming 650504, Yunnan, China
zhouxb@ynu.edu.cn

Abstract. Large text-to-image models allow for high-quality and diverse synthesis of images from a given text prompt. However, many scenarios require that the content creation be controllable. Recent methods add image-level controls, e.g., edge and depth maps, to manipulate the generation process together with text prompts to obtain desired images. In this work, we propose a decoupling control to disentangle one or multiple objects and individual objects' shapes and appearances in a given reference set while synthesizing novel renditions and rearranging them in different contexts. Given a set of images as input, we establish mapping relationships between the target's appearance and different "circles" through fine-tuning a pretrained text-to-image model. We achieve control over the local position of different "circles" by designing a novel local feature loss to decouple multi-targets. Extensive experiments demonstrate that our model can disentangle individual objects and allow for their translation within a scene, as well as arbitrary control over the combination of multiple targets while maintaining appearance consistency among the targets.

Keywords: Compositional and Consistent Generative · Disentangle Individual Objects · Local Feature Classification · Diversity Maintaining

1 Introduction

Have you ever imagined adding or removing elements in an image, wishing that only a specific object in the generated image could be moved a little to the left to meet the requirements better, or if it could be moved a bit to the right to be perfect? More complex scenarios, such as moving one object forward and another backward, without complex control conditions.

Recently developed large-scale text-to-image models have demonstrated unprecedented capabilities, enabling high-quality and diversified image synthesis through prompts written in natural language [1–3]. One of the main advantages of these models is the strong semantic priors learned from a large number of image-caption pairs. Though the ability of text-to-image synthesis models is becoming increasingly impressive, the quality of generated images is much worse when generating multiple objects. In text-to-image synthesis, there are some basic methods in text design [4, 5]. The text describes issues with the image generation pipeline, namely the lack of flexible user control to accurately guide generated images according to user ideas. To address this, descriptive information about objects in the images is needed. Some studies have attempted to use drawings, sketches, masks, or depth to control combined target creation, but these methods are mostly limited to single object scenarios and yield inconsistent results at higher resolutions and complexities. Currently, there are no methods that address the simultaneous generation and consistency of multiple targets. Thus, the paper proposes a decoupling control method based on categorizing targets, allowing independent control over different target categories. Additionally, control information is extracted from the text rather than being externally provided. The method aims to disentangle information between different targets [6, 7].

Our method can disentangle each target and the relationship between the targets and the background, allowing for independent control of each target. These attributes are crucial for various applications, such as film production, poster creation, dynamic generation of the target in videos, and the generation of complex object trajectories in a consistent manner. Therefore, our method has substantial practical value, enabling control over different targets while maintaining robust generation capabilities. It involves fine-tuning without the need for extensive computational resources or time.

2 Related Work

Conditional Image Synthesis: Generation based on diffusion models has achieved the best results [1–3]. Text-to-image synthesis has driven significant progress and has brought about tremendous changes. Text-to-image models, including Stable Diffusion (SD) [2], Dalle [3], and Imagen [8], have contributed largely to this advancement. There are also many methods emerging in the field of controllability research, using controls such as masks, human posture, depth maps, and sketches [9, 10]. These additional control conditions can be input into the model via a hypernetwork. The notion of hypernetworks originates from neural language processing methods [11, 12], where a smaller recursive neural network is trained to influence the weights of a larger neural network. By attaching a smaller neural network to a stable diffusion, the artistic style of its output image is altered [13–15].

In recent years, Transformer-based methods such as the GPT series [16, 17] and the BERT family [18, 19] have transformed the field of natural language processing. ChatGPT has excellent text parsing abilities, and Dalle3 has also been embedded within ChatGPT. Some methods use ChatGPT to generate intermediate control procedures to guide the generation process. Traditional studies on image layouts [20–22] tend to apply strategies like bounding boxes (bbox) or object categories for image synthesis. Neural network-based methods such as conditional GANs can generate controlled images with satisfactory results in specific scenes, but they lack generalizability and universality [23–25]. Some current research involves establishing a connection between specific targets and special characters, using the special character to express the specific target.

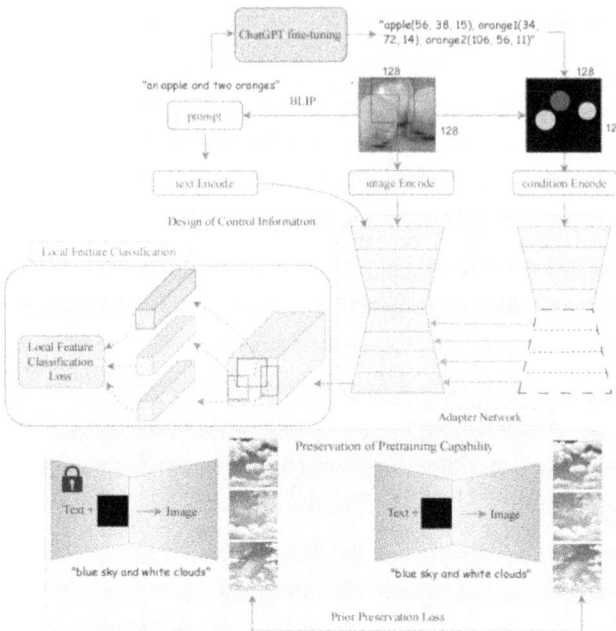

Fig. 1. Model architecture diagram, consisting of three components: the Control Condition Design Module, which automatically extracts control information from text and forms control conditions; the Adapter Network, which is a replicated version of the upper part of U-Net and is updated to be added to the corresponding lower part of U-Net; Local Feature Classification Network, which is used to supervise the position and category of the targets by classifying the features from U-Net locally.

3 Method

3.1 Adapter Network

Text-to-image models have achieved great success, allowing the generation of various images through text. We employ a small network to fine-tune the larger model, with a tiny adapter influencing the larger network. The adapter network allows for retaining the original pretrained model's knowledge, meaning one can capitalize on the extensive knowledge from training on large-scale datasets. This is particularly beneficial for scenarios with small datasets or a scarcity of data, allowing for the rapid fine-tuning of the model to suit new tasks or datasets.

The specific network model is depicted in Fig. 1. To incorporate the control module into Stable Diffusion, we transform the conditioned input image from an input size of 512×512 to a 64×64 feature space vector compatible with the size used by Stable Diffusion. Specifically, we use a tiny network $\varepsilon()$ consisting of four convolutional layers with 4×4 kernels and 2×2 strides. These layers are activated by ReLU and initialized with 16, 32, 64, and 128 channels, respectively. The network is initialized with Gaussian weights and trained jointly with the complete model. This is to encode the image space condition c_i into a feature space condition vector c_f. The formula is as follows.

$$c_f = \varepsilon(c_i) \tag{1}$$

The conditional vector c_f is passed to SD, forming the control.

Train the model by setting reconstruction loss between the denoised image and the real image. The reconstruction loss is for the entire image and is a global reconstruction loss. Given an initial noise map $\epsilon \sim \mathcal{N}(0, I)$, text prompts c_t, as well as a task-specific condition c_f, generates an image $X_{gen} = \widehat{X}_\theta(\epsilon, c_t, c_f)$.

They are trained using a squared error loss to denoise image or latent code $z_t := \alpha_t x + \sigma_t \epsilon$ as follows:

$$\mathcal{L}_{globe} = \mathbb{E}_{X,c_t,c_f,t,\epsilon}[W_t \|\widehat{X}_\theta(\alpha_t X + \sigma_t \epsilon, c_t, c_f) - X\|_2^2] \tag{2}$$

where X is the ground-truth image and α_t, σ_t, W_t are terms that control the noise schedule and sample quality, and are functions of the diffusion process time $t \sim \mu([0,1])$.

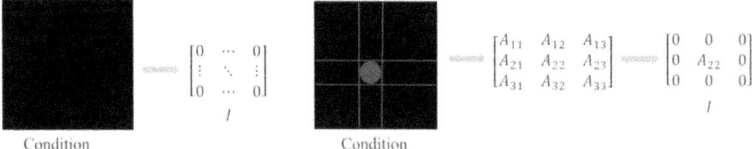

Fig. 2. Conversion of control conditions into a rectangular form.

3.2 Design of Control Information

In the previous section, the control conditions in the adapter network are generally edges, poses, depth, etc. However, it is not easy to obtain control conditions that meet user needs, and control conditions cannot be flexibly adjusted. Existing explicit control methods have resulted in models being biased towards visual control, significantly reducing their language control capabilities.

In this paper, we propose using different "circles" as conditions. The control conditions are simple and can be easily manipulated, allowing for a high degree of flexibility. By specifying the position and size of a circle, the corresponding image generation can be guided, ensuring that the generated results conform to specific layout or scene requirements. This decoupling allows individual control over each target, enabling composite and consistent generation.

As shown in Fig. 2, the control conditions are transformed into a matrix for analysis. The matrix, even after passing through the activation function, still contains a significant number of zeros. Therefore, its impact on the SD main network is minimal. When aiming to preserve the generation capabilities of the text-to-image model itself, where only text is used as input, the adapter network does not play a role. In this case, the adapter network receives a completely black image as input. The black image, where all the values in the matrix are set to 0, is passed as input to the pre-trained model without significantly affecting its pre-trained parameters, especially in a well-trained and robust model.

The information at the all-zero position does not add any additional information. When an all-black input is fed in, which means I is 0, $f(x) = I * W$ is approximately 0. Set I to 0, the gradient will also be 0, which means the parameters cannot be updated. Consequently, the standard deviation remains unchanged, effectively locking it. Once locked, it can generate the background as described by the text. The standard deviation combined with control represents the foreground, meaning that it generates this entity based on the foreground. We simply compute the gradients for the zero linear layer. Given an input map $I \in \mathbb{R}^{h \times w}$, the forward pass can be written as:

$$\mathcal{Z}(I; W, B) = B + I * W \tag{3}$$

When the matrix I is a zero matrix, the formula becomes as follows:

$$\mathcal{Z}(I; W, B) = B + 0 * W = B \tag{4}$$

When the matrix I is non-zero, the W matrix is also subjected to matrix partitioning, dividing W into nine corresponding smaller matrices. Thus, the formula becomes as follows:

$$\mathcal{Z}(I; W, B) = B + I * W = B + A_{22} * W_{22} \tag{5}$$

Using "circles" as control conditions, after passing through the adaptive network, the number of parameters is very small, and the impact on the original pre-trained model parameters is relatively small when sent to the stable diffusion. Still maintaining the prompt effect of the text, rather than relying solely on control conditions.

3.3 Local Feature Classification Loss

The global reconstruction loss minimizes the difference between the generated image and the input image, which leads to a lack of supervision and control over local information. Local classification loss can further improve the quality of generated samples. In the previous section, the control conditions are local, that is, the control condition circle, and the other black areas do not play a role. Enhance the control generation of local information based on local guidance.

In this paper, we propose the local feature classification loss, which addresses both the position and category loss. This approach stabilizes the generation of specific objects at fixed positions. Through experiments, we have observed that this local feature classification network does not create a jarring contrast between the target and the background. The local features are defined as w, and the category after passing through a linear function is denoted as $linear(W)$. The true category is defined as v, and the corresponding loss function is formulated as:

$$\mathcal{L}_{local} = MSE(v, linear(W)) \tag{6}$$

The U-Net part in the middle of the network is divided into an up-sampling layer, an intermediate layer, and a down-sampling layer, which are 64 * 64, 32 * 32, 16 * 16, and 8 * 8, respectively. We operate on the 16 * 16 features of the up-sampling layer, extract the corresponding local positions for classification calculation, and achieve supervision of local position targets.

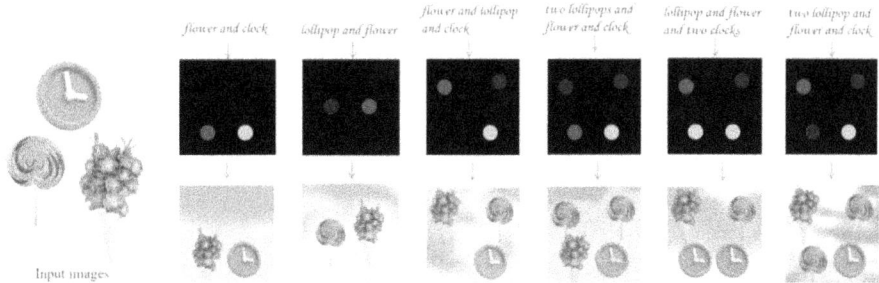

Fig. 3. Decontanglement control of multiple targets

3.4 Prior Preservation Loss

The loss of local feature classification is the control target, but to maintain the diversity of the background, we introduce the prior preservation loss in Dreambooth to maintain the strong generation ability of the large model. Specifically, we generate data $X_{pr} = \hat{X}(Z_{t_1}, C_{pr})$ by using the ancestral sampler on the frozen pre-trained diffusion model with random initial noise $Z_{t_1} \sim \mathcal{N}(0, I)$ and conditioning vector $c_{pr} := \gamma(f("abackgroundof"))$. The loss function is as follows.

$$\mathcal{L}_{pp} = \mathbb{E}_{X,c_t,c_f,t,\epsilon} \lambda W_{t'} \|X_\theta(\alpha_{t'}X_{pr} + \alpha_{t'}\hat{\epsilon}, c_{pr}, c_f) - X_{pr}\|_2^2 \tag{7}$$

where X is the ground-truth image, $\epsilon \sim \mathcal{N}(0, I)$, c_t is a conditioning vector obtained from a text prompt, c_f is the information used for controlling the target, which is input to the model through an adapter network, and α_t, σ_t, W_t are terms that control the noise schedule and sample quality, and are functions of the diffusion process time $t \sim \mu([0,1])$. The second term is the prior-preservation term that supervises the model with its own generated images, and λ controls for the relative weight of this term.

$$\mathcal{L}_{total} = \mathcal{L}_{globe} + \mathcal{L}_{local} + \mathcal{L}_{pp} \tag{8}$$

The three losses are combined as the overall loss function of the entire model. Guided by this loss function, the model can achieve control over the target positions while preserving the original generation capability of the pre-trained model.

4 Experiments

4.1 Experimental Design and Analysis

Stable Diffusion is an outstanding benchmark in text-to-image generation, providing a solid starting point for this research. We compute the similarity between the generated images and text using a pre-trained CLIP model to verify the alignment of the text with the generated images. The fidelity of the generated images is assessed by computing similarity with real images. To precisely evaluate the model's capability for target positioning control, we select texts from different categories containing positional relationship descriptions to generate images and calculate their similarity to the text. When target positional information is ambiguous, or the text does not specify target positioning, our model reverts to generative behavior on par with that of Stable Diffusion. This experiment was conducted on an NVIDIA 3090 GPU took approximately 5 h.

Table 1. Ablation studies on various components.

c_f	$\mathcal{L}_{globe}$	$\mathcal{L}_{local}$	$\mathcal{L}_{PP}$	Chat/Human operation	Clip-T C/H	Clip-I C/H
Stable Diffusion					0.3268	-
	✓	✓			0.2807	0.3314
	✓		✓		0.3269	0.3155
	✓	✓	✓		0.3257	0.3281
✓	✓			✓(C)/✓(H)	0.3023/0.3022	0.3216/0.3204
✓	✓	✓		✓(C)/✓(H)	0.2098/0.3011	0.3273/0.3273
✓	✓	✓		✓(C)/✓(H)	0.3279/0.3292	0.3145/0.3164
✓	✓	✓	✓	✓(C)/✓(H)	0.3308/0.3312	0.3308/0.3312

4.2 Experimental Results

This study relies primarily on two evaluation metrics, namely Clip-T and Clip-I. Clip-T represents the similarity between generated images and text, while Clip-I measures the similarity between real images and generated images. The entire experiment is divided into two major blocks: one without control conditions and another with control conditions. The absence of control conditions is intended to assess whether the model retains its original ability to generate images from text. Through ablation studies (Table 1), we observed that our model still possesses the inherent image generation capability to produce diverse images. Moreover, our model can also perform controlled generation, which sets it apart from many explicitly controlled models. In explicit models, control conditions must be provided during the inference stage; otherwise, the model fails to generate normal images. Our model can switch between controlled and uncontrolled. When no control conditions are applied, the input for control conditions becomes entirely black, effectively removing any control, thus reverting the model to its initial state of text-to-image generation.

The ablation experiments also primarily discuss the impact of $\mathcal{L}_{loc}$ and $\mathcal{L}_{pp}$ on the model, both in uncontrolled and controlled scenarios. It can be observed that $\mathcal{L}_{loc}$ facilitates control over the target position, while $\mathcal{L}_{pp}$ promotes the generation of diverse images. This diversity manifests in the ability to alter the target's posture or the background of specific objects.

4.3 Visualization Results

Visualizing Circles as Control Conditions. As shown in Fig. 3, visualize circles as control conditions, with circles of different colors representing different targets. The

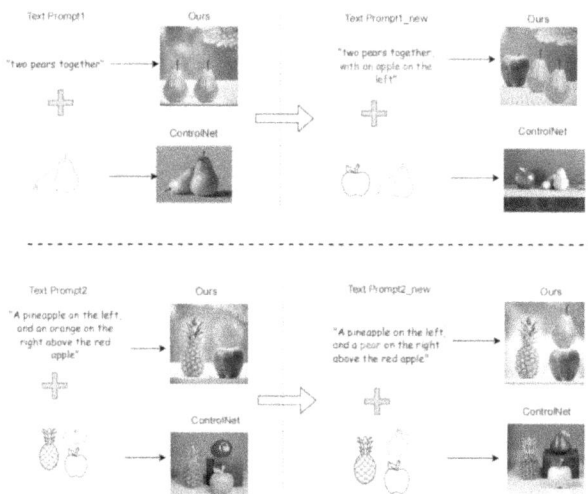

Fig. 4. Compare our method to the explicit information control model (ControlNet).

position of the circles can control the position of the targets generated. Through experiments, it can be seen that we can achieve any combination of these three goals, including understanding quantitative relationships. During the process of combining and generating images, it is possible to maintain consistency in the appearance of each target. In the subsequent visualization results, circles were not shown as implicit control conditions.

Comparison with Other Control Conditions. As shown in Fig. 4, preliminary experimental results indicate that our method outperforms the ControlNet network model in generating "complex" images with multiple object combinations. The advantage lies primarily in the simplicity and convenience of our approach to achieving controlled generation. Firstly, our method does not require additional control sketches. Instead, it extracts hidden information from textual cues to provide reasonable control over the spatial positions of individual objects. In contrast, ControlNet requires manual sketching, which significantly increases the complexity of user operations. Secondly, our project is also more straightforward in adjusting and modifying generated images. Modifying the text prompt can accomplish adjustments and modifications to the image. On the other hand, the ControlNet network model requires a new control sketch for such modifications.

Comparison with Existing Generative Models. The following compares this paper and wen xin yi ge, Stable Diffusion, Midjourney and DallE3 models regarding their generation performance. From the experimental results, it can be observed that these models achieve good results when generating images with relatively simple targets. However, when the generated scenes become "complex", the results generated by our model are more in line with the description in the text. As shown in Fig. 5, the description "Red cup, camera, desk lamp" denotes the need to generate multiple objects with a specific quantity relationship. "The camera is placed on the left side of the red cup" signifies the spatial relationship between different objects. "Desk lamp on the left, green bowl in the

Fig. 5. The qualitative results of text-to-image generation from different models vary.

middle, and red cup on the right" represent combinations of multiple objects and their positional relationships with each other. Compared with the four models in this article, when faced with multiple target combinations, the generated results cannot match the text highly. The quantity relationships are not clearly expressed in the generated images, and the combinations of different objects are also inaccurately generated, with the absence of crucial objects. In contrast, our method achieves more accurate generation results by accurately expressing the information from the textual descriptions and providing reasonable spatial distribution.

Fig. 6. Consistency generation of two objectives and one objective under different transformations.

Image Edit. As shown in Fig. 6, we complete consistency generation under different transformations for two targets and a single target. On the left side of the figure, we demonstrate controlled spawning of an object orbiting another object. In this process, you can maintain consistency in the appearance of two objects and understand that size and dimensions change as the distance between the objects changes. In the image on the right, when fed a specific image of a puppy, the model can generate consistent images of that specific puppy in different scenarios. The resulting image keeps the main subject as the input puppy, but the background, pose, number, and position change.

5 Conclusion

We propose a control method capable of orchestrating the arrangement and combination of multiple targets, whereby control over each target category is independent. This decoupling allows for the consistent generation of targets across various scenes. Additionally, our method facilitates seamless switching between controlled and uncontrolled scenarios. The cornerstone of our approach is the design of appropriate control conditions, which serve as a switch. Notably, this fine-tuning process requires only one image per category to generate high-quality pictures.

References

1. Shi, J., Wu, C., Liang, J., Liu, X., Duan, N.: DiVAE: photorealistic images synthesis with denoising diffusion decoder. arXiv preprint arXiv:2206.00386 (2022)
2. Rombach, R., Blattmann, A., Lorenz, D., Esser, P., Ommer, B.: High-resolution image synthesis with latent diffusion models. In: Proceedings of the IEEE/CVF Conference on Computer Vision and Pattern Recognition, pp. 10684–10695 (2022)
3. Ramesh, A., Dhariwal, P., Nichol, A., Chu, C., Chen, M.: Hierarchical text conditional image generation with clip latents. arXiv preprint arXiv:2204.06125 **1**(2), 3 (2022)
4. Liu, V., Chilton, L.B.: Design guidelines for prompt engineering text-to-image generative models. In: Proceedings of the 2022 CHI Conference on Human Factors in Computing Systems, pp. 1–23 (2022)
5. Pavlichenko, N., Ustalov, D.: Best prompts for text-to-image models and how to find them. In: Proceedings of the 46th International ACM SIGIR Conference on Research and Development in Information Retrieval, pp. 2067–2071 (2023)
6. Locatello, F., et al.: Challenging common assumptions in the unsupervised learning of disentangled representations. In: International Conference on Machine Learning, pp. 4114–4124. PMLR (2019)
7. Bengio, Y., Courville, A., Vincent, P.: Representation learning: a review and new perspectives. IEEE Trans. Pattern Anal. Mach. Intell. **35**(8), 1798–1828 (2013)
8. Saharia, C., et al.: Photorealistic text to image diffusion models with deep language understanding. Adv. Neural. Inf. Process. Syst. **35**, 36479–36494 (2022)
9. Zhang, L., Rao, A., Agrawala, M.: Adding conditional control to text-to-image diffusion models. In: Proceedings of the IEEE/CVF International Conference on Computer Vision, pp. 3836–3847 (2023)
10. Mou, C., et al.: T2I-Adapter: learning adapters to dig out more controllable ability for text-to-image diffusion models. arXiv preprint arXiv:2302.08453 (2023)

11. Alaluf, Y., Tov, O., Mokady, R., Gal, R., Bermano, A.: HyperStyle: StyleGAN inversion with hyper networks for real image editing. In: Proceedings of the IEEE/CVF conference on computer Vision and pattern recognition, pp. 18511–18521 (2022)
12. Dinh, T.M., Tran, A.T., Nguyen, R., Hua, B.S.: HyperInverter: improving StyleGAN inversion via hyper network. In: Proceedings of the IEEE/CVF Conference on Computer Vision and Pattern Recognition, pp. 11389–11398 (2022)
13. Chen, Z., et al.: Vision transformer adapter for dense predictions. arXiv preprint arXiv:2205.08534 (2022)
14. Stickland, A.C., Murray, I.: BERT and PALs: projected attention layers for efficient adaptation in multi-task learning. In: International Conference on Machine Learning, pp. 5986–5995. PMLR (2019)
15. Mallya, A., Davis, D., Lazebnik, S.: Piggyback: adapting a single network to multiple tasks by learning to mask weights. In: Proceedings of the European Conference on Computer Vision (ECCV), pp. 67–82 (2018)
16. Brown, T., et al.: Language models are few-shot learners. Adv. Neural. Inf. Process. Syst. **33**, 1877–1901 (2020)
17. Radford, A., Narasimhan, K., Salimans, T., Sutskever, I., et al.: Improving language understanding by generative pre-training (2018)
18. Devlin, J., Chang, M.W., Lee, K., Toutanova, K.: BERT: pre-training of deep bidirectional transformers for language understanding. arXiv preprint arXiv:1810.04805 (2018)
19. Liu, Y., et al.: ROBERTa: A robustly optimized BERT pretraining approach. arXiv preprint arXiv:1907.11692 (2019)
20. Li, Z., Wu, J., Koh, I., Tang, Y., Sun, L.: Image synthesis from layout with locality aware mask adaption. In: Proceedings of the IEEE/CVF International Conference on Computer Vision, pp. 13819–13828 (2021)
21. Zhao, B., Meng, L., Yin, W., Sigal, L.: Image generation from layout. In: Proceedings of the IEEE/CVF Conference on Computer Vision and Pattern Recognition, pp. 8584–8593 (2019)
22. Gafni, O., Polyak, A., Ashual, O., Sheynin, S., Parikh, D., Taigman, Y.: Make-A-Scene: scene-based text-to-image generation with human priors. In: European Conference on Computer Vision, pp. 89–106. Springer (2022). https://doi.org/10.1007/978-3-031-19784-0_6
23. Park, T., Liu, M.Y., Wang, T.C., Zhu, J.Y.: Semantic image synthesis with spatially-adaptive normalization. In: Proceedings of the IEEE/CVF Conference on Computer Vision and Pattern Recognition, pp. 2337–2346 (2019)
24. Chen, Q., Koltun, V.: Photographic image synthesis with cascaded refinement networks. In: Proceedings of the IEEE International Conference on Computer Vision, pp. 1511–1520 (2017)
25. Zhu, J.Y., Park, T., Isola, P., Efros, A.A.: Unpaired image-to-image translation using cycle-consistent adversarial networks. In: Proceedings of the IEEE International Conference on Computer Vision, pp. 2223–2232 (2017)

Arbitrary Scale Texture Synthesis with Feature Map Swapping

Di Sun[1], Yangde Lin[1], Sheng Shen[2], Zhiliang Zeng[2], Shizhao Zhang[2], and Qihang Wang[3](✉)

[1] College of Artificial Intelligence, Tianjin University of Science and Technology, Tianjin 300222, China
[2] Beijing Institute of Control and Electronic Technology, Beijing 100045, China
[3] College of Intelligence and Computing, Tianjin University, Tianjin 300350, China
164383983@qq.com

Abstract. Texture synthesis is a technique widely used in computer vision. Existing learning-based methods typically use fixed network structure, and they can only generate images that are the same size or integer multiples of the input sample. In this paper, we propose a swapping-aware texture synthesis method based on feature mapping using a deep generative model. To optimize the loss function, we conduct a dedicated exchange algorithm that operates directly in the feature map space. The texture matching is optimized by matching the feature map between the original image and the generated image. The model can generate texture images of any size based on input samples. The generated results can be extended from the inside of the image to the surrounding, resulting in an image larger than the original input size. The experimental results show that the proposed method effectively preserves more high-frequency details while maintaining the consistency of the generated content and texture, and obtains more realistic synthesized results.

Keywords: Textures synthesis · Arbitrary Size · GAN · Swap

1 Introduction

Texture synthesis (TS) is a process of taking a small texture and then make it larger in size, not by tiling, but by synthesizing it. Early example-based techniques [1–4] are widely used for creating perceptually similar, non-periodic textures from a single input. Due to the requirement of selecting samples for generating new textures, the selection of samples is a limitation. Furthermore, it is impossible to consider texture synthesis from the perspective of the global image, as it can only be synthesized from given samples. The recent research highlights the effectiveness of deep neural networks in image generation, with some using Convolutional Neural Networks (CNN) for texture synthesis [5–10]. These methods can roughly fall into single texture sample methods [5] and feed-forward network methods [7, 8].

More recently, Generative Adversarial Network (GAN)-based [9, 10] architectures gain significant traction in the realm of texture synthesis over recent years. This creates a competitive relationship between the two components, thereby enhancing the accuracy of the model's results. For instance, Zhou Yang et al. [9] use generative adversarial networks to synthesize textures. Given a texture sample, their model can generate integer multiples of the size of the input sample. These methods are suitable for images with small or large texture components. However, they typically have limitations in generating arbitrary size textures directly due to the fixed size input requirement, resulting in textures that match the input size or integer multiples of it.

The quality of image feature extraction has a significant impact on the performance of neural network models. The swapping is first proposed by Chen, T et al. [16]. They used it to accelerate the speed of Style Transfer to generate style images, but they only used the feature map of a certain layer of the CNN to swap. Inspired by them, we try to apply swapping to all layers of the loss network, and match and exchange the feature maps in the VGG-19 model of the loss network.

In this paper, we propose an algorithm capable of extrapolating to unknown areas with minimal neighboring information. Inspired by [12], we introduce an "arbitrary size generation texture network" based on the GAN architecture. Our model includes a generator for texture creation and a discriminator to compare the generator's output with the ground truth. During training, we use a patch-swap algorithm to optimize loss functions. The proposed approach can generate textures of any size, see Fig. 1. The swapping algorithm optimizes loss functions by calculating the similarity between feature maps and enhances texture synthesized results.

Our main contributions are: (1) We propose a GAN based texture synthesis framework. The combination of adversarial training with feature swapping allows the model to generate arbitrary textures directly from input images. (2) We design a patch-swap method to optimize loss functions and improve the synthesized contents.

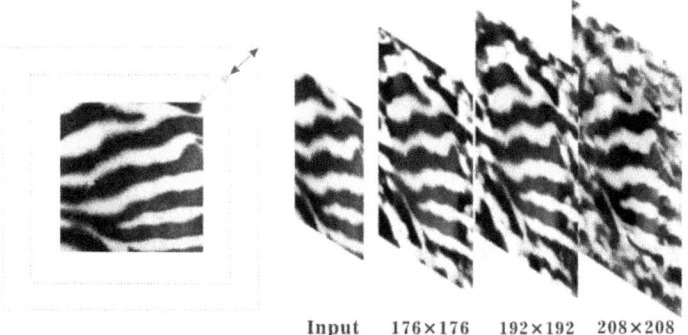

Fig. 1. Texture synthesis by the proposed method.

2 Related Work

In the early field of texture synthesis, sample-based methods are extensively used. Wei et al. [1] propose an effective example-based method to synthesize realistic textures quickly. Kwatra et al. [3] introduce an optimization-based method, while Darabui et al. [13] present the Image Melding method, which is based on patch-based optimization.

In recent years, there has been a growing focus on deep learning technologies [5, 8, 9, 14, 15]. Gatys et al. [5] demonstrate that CNN could generate textures from input samples by using feature maps to represent textures and calculating similarity between feature maps in different network layers. Their model introduces CNN as a new tool for texture synthesis. Li et al. [8] propose a texture synthesis method aimed at improving image quality, addressing issues such as generality, diversity, and suboptimality by designing a feed-forward network for synthesizing textures with meaningful interpolation. They improve the gram matrix loss by subtracting the feature mean. Ulyanov et al. [7] introduce texture networks based on the GAN model [11], capable of generating multiple samples from a single example of a texture and transferring artistic style from one image to another. Their model required training for a feed-forward Convolutional Network when given an input texture, with a loss function derived from [5]. Zhou et al. [9] use a GAN to synthesize textures, enabling their model to generate textures twice the size of the input sample, incorporating style loss and L1 loss into their GAN model.

Additionally, there are patch-based image synthesis methods. Chen et al. [16] achieve diverse style transfer, overcoming the limitations of existing methods. They use an inverse network to deterministically invert activation from stylized layers for stylized image generation and introduce a swap algorithm for style transfer. Li et al. [17] propose a Markov Random Field (MRF) loss function for optimizing image synthesis tasks applicable to style transfer and texture synthesis. Their MRF loss function calculates similarity from patches extracted from input samples. Song et al. [18] introduce a Convolutional Neural network-based image inpainting approach, enhancing results with a patch-swap algorithm that finds the closest-matching patch to fill missing information.

3 Method

Figure 2 shows the proposed framework that consists of a texture network and a loss network. For the texture network, the network structure is based on GANs network. The generator is used to extract visual features and synthesize the textural contents. The discriminator can improve the quality of synthesized results. For the loss network, the pre-trained VGG-19 serves as loss network. In addition, we design a swap module optimize the loss function.

3.1 Generator

The generator G follows the encoder-decoder fashion architecture. In contrast to [12, 21], we insert three residual blocks between them to increase network depth while preventing gradient disappearance, resulting in better generated images compared to models without these blocks. The generator comprises eight convolution layers and

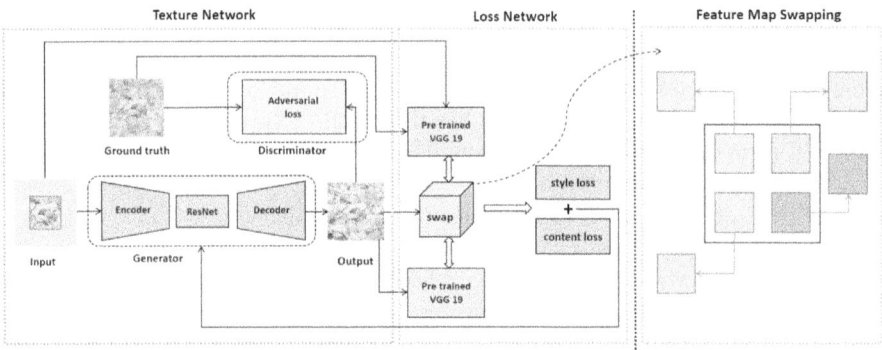

Fig. 2. Framework Overview. It includes a generator, a discriminator network, and a loss network. The generator's output serves as input for both the discriminator and the loss network, along with the texture samples. In the loss network, two input images traverse the network to calculate the style loss and content loss, with a swap operation matching the similarity of feature maps. In the Feature Map Swapping, squares represent the feature maps of different positions within the same layer of CNN, where different colors represent different feature maps at the same position. After calculation, the blue indicates that the feature map of this layer is most similar to the feature map of the input image, and then performs the exchange program, followed by further calculates style loss and content loss.

a deconvolution layer, with a 128×128 texture image as input. To enhance the quality of generated images, dilated convolution layers are added to increase the receptive field. Conv1 and decov7 layers employ 5×5 and 4×4 convolution kernels respectively, while the remaining convolution layers use 3×3 kernels. Conv2 and decov7 layers have a stride size of 2×2, whereas the rest have a stride size of 1×1. Except for conv9, which uses the Sigmoid activation function, ReLU activation function is applied in the other convolutional layers.

3.2 Discriminator

The discriminator is designed to use the output of itself and the generator to perform adversarial training to obtain the optimal results that the generator can obtain. To achieve this, we use the PatchGAN [20] network structure. In addition, Instance Norm and Max-pooling are utilized to enhance the stability of the training process.

3.3 Feature Map Matching Based on Swap

The swap algorithm is an operation on feature maps aimed at determining the similarity between input feature maps in the loss network. It's conceived as a specialized network layer for processing feature maps, comprising a convolutional layer and a deconvolutional layer. Unlike structures solely generating images within the original ones [16], our approach tackles image outpainting and applies the swap algorithm across all network layers.

The loss network could be divided into two models, $M_1(t_n)$ and $M_2(G)$. Model $M_2(G)$ extracts feature map patches of generated image, and model $M_2(G)$ extracts feature map patches of the ground truth I_{gt} which is similar as much as possible with those in generated images. The extract feature map patches should contain all channels. For feature map patches of generated image, the swap algorithm is defined by the following normalized cross-correlation measure, namely:

$$\alpha(G, t_n) := \underset{M_1(t_n)_i, i=1,2,...,N}{\mathrm{argmax}} \frac{\langle M_2(G), M_1(t_n) \rangle}{\|M_2(G), M_1(t_n)\|} \tag{1}$$

3.4 Loss Function

In this section, we introduce three loss functions: style loss, content loss and GAN loss.
Style Loss and Content Loss. Given a sample texture image I, the generator obtains the generated result I_0, then we feed I_0 into the loss network which is mentioned before to get the feature maps F_{I_0}. It is necessary to obtain the feature maps $F_{I_{gt}}$ of I_{gt} by using I_{gt} corresponding to I_0 as input for the loss network. Feature maps are extracted from {$relu1\_2$, $relu2\_2$, $relu3\_3$, $relu4\_3$, $relu5\_4$} of loss network. We use both output of generator and ground truth as input for the loss network. The architecture of loss network is shown in Fig. 3.

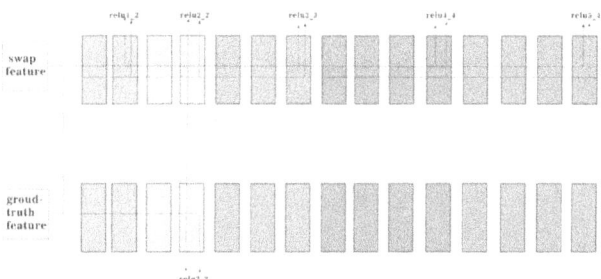

Fig. 3. Architecture of loss network. The loss network is based on VGG-19. The input of loss network is the swap feature and feature of ground truth. They go through the loss network and extract feature map from {$relu1\_2$, $relu2\_2$, $relu3\_3$, $relu4\_3$, $relu5\_4$}.

Assuming $F_{I_0} = \{F^l_{1_k}, F^l_{2_k}, \ldots, F^l_{n_k}\}$ represent the feature maps of I_0, $F_{I_{gt}}$ is extracted by I_0 from the loss network. $F_{I_{gt}} = \{F^l_{1_k}, F^l_{2_k}, \ldots, F^l_{n_k}\}$, where l and k represent the k_{th} feature map of the n_{th} position in the l layer. The feature maps of generated results I_0 and I_{gt} go through swapping to obtain a new feature map F_{swap}. $F_{\mathrm{swap}} = \{F^l_{\mathrm{swap}1_k}, F^l_{\mathrm{swap}2_k}, F^l_{\mathrm{swap}3_k}, \ldots, F^l_{\mathrm{swap}j_k}\}$. Where l and k represent the k_{th} feature map of the j_{th} position in the l layer. Then G_{swap} and G_{gt} could be calculated as:

$$G_{\mathrm{swap}} = \sum_k F^l_{\mathrm{swap}\,i_k} F^l_{\mathrm{swap}\,j_k} \tag{2}$$

$$G_{gt} = \sum k f^l_m f^l_n \tag{3}$$

By Eqs. (2) and (3), there is:

$$G_{\text{swap}} = G^1_{\text{swap}}, G^2_{\text{swap}}, \ldots, G^L_{\text{swap}} \quad (4)$$

$$G_{gt} = G^1_{gt}, G^2_{gt}, G^3_{gt}, \ldots, G^L_{gt} \quad (5)$$

where 1, 2, 3,…, L represents a layer in the loss network.

Then The style loss is calculated as the sum of the Euclidean distances between the gram matrix of the feature map after swapping and the ground truth's gram matrix.

$$L_{\text{style}} = \sum_{l=0}^{L} (G_{\text{swap}} - G_{gt})^2 \quad (6)$$

The content loss is the Euclidean distances between feature maps at different positions in the same layer from the Convolutional Network. Here, the features of I_0 and $I_g t$ are extracted in *relu3_1* from the loss network. The function is as follows:

$$L_{\text{content}} = \sum_{i=0, l=0, j=0}^{i,j,l} (F_{I_0}(i,j,l) - F_{gt}(i,j,l))^2 \quad (7)$$

In L_G, β is the tunable hyperparameter trading off the style loss and content loss with the standard generator GAN loss. The generator's loss function is defined as follows, where β is 4×10^{-4}:

$$L_G = L_{\text{style}} + L_{\text{content}} - \beta \log D(G(I_0)) \quad (8)$$

Adversarial Loss. Adversarial loss is based on Generative Adversarial Networks (GANs) and is defined as follows:

$$L_D = \max_D E[\log(D(I_0, I_g t)) + \log(1 - D(I_0, I_1))] \quad (9)$$

The input of discriminator are image pairs, the real image pair consisting of input image I_0 and ground truth I_{gt}, and the fake pair consisting of I_0 and image I_1 generated by generator, where γ is 1.0.

Therefore, the total loss function is defined as follows:

$$L_{\text{total}} = L_G + \gamma L_D \quad (10)$$

4 Experiments

4.1 Implementation Details

The experiments are carried out on the TensorFlow framework. The generator is trained on 6500 images with 128 × 128 size. We conduct experiments on two datasets DTD (Describing Textures in the Wild) and Places365. During the training phase, we divide 6500 images into 6000 training datasets and 500 testing datasets. Our model is trained on NVIDIA Titan V GPU, and it took three days to train our network for iterating over 500,000. The optimizer we use is Adam. The learning rate is 10^{-6}.

4.2 Quantitative Evaluation

In the evaluation of synthesized results, the proposed method is compared with representative methods such as TSCNN [5], TSFFN [8] and NTS [9] for texture synthesis. These comparisons are conducted on testing datasets from DTD, and Places365. Consistent with standard practices in texture synthesis research, we employ Peak Signal to Noise Ratio (PSNR), Structural Similarity (SSIM) as quantitative metrics. As detailed in Table, comparative experiments show that the proposed method outperforms existing approaches on these metrics.

4.3 Qualitative Evaluations

To validate the synthesis performance, Fig. 4 present a comparative analysis of the predicted results from different methods. As illustrated in Fig. 4, the synthesized result from TSCNN seems to produce distorted structures, particularly noticeable edge regions. NTS tends to produce texture noise during the reconstruction of features. TSFNN is capable of recovering reasonable content but often ignores texture details. In contrast, our method enhances the perception of textural regions.

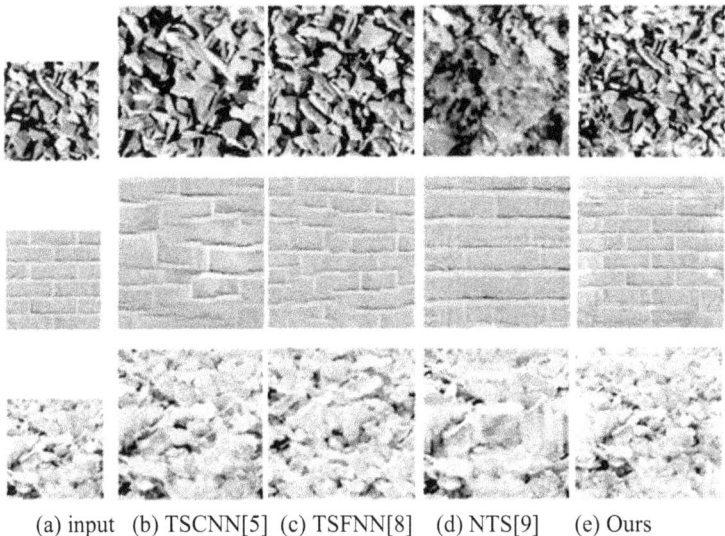

(a) input (b) TSCNN[5] (c) TSFNN[8] (d) NTS[9] (e) Ours

Fig. 4. Visual comparison of the proposed method with the others.

Figure 5 shows results for multi resolution images. The proposed method can generate different results from the original image. It can be seen that it is able to well preserve the important areas of input images and the overall structure over a large resolution span (176 × 176 to 208 × 208).

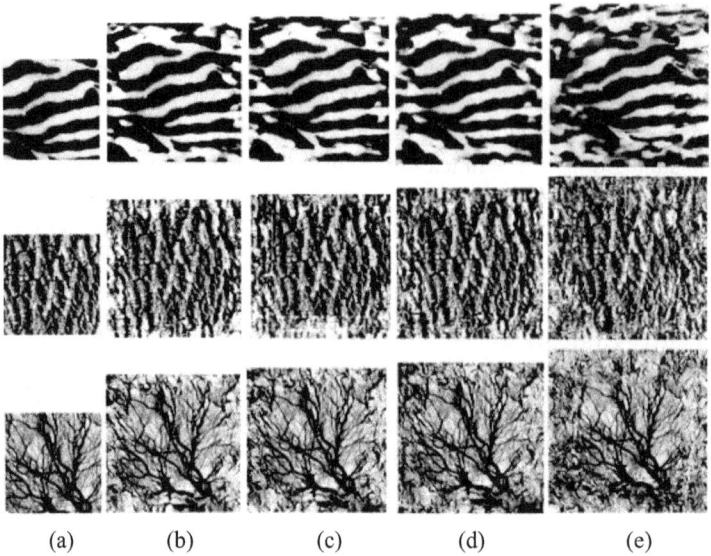

Fig. 5. Results for multi resolutions. (a) is the input with 128 × 128 size; (b) is the output with 176 × 176 size; (c) 184 × 184; (d) 192 × 192; (e) 208 × 208.

4.4 Ablation Study

In this subsection, we continue to analyze how the proposed modules contribute to the final performance of texture synthesis. Specifically, we verify the effectiveness of the backbone network by removing swap blocks. As can be seen from Fig. 6, the result with the swapping module is better than those without it. The reason is that after adding the swapping module, the generated feature map is compared with the reference image's feature map, and the optimal result is exchanged before calculating the loss function. This allows for the use of the optimal feature map to calculate the loss function, which is superior to directly using the extracted feature map for this purpose.In addition, PSNR, SSIM are all commonly used image evaluation. The larger their value, the better the image quality. It can be seen from Table 2 that when swap is added to the model, the evaluation result is the best (Table 1).

Table 1. Quantitative evaluations. ↑ means the higher the better.

Metric	TSCNN [5]	TSFNN [8]	NTS [9]	Ours
PSNR↑	17.39	17.75	18.62	**18.69**
SSIM↑	0.8988	0.9112	0.9010	**0.9187**

Table 2. Synthesized results in terms of PSNR, SSIM for ablation study.

Metric	w/o swapping	w swapping
PSNR↑	15.51	**16.65**
SSIM↑	0.39	**0.43**

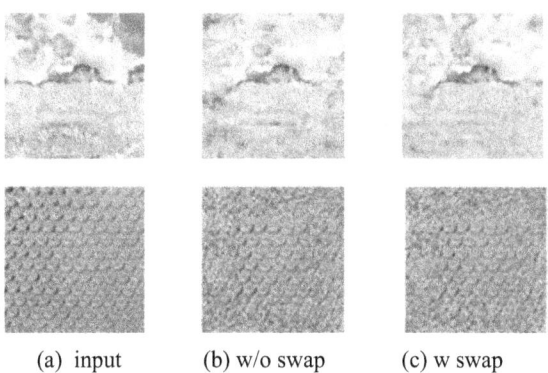

(a) input   (b) w/o swap   (c) w swap

Fig. 6. Ablation study.

5 Conclusion

In this paper, we have proposed a deep generative network for texture synthesis. The network is based on a GAN, with a feature mapping swapping strategy. Our method automatically synthesizes arbitrary texture images from input samples directly. We show that the feature swapping strategy significantly improves texture synthesized results. We provide in-depth comparisons with classic approaches and show visually plausible synthesized results.

References

1. Wei, L.-Y., Levoy, M.: Fast texture synthesis using tree-structured vector quantization. In: Proceedings of the 27th Annual Conference on Computer Graphics and Interactive Tecniques. SIGGRAPH '00, pp. 479–488. ACM Press/Addison Wesley Publishing Co., New York, NY, USA (2000)
2. Ashikhmin,M.: Synthesizing natural textures. In: Symposium on Interactive 3d Graphics (2001)
3. Kwatra, V., Essa, I., Bobick, A., Kwatra, N.: Texture optimization for example-based synthesis. ACM Trans. Graph. **24**(3), 795–802 (2005)
4. Efros, A.A., Freeman, W.T.: Image quilting for texture synthesis and transfer. In: Proceeings of the 28th Annual Conference on Computer Graphics and Interactive Techniques. SIGGRAPH '01, pp. 341–346. ACM, New York, NY, USA (2001)
5. Gatys, L., Ecker, A.S., Bethge, M.: Texture synthesis using convolutional neural networks. In: Cortes, C., Lawrence, N.D., Lee, D.D., Sugiyama, M., Garnett, R. (eds.) Advances in Neural Information Processing Systems 28, pp. 262–270. Springer, Heidelberg (2015)

6. Wilmot, P., Risser, E., Barnes, C.: Stable and controllable neural texture synthesis and style transfer using histogram losses. CoRR abs/1701.08893 (2017)
7. Ulyanov, D., Lebedev, V., Vedaldi, A., Lempitsky, V.: Texture Networks: feed-forward synthesis of textures and stylized images. arXiv e-prints (2016)
8. Li, Y., Fang, C., Yang, J., Wang, Z., Lu, X., Yang, M.-H.: Diversified texture synthesis with feed-forward networks. In: The IEEE Conference on Computer Vision and Pattern Recognition (CVPR) (2017)
9. Zhou, Y., Zhu, Z., Bai, X., Lischinski, D., Cohen-Or, D., Huang, H.: Nonstationary texture synthesis by adversarial expansion. CoRR abs/1805.04487 (2018)
10. Yu, N., Barnes, C., Shechtman, E., Amirghodsi, S., Lukac, M.: Texture mixer: A network for controllable synthesis and interpolation of texture. In: The IEEE Conference on Computer Vision and Pattern Recognition (CVPR) (2019)
11. Goodfellow, I., et al.: Generative adversarial nets. In: Ghahramani, Z., Welling, M., Cortes, C., Lawrence, N.D., Weinberger, K.Q. (eds.) Advances in Neural Information Processing Systems, vol. 27, pp. 2672–2680. Curran Associates, Inc., RedHook (2014)
12. Sabini, M., Rusak, G.: Painting outside the box: image outpainting with GANs. CoRR abs/1808.08483 (2018)
13. Darabi, S., Shechtman, E., Barnes, C., Dan, B.G., Sen, P.: Image melding: combining inconsistent images using patch-based synthesis. ACM Trans. Graph. **31**(4), 1–10 (2012)
14. Zhou, Y., Chen, K., Xiao, R., Huang, H.: Neural texture synthesis with guided correspondence. In: Conference on Computer Vision and Pattern Recognition (CVPR), pp. 18095–18104 (2023)
15. Ntavelis, E., Shahbazi, M., Kastanis, I., Timofte, R., Danelljan, M., Van Gool, L.: Arbitrary-scale image synthesis. In: Proceedings of the IEEE/CVF Conference on Computer Vision and Pattern Recognition, pp. 11533–11542 (2022)
16. Chen, T.Q., Schmidt, M.: Fast patch-based style transfer of arbitrary style. CoRR abs/1612.04337 (2016)
17. Li, C., Wand, M.: Combining markov random fields and convolutional neural networks for image synthesis. In: The IEEE Conference on Computer Vision and Pattern Recognition (CVPR) (2016)
18. Song, Y., et al.: Contextual-based image inpainting: infer, match, and translate. In: The European Conference on Computer Vision (ECCV) (2018)
19. He, K., Zhang, X., Ren, S., Sun, J.: Deep residual learning for image recognition. In: The IEEE Conference on Computer Vision and Pattern Recognition (CVPR) (2016)
20. Isola, P., Zhu, J.-Y., Zhou, T., Efros, A.A.: Image-to-image translation with conditional adversarial networks. In: The IEEE Conference on Computer Vision and Pattern Recognition (CVPR) (2017)
21. Iizuka, S., Simo-Serra, E., Ishikawa, H.: Globally and locally consistent image completion. ACM Trans. Graph. **36**(4), 107–110714 (2017)

A 3D-2D Hybrid Network with Regional Awareness and Global Fusion for Brain Tumor Segmentation

Wenxiu Zhao, Changlei Dongye[(✉)], and Yumei Wang

Shandong University of Science and Technology, Qingdao, China
dycl@sdust.edu.cn

Abstract. Accurate segmentation of brain tumors in MR images is crucial for their clinical diagnosis and treatment. Some existing methods do not adequately consider the relationship between tumor regions and the effect of fuzzy boundaries on segmentation. In this paper, we propose a 3D-2D Hybrid Network with Regional Awareness and Global Fusion for Brain Tumor Segmentation (HRGBTS). The model consists of three components: a hybrid encoder, a regional awareness module, and a feature fusion decoder. Specifically, the hybrid encoder uses 3D-2D hybrid convolutional blocks to extract multi-scale features from the brain tumor region. The regional awareness module (RAM) enhances the segmentation of tumor sub-regions by dynamically sensing the relationship between tumor cells and surrounding tissue cells through graph convolutional interactive inference. In the decoding stage, the feature fusion decoder, which consists of global fusion modules (GFMs) and cross-dimensional skip connections, is designed to improve boundary reconstruction. The GFM effectively fuses tumor information, enabling better tumor boundary reconstruction and addressing the challenge of boundary blurring. The cross-dimensional skip connections address the information mismatch problem caused by cross-dimensional changes. Extensive evaluations were made on three benchmark datasets, BraTS2018, BraTS2020, and BraTS2021, the Dice coefficients in the whole-tumor region (WT) were achieved to be 0.906, 0.917, and 0.903, respectively.

Keywords: Brain Tumor Segmentation · Global Fusion · Regional Awareness

1 Introduction

Brain tumors are the most prevalent and challenging primary tumors to treat, with varying degrees of invasiveness. Multimodal magnetic resonance imaging (MRI) technology [1] is widely used for diagnosing and surgically treating brain tumors. It plays a crucial role in monitoring, diagnosing, and predicting the prognosis of tumors. Therefore, accurate segmentation of gliomas from MRI images is a critical step in the diagnosis and treatment of this disease.

Automated MRI-based computerized segmentation not only means less time and cost, it also makes quantitative analysis more objective. In recent years, the widespread application of Convolutional Neural Networks (CNNs) in medical images has promoted the development of automatic segmentation of brain tumors [2, 3]. Fully Convolutional Neural Network (FCN) [4] achieves end-to-end semantic segmentation and shows a good performance in medical image segmentation. U-Net [5] has gained the most popularity for its ability to capture local characteristics in 2D or 3D space using its U-shaped structure. However, CNNs face challenges in effectively capturing global feature dependencies due to inherent limitations in the convolutional perceptual field. To address this limitation, researchers have proposed a two-stage approach that combines 3D and 2D networks to improve the extraction of single-layer contextual semantic information [6]. Specifically, this approach utilizes features learned by 2D convolutional neural networks (2D-CNNs) as input to the 3D-CNNs. This enables the acquisition of location information of the tumor from an even broader spatial environment. However, this method mainly focuses on the extraction and fusion of deep semantic features, without considering the relationship between different tumor regions and the importance of fuzzy boundaries for segmentation.

Xu et al. [7] proposed a multi-branch network that utilizes an attention mechanism to focus on each sub-region of the tumor so as to extract the tumor region. Wang et al. [8] incorporated a dynamic scale-aware context module that adapts contextual information dynamically. To deal with boundary-related information and effectively remove noise from MRI, they used an edge attention preserving (EAP) module. However, these efforts have ignored the critical role of global information in extracting tumor features.

In this paper, we present a new brain tumor segmentation model called HRGBTS, which consists of three components: a hybrid encoder, a region–aware module, and a feature fusion decoder. The hybrid encoder connects the 3DCNN and 2D MSCAN [9] in tandem, this combination effectively captures the spatial information of the tumor in 3D space. The regional awareness module is used to learn the texture and boundaries of tumor sub-regions by employing interactive graph inference. In the decoding process, we developed a feature fusion decoder that includes global fusion modules and cross-dimensional skip connections to reconstruct the tumor regions and address the boundary-blurring problem. To address the low percentage of tumor regions, we designed the Depth cropping algorithm and explored the impact of the normalization method in the cross-dimensional skip connections on the segmentation accuracy. Our research makes the following key contributions:

1. Hybrid encoder: This structure leverages multi-scale extraction of deep semantic features to effectively capture tumor shape and location information.
2. We designed a regional awareness module to extract texture features within the tumor to enable accurate segmentation of the sub-regions.
3. We introduce a feature fusion encoder during the decoding process. This encoder incorporates a global fusion module that effectively combines features from the tumor region, thereby reducing boundary ambiguity.
4. To mitigate the impact of low percentage of tumor regions on segmentation accuracy, we explored various data cropping methods aimed at balancing the dataset.

2 Method

2.1 Network Structure

The architecture of the 3D-2D Hybrid Network with Regional Awareness and Global.

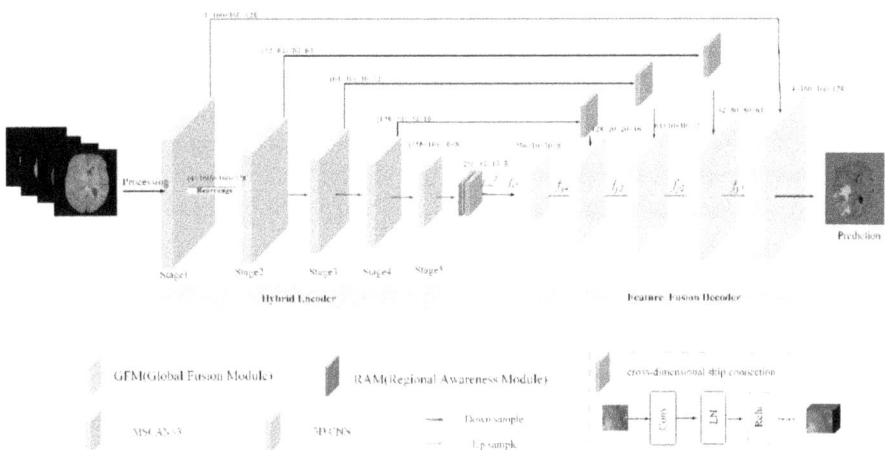

Fig. 1. Overview of the proposed network structure.

Fusion for Brain Tumor Segmentation(HRGBTS). This illustrated in Fig. 1. HRG-BTS comprises three key components: a hybrid encoder, a regional awareness module, and a feature fusion decoder. The hybrid encoder integrates both 2D and 3D convolutional blocks to extract deep semantic features from multimodal MRI scans. This hybrid design enables the network to capture comprehensive information from different dimensions of the input data. To address the challenge of distinguishing features from molecular regions, the regional aware-ness module (RAM) aggregates features from various regions. It employs inter-active graph inference to enhance the differentiation of molecular features, allowing for more precise segmentation. The feature fusion decoder consists of cross-dimensional skip connections and global fusion modules. The cross-dimensional skip connections act as a bridge between the hybrid encoder and the global fusion module, facilitating information interaction between the encoder and decoder. The global fusion module effectively fuses the semantic features of the different layers. This leads to better reconstruction of tumor boundaries, thus facilitating accurate and complete segmentation of brain tumors.

2.2 Hybrid Encoder

The hybrid encoder in our proposed model consists of a tandem structure that comprises a 3D convolutional blocks and a 2D Multi-Scale Convolutional Attention Network (MSCAN). This combination enables effective information capture in 3D space. To prevent overfitting, residual connectivity is integrated into the 3D convolutional block, as depicted in Fig. 2. We use rearranging to achieve dimensional transformation from 3D to 2D which solves the problem of dimensional mismatch. The encoder's four layers (stages 2–5) employ three Multi-Scale Convolutional Attention Network (MSCAN) structures to enhance feature extraction. The MSCAN structure uses a Multi-Scale Convolutional Attention (MSCA) module instead of multi-head attention for feature extraction (refer to Fig. 2 for the detailed structure). The MSCA module facilitates information exchange across multiple scales, thereby improving feature representation, particularly for capturing tumor location information. Furthermore, the MSCA module facilitates information sharing between different feature layers, enhancing the training efficiency of the model.

The hybrid encoder establishes a connection between 3D and 2D features and solves the problem of missing spatial information due to slice discontinuity, enabling information exchange and fusion. This approach can maximize the benefits of both 3D and 2D features, allowing for better capture of tumor shape and location information and facilitating accurate tumor segmentation.

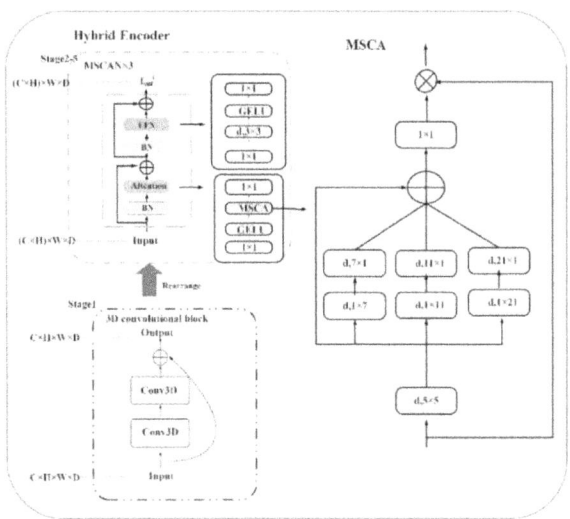

Fig. 2. Overview of the proposed network structure.

2.3 Regional Awareness Module

In order to be able to accurately segment the different subregions of a tumor (e.g. NCR/NET, ED and ET), we have designed a region awareness module. The mechanism of this module is shown in Fig. 2. The input features are given as $X \in R^{C \times H \times W}$, which $H \times W$ is the total number of features, and C denotes the feature dimension. The mapping of X is followed by contextual inference using the adjacency matrix A of the graph G (where the graph $G = (V, E, A)$ contains the set of nodes V, the edges E denotes the connection relationship between nodes and the adjacency matrix A is used to describe the degree of association between nodes.

Mapping method: The original feature $X \in R^{C \times H \times W}$ is mapped to the non-Euclidean interaction space to generate a mapping feature $G \in R^{C \times V}$. Then, pixels with similar features can be aggregated to a node, where the mapping feature vector X^{map} can be represented by a node in the interaction graph G as $v, v \in V$. Mathematically, this can be expressed as follows:

$$G = \mu_1(X) \times \mu_2(X) \tag{1}$$

where $\mu_1(X)$, $\mu_2(X)$ denote the convolution operation of the graph projection [10] and the feature dimensionality reduction convolution operation. Due to the fact that the shape, size and location of brain tumors in MRI images may vary significantly, we abandoned the traditional convolution approach and used a learnable (deformable convolution) method [11].

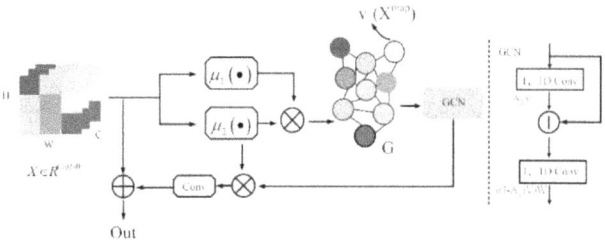

Fig. 3. Regional awareness module.

Graph convolutional region aware: After projecting The inference of the interaction graph is performed by learning the edge weights corresponding to the features of each node based on graph convolution [12]. The structure of the graph convolution is shown in Fig. 3, which performs a one-dimensional convolution operation in the channel and node directions. The graph convolution equation can be expressed as:

$$H = GCN(G) = \left((I - \hat{A}_g)V\right)W, \tag{2}$$

Back-projection: After the inference is complete, the non-Euclidean features are back-projected onto the original features using a linear interpolation algorithm. The final result is a set of $H \times W$ instances of Out features. Mathematically, this can be expressed as follows:

$$Out = X + Conv\left(\mu_2(X)^T \times H\right), \tag{3}$$

2.4 Feature Fusion Decoder

In this section, we design a feature fusion decoder aimed at reconstructing the tumor region and addressing the boundary blurring issue. The decoder consists of two parts: cross-dimensional skip connections and global fusion modules. Cross-dimensional skip connection(CSC) aims to bridge the semantic gap between the hybrid decoder and the global fusion modules by providing pixel-level features on features extracted from the hybrid decoder. The CSC can be mathematically represented as follows:

$$Y = Rearange(ReLU(LN(Conv(X)))), \tag{4}$$

where X represents the side output of the hybrid feature extraction network and Y represents the result of the transformation. $Conv$ represents a convolution with the 1×1 kernel, and $Rearange$ denotes the transformation function.

Global Fusion Module. The global fusion module involves multiple fusion operations, as depicted in Fig. 4. We define the feedforward features obtained from the aforementioned sampling and transformation connections as f_y and f_{out}^i, respectively, and the first fusion and convolution operations obtain the initial fusion features f_{fuse}. Then the process is represented by Eq. (6).

$$f_{fuse} = Conv_{3D}\left(Concat\left(f_y, f_{out}^i\right)\right) + f_y + f_{out}^i, \tag{5}$$

We employed a channel attention mechanism based on an attention vector $C_{weight} \in R^{C \times 1 \times 1 \times 1}$ learned from the initial fused features, The $C_{weight} \in R^{C \times 1 \times 1 \times 1}$ is learned through a sequence of operations, including global average pooling (GAP) and a fully connected layer (FC), with C denoting the number of channels. The output of the global fusion module, denoted as f_{out}, is obtained using the following equation:

$$C_{weight} = FC(GAP(f_{fuse})), f_{out} = (C_{weight} \times f_{fuse}) + f_y + f_{out}^i, \tag{6}$$

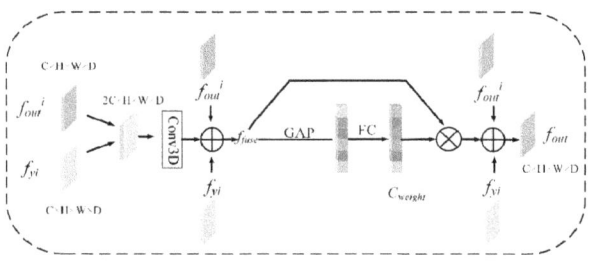

Fig. 4. Global fusion Module

2.5 Loss Function

We define the loss function L_{Seg} as a combination of a weighted binary cross-entropy loss L_{BCE}^w and a Dice coefficient loss L_{Dice}, with Laplace smoothing added to perform the task of segmenting brain tumors. The formula is as follows:

$$\begin{aligned}
L_{Seg} &= L_{BCE}^{w} + L_{Dice}, \\
L_{BCE}^{w} &= w \times \left[-y \log(\hat{y}) + (1-y) \log(1-\hat{y})\right], \\
L_{Dice} &= 1 - \frac{2|x \cap y| + 1e-5}{|x| + |y| + 1e-5}
\end{aligned} \quad (7)$$

where $x, \hat{y}$ represents predicted output; y represents Ground truth. w is the weighting coefficient with a value of 2. L_{Seg} provides effective image-level and pixel-level supervision for precise segmentation, resulting in high-quality region segmentation.

3 Experiment

3.1 Experimental Details

Dataset. To evaluate the effectiveness of the HRGBTS network, we conducted experiments using three datasets obtained from BraTS (Brain Tumor Segmentation) challenges 2018, 2020, and 2021 [13]. The input data was cropped to a size of 160 × 160 × 128 along the D axis. We applied several data augmentation techniques during the training phase. These techniques included random scaling, random flipping in three directions, the addition of Gaussian noise, Gaussian blurring, and random contrast adjustments.

3.2 Ablation Experiments and Analysis

Table 1. Results of ablation experiments with different cutting methods. The best value for each metric is shown in bold.

Method	DICE		
	WT	ET	TC
Depth cropping	0.907	**0.765**	**0.830**
Center Cropping	0.904	0.762	0.814
Random cropping	**0.909**	0.750	0.799

First, we have analyzed the impact of different cropping methods on the segmentation results. We designed experiments and evaluated three methods: depth cropping, center cropping and random cropping. The results of our experiments, shown in Table 1, demonstrate the best overall performance of the model when Depth cropping is employed, suggesting that Depth cropping solves the problem of data imbalance to some extent. Therefore, we chose Depth cropping as the method to process the data in our experiments.

Secondly, we investigated the impact of three key components: the hybrid feature extraction encoder, the regional awareness module(RAM) and the feature fusion decoder. The experimental results for different models are shown in Table 2.

Table 2. Results of ablation experiments with different cutting methods. The best value for each metric is shown in bold.

Model	DICE		
	WT	ET	TC
(1) Baseline	0.907	0.765	0.830
(2) Baseline + Hybrid Encoder	0.916	0.777	0.840
(3) Baseline + RAM	0.915	0.771	0.838
(4) Baseline + Feature Fusion Decoder	0.917	0.773	0.841
(5) HRGBTS	**0.917**	**0.782**	**0.853**

Effectiveness of hybrid encoders. The effectiveness of the hybrid encoder is verified by comparing it with Baseline, called model (1).Model (2) employs a hybrid encoder and has a significantly higher Dice score compared to model (1). Our analysis of Fig. 5, Case 2 demonstrates that the hybrid encoder reduces erroneous segmentation, and these results show that the hybrid encoder is able to capture global information effectively.

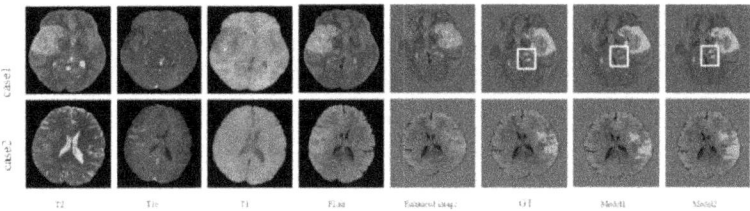

Fig. 5. Results of ablation experiment for model (2).

Effectiveness of the region awareness module. The results demonstrating the effectiveness of the region awareness module (model (3)) are given in Table 2. Compared to model (1), model (3) improves the Dice score by 0.6% for enhanced tumor segmentation and 0.8% for tumor core segmentation. This indicates that the use of the region awareness module can improve the performance of accurately segmenting tumor subregions Fig. 6 provides a visualisation of the segmentation results. In Case 1, it is clear that model (3) places more emphasis on the segmentation of sub-regions.

Effectiveness of feature fusion decoder. In this experiment, we replace the conventional CNN decoder with the global fusion module and utilized the cross-dimensional skip connection to connect it to the hybrid encoder. The inclusion of the feature fusion decoder in Model (4) further improved the segmentation results compared to Model(1).

(Model (4): WT:0.917 ET:0.773 TC:0.841, Model (1) WT:0.907 ET:0.765 TC:0.830). As shown in Fig. 7, the segmentation results of Model (4), which benefits from the global fusion module, are more accurate. Conversely, Model (1) exhibited a tendency for over-segmentation (as indicated by the white box in Case 2. Consequently, the global fusion module facilitates the learning of tumor regions while suppressing redundant information.

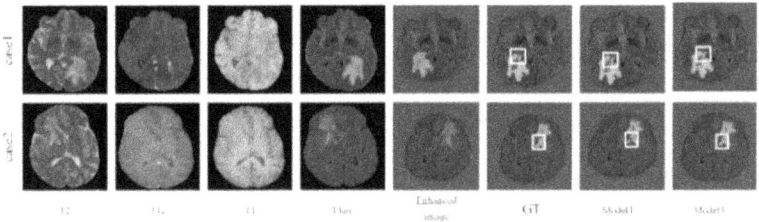

Fig. 6. Results of ablation experiment for model (3).

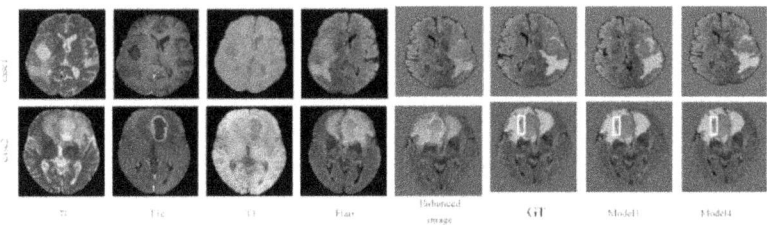

Fig. 7. Results of ablation experiment for model (4).

3.3 Comparison with State-of-the-Arts

To compare the performance of our model, we conducted a comprehensive analysis by comparing it with several classical brain tumor segmentation methods. HRGBTS is based on the architecture of 3DUNet, and our results demonstrate its superiority over 3DUNet in terms of average Dice scores for the three datasets and the three tumor regions.

Table 3. Comparison of this model with other SOTA models. (The best result for each metric is shown in bold.)

Method	BraTS2018				BraTS2020				BraTS2021			
	DICE				DICE				DICE			
	WT	ET	TC	Mean	WT	ET	TC	Mean	WT	ET	TC	Mean
3D-UNet	0.887	0.725	0.798	0.865	0.904	0.762	0.814	0.874	0.891	0.792	0.844	0.853
DMFNet	0.868	0.753	0.778	0.832	0.884	0.748	0.759	0.874	0.872	0.763	0.798	0.826
TransBTS	0.900	0.772	0.839	0.843	0.902	0.772	0.823	0.863	0.870	0.818	0.850	0.884
VNet	0.886	0.770	0.803	0.847	0.916	0.762	0.836	0.882	0.900	0.766	0.823	0.875
E1D3	0.892	0.742	0.832	0.825	0.902	0.781	**0.877**	0.891	0.894	0.816	**0.861**	0.891
AttU-Net	0.901	0.763	0.832	0.876	0.915	0.770	0.840	0.894	0.879	0.809	0.838	0.886
Kong et al	0.871	0.741	0.789	0.814	0.888	0.752	0.783	0.825	0.886	0.775	0.792	0.832
MISSFormer	0.893	0.744	0.820	0.868	0.906	0.775	0.792	0.872	**0.905**	0.802	0.836	0.874
Zhu et al	0.868	**0.773**	0.832	0.853	0.901	0.732	0.848	0.822	**0.905**	0.798	0.834	0.852
Ours	**0.906**	0.742	**0.858**	**0.891**	**0.917**	**0.782**	0.853	**0.899**	0.903	**0.821**	0.860	**0.893**

Specifically, HRGBTS achieved average improvements of 3.4%, 2.5%, and 4% across the three datasets, respectively. We also compared HRGBTS with VNet [14], which utilizes feature fusion from compressed and decompressed paths through stitching for medical image segmentation. As shown in Table 3, VNet obtained better results in segmenting the ET regions. Furthermore, we compared HRGBTS with AttU-Net [15], which incorporates a self-attention gating module to highlight features in local regions. HRG-BTS achieved a significant improvement of 1.5% in the mean Dice score for the BraTS2018 dataset when compared to AttU-Net.

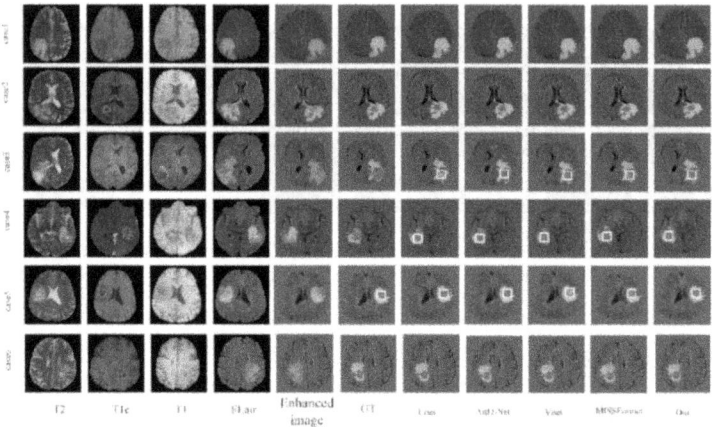

Fig. 8. Visualisation of segmentation results.

TransBTS [16] represents the first attempt to combine 3DCNN with Transformer for brain tumor segmentation. This method capitalizes on the spatial relationships of 3D images and leverages the features of the Transformer to predict both local and global brain tumor characteristics. As a result, TransBTS achieves the best Dice results in the ET region. E1D3 [17], consists of one encoder and three independent decoders, each specializing in a different tumor region. As demonstrated in Table 3, E1D3 achieves optimal performance in the core tumor region (TC). Kong et al. [18] introduce a dual attention mechanism, They assign weights to different sub-regions based this mechanism. Furthermore, MissFormer [19] introduces a novel hierarchical codec structure for medical image segmentation, incorporating both global dependency and local correlation. Notably, the average Dice improvement achieved by HRGBTS on the three datasets is 2.3%, 2.7%, and 1.9%, respectively. Zhu et al. [20] used Swin transformer as a feature extraction network and utilised graph convolution for feature inference. This combination effectively improves the segmentation accuracy, especially in the whole tumor region.

Figure 8 shows the qualitative results obtained by comparing our proposed model with several representative models. The regions in the white rectangles in all segmentation results indicate the dominance of HRGBTS. Notably, in Case 2 of Fig. 8, our model effectively avoids the false-positive results observed from other models (marked with white rectangles), and is much closer to the true labels in terms of the segmentation of peri-tumor oedema regions. In Cases 3 and 5, our model achieves more complete and precise boundaries, and even though MISSFormer applies the idea of global dependency, the segmentation results show that there is still mis-segmentation in the segmentation of necrotic regions.

4 Conclusion

In this paper, we propose a 3D-2D Hybrid Network with Regional Awareness and Global Fusion for Brain Tumor Segmentation (HRGBTS). HRGBTS consists of a hybrid encoder, a Regional awareness module, and a feature fusion decoder. The performance of HRGBTS has been extensively evaluated on the BraTS 2018, 2020, and 2021 datasets. The results unequivocally demonstrate the effectiveness of our approach in accurately segmenting tumor regions. In the future, we plan to investigate the impact of imaging modalities on tumor segmentation.

Acknowledgments. The authors did not receive support from any organization for the submitted work.

Disclosure of Interests. The authors declare that they have no known competing financial interests or personal relationships that could have appeared to influence the work reported in this paper.

References

1. Menze, B.H., et al.: The multimodal brain tumor image segmentation benchmark (brats). IEEE Trans. Med. Imaging **34**(10), 1993–2024 (2014)
2. Huo, Y., et al.: 3D whole brain segmentation using spatially localized atlas network tiles. NeuroImage **194**, 105–119 (2019)
3. Saouli, R., Akil, M., Kachouri, R., et al.: Fully automatic brain tumor segmentation using end-to-end incremental deep neural networks in MRI images. Comput. Methods Programs Biomed. **166**, 39–49 (2018)
4. Long, J., Shelhamer, E., Darrell, T.: Fully convolutional networks for semantic segmentation. In: Proceedings of the IEEE Conference on Computer Vision and Pattern Recognition, pp. 3431–3440 (2015)
5. Ronneberger, O., Fischer, P., Brox, T.: U-Net: convolutional networks for biomedical image segmentation. In: Medical Image Computing and Computer-Assisted Intervention–MICCAI 2015: 18th International Conference, Munich, Germany, October 5–9, 2015, Proceedings, Part III 18, pp. 234–241. Springer (2015). https://doi.org/10.1007/978-3-319-24574-4_28
6. Mlynarski, P., Delingette, H., Criminisi, A., Ayache, N.: 3D convolutional neural networks for tumor segmentation using long-range 2D context. Comput. Med. Imaging Graph. **73**, 60–72 (2019)
7. Xu, H., Xie, H., Liu, Y., Cheng, C., Niu, C., Zhang, Y.: Deep cascaded attention network for multi-task brain tumor segmentation. In: Medical Image Computing and Computer Assisted Intervention–MICCAI 2019: 22nd International Conference, Shenzhen, China, October 13–17, 2019, Proceedings, Part III 22, pp. 420–428. Springer (2019). https://doi.org/10.1007/978-3-030-32248-9_47

8. Wang, K., Zhang, X., Zhang, X., Yuting, L., Huang, S., Yang, D.: Eanet: Iterative edge attention network for medical image segmentation. Pattern Recogn. **127**, 108636 (2022)
9. Guo, M.-H., Lu, C.-Z., Hou, Q., Liu, Z., Cheng, M.-M., Hu, S.-M.: SegNext: rethinking convolutional attention design for semantic segmentation. arXiv preprint arXiv:2209.08575 (2022)
10. Chen, Y., Rohrbach, M., Yan, Z., Shuicheng, Y., Feng, J., Kalantidis, Y.: Graph-based global reasoning networks. In: Proceedings of the IEEE/CVF Conference on Computer Vision and Pattern Recognition, pp. 433–442 (2019)
11. Dai, J., et al.: Deformable convolutional networks. In: Proceedings of the IEEE International Conference on Computer Vision, pp. 764–773 (2017)
12. Li, Q., Han, Z., Wu, X.-M.: Deeper insights into graph convolutional networks for semi-supervised learning. In: Proceedings of the AAAI Conference on Artificial Intelligence, vol. 32 (2018)
13. Bakas, S., et al.: Identifying the best machine learning algorithms for brain tumor segmentation, progression assessment, and overall survival prediction in the brats challenge. arXiv preprint arXiv:1811.02629 (2018)
14. Milletari, F., Navab, N., Ahmadi, S.-A.: V-Net: fully convolutional neural networks for volumetric medical image segmentation. In: 2016 Fourth International Conference on 3D Vision (3DV), pp. 565–571. IEEE (2016)
15. Wang, S., Li, L., Zhuang, X.: AttU-NET: attention U-Net for brain tumor. In: Brainlesion: Glioma, Multiple Sclerosis, Stroke and Traumatic Brain Injuries: 7th International Workshop, BrainLes 2021, Held in Conjunction with MICCAI 2021, Virtual Event, September 27, 2021, Revised Selected Papers, Part II, pp. 302–311. Springer (2022). https://doi.org/10.1007/978-3-031-09002-8_27
16. Wang, W., Chen, C., Ding, M., Yu, H., Zha, S., Li, J.: TransBTS: multimodal brain tumor segmentation using transformer. In: Medical Image Computing and Computer Assisted Intervention–MICCAI 2021: 24th International Conference, Strasbourg, France, September 27–October 1, 2021, Proceedings, Part I 24, pp. 109–119. Springer (2021). https://doi.org/10.1007/978-3-030-87193-2_11
17. Bukhari, S.T., Mohy-ud Din, H.: E1D3 U-Net for brain tumor segmentation: submission to the RSNA-ASNR-MICCAI brats 2021 challenge. In: Brainlesion: Glioma, Multiple Sclerosis, Stroke and Traumatic Brain Injuries: 7th International Workshop, BrainLes 2021, Held in Conjunction with MICCAI 2021, Virtual Event, September 27, 2021, Revised Selected Papers, Part II, pp. 276–288. Springer (2022). https://doi.org/10.1007/978-3-031-09002-8_25
18. Kong, D., Liu, X., Wang, Y., Li, D., Xue, J.: 3D hierarchical dual attention fully convolutional networks with hybrid losses for diverse glioma segmentation. Knowl.-Based Syst. **237**, 107692 (2022)
19. Huang, X., Deng, Z., Li, D., Yuan, X., Fu, Y.: Missformer: An effective transformer for 2d medical image segmentation. IEEE Trans. Med. Imaging **42**, 1484–1494 (2022)
20. Zhu, Z., He, X., Qi, G., Li, Y., Cong, B., Liu, Y.: Brain tumor segmentation based on the fusion of deep semantics and edge information in multimodal MRI. Inf. Fus. **91**, 376–387 (2023)

GLAD: A Global-Attention-Based Diffusion Model for Infrared and Visible Image Fusion

Haozhe Guo[1], Mengjie Chen[1], Kaijiang Li[1], Hao Su[1(✉)], and Pei Lv[1,2,3]

[1] School of Computer and Artificial Intelligence, Zhengzhou University, Zhengzhou, China
ghzsqmr@stu.zzu.edu.cn, {chenmj,riversky}@gs.zzu.edu.cn,
{iesuhao,ielvpei}@zzu.edu.cn
[2] Engineering Research Center of Intelligent Swarm Systems, Ministry of Education, Zhengzhou, China
[3] National Supercomputing Center in Zhengzhou, Zhengzhou, China

Abstract. Infrared and visible image fusion (IVIF) is a widely used approach to enhance scenario understanding, which fuses the salience of infrared images and the texture details of visible images. Existing methods typically focus on extracting local feature maps between connected layers while ignoring the global features, which incurs the issue of fine-grained loss (e.g., texture and edge blurring) in the fused images. To address the issue, we propose *GLAD (GLobal-Attention-based Diffusion model)*, a novel IVIF approach to produce high-quality fused images with fine-grained. In GLAD, we first tailor a denoising network of the diffusion model to learn the joint distribution of multi-channel data. Next, we proposed a global attention fusion module to synthesize the global features extracted from the denoising network into a fine-grained fused image. Moreover, considering the influences of illumination factors, we design a fusion loss function to improve the denoising network for IVIF task. Qualitative and quantitative experiments demonstrate that our GLAD is 7.08% better than other state-of-the-art methods on the MSRS dataset.

Keywords: Image fusion · Diffusion process · Global attention

1 Introduction

Image fusion [1–5] is a longstanding task to integrate images from different sensors to enhance the scenario understanding. In the field of image fusion, infrared and visible image fusion (IVIF) is the most widely used method. Although infrared images can effectively capture objects and decrease the illumination influence, they focus on objects' heat salience and lack of texture details. In contrast, visible images contain rich texture and structural details but are sensitive to illumination influence. Therefore, their complementary nature allows IVIF to enhance the representations of object salience and texture details simultaneously.

Recently, IVIF techniques have been ubiquitously applied in fields of object detection [6], tracking [7], pedestrian re-identification [8], semantic segmentation [9], and so on.

Existing studies of IVIF have made remarkable achievements, which are mainly divided into traditional approaches and learning-based approaches [10]. Traditional approaches primarily consist of multi-scale transform-based approaches [11], sparse representation-based approaches [12], salience-based approaches [13], and hybrid approaches [14]. These approaches offer high interpretability but heavily rely on manual design. Specifically, these approaches lack versatility since they extract and fuse features by pre-defined algorithms that require manual adjustments for different fusion tasks [15]. Learning-based approaches can be further categorized into extraction-based approaches and generation-based approaches. Extraction-based approaches [17] extract features from source images using convolutional neural networks (CNN), and then fuse features from different source images using tailored rules. Next, the fused image is produced by combining the extracted features. Generation-based approaches are popular in computer vision, which aims to train a generative model (e.g., generative adversarial network (GAN) [18, 19], diffusion model [21, 22]) to generate fused images by simulating the sample distribution of the training dataset.

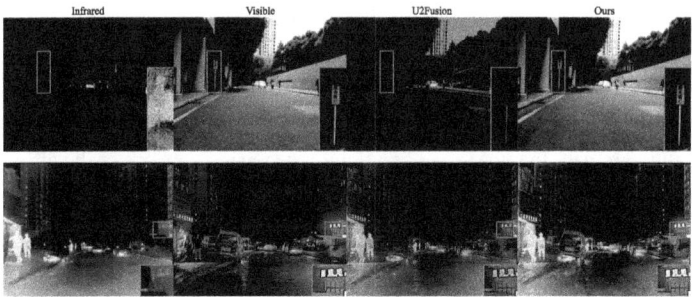

Fig. 1. Samples of IVIF results. Compared with related studies, our proposed GLAD generates better fine-grained fused images (red boxes). (Color figure online)

Although existing learning-based approaches have made considerable progress in IVIF, they focus on extracting local features without adequately considering global features. Specifically, these studies typically extract local feature maps between connected layers [21], which incurs the issues of fine-grained information loss (e.g., texture and edge blurring) in the fused images. For example, as shown in the red boxes of Fig. 1, U2Fusion [20] cannot produce a fine-grained fused image, and there are blurred edges and textures in signposts, and the text in the zoomed-in area.

To address the issues, we propose GLAD (GLobal-Attention-based Diffusion model), a novel IVIF approach that can produce high-quality fused images with fine-grained. In GLAD, we first tailor a denoising network of the diffusion model to learn the joint distribution of multi-channel information. Then, global features are extracted from the five steps of the denoising network, and we combine these global features into a fine-grained fused image by a proposed global attention fusion module (GAFM). Moreover, considering the influences of illumination environment factors, we design a fusion loss function to improve the diffusion model for the IVIF task. Qualitative and quantitative experiments demonstrate that our GLAD is 7.08% better than other related state-of-the-art methods on the MSRS dataset [17].

To summarize, our main contributions are three-fold:

- We propose a global-attention-based diffusion model, named GLAD, which is a novel IVIF approach that can produce high-quality fine-grained fused images.
- We propose a GAFM to effectively synthesize global features to fine-grained fused images, and design a novel fusion loss to improve the fusion performance by considering structure information and illumination factors.
- Extensive experiments demonstrate that GLAD can output impressive results and reach the state-of-the-art methods level.

2 Related Work

Below we summarize the representative studies most related to IVIF. In this field, researchers have made remarkable achievements, which are primarily categorized into the traditional methods [11–13] and the learning-based methods [10, 18, 19].

Traditional Method. The key of traditional methods lies in feature extraction and fusion, which can be roughly categorized into multi-scale transform-based approaches [11], sparse representation-based approaches [12], salience-based approaches [13], and hybrid approaches [14]. Although these approaches offer high interpretability, they heavily rely on manual design rule.

Learning-based Method. To solve the complexity problem of manually designing fusion rules in traditional methods, researchers introduce learning-based methods for the IVIF task. The representative learning-based methods can be further classified into extraction-based approaches and generation-based approaches.

Extraction-based approaches use CNN to extract features from source images and then fuse features with tailored rules. Next, the fused image is produced by combining the extracted features. Researchers modify the network architecture or combine multiple loss functions to improve the fusion performance of the network. Li et al. [16] propose DenseFuse, an IVIF approach based on CNN and dense connection. Tang et al. [17] consider the effect of the light factor and propose a light-aware CNN fusion approach called PIAFusion.

Generation-based approaches consider the image fusion task as a transformation from source images to target images. Ma et al. propose FusionGAN [18] to ingeniously frame the task as a competitive interplay between the generator and discriminator, treating it like a game. Then, Ma et al. [19] further used multi-classification GAN in GANMcC to estimate visible and infrared domain distributions simultaneously. However, GAN has the disadvantage of unstable training, and it is difficult to explain its internal mechanism. With the excellent performance of diffusion models [24] in visual tasks in recent years, some scholars have tried to apply diffusion models in this field. Yue et al. proposed [21] Dif-Fusion to produce fused images with high color fidelity, and DDFM [22] as a generalized image fusion model proposed by Zhao et al. achieved excellent performance.

In this paper, we propose a new IVIF approach, named GLAD, to produce high-quality fine-grained fused images. GLAD introduces a GAFM and fusion loss to the diffusion model [21], and reaches the state-of-the-art level.

3 Method

3.1 Overview

Given an infrared image I_{ir} and a visible image I_{vi}, our method GLAD is modeled as a function Ψ to generate a high-quality fine-grained fused image $I_{fu} = \Psi(I_{ir}, I_{vi})$, where $I_{ir} \in R^{H \times W \times 1}, I_{vi} \in R^{H \times W \times 3}$, and $I_{fu} \in R^{H \times W \times 3}$.

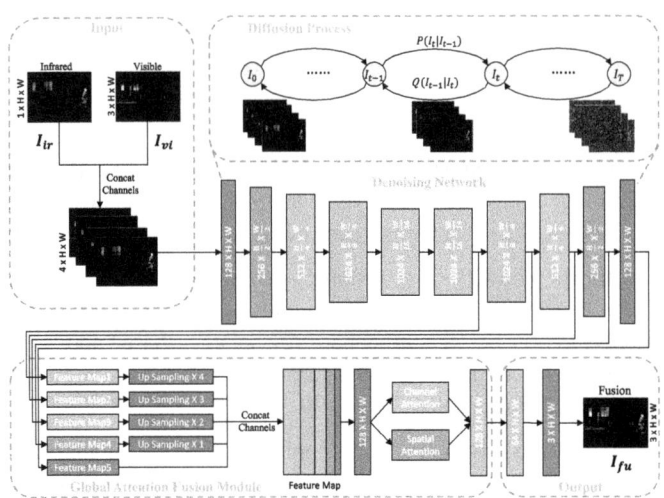

Fig. 2. System Pipeline. Given an infrared image I_{ir} and a visible image I_{vi}, our GLAD is modeled as a function Ψ to generate a high-quality fused image $I_{fu} = \Psi(I_{ir}, I_{vi})$.

Figure 2 shows the overall pipeline of GLAD. The proposed GLAD consists of two stages. In the first stage, we tailor a denoising network of diffusion model, and concatenate I_{ir} and I_{vi} along the channel dimensions and input them into the denoising network [21]. Through the diffusion process, we train the denoising network to learn the distribution of image data. In the second stage, we input the data into the trained denoising network, and utilize a designed fusion loss to train proposed GAFM. Finally, we extract global feature maps from five stages in the denoising network, and these global feature maps are constructed to a fine-grained fused image I_{fu}.

We will detail the diffusion model, the GAFM, and the fusion loss in Sect. 3.2, Sect. 3.3, and Sect. 3.4, respectively.

3.2 Diffusion Model

We tailor a diffusion model [21] to extract the image features more effectively. Specifically, we leverage the U-Net architecture in SR3 [23] as a denoising network to synthesize the distribution of infrared and visible image data through the diffusion process in the denoising diffusion probability model [24].

Input. Unlike most fusion methods, aiming at learning the joint distribution and the underlying feature structures of infrared and visible image pairs, we concatenate a pair of aligned infrared image $I_{ir} \in R^{H \times W \times 1}$ and visible image $I_{vi} \in R^{H \times W \times 3}$ (H and W indicate the image height and width) in channel dimensions to form a four-channel input data fed into the denoising network and learn the data distribution [21].

Forward Diffusion Process. As shown in Fig. 2, we gradually add Gaussian noise to the input data during the forward diffusion process until the data approaches pure noise. From the DDPM [24], it is known that given the input data I_0, timestep t, variance schedule $\alpha_1, \ldots, \alpha_t$, and the sampled noise, the noise multi-channel distribution image I_t can be calculated by

$$P(I_t|I_0) = \mathcal{N}\left(I_t; \sqrt{\overline{\alpha_t}}I_0, (1 - \overline{\alpha_t})Z\right) \quad (1)$$

where Z represents the standard normal distribution, $\overline{\alpha_t} = \prod_{i=1}^{t} \alpha_i$.

Reverse Diffusion Process. In the reverse diffusion process, the denoising network performs a series of small denoising operations at each timestep to obtain the image of the previous timestep and obtains the original image by gradual denoising [25]. Similarly, given the noisy image I_t corresponding to timestep t, the probability distribution of It − 1 under the condition It can be calculated by

$$Q(I_{t-1}|I_t) = \mathcal{N}\left(I_{t-1}; \mu_\theta(I_t, t), \sigma_t^2 Z\right) \quad (2)$$

where $\mu_\theta(I_t, t)$ is the mean value of $Q(I_{t-1}|I_t)$ and σ_t^2 is the variance, they also can be calculated.

3.3 Global Attention Fusion Module

After training the denoising network, to ensure that the model can focus on both global features and local details, we first utilize the trained denoising network to extract feature maps from each stage. Then, we design a GAFM to synthesize global feature maps to a fine-grained fused image.

As shown in the denoising network of Fig. 2, we use the backbone [21, 23] as our denoising network, there are five convolutional layers in the right part. We extract five stages of the feature maps and the size of five feature maps are $\frac{H}{16} \times \frac{W}{16}, \frac{H}{8} \times \frac{W}{8}, \frac{H}{4} \times \frac{W}{4}, \frac{H}{2} \times \frac{W}{2}$ and $H \times W$, each of which extracts features generated by the trained denoising network at three timesteps (i.e., 5, 50, 100). As shown in the GAFM in Fig. 2, for the model to pay attention to both global features and local details, after obtaining the diffusion feature maps, the feature maps of the five stages are enlarged into $H \times W$ dimensions by the corresponding upsampling operations. Then, the feature maps are concatenated in the channel dimension to obtain the global feature map, and the same channel attention mechanism and spatial attention mechanism as in scSE [26] are used for the global feature map to obtain the new feature map. Finally, the feature map is transformed into 128 channels by a fully connected layer, and the final 3-channel output fusion image is obtained through the 3 × 3 convolution layer.

3.4 Fusion Loss

To better focus on infrared images' salience and visible images' texture details while adapting to the influence of environmental illumination, we train our GAFM by a designed fusion loss $\mathcal{L}_{fus}$ that consists of illumination loss $\mathcal{L}_{ill}$, intensity loss $\mathcal{L}_{int}$, and gradient loss $\mathcal{L}_{gra}$.

Illumination Loss. Aiming to better adapt to the illumination conditions and preserve semantic information from the source image, we introduce an illumination loss [17]. Specifically, by using the light binary classification network to output the light probability P of the image, and then assigning the light weights $W_{ir} = P$ and $W_{vi} = 1 - P$. The illumination loss $\mathcal{L}_{ill}$ is finally defined as

$$\mathcal{L}_{ill} = W_{ir} \cdot \frac{1}{HW} ||I_{fu} - I_{ir}||_1 + W_{vi} \cdot \frac{1}{HW} ||I_{fu} - I_{vi}||_1 \qquad (3)$$

where I_{fu}, I_{ir} and I_{vi} represent fused image, infrared image, and visible image respectively, and $||\cdot||_1$ represents $L1$ loss.

Intensity Loss. In order to maintain the best intensity distribution for the fused image obtained by GLAD, we employ an auxiliary intensity loss [21], defined as

$$\mathcal{L}_{int} = \frac{1}{HW} ||I_{fu} - max(I_{ir}, I_{vi})||_1 \qquad (4)$$

Gradient Loss. Aiming to retain sufficient texture information in the final fused image while maintaining intensity distribution, we use a gradient loss [21], defined as

$$\mathcal{L}_{gra} = \frac{1}{HW} ||\nabla I_{fu} - max(\nabla|I_{ir}|, \nabla|I_{vi}|)||_1 \qquad (5)$$

where ∇ indicates the gradient operator.

Finally, the total fusion loss $\mathcal{L}_{fus}$ utilized to train our model is defined as

$$\mathcal{L}_{fus} = \mathcal{L}_{ill} + \mathcal{L}_{int} + \mathcal{L}_{gra} \qquad (6)$$

4 Experiments

In this section, we first present our experiment implementation, including datasets, metrics, and implementation details. Next, we perform some comparison and generalization experiments to show the superiority of GLAD. Finally, we reveal the effectiveness of using the global attention fusion module based on the ablation study.

4.1 Implementation

Datasets. To evaluate the performance of our framework, we conduct extensive experiments on three public datasets, i.e., **MSRS** [17], **KAIST** [27], and **M3FD** [6]. **MSRS** dataset is an multispectral dataset based on the MFNet dataset, containing 1444 pairs of high-quality aligned infrared and visible images. **KAIST** dataset captures a variety of regular traffic scenes, including campuses, streets, and countryside, both day and night, respectively. The image size is 640 × 480. **M3FD** dataset includes scenes such as campuses, resorts, roads, etc., and most of the images are 1024 × 768 pixels.

Metrics. In our comparative experiments, we utilize six metrics to comprehensively evaluate the fused effect: entropy (**EN** [28]), standard deviation (**SD**), mutual information (**MI**), visual information fidelity (**VIF** [29]), quality assessment based on blur and noise factors (**Qabf** [30]), and structural similarity index measure (**SSIM**). **EN** measures the amount of information the fused image contains. **SD** reflects the extent to which the values of individual pixels in the image are deviated from the average value. **MI** primarily evaluates how well the fused image aggregates information from the original image pairs. **VIF** measures the information fidelity of the fused image. **Qabf** quantifies the edge information and granularity level in the fused image. **SSIM** measures the structural similarity between source images and fused images [10].

Implementation Details. Our proposed GLAD is trained on the MSRS dataset and we adopt the training settings in Dif-Fusion [21]. During training, we randomly select 160 × 160 patches from both visible and infrared images and extract diffusion features from these patches produced at three time steps (e.g., 5, 50, 100) to construct multi-channel features. For training the fusion module, we employ the Adam optimizer to minimize loss, with a fixed learning rate of 0.0001. The training process utilizes a batch size of 24, and we iterate through 300 epochs to train the model. All of the training process is performed on a server equipped with an NVIDIA RTX3090 GPU.

4.2 Comparison with State-of-the-Art Methods

Below we compare our model with five state-of-the-art methods, FusionGAN [18], GANMcC [19], U2Fusion [20], TarDAL [6] and Dif-Fusion [21]. U2Fusion is based on CNN architectures, while FusionGAN, GANMcC, TarDAL, and Dif-Fusion are based on generative models and their variants.

Qualitative Comparison. The qualitative results of different fusion methods on the MSRS 00537D image are shown in Fig. 3. Overall, our method, TarDAL, and Dif-Fusion effectively preserve the texture details of the visible image while highlighting the salient targets of the infrared image. However, the fused image obtained by U2Fusion appears darker. In some details, as depicted in the zoomedin areas of the red and green boxes, the fusion results obtained by FusionGAN and GANMcC are slightly misaligned compared to the original image, with a significant loss of texture details in the zoomed-in areas. In contrast, our method preserves the texture details of the notice boards in the figure well, resulting in fine-grained fused images.

Quantitative Comparison. The quantitative results are shown in Fig. 4. Our method achieves superior performance across all six metrics. Particularly noteworthy is the significant improvement observed in four metrics (i.e., EN, SD, VIF, and Qabf). The highest SD and VIF values indicate that the fused images obtained by our method have high contrast and sizable visual effects. The highest MI and SSIM indicate that our method retains more structural information and features from the source images. Furthermore, thanks to our global attention fusion module, our method achieves the highest Qabf, indicating that our fusion results retain more edge information and achieve the finest level of granularity.

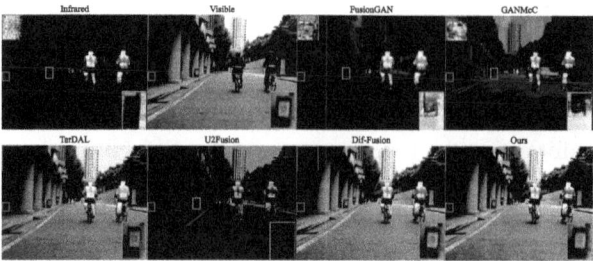

Fig. 3. Qualitative comparison on the 00537D image pair from the MSRS dataset.

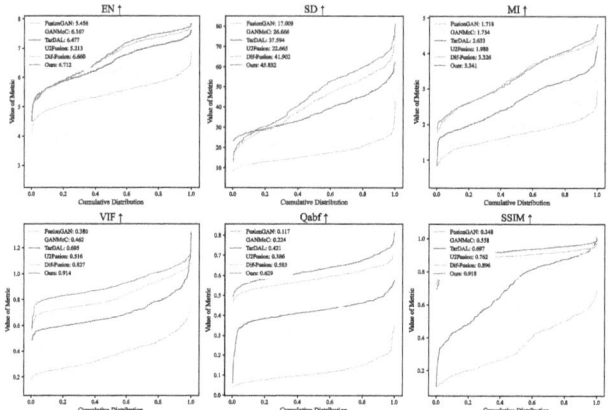

Fig. 4. Quantitative comparisons of the six metrics, i.e., EN, SD, MI, VIF Qabf and SSIM, on 361 image pairs from the MSRS dataset.

4.3 Generalization Experiment

Below we conduct experiments on the KAIST and M3FD datasets to assess GLAD's generalizability. Specifically, our fusion model was trained on the MSRS dataset and then directly evaluated on the KAIST and M3FD datasets.

Qualitative Comparison. The qualitative results of different fusion methods on the KAIST set09_V000_I02542 are shown in Fig. 5. From the red-boxed zoomed-in area in the figure, all six methods highlight the infrared pedestrian target, with FusionGAN having a more prominent target and U2Fusion having a darker target. However, from the zoomed-in area in the green box, FusionGAN and GANMcC lose the texture details of the visible image, such as the traffic sign. Figure 6 shows the fusion results of different fusion methods on M3FD00572. From the figure, all six methods can retain the infrared pedestrian targets well, but only our method and the Dif-Fusion method based on the diffusion model better retain the textual details in the zoomed-in area of the red box in the figure. Overall, benefiting from the learning of image features by the diffusion model and the application of the global attention fusion module, our method retains more feature details from the source images and gains finely-grained fused images.

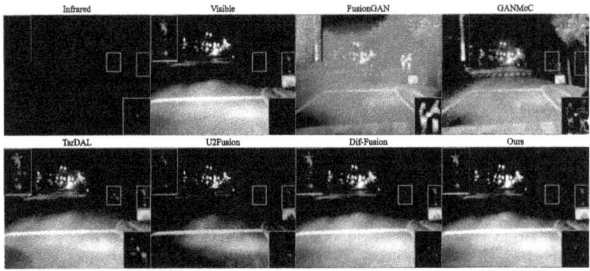

Fig. 5. Qualitative comparison on the set09_V000 _I02542 image pair from the KAIST dataset.

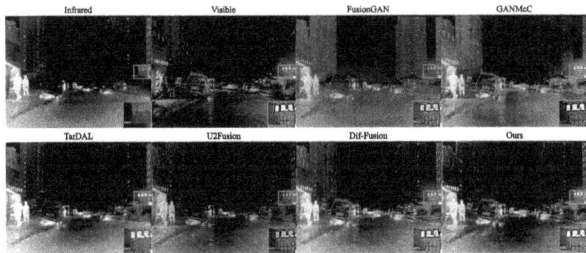

Fig. 6. Qualitative comparison on the 00572 image pair from the M3FD dataset.

Table 1. Fusion quality evaluation on 2257 aligned image pairs from the KAIST dataset. **Bold** represents the best results, and underlining represents the second-best results.

Methods	EN ↑	SD ↑	MI ↑	VIF ↑	Qabf ↑	SSIM ↑
FusionGAN	6.361	25.383	2.438	0.444	0.168	0.321
GANMcC	6.875	38.112	2.344	0.432	0.251	0.458
TarDAL	7.048	50.239	3.336	0.715	0.508	0.858
U2Fusion	6.559	32.623	2.537	0.689	0.521	**0.878**
Dif-Fusion	7.089	52.509	**3.916**	0.799	0.615	0.864
Ours	**7.109**	**57.921**	3.842	**0.832**	**0.638**	0.862

Quantitative Comparison. The fusion results on 2257 pairs of KAIST datasets are presented in Table 1. Compared with the other five methods, our approach achieves the highest EN, SD, VIF, and Qabf values, as well as the second-highest MI values. This indicates that the fusion results obtained by our method closely resemble the visual perception of the human eye and better retain both the local details and global information of the source images. Following the most work, we randomly select 25 pairs of M3FD datasets, and the test results of different fusion methods are shown in Table 2. Our method performs well across five metrics, namely EN, SD, MI, VIF, and Qabf, further validating the generalization ability of our proposed GLAD.

Table 2. Fusion quality evaluation on 25 image pairs from the M3FD dataset. **Bold** represents the best results, underlining represents the second best results.

Methods	EN ↑	SD ↑	MI ↑	VIF ↑	Qabf ↑	SSIM ↑
FusionGAN	6.907	32.707	2.102	0.256	0.158	0.482
GANMcC	6.997	35.838	1.735	0.332	0.168	0.595
TarDAL	<u>7.493</u>	<u>47.750</u>	2.471	0.447	0.407	<u>0.871</u>
U2Fusion	7.042	35.686	1.876	0.476	0.549	**0.973**
Dif-Fusion	7.390	43.829	<u>2.820</u>	<u>0.498</u>	<u>0.570</u>	0.869
Ours	**7.598**	**53.276**	**3.243**	**0.614**	**0.641**	0.856

4.4 Ablation Study

We propose a global attention fusion module(GAFM) to enable the model to focus on both local details and global features. We further conduct ablation experiments to confirm the effectiveness of the GAFM. Specifically, all other modules remain unchanged and are trained for 300 epochs under identical settings without the GAFM. The final results of the ablation experiments on the MSRS test set are presented in Table 3. 错误!未找到引用源。. It is evident that the removal of the global attention module results in a performance decrease in our method across five metrics (namely, EN, SD, VIF, Qabf, and SSIM). This further validates the capability of our proposed global attention module to effectively capture both the global and local information of the source image.

Table 3. The fusion performance with and without the GAFM on the MSRS dataset.

Methods	EN ↑	SD ↑	MI ↑	VIF ↑	Qabf ↑	SSIM ↑
w/o GAFM.	6.644	41.828	**3.344**	0.831	0.576	0.900
w GAFM.	**6.712**	**45.832**	3.341	**0.914**	**0.629**	**0.919**

5 Conclusion

In this paper, we propose GLAD, an IVIF method that can produce high-quality fused images with fine-grained. In GLAD, we tailor a denoising network of the diffusion model, propose a GAFM, and design a fusion loss function to improve our performance for the IVIF task. Through qualitative and quantitative experiments experiments conducted on multiple datasets, including MSRS, KAIST, and M3FD, we have demonstrated the superior performance of GLAD compared with other SOTA methods.

Acknowledgements. Thanks for the suggestion of reviewers. This work was supported in part by National Key R&D Program Project under Grant 2022YFC3803203, Joint Fund of the Ministry of Education for Equipment Pre Research with Grant 8091B032257, and National Natural Science Foundation of China under Grant 62372415.

References

1. Dogra, A., Goyal, B., Agrawal, S.: From multi-scale decomposition to non-multiscale decomposition methods: a comprehensive survey of image fusion techniques and its applications. IEEE Access **5**, 16040–16067 (2017)
2. Sun, C., Zhang, C., Xiong, N.: Infrared and visible image fusion techniques based on deep learning: a review. Electronics **9**(12), 2162 (2020)
3. Ma, W., et al.: Infrared and visible image fusion technology and application: a review. Sensors **23**(2), 599 (2023)
4. Tang, L., Zhang, H., Xu, H., Ma, J.: Rethinking the necessity of image fusion in high-level vision tasks: a practical infrared and visible image fusion network based on progressive semantic injection and scene fidelity. Inf. Fus. **99**, 101870 (2023)
5. Zhang, X., Demiris, Y.: Visible and infrared image fusion using deep learning. IEEE Trans. Pattern Anal. Mach. Intell. (2023)
6. Liu, J., et al.: Target-aware dual adversarial learning and a multi-scenario multi-modality benchmark to fuse infrared and visible for object detection. In: Proceedings of the IEEE/CVF Conference on Ccomputer Vision and Pattern Recognition, pp. 5802–5811 (2022)
7. Li, C., Zhu, C., Huang, Y., Tang, J., Wang, L.: Cross-modal ranking with soft consistency and noisy labels for robust RGB-T tracking. In: Proceedings of the European Conference on Computer Vision (ECCV), pp. 808–823 (2018)
8. Lu, Y., et al.: Cross-modality person re-identification with shared-specific feature transfer. In: Proceedings of the IEEE/CVF Conference on Computer Vision and Pattern Recognition, pp. 13379–13389 (2020)
9. Zhou, W., Liu, J., Lei, J., Yu, L., Hwang, J.N.: GMNet: Graded-feature multilabel-learning network for rgb-thermal urban scene semantic segmentation. IEEE Trans. Image Process. **30**, 7790–7802 (2021)
10. Ma, J., Ma, Y., Li, C.: Infrared and visible image fusion methods and applications: a survey. Inf. Fus. **45**, 153–178 (2019)
11. Liu, Y., Liu, S., Wang, Z.: A general framework for image fusion based on multiscale transform and sparse representation. Inf. Fus. **24**, 147–164 (2015)
12. Liu, Y., Chen, X., Ward, R.K., Wang, Z.J.: Image fusion with convolutional sparse representation. IEEE Signal Process. Lett. **23**(12), 1882–1886 (2016)
13. Bavirisetti, D.P., Dhuli, R.: Two-scale image fusion of visible and infrared images using saliency detection. Infrared Phys. Technol. **76**, 52–64 (2016)
14. Ma, J., Zhou, Z., Wang, B., Zong, H.: Infrared and visible image fusion based on visual saliency map and weighted least square optimization. Infrared Phys. Technol. **82**, 8–17 (2017)
15. Li, S., Kang, X., Fang, L., Hu, J., Yin, H.: Pixel-level image fusion: A survey of the state of the art. information Fusion **33**, 100–112 (2017)
16. Li, H., Wu, X.J.: DenseFuse: a fusion approach to infrared and visible images. IEEE Trans. Image Process. **28**(5), 2614–2623 (2018)
17. Tang, L., Yuan, J., Zhang, H., Jiang, X., Ma, J.: PIAFusion: a progressive infrared and visible image fusion network based on illumination aware. Inf. Fus. **83**, 79–92 (2022)
18. Ma, J., Yu, W., Liang, P., Li, C., Jiang, J.: FusionGAN: a generative adversarial network for infrared and visible image fusion. Inf. Fus. **48**, 11–26 (2019)
19. Ma, J., Zhang, H., Shao, Z., Liang, P., Xu, H.: GANMcC: a generative adversarial network with multiclassification constraints for infrared and visible image fusion. IEEE Trans. Instrum. Meas. **70**, 1–14 (2020)
20. Xu, H., Ma, J., Jiang, J., Guo, X., Ling, H.: U2Fusion: a unified unsupervised image fusion network. IEEE Trans. Pattern Anal. Mach. Intell. **44**(1), 502–518 (2020)

21. Yue, J., Fang, L., Xia, S., Deng, Y., Ma, J.: Dif-Fusion: towards high color fidelity in infrared and visible image fusion with diffusion models. IEEE Trans. Image Process. (2023)
22. Zhao, Z., et al.: DDFM: denoising diffusion model for multi-modality image fusion. In: Proceedings of the IEEE/CVF International Conference on Computer Vision, pp. 8082–8093 (2023)
23. Saharia, C., Ho, J., Chan, W., Salimans, T., Fleet, D.J., Norouzi, M.: Image superresolution via iterative refinement. IEEE Trans. Pattern Anal. Mach. Intell. **45**(4), 4713–4726 (2022)
24. Ho, J., Jain, A., Abbeel, P.: Denoising diffusion probabilistic models. Adv. Neural. Inf. Process. Syst. **33**, 6840–6851 (2020)
25. Baranchuk, D., Rubachev, I., Voynov, A., Khrulkov, V., Babenko, A.: Label-efficient semantic segmentation with diffusion models. arXiv preprint arXiv:2112.03126 (2021)
26. Roy, A.G., Navab, N., Wachinger, C.: Concurrent Spatial and Channel 'Squeeze & Excitation' in Fully Convolutional Networks. In: Frangi, A.F., Schnabel, J.A., Davatzikos, C., Alberola-López, C., Fichtinger, G. (eds.) MICCAI 2018. LNCS, vol. 11070, pp. 421–429. Springer, Cham (2018). https://doi.org/10.1007/978-3-030-00928-1_48
27. Choi, Y., et al.: Kaist multi-spectral day/night data set for autonomous and assisted driving. IEEE Trans. Intell. Transp. Syst. **19**(3), 934–948 (2018)
28. Qu, G., Zhang, D., Yan, P.: Information measure for performance of image fusion. Electron. Lett. **38**(7), 1 (2002)
29. Han, Y., Cai, Y., Cao, Y., Xu, X.: A new image fusion performance metric based on visual information fidelity. Inf. Fus. **14**(2), 127–135 (2013)
30. Xydeas, C.S., Petrovic, V., et al.: Objective image fusion performance measure. Electron. Lett. **36**(4), 308–309 (2000)

An Approach for Extracting Road Network from Remote Sensing Images

Zhihui Wang[1,2(✉)], Yu Wang[1,2], and Yuliang Ni[1,2]

[1] School of Computer Science, Fudan University, Shanghai, China
zhhwang@fudan.edu.cn
[2] Shanghai Key Laboratory of Data Science, Shanghai, China

Abstract. In recent years, the neural network architecture has developed rapidly and has been widely used in the semantic segmentation of remote sensing images. In this paper, we apply the neural network to the road network extraction of high-resolution remote sensing images. Subsequently, a series of single-pixel coordinate points are obtained by using the refinement method. Given the different lengths of road sections, our algorithm uses a double-loop mechanism to perform multi-scale fitting of them, which improves the rough results of the neural network and enhances the accuracy of road network extraction. For multiple line segments that may be on the same road, we also propose appropriate rules to classify and merge them. Our experimental results show that compared with other methods of road network extraction, our approach can obtain better results.

Keywords: Road Network · Deep Learning · Image Recognition

1 Introduction

Research related to high-resolution remote sensing images has developed into many fields, such as image classification, parcel segmentation, and semantic segmentation. Geographic information extracted by remote sensing images can be well applied in the valuable directions of life such as rail transit, meteorology, and agriculture. Therefore, road network extraction in remote sensing images is still an important direction [9]. Recently, China's urbanization process has got faster and faster. Road network construction and spatial layout development in first-tier cities are particularly important. In the big cities, the irregular shapes of the street blocks, the shadings of tall buildings and green plants, and other factors lead to a low contrast between road network features and non-road network features, which poses a great challenge to the road network extraction task.

In this paper, we use the convolutional neural network model to extracting road network from remote sensing images, and then perform further post-processing on the rough road network extracted by the model, including road network skeleton extraction, and the improved RANSAC [2, 6] algorithm for the vectorization of road network. Finally, the Ramer-Douglas-Peucker (RDP) [1, 7] algorithm is used for vector path compression.

Our contributions in this paper are mainly as follows: Firstly, through neural network training and parameter adjustment, our approach can handle the considerable large scale of remote sensing images and optimized them through model fusion. Secondly, based on the results of the neural network, our approach can further carry out a series of post-processing, especially for the improvement of the road fitting algorithm, so that our road network extraction approach can obtain a higher precision. Thirdly, compared with other methods of extracting the road network, we have proposed a set of practical methodology. Our approach can process the input of images and output the vectorized road network for further processing.

2 Our Approach

The structure of our neural network model is based on U-Net [8]. In order to obtain better result, we have fine-tuned the network structure, such as the use of the pre-training model, the alignment of the size of the up-sampled feature map, the fusion of multiple model results, etc. At the beginning of the road network post-processing, we introduced some morphological knowledge; in the task of road vector fitting, the improved RANSAC algorithm allows our experiments to proceed smoothly; for the road after fitting, classification reconstruction and vector compression are carried out, we combined some mathematical knowledge to make our method more convincing.

2.1 Model Structure and Model Fusion

U-Net is an improved version of fully convolutional network (FCN) [5]. We furtherly improve the idea of the U-Net structure and replace the down-sampling part with the pre-trained ResNet [3] structure in PyTorch. In addition, we use different variants of ResNet (ResNet50 / ResNet101 / ResNet152) as the up-sampling part for training different models, and select the models for each variant for prediction, then finally voted on the prediction of a single-pixel to achieve model fusion. For convenience, we call the model U-Net*.

2.2 Road Refinement

The choice of the refinement algorithm is determined according to the actual situation. Since the refinement algorithm has discontinuous results for skeleton extraction in the practical applications, we do not focus on the integrity and connectivity of the skeleton. Instead, we only need to obtain the discrete pixel feature map with the road network structure. We compared the effects of Hilditch's algorithm [4] and Zhang's algorithm [10] on road network skeleton extraction, and the results of these two algorithms are different. In our experiments, the Zhang's algorithm can get more suitable results, and the skeleton produced by Hilditch's algorithm is ambiguous.

2.3 DL-RANSAC Algorithm

By drawing the lessons from the idea of cyclically using RANSAC [2, 6], we made the improvement and presented the approach of Double Loop RANSAC (DL-RANSAC). This method can perform more robust multi-scale fitting and improve the road network coverage.

In RANSAC, the result returned by the fitting contains three parts: the coordinate point set, the slope k of the fitted line, and the offset b. To facilitate the representation and storage of line segments, we only retain the coordinates of the two endpoints of the straight line, so the data structure of the line segment is $line = [point_{left}, point_{right}]$.

A single loop RANSAC can fit multiple line segments in a binary image. However, the position of pixels is expressed based on the Cartesian coordinate system, the least-squares fit in RANSAC cannot fit the straight line that perpendicular to the x-axis, we fixed this problem in the algorithm. In addition, there is a fixed parameter N in RANSAC, which is the number of minimum pixels that meet the straight-line fit. If this parameter is too large, the shorter line segment will not fit. On the contrary, it is easy to fit the wrong line segment. So we improved the algorithm to achieve dynamic multi-scale fitting and called it double loop RANSAC(DL-RANSAC): nesting an outer loop and setting the dynamic parameter N (specifically, the outer loop gradually decreases, but will not fall below the minimum threshold). In this case, the longer line segment will be fitted first, and then the shorter line segment will be fitted. The specific algorithm is shown by Algorithm 1.

2.4 Segment Classification

In the process of circular line fitting using discrete pixels with a road network architecture, multiple similar lines will be fitted on the same road segment, so we set certain clustering rules to cluster the same line segment.

We consider using the angle of the straight lines as one of the similarity measures to cluster different straight lines. In the following, we will define the rule for the intersection of straight lines from the parallel and intersection of line segments.

Algorithm 1 Double Loop RANSAC Algorithm

Input:
    Binary image with road skeleton: $Image_{data}$
    The minimum number of pixels needed to fit a straight line: n
    Inner loop RANSAC iterations: k
    Error threshold of fitted model and external points: t
        The number of minimum demand points that meet the qualified straight line and the minimum threshold of the outer circle: $N_{miniFit}$, $N_{miniGap}$

Output:
    Set of line segments that are not perpendicular to the x axis $Lines_{Novx}$
    Set of line segments that are perpendicular to the x axis $Lines_{Vx}$

1: Initialize $Image_{data}$ and return the pixel coordinate set P_{XYs} of road features, and declare that a $P_{original}$ is equal to P_{XYs}
2: Initialization result coordinate point set $Lines_{Novx}$ and $Lines_{Vx}$ are empty
3: Initialize the outer loop number batch to 1
4: **while** $P_{XYs}/P_{original} \geq 0.1$ && $N_{miniFit}/batch >= N_{miniGap}$ **do**
5:     $N_{miniFit} / = batch$
6:     **while** $line_{Novx}$ is exist **do**
7:         Get $RANSAC_{fitmodel}$ and $RANSAC_{fitdata}$ from $RANSAC(n, k, t, N_{miniFit})$
8:         Obtain line segment endpoints from the fitted model and data to form a line segment representation $line_{Novx}$
9:         $P_{XYs} = P_{XYs} - RANSAC_{fitdata}$
10:        $Lines_{Novx}.append(line_{Novx})$
11:    **end while**
12:    **while** $line_{Vx}$ is exist **do**
13:       Get $line_{Vx}$
14:       $P_{XYs} = P_{XYs} -$ data in $line_{Vx}$
15:       $Lines_{Vx}.append(line_{Vx})$
16:    **end while**
17:    $batch$ += 1
18: **end while**
19: **return** $Lines_{Novx}$ and $Lines_{Vx}$

Parallel Line Segments. If the slope k of the two straight lines is equal, but the offset b is inconsistent (shown in Fig. 1(a)), we set the threshold th_1 to determine the relationship between the distance D_1 of the two straight lines and the threshold. D_1 can be calculated by $D_1 = \frac{|b_1 - b_2|}{\sqrt{k^2+1}}$.

If the slope k and the offset b of the two straight lines are equal (shown in Fig. 1(b)), two cases are considered: (1) If two lines intersect directly, they are classified into the same category; (2) If the lines are parallel, we determine the relationship by comparing the distance D_2 with a predefined threshold th_2, where D_2 is calculated as $D_2 = min(distance(B_1, A_2), distance(A_1, B_2))$.

Intersecting Line Segments. If the angle θ between two straight lines is greater than the predefined threshold th_θ, they must not be of the same type. The angle θ can be

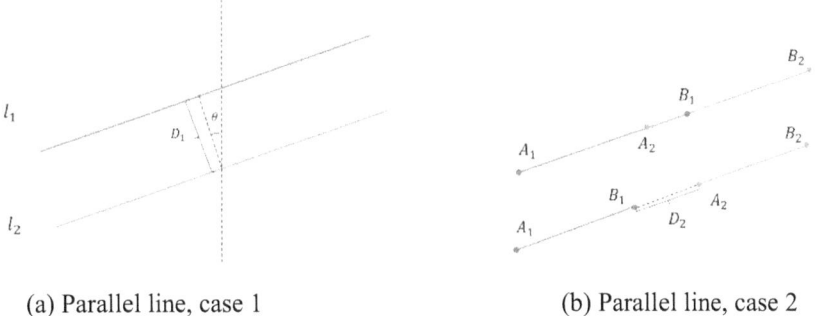

(a) Parallel line, case 1   (b) Parallel line, case 2

Fig. 1. Examples of parallel line segments.

obtained by $\theta = abs(arctan(\frac{k_1-k_2}{1+k_1*k_2}))$, where k_1 and k_2 are the slopes of the two lines, respectively.

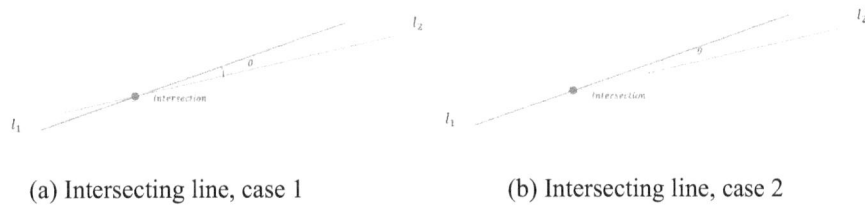

(a) Intersecting line, case 1   (b) Intersecting line, case 2

Fig. 2. Examples of intersecting line segments (case 1 & case 2).

If the angle between two straight lines is less than the threshold th_θ, consider the following situations:

1. If the intersection falls on two straight lines at the same time (shown in Fig. 2(a)), the lines are directly classified into the same category, and the coordinates of the intersection point are retained. The x and y of the intersection coordinate can be obtained by the following formula:

$$x = \frac{b_2 - b_1}{k_1 - k_2}, y = \frac{b_2*k_1 - b_1*k_2}{k_1 - k_2} \quad (1)$$

2. If the intersection point is located only on one of the straight lines, but the two straight lines intersect in the value range of x (shown in Fig. 2(b)), the lines are classified into the same category, but the coordinates of the intersection point are not retained.

3. If the intersection point is located only on one of the straight lines, and the two straight lines do not intersect in the value range of x (shown in Fig. 3(a)), we need another predefined distance threshold th_3. If the distance D_3 between the endpoints of the two straight lines is less than the threshold th_3, the lines are of the same type.

4. If the intersection point is not on any straight line, but is located in the middle of the two lines (shown in Fig. 3(b)), the threshold th_3 and the distance D_3 are also used to

(a) Intersecting line, case 3   (b) Intersecting line, case 4

Fig. 3. Examples of intersecting line segments (case 3 & case 4).

determine whether the two lines are of the same type. However, the position of the intersection point needs to be further judged here. If the intersection point is within the range of the current image, the coordinates of the intersection point are retained. Otherwise, they are not retained.

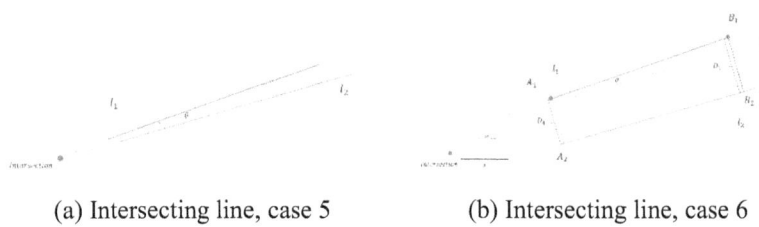

(a) Intersecting line, case 5   (b) Intersecting line, case 6

Fig. 4. Examples of intersecting line segments (case 5 & case 6).

5. Consider the last case, where the intersection point is not on any straight line. Ideally, the situation that satisfies the same category is shown in Fig. 4(a). However, it may be as shown in Fig. 4(b). That is, the intersection point of the two-line segments is far outside the picture range. At this case, we need a pre-define distance threshold th_4, and calculate the vertical distances D_4 and D_5 from A_1 and B_1 to another line. If both D_4 and D_5 are smaller than the threshold th_4, the lines are classified into the same category. Here D_4 (or D_5) can be obtained by the following formula:

$$D_4(\text{dis from } A_1 \text{ to } l_2) = \left| \overrightarrow{A_1A_2} - \frac{\overrightarrow{A_1A_2}\overrightarrow{A_2B_2}}{|\overrightarrow{A_2B_2}|^2} \overrightarrow{A_2B_2} \right| \quad (2)$$

2.5 Vector Path Compression

After we classify the line segments by the above line segment rules, the set of line segments of each category is $L = l_1, l_2, \ldots, l_n$, where l_i has two endpoints. We convert the line segment set into a point set and sort all the endpoints according to the coordinate size, then use the Ramer-Douglas-Peucker (RDP) [1, 7] algorithm to perform vector path compression on the ordered coordinate points. After that, we can delete unnecessary endpoints, and connect the retained points to obtain the final vectorization result of road network.

3 Experimental Results

3.1 Data Description

The road network source data we obtained is vector data stored in the format of GeoJSON. Each node of the road label is represented by the latitude and longitude coordinates based on the Mercator coordinate system. We use relevant toolkits in Python to convert these nodes into tiles annotate and download the corresponding tilemap on Google Maps. The downloaded annotations and data are as shown in Fig. 5, and the size is 256 * 256. Because the downloaded tile labels are single-pixel binary images, we performed morphological dilation preprocessing to better match the width of the roads in the map data. Similarly, before the neural network training, we conducted artificial screening and elimination of dirty data.

3.2 Model Training and Prediction

Through the experiment and parameter adjustment process, we found that adding loss weights has a critical effect on the experimental results. We regard the road network extraction task as a semantic binary classification task, using *CrossEntropyLoss* in PyTorch as a loss function, and the specific calculation method of the function is as the following formula.

$$\text{loss}(x, \text{class}) = -\log(\frac{\exp(x[\text{class}])}{\Sigma_j \exp(x[j])}) = -x[\text{class}] + \log(\sum_j \exp(x[j])) \quad (3)$$

When using *CrossEntropyLoss* without adding any parameters for model training, our binary prediction results account for almost 0% of the road network. Through analysis and thinking, we found that the ratio of the road network to the non-road network in the data has a large skew. In the case where the non-road network accounts for a large amount, the network tends to determine the pixels as non-road networks during the gradient descent optimization process. Because in this case, even if all road networks are predicted to be non-road networks, the accuracy of classification prediction will also be considerable.

Notice that in *CrossEntropyLoss*, the calculation formula with weight is (*default weight = None*): $\text{loss}(x, \text{class}) = \text{weight}[\text{class}](-x[\text{class}] + (\sum_j \exp(x[j])))$. We use the following calculation method for the weight of determining the two-class (i.e., road and non-road), $\text{weight} = \frac{1}{\log(w_b + P)}$, where P represents the ratio of the sum of road pixels (or the sum of non-road pixels) to the total number of pixels in the data, w_b represents a pre-defined bias parameter.

With the help of the weight, our approach can obtain quite impressive results especially for the experiments on the skew data of the test set. Several representative results are shown in Fig. 5. Each subgraph contains the original image of the test picture, the single-pixel annotated image, the experimental annotated image, and the predicted image (because we predict and return a probability of (0–1) for each pixel value p, so the value of a single-pixel in the prediction map comes from $p * 255$, not only 0 and 255).

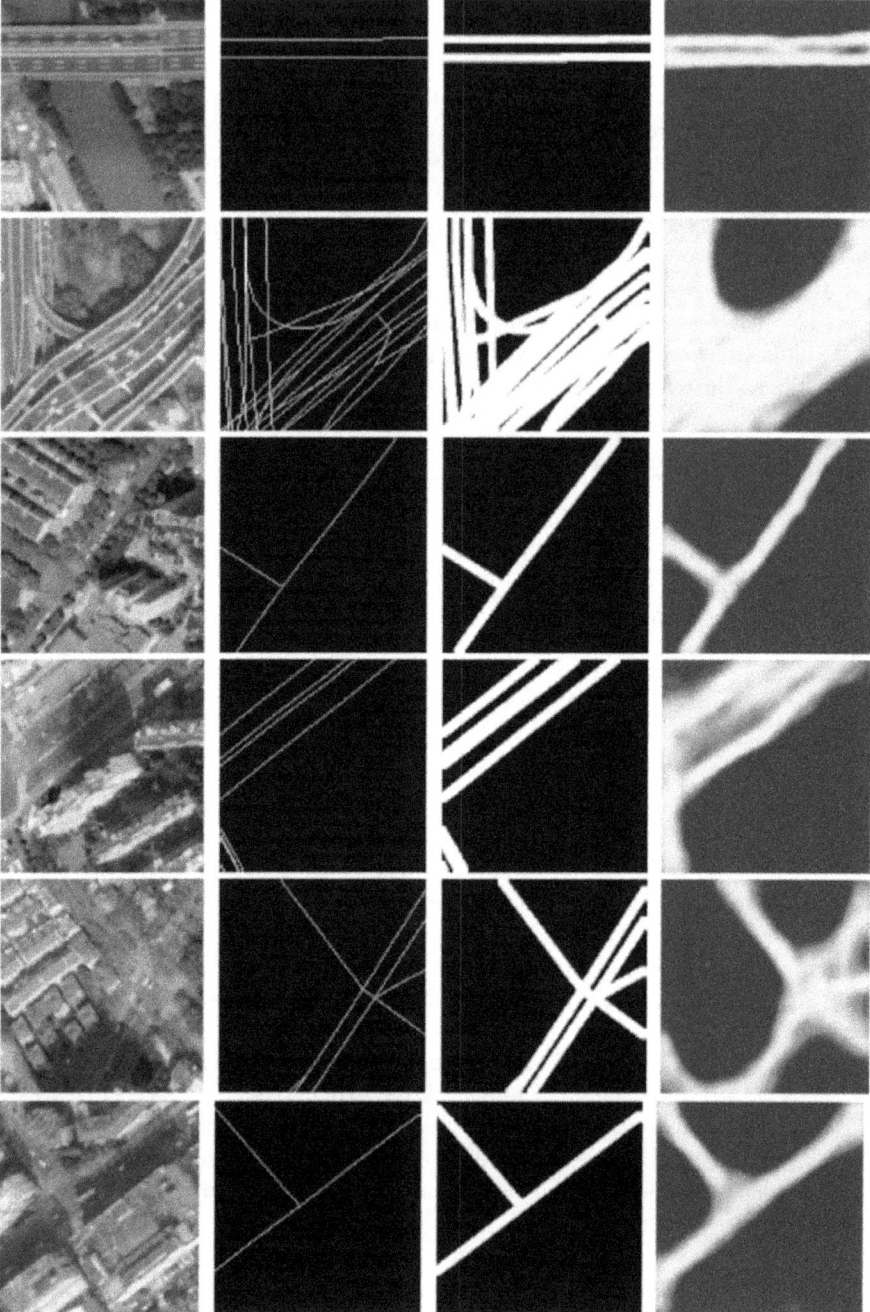

Fig. 5. Datasets and test predictions. There are six groups of sample pictures. From left to right, in each group are the original satellite image, the vector single-line road network label, the road network label after morphological expansion, and the U-Net* prediction result.

3.3 Road Refinement and DL-RANSAC

In our experiments, we set the number of pixels of randomly generated lines as 2. In addition, we set the random number k to 500, the distance threshold between the non-fitting point and the fitted line is set to 100, and the minimum number of pixels required to meet the required straight line is dynamically decreased from 125 in the outer loop of Algorithm 1 until it is less than the minimum threshold of 50.

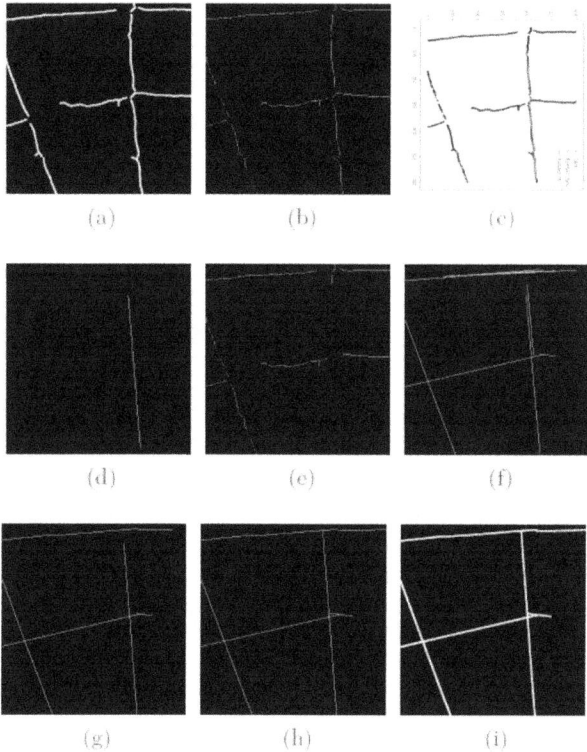

Fig. 6. The results of our DL-RANSAC: a) Filter results of U-Net*. b) Skeleton extraction results. c) RANSAC fitting. d) Fitted line. e) Skeleton after removing fitting results. f) After DL-RANSAC iterative fitting. g) Reconstruction result. h) The result after repairing. i) Final result.

Our fitting results on the sample data are shown in Fig. 6. It can be seen that we perform a route fitting on a binary image with a road skeleton, and the pixels of the fitting will be deleted before the next round of fitting until the final fitting is completed. Compared with the original results, the fitted straight line removed burrs and repaired the disconnection of the intersection to some extent.

3.4 Classification and Reconstruction

It can be seen that in the results of DL-RANSAC, we have multiple straight line fittings on the same road segment at the same time. Therefore, based on the line segment classification rules introduced in the previous section, we further reconstruct the fitting results of DL-RANSAC. It is worth mentioning that, with the help of vector path compression based on Ramer-Douglas-Peucker (RDP) algorithm, we can also repair some small line segments which are disconnected incorrectly.

The segment classification and reconstruction results for the previous picture are shown in Fig. 6. After the classification and reconstruction, the redundant lines of the same road segment disappeared, and the reconstructed road segments also retained the characteristics of the original set of road segments.

3.5 Experiments on the Road Network

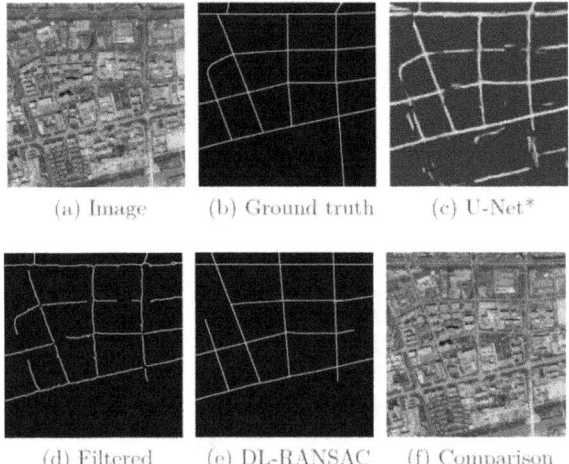

Fig. 7. The results of our approach.

In this set of experiments, we have conducted road network prediction experiments on the large size of maps that we grabbed. Some of the results are shown in Fig. 7. It can be seen that compared to the rough results of the neural network, the vector results fitted by DL-RANSAC look more comfortable, they do not have too much burr effect, and achieve connections for some broken intersections. However, the disadvantage is that due to the uncertainty defect of the RANSAC algorithm itself, a small part of the road network will be lost and the fitting errors will occur. A final road network coverage result is shown in Fig. 8.

Fig. 8. The result of a road network.

4 Conclusion

In the road network extraction task, the data requirements using traditional mathematical methods are relatively more stringent, and the boundary conditions that need to be considered in a certain scene are also more detailed. For the road network extraction task for urbans, such as Shanghai, the traditional method is difficult.

In this paper, we present an approach for extracting road network from remote sensing images, and also provide the approach for processing the results of image recognition to improve the quality of extracted road network. The experimental results show that our approach can get better results, especially in the settings of an urban.

Acknowledgments. This work was supported in part by the Scientific & Technological Innovation 2030 - "New Generation AI" Key Project (No. 2021ZD0114001; No. 2021ZD0114000), and the Science and Technology Commission of Shanghai Municipality (No. 21511102200). Zhihui Wang is the corresponding author of this work.

References

1. Douglas, D.H., Peucker, T.K.: Algorithms for the reduction of the number of points required to represent a digitized line or its caricature. Cartographica Int. J. Geogr. Inf. Geovisualization **10**(2), 112–122
2. Fischler, M.A., Bolles, R.C.: Random sample consensus: a paradigm for model fitting with applications to image analysis and automated cartography. Commun. ACM **24**(6), 381–395 (1981)
3. He, K., Zhang, X., Ren, S., Sun, J.: Deep residual learning for image recognition. In: Proceedings of the IEEE Conference on Computer Vision and Pattern Recognition, pp. 770–778 (2016)
4. Hilditch, C.J.: Linear skeleton from square cupboards. Mach. Intell. **6**, 403–420 (1969)

5. Long, J., Shelhamer, E., Darrell, T.: Fully convolutional networks for semantic segmentation. In: Proceedings of the IEEE Conference on Computer Vision and Pattern Recognition, pp. 3431–3440 (2015)
6. Miao, Z., Shi, W., Samat, A., Lisini, G., Gamba, P.: Information fusion for urban road extraction from VHR optical satellite images. IEEE J. Sel. Top. Appl. Earth Observations Remote Sens. **9**(5), 1817–1829 (2016)
7. Ramer, U.: An iterative procedure for the polygonal approximation of plane curves. Comput. Graph. Image Process. **1**(3), 244–256 (1972)
8. Ronneberger, O., Fischer, P., Brox, T.: U-Net: convolutional networks for biomedical image segmentation. In: Proceedings of the 18th International Conference on Medical Image Computing and Computer-Assisted Intervention - MICCAI, Part III. Lecture Notes in Computer Science, vol. 9351, pp. 234–241. Springer (2015). https://doi.org/10.1007/978-3-319-24574-4_28
9. Soni, P.K., Rajpal, N., Mehta, R.: A comparison of road network extraction from high resolution images. In: Proceedings of the First International Conference on Secure Cyber Computing and Communication (ICSCCC), pp. 525–531. IEEE (2018)
10. Zhang, T., Suen, C.Y.: A fast parallel algorithm for thinning digital patterns. Commun. ACM **27**(3), 236–239 (1984)

Sparse Point Cloud Upsampling Based on Neural Implicit Functions

Wenjun Wang[1,2], Xiangyu Kong[2], Daole Wang[1,2], and Xiuyang Zhao[2(✉)]

[1] Shandong Provincial Key Laboratory of Network Based Intelligent Computing, University of Jinan, Jinan, China
[2] School of Information Science and Engineering, University of Jinan, Jinan, China
zhaoxy@ujn.edu.cn

Abstract. In this paper, we propose a novel point cloud representation method based on neural implicit functions - spatial fields. This method utilizes neural implicit functions to transform three-dimensional coordinate points into local spatial fields, converting the original "discrete-discrete" point cloud representation into a "discrete-continuous" geometric representation, thereby to obtain continuous point cloud representations and richer geometric detail expression. In this method, each three-dimensional coordinate point in the original sparse point set is transformed into a local spatial field embedding multi-layer neighborhood information by means of implicit functions. Eventually, multiple such local spatial fields are aggregated into a continuous high-resolution spatial field to approximate the object surface as closely as possible. At last, arbitrary-scale sampling can be conducted in the high-resolution spatial field for point cloud densification needs at arbitrary resolutions in downstream applications such as 3D medical image reconstruction and autonomous driving. This paper provides an example to illustrate how to utilize the results of the proposed solution for 3D model reconstruction.

Keywords: Sparse point cloud · neural implicit functions · upsampling · Three-dimensional reconstruction

1 Introduction

As one of the most commonly used 3D data formats, point clouds have extensive applications in various fields such as geometric analysis and autonomous driving. Point clouds can exist with extremely low or high densities and can provide both global shape and refined geometric information of objects. Common 3D scanning devices include LiDAR sensors, depth cameras, and specialized cameras. However, this method is susceptible to the influence of equipment and environment, resulting in sparse, noisy, and unevenly distributed points. The sparsity and non-uniformity of the clouds can adversely affect the performance of downstream tasks, including semantic classification [1], rendering [2], 3D reconstruction [3–5], virtual/augmented reality [6] [7], and autonomous driving [8] [9]. Additionally, point clouds can also be applied in traditional automotive industries, mechanical, or architectural designs. Therefore, converting point clouds into dense, uniform, and clean representations is crucial. The process is known as point cloud upsampling.

The purpose of point cloud upsampling is to increase the density of point cloud data while ensuring that the quality of the object's global shape and geometric details remains intact, thus obtaining a high-resolution regular point cloud. However, increasing the density of points implies adding interpolated information, which can make local edge details handing extremely challenging.

Existing point cloud upsampling methods [10–17] can broadly be divided into two types: optimization-based methods and deep learning-based methods. Optimization-based methods heavily rely on prior knowledge, such as fitting local geometric information. Though the optimization-based methods are demonstrated to have some effectiveness in upsampling smooth surfaces, they often encounter difficulties when dealing with complex corners and edge regions. Learning-based methods break though this limitation by using various networks [18–22] (such as convolutional neural networks and multi-layer perceptrons) to learn multi-scale and multi-feature structures [10–24], thereby significantly improving traditional optimization-based methods. However, the existing methods still face some challenges, such as unevenly distributed dense points generating or certain local edge features neglect, which will leading to a significant decrease in the quality of reconstructed point clouds. Furthermore, the existing methods mostly consider fixed-factor upsampling, such as 4x or 8x. When practical applications require point cloud densification at multiple different scales, training multiple models separately for different scales will results in inefficiency and resource wastage.

NePs [25] introduced a new point cloud representation method to address the upsampling issue with fixed factors, but simply combining the upsampled blocks into a complete point cloud as the prediction result ignores the inconsistency between local patches [27]: Firstly, without global shape information, it is difficult to determine the geometric shape of block boundaries, leading to outliers on dense point clouds. Secondly, combining inconsistent blocks can result in holes or uneven points in the predicted point cloud. This paper extracts multi-dimensional features from a given uneven sparse point set and embeds multi-scale features from the graph structure formed by neighborhood information and the neighborhood information of the neighborhood information, as a supplement to global shape information, to eliminate the problem of outliers in dense point clouds.

Addressing the aforementioned challenges, this paper introduces a novel and powerful point cloud upsampling method. By designing a simple and efficient multi-scale sampling model based on neural implicit functions, it generates accurate and uniformly dense point sets. This model converts sparse point clouds into high-quality dense point sets and can be applied to various downstream tasks such as point cloud object classification and segmentation. Traditional point cloud upsampling methods typically follow three steps: (1) feature extraction, (2) feature expansion, and (3) coordinate reconstruction. The limitation of this approach lies in the fact that, during feature extraction, only the central point and local features are usually considered, neglecting features from local neighborhoods and their adjacent points. Furthermore, during feature expansion, only simple operations like replication and convolution pooling are applied, resulting in unevenly distributed dense point sets often clustering together, making complete coverage of the object surface challenging.

This paper abandons the traditional three-step approach and proposes a point cloud upsampling method based on implicit functions. Specifically, this paper introduces the concept of spatial fields and designs a bidirectional neural implicit function, which achieves a dual mapping between the feature space of sparse point sets and the implicit spatial field, obtaining continuous spatial fields as information about the object surface. To ensure that the spatial fields approximate the object surface, this paper emphasizes the importance of features extracted from sparse point sets. Advanced semantic features and low-dimensional geometric features are extracted from the central points of sparse point sets, embedding local neighborhood features, while ensuring the final features are rich and expressive through the connection of local neighborhood information with different weights. Finally, this paper maps the features obtained from the central points of continuous spatial fields back to sparse point sets, generating dense and uniformly distributed target point sets. By using a comprehensive loss function, this paper ensures that the generated point sets approximate the original point cloud and are evenly distributed on the shape surface.

The contributions of this work can be described as follows:

- This paper introduces a novel point cloud representation method based on neural implicit functions called Spatial Fields. By utilizing neural implicit functions to transform three-dimensional coordinate points into local spatial fields, this method achieves continuous point cloud representation and richer geometric detail expression.
- This paper designs a point cloud upsampling network based on neural implicit functions to apply the proposed point cloud representation method to point cloud densification tasks. It achieves high-precision upsampling at arbitrary scaling factors.
- The method proposed in this paper achieves competitive upsampling results on public datasets, demonstrating its effectiveness in point cloud upsampling tasks.

2 Method

Assuming a sparse and unevenly distributed three-dimensional point cloud X, where N represents the number of points, and each point is associated with three-dimensional coordinates, the network model in this paper undergoes a series of processes to transform it into a dense and uniformly distributed point cloud Y. Additionally, it is expected that this dense point cloud can closely approximate the surface of the three-dimensional object as closely as possible while minimizing noise or outliers. Previous works often directly established a mapping between sparse point clouds and dense point clouds, leading to information overload and reduced accuracy. This paper utilizes a neural implicit function to learn a continuous mapping as shown in Eq. (1), transforming discrete point cloud information into a continuous geometric representation, enhancing the expressive power of the point set while reducing resource wastage caused by excessive storage costs.

$$\mathbf{P} = \{(p_i \in R^6)\}_{i=1}^{n} \to^{NIFs} \{p_i^r \in s_i\}_{i,r=1}^{n,R}, \quad (1)$$

where pi represents each point in the point cloud, including the three-dimensional coordinate information of the points.

The point cloud representation method based on neural implicit functions proposed in this paper can transform discrete pi into a continuous spatial field si. Si contains the multi-scale neighborhood information and global shape of pi, representing a continuous geometric surface. By transforming each point in the point set into a spatial field and aggregating them together, a continuous smooth high-resolution spatial field is eventually formed to approximate the object surface as closely as possible, as shown in Eq. (2).

$$S = \bigcup_{i=1}^{n} s_i \xrightarrow{\text{resample}} S' \in S \qquad (2)$$

Subsequently, upsampling at arbitrary resolution factors is performed on the high-resolution spatial field to achieve multi-scale point cloud densification.

Specifically, to generate a more accurate and uniformly dense point set, this paper extracts multi-dimensional features from the given unevenly sparse point set and embeds multi-scale features from neighborhood information and graph structures formed by the neighborhood information of the neighborhood information. Subsequently, a bidirectional mapping from sparse point sets to local spatial fields is established. By learning the final features obtained from the unevenly sparse point set, this paper generates a continuous spatial field in three-dimensional space, aiming to simulate the object's surface as closely as possible. The inverse mapping here maps the spatial field features meeting specific conditions back to the unevenly sparse point set to generate a dense and uniformly distributed point set.

Local Spatial Field: This paper proposes a point set representation based on neural implicit functions. It first assumes that each center point in 3D space can be linearly expressed through its neighboring points. Then, it transforms the three-dimensional coordinate point features in the point set into a latent implicit representation of embedded multi-scale neighborhood features with the three-dimensional coordinate point as the starting point. These latent implicit representations are defined as local spatial fields, as shown in Eq. (3).

$$\mathbf{s} = f_\theta(p_i, c_i, q) \qquad (3)$$

where pi represents any three-dimensional coordinate point in the point set, ci represents the k local neighborhood features of pi, and q is the input sparse point cloud set.

Meanwhile, to improve the accuracy of the spatial field, this paper sets distance constraints to select points with stronger semantic features, as shown in Eq. (4).

$$\mathbf{Dist}(\mathbf{c}_{(x,y,z)}, \mathcal{S}) \in [D_l, D_u] \qquad (4)$$

where c represents a point containing three-dimensional coordinate information (x, y, z), s represents the local spatial field centered at c, Dl and Du represent the lower and upper distance limits set in this paper, respectively.

Since it is not possible to calculate the distance from a three-dimensional coordinate point to an unknown local spatial field, this paper divides the input sparse point cloud into multiple overlapping patches centered at three-dimensional coordinate points. Three points are randomly selected within each patch to form a three-dimensional local surface, and the distance from the center point to the three-dimensional local surface is defined as the distance from the three-dimensional coordinate point to the unknown local spatial field.

The points that meet the distance constraints are selected and transformed into local spatial fields, as illustrated in Fig. 1.

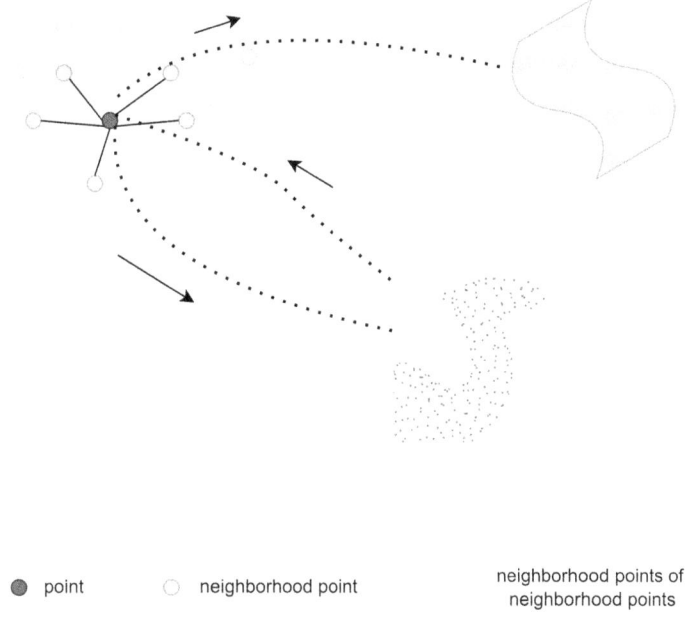

Fig. 1. Local spatial field structure diagram.

The ultimate goal of point cloud upsampling is to obtain a densely distributed point set that uniformly covers the surface of an object. However, directly solving for the surface is a challenging task. Local spatial fields extend the representation range of point sets, enhance semantic features, and represent part of the object surface information composed of new points that do not exist in the sparse point set. When aggregated together, sufficiently large local spatial fields can be regarded as the object surface.

Surface Reconstruction: The method proposed in this paper based on neural implicit functions transforms each three-dimensional coordinate point in the sparse point cloud into a continuous local spatial field. By aggregating all local spatial fields, a sufficiently large continuous high-resolution spatial field is generated to simulate the object surface, thus achieving point cloud densification at arbitrary sampling factors. However, since different local spatial fields are based on different coordinate systems, this paper calculates a weight based on the features of the three-dimensional coordinate point and its neighborhood points. Continuous high-resolution spatial field generation is achieved through weighted aggregation of multiple local spatial fields, as shown in Eqs. (5) and (6).

$$w_k = e^{-\alpha_1 |x - x_k|_2^2}, \forall k \in N(x) \tag{5}$$

$$S = \left(\sum w_j \cdot s_j\right) / \left(\sum w_j\right) \tag{6}$$

The next step is the design of the network architecture.

Network Architecture Design: In the feature extraction stage, given the input sparse point cloud, this paper designs feature extraction modules at different levels. Lower-level network modules extract local features of points, while higher-level network modules capture global features of points. Finally, these features are aggregated to form multi-level features of points with stronger expressiveness. Specifically, for each point in the sparse point cloud, this paper utilizes the state-of-the-art method DGCNN to extract K multi-scale neighborhood features of the three-dimensional coordinate point. Subsequently, after passing through a max-pooling layer, the final features used for embedding in the dual mapping layer are obtained, as shown in Fig. 2.

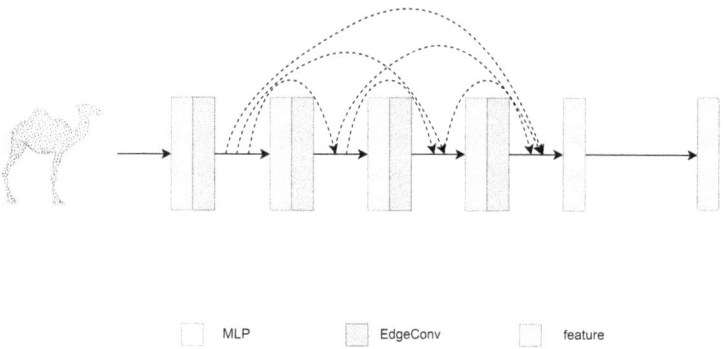

Fig. 2. Feature extraction architecture.

The generation of local spatial fields relies on the design of the bidirectional implicit functions. Here, this paper adopts an encoder-decoder approach. Points in the sparse point cloud act as center points, while random points in the spatial field are selected as query points. Local features, center points, and query points are concatenated as inputs to the implicit function. Through multiple blocks consisting of MLP layers, normalization layers, and ReLU activation layers, the final output forms the continuous high-resolution spatial field. Points features obtained through arbitrary sampling in the continuous high-resolution spatial field are mapped back to three-dimensional coordinate space to generate a densified point set with the desired sampling factor. The overall architecture is shown in Fig. 3.

Loss Function: To ensure that the generated dense point set is more evenly distributed on the object surface, this paper utilizes Chamfer Distance (CD) as shown in Eq. (7).

$$d_{\text{cD}}(S_1, S_2) = \frac{1}{S_1} \sum_{x \in S_1} \min_{y \in S_2} |x - y|_2^2 + \frac{1}{S_2} \sum_{x \in S_2} \min_{y \in S_1} |y - x|_2^2 \qquad (7)$$

Hausdorff Distance (HD) as shown in Eq. (8).

$$d_{HD}(S_1, S_2) = max(h(S_1, S_2), h(S_2, S_1)) \qquad (8)$$

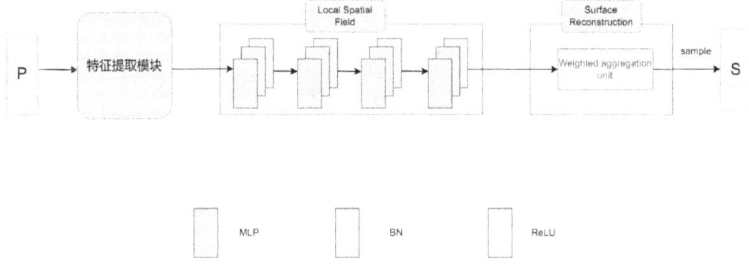

Fig. 3. Overall architecture.

and Point-to-Plane Distance (P2F) as shown in Eq. (9) to evaluate the reconstruction error between the generated point set S1 and the ground truth point set S2.

$$d_{P2F}(S_1, \boldsymbol{\beta}) = \frac{1}{|S_1|} \sum_{x \in S_1} d(x, \boldsymbol{\beta}) \tag{9}$$

3 Experiments

Dataset: This paper utilizes the PU-GAN dataset, which consists of 147 3D models of various shapes collected from the PU-Net, MPU dataset, and Visionair library. The dataset includes a diverse range of representative 3D models, such as smooth models like polyhedrons and models with complex and intricate details like sculptures. This enhances the robustness of the experiments conducted in this paper. 120 point cloud models were randomly selected for training, while the remaining were used for testing. From each training point cloud, 200 patches were randomly cropped, resulting in 24,000 patches used for training.

Training Details: To enhance the robustness of the network, this paper applies rotation, scaling, and Gaussian noise perturbation to the input point sets. In all experiments conducted on the PyTorch platform, the training duration was set to 200 epochs, the batch size was 64, the initial learning rate of the Adam optimizer was 0.0001, with a decay rate of 0.9.

Evaluation Metrics: This paper adopts Chamfer Distance (CD), Hausdorff Distance (HD), and Point-to-Plane Distance (P2F) as evaluation metrics. For all metrics, smaller values indicate better result quality.

Results and Comparison: We conducted comparisons of our proposed method with PU-Net, MPU, PU-GAN, PU-GCN, PU-EVA, and APU. Training was carried out separately at 4x and 16x to ensure fairness, maintaining identical batch sizes, iteration counts, and learning rates. The comparative results are as follows:

(1) Upsampling evaluation metrics on the PU-GAN dataset are presented in Table 1.
(2) Specific metric changes in terms of CD and HD are illustrated in Fig. 4.
(3) Visualization of large-scale sampling factors is shown in Fig. 5.
(4) Visual comparisons with baseline experiments on the PU-GAN dataset are depicted in Fig. 6.

Our method consistently demonstrates outstanding performance across all scenarios. Additionally, Fig. 7 showcases a reconstruction example designed by us, including the input sparse point cloud, the dense point cloud upsampled using our method, and the three-dimensional model reconstructed using Poisson reconstruction.

Ablation Study: We conducted ablation experiments by removing the CD loss, removing the HD loss, and replacing the final features extracted from local spatial fields with features extracted by PointNet to verify the effectiveness of the method. Specific results are shown in Table 2.

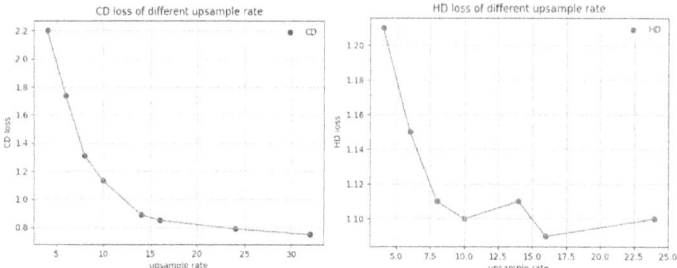

Fig. 4. CD and HD of differents upsample rate.

Fig. 5. Results of upsampling with a large scaling factor. From left to right, they are 8x upsampling, 16x upsampling, 32x upsampling, and 256x upsampling.

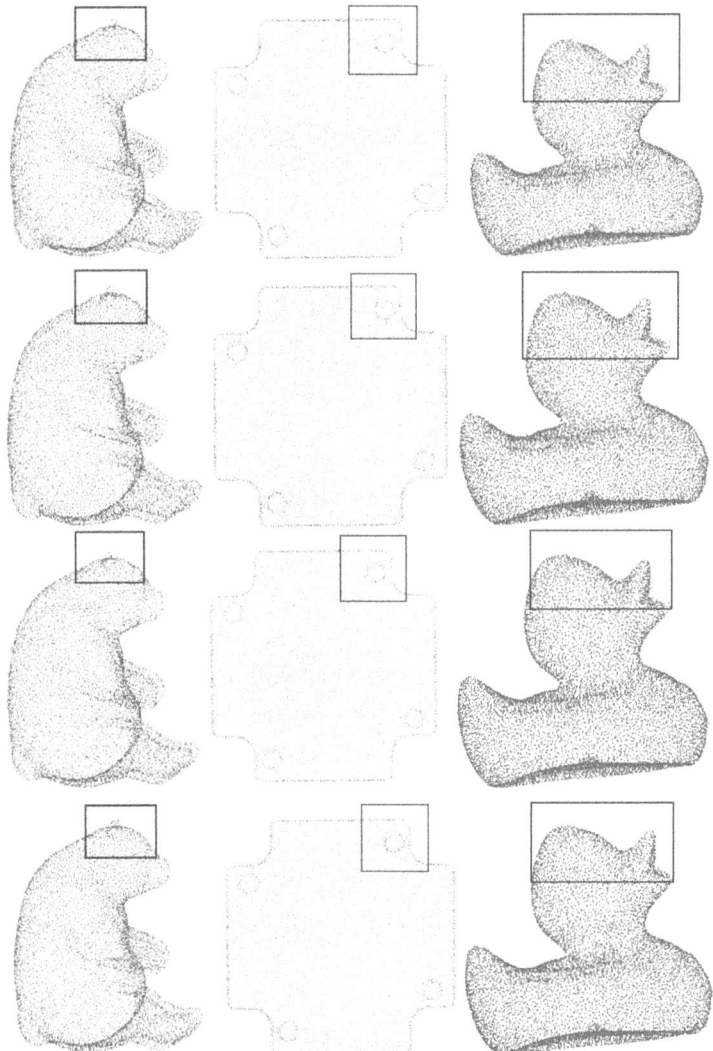

Fig. 6. Visualizing Experimental Results Comparison, The images from top to bottom are: PU-GCN, PU-EVA, APU and ours.

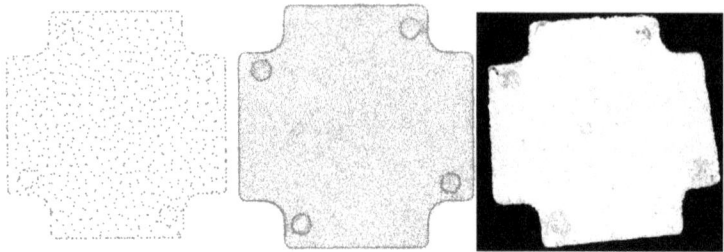

Fig. 7. One downstream application - Example of three-dimensional econstruction.

Table 1. Results and comparisons for 4 ×, 8 ×, and 16 × upsampling on PU-GAN dataset with supervised training.

Method	CD(r = 4)↓	HD(r = 4)↓	P2F(r = 4)↓	CD(r = 8)↓	HD(r = 8)↓	P2F(r = 8)↓	CD(r = 16)↓	HD(r = 16)↓	P2F(r = 16)↓
PU-Net[16]	4.04	3.53	12.74	3.97	3.26	9.92	3.98	3.03	8.92
MPU[14]	2.26	1.9	8.02	1.42	2.45	8.04	0.95	2.41	7.26
PU-GAN[10]	2.25	2.08	7.87	1.35	1.62	7.4	0.88	1.58	6.65
PU-GCN[24]	2.22	1.28	7.64	1.34	**1.11**	7.25	0.87	1.12	6.50
PU-EVA[12]	2.27	2.93	7.78	1.36	3.09	6.53	0.93	3.50	6.39
APU[26]	2.36	2.17	9.03	1.39	1.61	7.27	0.89	2.07	6.47
NePs[25]	2.49	2.39	**7.32**	1.52	2.31	7.14	0.94	2.43	6.52
Ours	**2.2**	**1.21**	**7.32**	**1.31**	**1.11**	**6.29**	**0.85**	**1.09**	**6.37**

Table 2. Results of the ablation study on PU-GAN dataset.

	CD↓	HD↓	P2F↓
w/o Lcd	2.37	1.42	8.68
w/o Lhd	2.25	1.81	7.94
w/o Fields	2.39	2.01	7.71
ours	**2.20**	**1.21**	**7.32**

4 Conclusion

This paper presents an innovative strategy for point cloud upsampling leveraging neural implicit functions, which possess the flexibility to handle arbitrary scaling factors. The methodology involves establishing bidirectional implicit functions that establish connections between the feature space and the implicit surface. This allows for the extraction of both high-level semantic features and low-dimensional geometric features from central points. Moreover, the process entails aggregating local spatial fields generated by each three-dimensional coordinate point, resulting in the derivation of a continuous and highly precise implicit spatial field of latent features.

Through random sampling within this spatial field, the method achieves point cloud densification across a spectrum of scaling factors. Experimental results provide compelling evidence of the robustness and generalization capabilities of our proposed approach. Consequently, our method emerges as a competitive alternative to existing state-of-the-art upsampling techniques.

References

1. Xiang, T., et al.: Walk in the cloud: Learning curves for point clouds shape analysis. In: Proceedings of the IEEE/CVF International Conference on Computer Vision, pp. 915–924 (2021)
2. Dai, P., et al.: Neural point cloud rendering via multi-plane projection. In: Proceedings of the IEEE/CVF Conference on Computer Vision and Pattern Recognition, pp. 7830–7839 (2020)
3. Hoppe, H., et al.: Surface reconstruction from unorganized points. Proceedings of the 19th Annual Conference on Computer Graphics and Interactive Techniques, pp. 71–78 (1992)
4. Kazhdan, M., Hoppe, H.: Screened poisson surface reconstruction[J]. ACM Trans. Graph. (ToG) **32**(3), 1–13 (2013)
5. Newcombe, R.A., et al.: Kinectfusion: real-time dense surface mapping and tracking. In: 2011 10th IEEE International Symposium on Mixed and Augmented Reality, pp. 127–136. IEEE (2011)
6. Held, R., et al.: 3D puppetry: a kinect-based interface for 3D animation. UIST. **12**, 423–434 (2012)
7. Santana, J.M., Wendel, J., Trujillo, A., et al.: Multimodal location based services—semantic 3D city data as virtual and augmented reality[C]//Progress in location-based services. Springer International Publishing **2017**, 329–353 (2016)
8. Lang, A.H., et al.: Pointpillars: fast encoders for object detection from point clouds. In: Proceedings of the IEEE/CVF Conference on Computer Vision and Pattern Recognition, pp. 12697–12705 (2019)
9. Wang, Y., et al.: Pseudo-lidar from visual depth estimation: Bridging the gap in 3D object detection for autonomous driving. In: Proceedings of the IEEE/CVF Conference on Computer Vision and Pattern Recognition, pp. 8445–8453 (2019)
10. Li, R., et al.: Pu-gan: a point cloud upsampling adversarial network. In: Proceedings of the IEEE/CVF International Conference on Computer Vision, pp. 7203–7212 (2019)
11. Li, R., et al.: Point cloud upsampling via disentangled refinement. In: Proceedings of the IEEE/CVF Conference on Computer Vision and Pattern Recognition, pp. 344–353 (2021)
12. Luo, L., et al.: Pu-eva: an edge-vector based approximation solution for flexible-scale point cloud upsampling. In: Proceedings of the IEEE/CVF International Conference on Computer Vision, pp. 16208–16217 (2021)
13. Qian, Y., Hou, J., Kwong, S., et al.: Deep magnification-flexible upsampling over 3d point clouds [J]. IEEE Trans. Image Process. **30**, 8354–8367 (2021)
14. Yifan, W., et al.: Patch-based progressive 3D point set upsampling. In: Proceedings of the IEEE/CVF Conference on Computer Vision and Pattern Recognition, pp. 5958–5967 (2019)
15. Ye, S., Chen, D., Han, S., et al.: Meta-PU: An arbitrary-scale upsampling network for point cloud [J]. IEEE Trans. Visual Comput. Graphics **28**(9), 3206–3218 (2021)

16. Yu, L., et al.: Pu-net: Point cloud upsampling network. In: Proceedings of the IEEE Conference on Computer Vision and Pattern Recognition, pp. 2790–2799 (2018)
17. Zhao, Y., Hui, L., Xie, J.: Sspu-net: Self-supervised point cloud upsampling via differentiable rendering. In: Proceedings of the 29th ACM International Conference on Multimedia, pp. 2214–2223 (2021)
18. Li, Y., et al.: Pointcnn: convolution on x-transformed points [J]. Adv. Neural Inf. Process. Syst. **31** (2018)
19. Wu, W., Qi, Z., Fuxin, L.: Pointconv: deep convolutional networks on 3D point clouds. In: Proceedings of the IEEE/CVF Conference on computer vision and pattern recognition, pp. 9621–9630 (2019)
20. Liu, Y., et al.: Relation-shape convolutional neural network for point cloud analysis. Proceedings of the IEEE/CVF Conference on Computer Vision and Pattern Recognition, pp. 8895–8904 (2019)
21. Maturana, D., Scherer, S.: Voxnet: a 3D convolutional neural network for real-time object recognition. In: 2015 IEEE/RSJ International Conference on Intelligent Robots and Systems (IROS), pp. 922–928. IEEE (2015)
22. Riegler, G., Osman Ulusoy, A., Geiger, A.: Octnet: learning deep 3D representations at high resolutions. In: Proceedings of the IEEE Conference on Computer Vision and Pattern Recognition, pp. 3577–3586 (2017)
23. Long, C., et al.: Pc2-pu: patch correlation and point correlation for effective point cloud upsampling. In: Proceedings of the 30th ACM International Conference on Multimedia, pp. 2191–2201 (2022)
24. Qian, G., et al.: Pu-gcn: point cloud upsampling using graph convolutional networks. In: Proceedings of the IEEE/CVF Conference on Computer Vision and Pattern Recognition, pp. 11683–11692 (2021)
25. Feng, W., et al.: Neural points: point cloud representation with neural fields for arbitrary upsampling. Proceedings of the IEEE/CVF Conference on Computer Vision and Pattern Recognition, pp. 18633–18642 (2022)
26. Dell'Eva, A., Orsingher, M., Bertozzi, M.: Arbitrary point cloud upsampling with spherical mixture of gaussians. In:2022 International Conference on 3D Vision (3DV), pp. 465–474 IEEE (2022)
27. He, Y., et al.: Grad-pu: arbitrary-scale point cloud upsampling via gradient descent with learned distance functions. Proceedings of the IEEE/CVF Conference on Computer Vision and Pattern Recognition, pp. 5354–5363 (2023)

Adaptive Non-local Means Filter Based on Multi-kernel for Complicated Noise

Qian long[1], Hongwei Qu[3(✉)], Yiping Wang[1], Gaihua Wang[1,2(✉)], and Bolun Zhu[1]

[1] College of Artificial Intelligence, Tianjin University of Science & Technology, Tianjin 300457, China
{longqian,wanggh}@tust.edu.cn
[2] Hubei Key Laboratory of Optical Information and Pattern Recognition, Wuhan Institute of Technology, Wuhan 430205, China
[3] Wuhan Electronic Information Institute, Wuhan 430019, China
394139525@qq.com

Abstract. In the paper, we propose a modified denoising filter based on multi-kernel for color images. To compare the similarity of patches, the patch standard deviation is taken to discriminate flat area and edges, which can capture local geometric structures. It gets rid of the effect of highly dissimilar image patches by setting the weights to zero. Then, we add multi-kernel weights to denoising filter. Different kernel parameters are used to remove complicated noise. The experimental results show that the proposed method has superior performance to existing approaches in terms of noise suppression and detail preservation, especially for the case of low signal-to-noise ratio (SNR). As our future research work, we intend to apply the method to speech and other intelligent recognition system.

Keywords: Non-local means · Multi-kernel · Gaussian noise · Adaptive filter

1 Introduction

Images are often corrupted by all kinds of noise. To remove noise and preserve the fine structures and textures, many approaches have been proposed, such as the total variation filter [1–3] and the wavelet filter [4]. However, these methods cannot be extended to color images. The vector median filter is a kind of traditional effective vector filter, which is used widely [5–7] to remove impulse noise. They have been developed with switching schemes [8–10] and detectors [11]. However, the effect is dropped dramatically with Gaussian noise.

Non-local means (NLM) [12], which operates on a non-local area, has attracted significant interest. Under the conditions of Gaussian noise contamination, the NLM filters outperform other classic filters. In [13, 14], it is an adaptive median filter based on NLM, which uses the piecewise function to compute weight. The paper [15] proposes modified NLM, which is based on unweighted Euclidean distance and integral image method, to denoise gravity datasets. The paper [16] makes full use of redundant texture and self-similarity of multidimensional data, which can obtain the estimated denoising result by the weighted average of pixels with similar neighborhood structures.

Above all these denoising methods can not consider texture feature effectively. When confronting with different level noise, the robust of these methods is worse. In this paper, we propose multi-kernel method to modify the NLM. First, we take a patch standard deviation to discriminate texture feature, and add weight strategic of similarity measure. Then we use the multi-kernel methods to remove the wide level noises. The proposed method is shown to have better performance than some popular methods through experiments.

2 Methodology

2.1 The Weight

For the NLM, weights of candidate patch are assigned solely based on similar measure between pixels, which may cause loss of fine structures and edge blurring. For example, suppose Fig. 1 (a) and (b) are neighbor patch window, and Fig. 1 (c) is central patch window. If only intensity similarity between corresponding pixels is considered, Fig. 1 (a) and (b) patch window have same weight for the NLM. But, in fact, Fig. 1 (a) has more similar property to Fig. 1 (c), and tends to edge area. To use local and non-local information, we add texture information to compare the similarity of patch image.

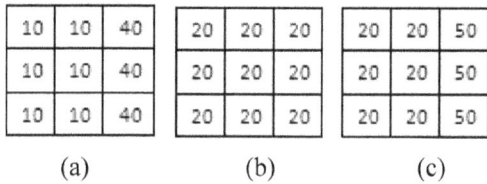

Fig. 1. The similarity properties of different patch windows

Given a patch standard deviation D. It is defined as.

$$D = \frac{1}{\sqrt{3S}} \sum_{s=0}^{S=1} \|f_p(x,y) - g_p\|_2 \tag{1}$$

Where g_p is the average of patch window, $f_p(x,y)$ is each pixel of patch window. It follows that the new weight of the NLM is.

$$w_0(x,y,x_0,y_0) = \exp\left(-\frac{(D_{x,y} - D_{x_0,y_0})^2}{h_3}\right) \tag{2}$$

where h_3 is a new parameter controlling the smooth degree.

Given thresholds T_1 and T_2, based on the idea of the paper [17], we are still setting the weights to zero when the Euclidean distances are quite large. It is expressed by.

$$w_0(x,y,x_0,y_0) = \begin{cases} 0, \text{ IF } \sum_{s_1,s_2 \in S} \|f_p(x+s_1,y+s_2) - f_p(x_0+s_1,y_0+s_2)\|_2 \geq T_1 \text{ and } (D_{x,y} - D_{x_0,y_0})^2 \geq T_2 \\ w_0(x,y,x_0,y_0), \text{ otherwise} \end{cases} \quad (3)$$

It reflects the dissimilar properties from two parts, dissimilar properties between pixels and dissimilar properties on texture.

2.2 Multi-kernel NLM

To compensate the weakness of the NLM in removing the complicated noises, we use multi-kernel filter based on the GNLMKIM [20]. The similarity between two image patches $f_p(x+s_1, y+s_2)$ and $f_p(x_0+s_1, y_0+s_2)$ is expressed by.

$$K_i = \exp\left(\frac{\sum_{s_1,s_2 \in S} \|f_p(x+s_1,y+s_2) - f_p(x_0+s_1,y_0+s_2)\|_{2,\alpha}^2}{h_i^2}\right) \quad (4)$$

where h_i are the kernel parameter ($h_1, h_2 \in h_i$). We modify the weight of the NLM by.

$$w_0(x,y,x_0,y_0) = \sum_{t=1}^{2} \widehat{\lambda}_t K_t + w_0(x,y,x_0,y_0) \quad (5)$$

where $\widehat{\lambda}_t$ is the parameter of penalty, computed as.

$$\widehat{\lambda}_t = \frac{\exp\left(\frac{1}{P} \sum_{i \in S \in j \in N} \sum K_t(X_i, X_j)\right)}{\exp\left(\frac{1}{P}\right)\left(\sum_{i \in S \in j \in N} \sum K_t(X_i, X_j)\right)} \quad (6)$$

where P is a non-negative parameter controlling the degree of penalty for the $\widehat{\lambda}_t$. The new filtering output is expressed by.

$$g_p(x_0,y_0) = \frac{1}{\sum_{j \in N} w(x,y,x_0,y_0)} \sum_{j \in N} w(x,y,x_0,y_0) f_p(x,y) \quad (7)$$

We set $h_1 = 10, h_2 = 15, h_3 = 50$. . The proposed modified non-local means based on multi-kernel (MKNLM) algorithm is described as follows.

> Input: The noisy image $f_p(x,y)$, with size of $H \times W \times 3$
> Output: The restored image $g_p(x,y)$
>
> 1: Initialize (searching window) $N = 7 \times 7$, (patch window) $S = 3 \times 3$, $h_1 = 10$, $h_2 = 15$, $h_3 = 50$
> 2: $D = \dfrac{1}{\sqrt{3s}} \sum\limits_{s=0}^{S-1} \left\| f_p(x,y) - g_p \right\|_2, f_p(x,y) \in PatchWindow$ (Compute the standard deviation of each patch window).
> 3: for $x = 1$ to H; $y = 1$ to W
> 4:   for Searching window $n = 1$ to N
> 5:   for Patch Window $s = 1$ to S
> 6:   Use (4) to compute K_i
> 7:   Use (6) to compute $\hat{\lambda}_t$
> 8:   end for
> 9:   Compute w_0, $w(x,y,x_0,y_0)$ according to (3) and (5)
> 10: end for
> 11: Use (7) to get the filtering value $g_p(x,y)$ of position (x_0, y_0)
> 12: end for
> Output: The restored image $g_p(x,y)$

3 Experiments and Results

3.1 Quantitative Comparison

To compare the performance of the proposed algorithm, the experiments are tested. The execution time (in seconds) running on a desktop PC with 2.50GHz CPU and 4.0G RAM is measured.

We also give a quantitative comparison between the pro-posed algorithm and the recently methods through Peak Signal-to-Noise Ratio (PSNR), normalized mean square error (NMSE), mean squared error (MSE) and structural similarity (SSIM). The MSE and NMSE are represented in pixels, and PSNR is represented in decibels (dB). In this experiment, the public color images are from Matlab 7.0 and the database "google thing". We use the "image1" with 203 × 162 and "image2" with 150 × 150 in "google_things" (Fig. 2).

The results of performance are shown in Tables 1–2, the color images are degraded by Gaussian noise with zero means and different deviation. As is shown in Tables 1–2, the proposed method outperforms NLM, Bilateral Filter (BILF), FDNLM and GNLMKIM. The BILF is a non-linear filter. In Table 1, the variance of Gaussian noise ranges from 0.01 to 0.05. Our method did not experience a significant decline. For variance 0.05, the PSNR is 24.0002. The performance of BILF is worst. For the NLM and GNLMKIM,

Fig.2. The original images: (a) "image1" (b) "image2"

they are effective at low noise level. When the variance is 0.05, the PSNR of NLM and GNLMKIM are 23.1770 and 23.1710. The FDNLM is mainly to denoise impulse noise and mixture noise. For Gaussian noise, the FDNLM is not better than the NLM.

3.2 Discussion

From experimental results, the NLM performs better than the BILF when the level of Gaussian noise increases. The FDNLM, GNLMKIM and the proposed method are modified methods based on the NLM. The GNLMKIM is a multi-kernel method that is more robust and effective in tackling complex problems than single-kernel ones. From Fig. 3, when the density of Gaussian noise increases from 0.01 to 0.03, the NLM has a better performance than BILF.

From Fig. 3, we can see that the similar neighbors in patch image are well identified and the weights are good enough to average the central pixel at low noise levels. The NLM and GNLMKIM can remove the low-level noise effectively. When noise is higher, the proposed method is best. Especially, the "image 1" in Fig. 3, when the noise level is higher, the performance of the proposed method doesn't drop dramatically. The robust of the proposed method is better.

Figure 4 shows the filtering outputs from "image1". Gaussian noise is added with mean of 0 and variance of 0.05. When the size of searching window is increasing, the blurring become more severe and the computational time is also increasing. For NLM, GNLMKIM and the proposed method, the size of the searching window is set to 7×7. And the size of the patch window is 3×3. For BILF, the filtering window is 3×3. For the FDNLM, the size of the searching window is 5×5 and the size of the patch window is 3×3. By comparing the result, it is obvious that the result of the BILF is bad, and the FDNLM is not effective to denoise Gaussian noise. The NLM, GNLMKIM and the proposed method have better results.

Table 1. Performance Comparison for the "image1" with different Gaussian noise

Noise Algorithms	Gaussian noise of mean 0 and variance 0.01					Gaussian noise of mean 0 and variance 0.02				
	PSNR	NMSE	MSE	SSIM	Time(s)	PSNR	NMSE	MSE	SSIM	Time(s)
NLM	25.4301	0.0066	186.2408	0.7379	11.45593	25.0926	0.0072	201.2910	0.7368	13.521567
BILF	22.0681	0.0144	403.8954	0.5841	**9.093267**	21.4976	0.0164	460.5993	0.5475	11.189882
FDNLM	24.3697	0.0085	237.7469	0.7228	12.86418	23.6930	0.0099	277.8306	0.6853	12.655751
GNLMKIM	25.4248	0.0066	186.4654	0.7437	9.956551	25.0819	0.0072	201.7876	0.7425	**10.474830**
MKNLM	**25.6321**	**0.0056**	**180.2258**	**0.7683**	11.73104	**25.3421**	**0.0062**	**190.1203**	**0.7522**	12.494737

Noise Algorithms	Gaussian noise of mean 0 and variance 0.03					Gaussian noise of mean 0 and variance 0.05				
	PSNR	NMSE	MSE	SSIM	Time(s)	PSNR	NMSE	MSE	SSIM	Time(s)
NLM	24.4861	0.0082	231.4592	0.7351	11.27403	23.1770	0.0111	312.8854	0.7306	11.523196
BILF	21.0864	0.0180 lePara>	506.3385	0.5135	22.03590	20.5120	0.0206	577.9309	0.4710	**8.9323334**
FDNLM	23.1144	0.0113	317.4252	0.6595	12.79744	22.0551	0.0144	404.1034	0.6019	13.178568
GNLMKIM	24.5859	0.0080	226.1989	0.7353	**9.709179**	23.1710	0.0111	313.3157	0.7341	10.110937
MKNLM	**25.0205**	**0.0070**	**217.8053**	**0.7517**	11.45487	**24.0020**	**0.0100**	**283.6257**	**0.7414**	11.873625

Table 2. Performance Comparison for the "image2" with different Gaussian noise

Noise Algorithms	Gaussian noise of mean 0 and variance 0.01					Gaussian noise of mean 0 and variance 0.02				
	PSNR	NMSE	MSE	SSIM	Time(s)	PSNR	NMSE	MSE	SSIM	Time(s)
NLM	27.1190	0.0078	126.2339	0.6890	7.65134	26.5247	0.0090	144.7470	0.6888	7.457209
BILF	24.8563	0.0132	212.5427	0.5849	**5.98015**	24.0521	0.0159	255.7824	0.5313	**6.011340**
FDNLM	26.8471	0.0083	134.3896	0.7060	8.72527	25.8025	0.0106	170.9352	0.6601	8.717982
GNLMKIM	27.1337	0.0078	125.8080	0.6863	6.56518	26.5494	0.0089	143.9279	0.6844	6.457455
MKNLM	**27.2863**	**0.0075**	**121.4639**	0.5970	7.69934	**26.6182**	**0.0088**	**141.6640**	**0.6897**	7.644170
Noise Algorithms	Gaussian noise of mean 0 and variance 0.03					Gaussian noise of mean 0 and variance 0.05				
	PSNR	NMSE	MSE	SSIM	Time(s)	PSNR	NMSE	MSE	SSIM	Time(s)
NLM	25.7482	0.0107	173.0848	0.6845	7.877205	23.7396	0.0171	274.8686	0.6839	7.608955
BILF	23.4217	0.0184	295.7384	0.4884	**6.149082**	22.5805	0.0223	358.9439	0.4308	**5.836560**
FDNLM	25.0970	0.0125	201.0842	0.6263	8.95965	23.3919	0.0185	297.7750	0.5386	8.592263
GNLMKIM	25.6979	0.0109	175.1037	0.6880	6.86835	23.7678	0.0169	273.0866	0.6786	6.588775
MKNLM	**25.8179**	**0.0106**	**170.3281**	**0.6935**	8.90800	**23.9617**	**0.0160**	**263.2485**	**0.6907**	7.589522

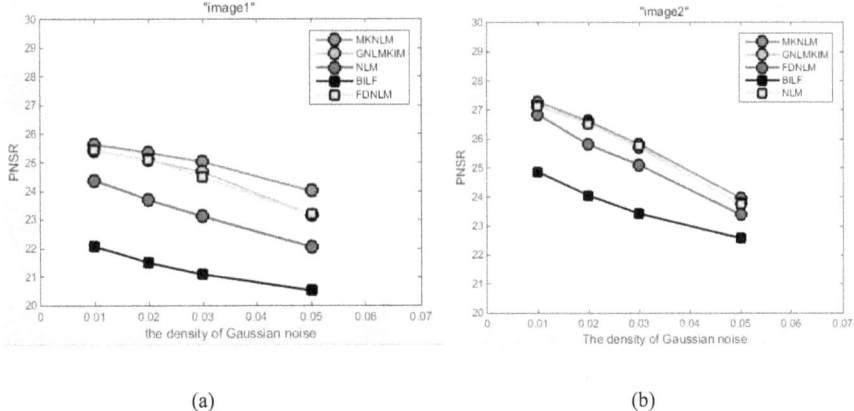

Fig.3. The results in PSNR (dB) from the different filters applied to the images: (a) PSNR for the "image1" (b) PSNR for the "image2"

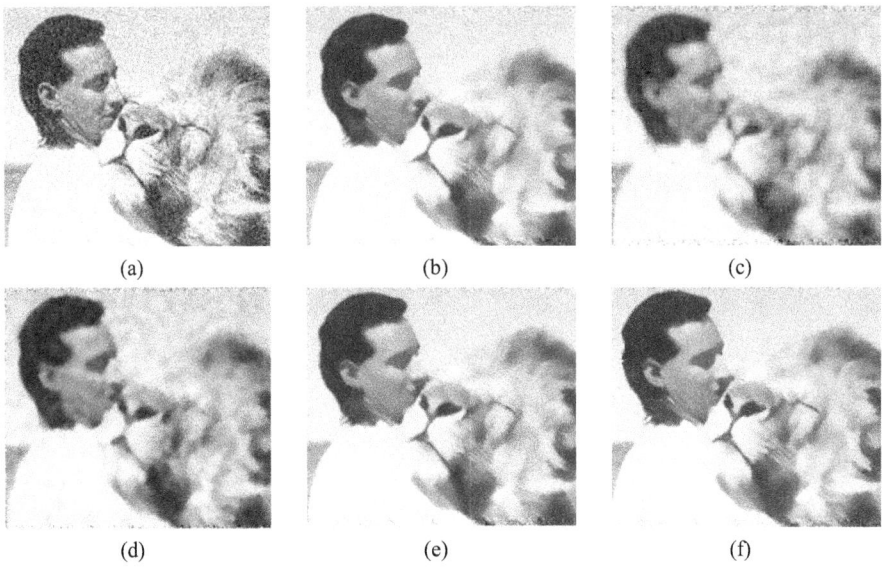

Fig.4. The output of "image1": (a) the "image1" with Gaussian noise of 0.05 variance (b) the output of NLM (c) the output of BILF (d) the output of FDNLM (e) the output of GNLMKIM (f) the output of the proposed algorithm

4 Conclusions

In this paper, we proposed a modified non-local means based on multi-kernel (MKNLM) filter for color image. Constructed by two individual kernel members, the multi-kernel methods can remove noises effectively. It calculates a weight by adding texture feature. And when the neighbor pixel is dissimilarity, the weight is set to zero. The proposed filter can remove Gaussian noise and preserve the image details effectively. Experimental results indicate that the proposed method has superior denoising performance to some classic filters. However, our method mainly aims to Gaussian noise. In the next work, we will further develop it to remove mixed noise and study its performance on real images.

Acknowledgments. This work is supported by the Open Foundation Project of Hubei Key Laboratory of Optical Information and Pattern Recognition, Wuhan Institute of Technology (grant No. 202306).

References

1. Srivastava, R., Gupta, J., Parthasarthy, H.: Comparison of PDE based and other techniques for speckle reduction from digitally reconstructed holographic images. Opt. Lasers Eng. **48**, 626–635 (2010)
2. Shih, Y., Rei, C., Wang, H.: A novel PDE based image restoration: convection diffusion equation for image denoising. J. Comput. Appl. Math. **231**, 771–779 (2009)
3. Liu, M., Vemuri, B.C., Deriche, R.: A robust variational approach for simultaneous smoothing and estimation of DTI. Neuro. Image **67**, 33–41 (2013)
4. Nowak, R.D.: Wavelet-based Rician noise removal for magnetic resonance imaging. IEEE Trans. Image Process. **10**(8), 1408–1419 (1999)
5. Astola, J., Haavisto, P., Neuvo, Y.: Vector median filters. Proc. IEEE **78**(4), 678–689 (1990)
6. Jin, L., Xiong, C., Li, D.: Adaptive center-weighted median filter. J. Huazhong Univ. Sci. Technol. **36**(8), 9–12 (2008)
7. Kang, C., Wang, W.: Fuzzy reasoning-based directional median filter design. Signal Process. **89**, 344–351 (2009)
8. Wang, G., et al.: Modified switching median filter for impulse noise removal. Signal Process. **90**(5), 3213–3218 (2010)
9. Chou, H., Hsu, L.: A noise-ranking switching filter for images with general fixed-value impulse noises. Signal Process. **106**, 198–208 (2015)
10. Wang, G., Liu, Y., Zhao, T.: Quaternion switching filter for suppression of impulse noise in color images. Signal Process. **102**(9), 216–225 (2014)
11. Luo, Z., Lu, P., Zhang, G.: Locally optimal detector design in impulsive noise with unknown distribution. EURASIP J. Adv. Signal Process. **2018**(1), 1–10 (2018). https://doi.org/10.1186/s13634-018-0560-x
12. Buades, A., Coll, B., Morel, J.M.: A review of image denoising algorithms with a new one. Multiscale Model. Simul. **2**(4), 490–530 (2005)
13. Sun, Z., Chen, S.: Modifying NLM to a universal filter. Opt. Commun. **285**, 4918–4926 (2012)
14. Zhang, X., Zhan, Y., et al.: Decision-based non-local means filter for removing impulse noise from digital images. Signal Process. **93**, 517–524 (2013)
15. Ai, H., Ahmad A., Ghanati, R.: Modified non-local means: a novel denoising approach to process gravity field data. Open Geosci. **15**(1), 20220551 (2022). https://doi.org/10.1515/geo-2022-0551
16. Li, J., Wang, Y., Xiao, L.: SNR enhancement with a non-local means image-denoising method for a Φ-OTDR system. Appl. Opt. **63**(9), 2283–2291 (2023)
17. Verma, R., Pandey, R.: Adaptive selection of search region for NLM based image denoising. Optik **147**, 151–162 (2017)

One-Stage Lightweight Network of Object Detection for Rectangular Panoramic Images

Yingying Lu[✉], Yun Tie, and Lin Qi

Zhengzhou University, Zhengzhou Henan 450000, China
luyingy2021@163.com

Abstract. Nowadays, object detection has developed rapidly and the application scenarios of panoramic image detection are increasing. Compared with ordinary images, panoramic images have a certain degree of distortion of the objects and the number of objects is greater. Therefore, the traditional target detection network designed for vanilla images will bring problems such as insufficient feature extraction and slow inference speed of object detection. In this paper, we proposed a one-stage detection network to solve the problems. First, we constructed the ELAN-P module with Partial Convolution (PConv) to reduce the computational complexity. Second, we introduced the bi-level attention mechanism Biformer into the network to improve the robustness of the detection network and better capture the distortion information. Finally, we made a panoramic dataset to train the detection model and evaluate the performance of the proposed model. The experiment results verified the effectiveness of our model compared to the popular networks.

Keywords: Object detection · Biformer · Partial Convolution · Panoramic images

1 Introduction

Currently, with the development of the high bandwidth and low latency with 5G, people have an increasing demand for wider image representation. The imperative of research based on panoramic videos has become increasingly pronounced. In daily life, panoramic video has made remarkable contributions in areas such as autonomous driving [1], VR [2], and video surveillance [3], leveraging its inherent advantages. As a fundamental task in computer vision, many researchers have begun to study object detection [4], semantic segmentation [5], and other basic tasks of image processing based on panoramic images. As shown in Fig. 1, the panoramic image contains more details and distorted parts compared to ordinary images, which greatly limits the application of target detection in panoramic images.

There are three difficulties that panoramic images face in object detection. First, the objects in panoramic images have various degrees of distortion to a certain extent, and the detection network's ability to recognize objects is weaker than that of conventional objects. Second, because the panoramic image includes all objects in the 360° angle of view, it makes the reasoning speed of the network correspondingly slow, the panoramic image needs a lighter network to improve the overall performance of the network. Third, the datasets of panoramic images with rectangular boxes are scarce, and it is necessary to build one.

Fig. 1. Comparison between panoramic and vanilla images.

To crack the above nuts, we are dedicated to researching a fast and accurate panoramic image object detection network based on YOLOv7 architecture which is initially used for object detection of vanilla images and is not suitable for panoramic images. The main contributions are as follows:

1. **Effective fine-grained feature extraction.** An attention mechanism, Biformer is introduced to the basic network, which enables part of the vital features of the distorted graphics to be extracted effectively. Additionally, Biformer balances efficient feature extraction ability with computational complexity due to the designed bi-level routing attention architecture.
2. **Lower computational complexity.** The ELAN-P module with Partial Convolution (PConv) is introduced into our model to reduce the calculation complexity of the reasoning process and speed up the inference time. As a result, our model achieves a balance between computational efficiency and inference speed through the distinct design of both Biformer and ELAN-P with PConv.
3. **Self-build panoramic dataset.** To fill up the absence of a panoramic image dataset and train as well as evaluate the detection models, we established a panoramic dataset, namely Panowe. Finally, we conducted extensive experiments on both the public dataset and the self-built panoramic dataset. The experimental results show that the proposed model has better performance on the public dataset and self-build dataset.

2 Relate Work

According to the characteristics of panoramic images, researchers have devised several object detection frameworks, which can primarily be categorized into three categories. One is mapping panoramic images to the sphere to better extract object features, the second approach puts the focus on image pre-processing, and the last is based on the traditional detection algorithm [6–8]. In this paper, we design the network based on traditional algorithms, focusing on attention mechanisms and lightweight aspects.

The core idea of the attention mechanism is to mimic the human visual system, capable of automatically focusing on important parts of information. Its key structures include modules for computing attention weights and mechanisms for reallocating resources based on these weights. The design and implementation of these structures are crucial for the performance of the model. Currently, research on attention mechanisms encompasses various aspects such as channel attention [9], spatial attention, mixed channel-spatial attention [10, 11], and self-attention. These studies continuously advance the theory and practical applications of attention mechanisms, demonstrating their outstanding performance in different tasks and domains. The Transformer [12] model employs the Self-Attention mechanism as its core component to enable direct interactions between different positions within a sequence. To elaborate, traditional Recurrent Neural Networks (RNNs) face the issue of long-term dependency when processing sequential data. This means that the computational complexity of interactions between distant elements in a sequence increases with the distance between them. The Transformer addresses this by incorporating the Self-Attention mechanism, which allows for direct interaction between any two elements in the sequence, regardless of the distance separating them. This design facilitates information propagation in a single step, unlike the sequential transmission in RNNs, effectively resolving the problem of long-term dependencies. [13] is a transformer-based architecture designed for image recognition tasks. It represents a significant departure from the traditional convolutional neural network (CNN) approach that has dominated computer vision for many years.

Lightweight networks have always been a hot topic in the field of image processing. They maintain high accuracy while reducing the demand for computational resources. By employing knowledge distillation [14] to eliminate redundant information and preserve key insights, large complex models are compressed into smaller versions. Some studies have designed more efficient network structures, such as using depthwise separable convolution [15] to reduce the number of parameters and computations. Reference [16, 17] redesigns network layers to lower complexity. Several mature lightweight network models are already available, such as SqueezeNet, ShuffleNet, and MobileNet. Through innovations in these algorithms [18, 19], significant improvements in lightweight performance can also be achieved.

3 Proposed Method

The overall structure of the proposed model is shown in Fig. 2. In the feature extraction part, to reduce the parameters, the ELAN-P module with partial convolution is introduced. In the feature fusion part, the attention mechanism Biformer is introduced to realize more flexible calculation allocation and content awareness, and the distorted object features can be extracted more effectively.

3.1 Fine-Grained Feature Extraction

Due to the distortion of the object existing in the panoramic image, the vanilla object detection network has shown unsatisfactory detection effectiveness. Traditional convolution does not have enough representation ability to extract useful information from raw panoramic images. Currently, the multi-head self-attention (MHSA) mechanism is used in object detection to enhance representation capability. Compared to the normal convolution, MHSA has higher computational and storage requirements. However, an explosive amount of computation is inevitable in such a network.

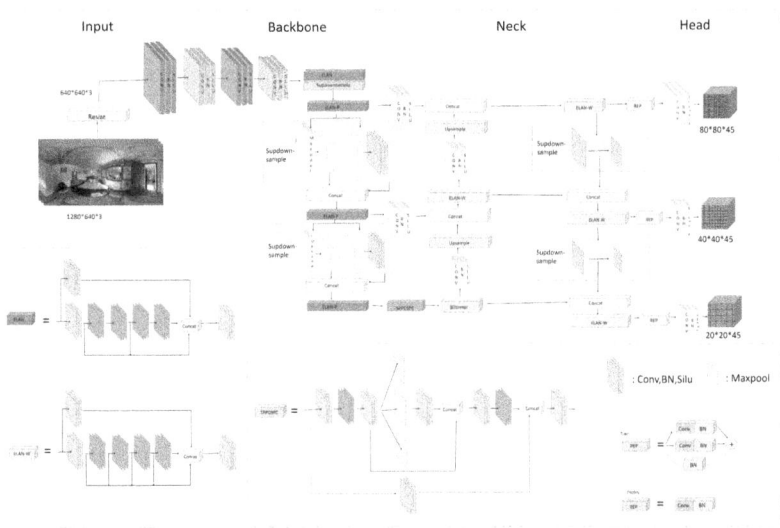

Fig. 2. The overall structure of the proposed model. The network includes three parts: backbone to extract the information, neck to fuse the information, and head to predict.

Therefore, inspired by MHSA, we introduce an effective module BiFormer to realize fine-grained feature extraction to maintain the feature extraction ability while accessing relatively little computation, which takes the feature representation capability and computation complexity into consideration. In particular, it adopts bi-level routing attention to speed up computation and employs a shortcut trick to maintain useful information.

To improve the feature extraction ability while accessing relatively little computation, a dynamic and query-aware sparse attention mechanism called BiFormer was introduced to our model. The fundamental concept of BiFormer is to filter out irrelevant key-value pairs at a coarse-grained region level, thereby retaining only a small subset that contains valuable information while eliminating redundancy. Additionally, BiFormer employs fine-grained token-to-token attention within these selected regions.

The structure of the BiFormer is shown in Fig. 3. It follows the common design of most vision transformer architectures, employing a four-level pyramid structure that achieves a downsampling factor of 32. In the first stage, BiFormer utilizes overlapping block embeddings, while in the second to fourth stages, block merging modules are employed to decrease the input spatial resolution while increasing the number of channels. Subsequently, a series of BiFormer blocks is used for feature transformation. Each Biformer block begins with a 3x3 depth-wise convolution to implicitly encode relative positional information. The BRA module and Multi-Layer Perceptron (MLP) module are then successively applied to the model positional relationships and embed information at each position. The most important construction of BiFormer is the BRA module. The BRA module includes the region-to-region routing step and token-to-token attention.

Equations (1), and (2) first calculate the semantic correlation between two regions and then filter out the most relevant regions. Among them, suppose that the feature map is divided into S*S non-overlapped regions. In the equation, $Q^r, K^r \in R^{S^2*C}, A^r \in R^{S^2*S^2}$. Equations (3), and (4) first gather the scattered key and value and then apply attention to the gathered key-value pairs. It collects key-value pairs from the top-k relevant windows and utilizes sparse operations to skip computations in the least relevant regions, thereby reducing parameter and computational costs. In the equation, $K^g, V^g \in R^{S^2*\frac{kHW}{S^2}*C}$, , LCE(V) [20] is used to enhance the local context.

$$A^r = Q^r(K^r)^T \qquad (1)$$

$$I^r = topkIndex(A^r) \qquad (2)$$

$$K^g = gather(K, I^r), V^g = gather(V, I^r) \qquad (3)$$

$$O = Attention(Q, K^g, V^g) + LCE(V) \qquad (4)$$

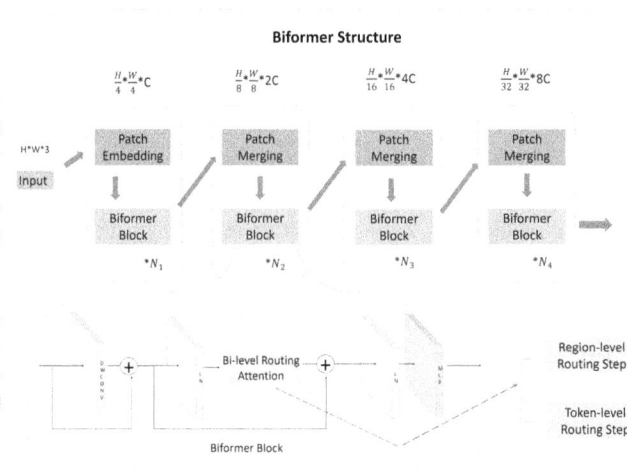

Fig. 3. The structure of the Biformer.

Due to the superior performance of the Biformer and the particularity of panoramic images, we introduced Bifomer into our module to improve the distortion characteristics feature extraction capability, and global dependency modeling capability.

3.2 Lightweight Operation

The task of object detection typically demands high real-time performance, particularly when applied to panoramic images, which encompass a 360-degree view of a scene.

Unlike standard images, panoramas inherently contain a greater number of objects, leading to an abundance of redundant information. Consequently, this results in excessive computations, leading to prolonged inference times and a reduction in the number of frames detected per second. Thus, the imperative arises to devise a lightweight network architecture to address this challenge.

Inspired by a novel technique called partial convolution in Faster Net, we reconstructed a module ELAN-P into our model. The introduction of the PConv addressed the issue of redundant computations and memory access while effectively extracting spatial features. PConv takes advantage of the high similarity among different channels in the feature map. It applies regular convolution selectively to a subset of input channels for spatial feature extraction while keeping the remaining channels unchanged. The structure of the PConv is shown on the right of Fig. 4. The researchers have found that the reduction in FLOPs does not always correspond to a proportional decrease in latency. This discrepancy primarily arises from the inefficiency of low-floating-point operations per second (FLOPS), which is caused by frequent memory access by operators. To facilitate contiguous or regular memory access, either the first or last contiguous channels are treated as representatives of the entire feature map during computation. Without loss of generality, it is assumed that the input and output feature maps have an equal number of channels. This approach greatly reduces the frequency of memory access by operators, resulting in faster and more efficient operation of neural networks. The FLOPs of a PConv are shown in Eq. (5), and the FLOPs of a Conv are shown in Eq. (6). The relationship between the c and c_p is shown in Eq. (7). We can see that the FLOPs of PConv are much less than Conv. Moreover, PConv demonstrates high efficacy in extracting spatial features.

$$FLOPs_{(Pconv)} = h*w*k^2*c_p^2 \tag{5}$$

$$FLOPs_{(Conv)} = h*w*k^2*c^2 \tag{6}$$

$$c_p = 1/4*c \tag{7}$$

Considering the above characteristics of PConv, we constructed the module ELAN-P. In the ELAN-P, the convolution of the residual branch remains unchanged and in the other branch, we changed four ordinary convolutions into PConv. The structure of the ELAN-P is shown on the left of Fig. 4.

3.3 Loss Function

In the process of backpropagation of the neural network, the loss function plays an important part in network adaptive parameter updating. The loss function of the model includes confidence loss, localization loss, and classification loss. The contribution to the network of the three is different and the weight allocation is shown in Eq. (8). In the equation, $Loss_{con}$ stands for the confidence loss, $Loss_{cla}$ stands for the classification loss, $Loss_{loc}$ stands for the localization loss, Among them, the loss of confidence and classification is calculated by binary cross-entropy with Eq. (9), where N represents the

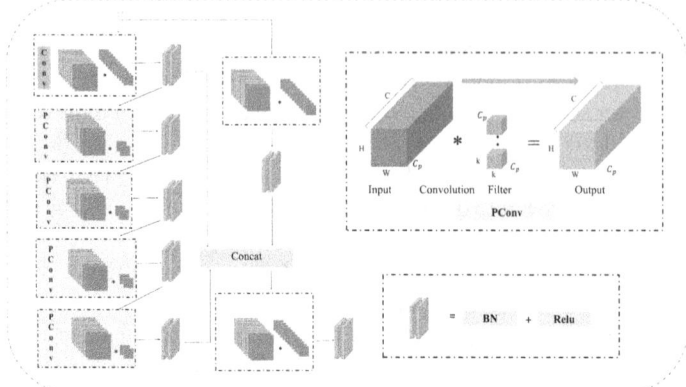

Fig. 4. The structure of the ELAN-P and PConv. The structure of ELAN-P is shown on the left, and the top right illustrates the convolution process of the PConv

categories, y_i is the binary label 0 or 1, and p_i is the probability that the output corresponds to the y label. The loss of localization is calculated by CIoU loss with Eq. (10), where IoU is used to measure the relevance between the prediction box and the real box, b and b^{gt} represents the center point of the prediction box and the real box respectively, and η represents the Euclidean distance between the two center points, c represents the diagonal length of the smallest external rectangle that can contain both the prediction box and the real box, α is the weight parameter, and υ is used to measure the consistency of the aspect ratio.

$$Loss_{total} = 0.1 * Loss_{con} + 0.125 * Loss_{cla} + 0.05 * Loss_{loc} \tag{8}$$

$$Loss = -\frac{1}{N}\sum_{i=1}^{N}[y_t log(p_t) + (1-y_i)log(1-p_i)] \tag{9}$$

$$L_{CIoU} = 1 - IoU + \frac{\eta^2(b, b^{gt})}{c^2} + \alpha\upsilon \tag{10}$$

4 Experiments

4.1 Implementation Details

The experimental setting is based on the Ubuntu20.04 platform, GTX1080Ti × 2 (12G) GPU, and Pytorch 1.10 library. In the training process, batch size and learning rate are set to 64 and 1e-3, respectively. Adam optimizer and weight decay are used for optimization. For experimental fairness and preciseness, the pre-trained strategy is employed in all models in this study.

To enhance the model's ability to swiftly learn the target features of objects within panoramic images, we adopted a transfer learning approach. Initially, we pre-trained the model on a publicly available dataset PASCAL VOC2007. Subsequently, since there is a large similarity in the information contained in the images. we employed this pre-trained model as the base for training on panoramic images.

4.2 Dataset

Due to the absence of a publicly available panoramic image object detection dataset, we created a self-built dataset named Panowe. This dataset is sourced from three primary origins: online searches, and images captured using KanDao four-eye and Teche six-eye cameras. The dataset includes images with three different resolutions: 9104x4552, 7680x3840, and 3840x1920.

To generate the panoramic images, the cameras were used to capture pictures from various angles. These images were then stitched together using KandaoStudio and TecheStudio software. Once the panoramic images were assembled, we used LabelImg to annotate them.

Panowe encompasses eight categories of objects found in both indoor and outdoor environments: person, chair, car, window, table, sofa, door, and bed, as illustrated in Fig. 5. The dataset consists of a total of 1,816 images, which were divided into training, validation, and test sets with a 7:2:1 ratio. This structured approach ensures a comprehensive and balanced dataset for developing and evaluating panoramic image object detection models.

Fig. 5. Panoramic images in the Panowe dataset.

In addition, the public dataset VOC2007 is also employed in this study to ensure experimental fairness and evaluate the generalization of the models. The VOC2007 dataset contains 20 categories, and all of them are representative targets in object detection.

4.3 Baselines

To demonstrate the enhancement of our proposed method, we selected the YOLOv7 series as our baseline and conducted a comparative analysis. As shown in Table 1, our model exhibits significant improvements over YOLOv7 on the VOC2007 dataset. Specifically, our model has 3.5% fewer parameters, 4.46% less computation, and achieves a 0.92% higher mean Average Precision (mAP). Similarly, Table 2 presents a comparative evaluation of the Panowe dataset, where our model again outperforms the baselines, showing 3.5% fewer parameters, 3.8% less computation, and a 0.72% higher mAP than YOLOv7.

These experimental results clearly demonstrate the superiority and robustness of our proposed model, which integrates Biformer and ELAN-P with the Pconv module. The consistent performance improvements across different datasets underscore the efficacy of our enhancements in reducing computational complexity while boosting accuracy.

Table 1. Comparison with Baselines YOLOV7 on the VOC2007 dataset.

Model	Params(M)	FLOPs (G)	Size	mAP
YOLOv7	37.2	105.3	640*640	0.871
YOLOv7-X	71.5	189.9	640*640	0.887
YOLOv7-tiny	6.2	3.5	640*640	0.598
YOLOv7-E6	97.4	516.3	640*640	0.921
YOLOv7-E6E	152.3	846.2	640*640	0.936
Ours	35.89	100.6	640*640	0.879

Table 2. Comparison with Baselines YOLOV7 on the Panowe dataset.

Model	Params(M)	FLOPs (G)	Size	mAP
YOLOv7	37.2	106.7	640*640	0.839
YOLOv7-X	71.5	192.9	640*640	0.856
YOLOv7-tiny	6.2	3.8	640*640	0.573
YOLOv7-E6	97.4	526.3	640*640	0.908
YOLOv7-E6E	152.3	853.2	640*640	0.916
Ours	35.89	102.6	640*640	0.845

4.4 Comparison Study

To demonstrate the algorithm's effectiveness and applicability, we trained and tested the network model on the public dataset PASCAL VOC2007. We compared our model with other object detection algorithms, the results are shown in Table 3. From the results, we can see that although our model is designed for the detection of panoramic images, it also has a good performance on the ordinary object detection task. The detection accuracy and detection speed all have improved.

Table 3. Comparison of the popular object detection algorithms on the VOC2007 dataset.

Model	Image size	mAP	FPS
YOLOv5s	640*640	0.842	40
YOLOv7	640*640	0.871	51
YOLOv8s	640*640	0.867	47
Faster R-CNN	1000 * 600	0.732	7
SSD	512 * 512	0.767	18
Ours	640*640	0.879	53

Then the transfer learning method is adopted on the model we trained on the PASCAL VOC2007 dataset, we used it as our pre-trained model and then trained the model on the self-collected dataset Panowe. The comparison test results are shown in Table 4. From the table, we can see that the model we proposed performs best.

Table 4. Comparison of the popular object detection algorithms on the Panowe dataset.

Model	Image size	mAP	FPS	person	car	chair	window	table	sofa	door	bed
YOLOv5s	640*640	0.827	37	0.867	0.873	0.838	0.801	0.795	0.799	0.812	0.831
YOLOv7	640*640	0.839	48	0.919	0.927	0.833	0.77	0.799	0.809	0.819	0.836
YOLOv8s	640*640	0.823	45	0.911	0.917	0.77	0.782	0.778	0.805	0.803	0.818
Faster R-CNN	1000*600	0.722	6	0.829	0.843	0.63	0.668	0.671	0.698	0.711	0.726
SSD	512*512	0.745	15	0.814	0.826	0.706	0.722	0.699	0.709	0.725	0.759
Ours	640*640	0.845	50	0.928	0.941	0.801	0.792	0.813	0.811	0.823	0.851

4.5 Ablation Study

To explore the impact of different modules on network performance, we conducted ablation experiments, with results shown in Table 5. The introduction of Biformer significantly enhanced the feature extraction capability for distorted objects, thanks to its Bi-level routing attention, which effectively captures fine-grained information. However, this improvement also increased parameters and computational load.

ELAN-P addresses this issue by reducing computational complexity and improving detection speed through efficient convolution, significantly minimizing redundant operations. Panoramic images contain substantial extraneous information, and using standard convolution leads to redundancy. While PConv alone can reduce redundancy, it risks ignoring important features, particularly edges and text of distorted objects. Biformer effectively resolves this issue by maintaining critical feature extraction without excessive computation.

Table 5. Ablation study on Panowe dataset[1] with Biformer and ELAN-P.

Model	mAP	FPS	FLOPs(G)	Params(M)
Baseline	0.839	48	107.3	37.25
Baseline + B	0.847 (+0.008)	45 (−3)	133.6 (+26.3)	46.3 (+9.05)
Baseline + P	0.838 (−0.001)	54 (+6)	86.1 (−21.2)	32.9 (4.35)
Baseline + B + P (Ours)	0.845 (+0.006)	50 (+2)	102.6 (−4.7)	35.89 (−1.36)

---

[1] B represents Biformer and P represents ELAN-P.

To explore the best way to construct ELAN-P so that the detector performance is optimal, we combine the general convolution with the partial convolution. The model structure and experimental results are shown in Table 6. Since the ELAN-P network has a residual network connection at the input side, the convolution collocation with the proper structure makes the network play a better performance. It can effectively reduce the number of network parameters and make the model lighter with little loss in accuracy. From the experimental results, it can also be analyzed that keeping the original convolution at the initial end of the network tends to make the network more stable.

Table 6. Ablation study on ELAN-P modules[2] with different distributions of PConv.

Convolution permutation	mAP	FPS	FLOPs(G)	Params(M)
PPPPP	0.813	60	70.3	30.7
CPPPP (Ours)	0.828	54	86.1	32.9
CCPPP	0.826	48	97.3	35.9
PPPCC	0.824	49	96.6	34.8
PPPPC	0.821	53	87.4	33.1

5 Conclusion

In this study, we address two key challenges in panoramic image object detection: distortion and network lightweighting. To enhance effective information capture and better handle distorted objects in panoramic images, we incorporated Biformer into our model. To reduce computational complexity and improve detection speed, we introduced the ELAN-P module, which significantly reduces redundant computations while maintaining exceptional detection performance.

We created a panoramic image dataset named Panowe to train our model effectively. We evaluated our model's detection capabilities against popular algorithms, and the results demonstrated superior performance. Additionally, ablation studies were conducted to assess the impact of the different modules in our network. The results confirmed that both modules effectively address the identified challenges.

References

1. Kinzig, C., Cortés, I., Fernández, C., Lauer, M.: Real-time seamless image stitching in autonomous driving. In: 2022 25th International Conference on Information Fusion (FUSION), pp. 1–8. IEEE (2022)
2. Nieto-Escamez, F., Cortés-Pérez, I., Obrero-Gaitán, E., Fusco, A.: Virtual reality applications in neurorehabilitation: Current panorama and challenges (2023)

---

[2] In the table, P represents PConv and C represents Conv.

3. Gao, J., Hu, Z., Bian, K., Mao, X., Song, L.: Aq360: Uav-aided air quality monitoring by 360-degree aerial panoramic images in urban areas. IEEE Internet Things J. **8**(1), 428–442 (2020)
4. Kashika, P., Venkatapur, R.B.: Deep learning technique for object detection from panoramic video frames. Int. J. Comput. Theory Eng. **14**(1), 20–26 (2022)
5. Orhan, S., Bastanlar, Y.: Semantic segmentation of outdoor panoramic images. SIViP **16**(3), 643–650 (2022)
6. Lee, Y., Jeong, J., Yun, J., Cho, W., Yoon, K.J.: Spherephd: Applying cnns on a spherical polyhedron representation of 360deg images. In: Proceedings of the IEEE/CVF Conference on Computer Vision and Pattern Recognition, pp. 9181–9189 (2019)
7. Cao, M., Ikehata, S., Aizawa, K.: Field-of-view iou for object detection in 360° images. IEEE Trans. Image Process. (2023)
8. Tateno, K., Navab, N., Tombari, F.: Distortion-aware convolutional filters for dense prediction in panoramic images. In: Proceedings of the European Conference on Computer Vision (ECCV), pp. 707–722 (2018)
9. Hu, J., Shen, L., Sun, G.: Squeeze-and-excitation networks. In: Proceedings of the IEEE Conference on Computer Vision and Pattern Recognition, pp. 7132–7141 (2018)
10. Woo, S., Park, J., Lee, J.Y., Kweon, I.S.: Cbam: convolutional block attention module. In: Proceedings of the European Conference on Computer Vision (ECCV), pp. 3–19 (2018)
11. Zhang, Q.L., Yang, Y.B.: Sa-net: shuffle attention for deep convolutional neural networks. In: ICASSP 2021–2021 IEEE International Conference on Acoustics, Speech and Signal Processing (ICASSP), pp. 2235–2239. IEEE (2021)
12. Ł., Polosukhin, I.: Attention is all you need. Advances in neural information processing systems 30 (2017)
13. Dosovitskiy, A., et al.: An image is worth 16x16 words: Transformers for image recognition at scale. arXiv preprint arXiv:2010.11929 (2020)
14. Yang, Z., Zeng, A., Li, Z., Zhang, T., Yuan, C., Li, Y.: From knowledge distillation to self-knowledge distillation: a unified approach with normalized loss and customized soft labels. In: Proceedings of the IEEE/CVF International Conference on Computer Vision, pp. 17185–17194 (2023)
15. Chollet, F.: Xception: deep learning with depthwise separable convolutions. In: Proceedings of the IEEE Conference on Computer Vision and Pattern Recognition, pp. 1251–1258 (2017)
16. Gu, M., et al.: A lightweight convolutional neural network hardware implementation for wearable heart rate anomaly detection. Comput. Biol. Med. **155**, 106623 (2023)
17. Zhang, D., et al.: An efficient lightweight convolutional neural network for industrial surface defect detection. Artif. Intell. Rev. **56**(9), 10651–10677 (2023)
18. Ullah, N., Khan, J.A., El-Sappagh, S., El-Rashidy, N., Khan, M.S.: A holistic approach to identify and classify covid-19 from chest radiographs, ecg, and ct-scan images using shufflenet convolutional neural network. Diagnostics **13**(1), 162 (2023)
19. Kaya, Y., Gürsoy, E.: A mobilenet-based cnn model with a novel fine-tuning mechanism for covid-19 infection detection. Soft. Comput. **27**(9), 5521–5535 (2023)
20. Ren, S., Zhou, D., He, S., Feng, J., Wang, X.: Shunted self-attention via multi-scale token aggregation. In: Proceedings of the IEEE/CVF Conference on Computer Vision and Pattern Recognition, pp. 10853–10862 (2022)
21. Zhu, L., Wang, X., Ke, Z., Zhang, W., Lau, R.W.: Biformer: Vision transformer with bi-level routing attention. In: Proceedings of the IEEE/CVF Conference on Computer Vision and Pattern Recognition, pp. 10323–10333 (2023)

ISE-UFDS: A Dataset for Detecting the Degree of Danger to Vehicles in Urban Flooding and Performance Assessment

Jiwu Sun[1], Cheng Zhang[1], Cheng Xu[1], Pengfei Wang[1,2], and Hongzhe Liu[1]($\boxtimes$)

[1] Beijing Key Laboratory of Information Service Engineering, Beijing Union University, Beijing, China
liuhongzhe@buu.edu.cn

[2] Big Data Center, Ministry of Emergency Management, Beijing, China

Abstract. As global warming and urbanisation continue to accelerate, resulting in the increasing likelihood and uncertainty of extreme rainstorms and floods, how to detect things in flooding scenarios and implement relevant rescue measures has become an urgent problem to be solved. Flooding scenarios are difficult and dangerous to obtain data, which leads to relatively few data sets dedicated to the detection of the degree of danger of vehicles in flooding scenarios. To this end, a dataset for vehicle hazard detection in urban flooding is proposed and the YOLOv8s algorithm is improved to increase the detection accuracy. The proposed dataset aims to provide realistic, diverse and challenging vehicle images in flooding scenarios, including different flood hazard scenarios and time periods. The dataset contains a total of 20,152 images, which are divided into training, validation and test sets in the ratio of 8: 1: 1 and evaluated and validated on the existing target detection algorithms. The authenticity and accuracy of the dataset is ensured by collecting data from real flooding sites.

Keywords: Vehicle Detection · Urban Waterlogging · Hazard Detection Dataset · YOLO · Performance Evaluation

1 Introduction

Several studies have shown that there is a complex interplay between urbanisation and flooding [1] With the acceleration of global warming and urbanisation, the likelihood and uncertainty of flooding triggered by extreme rainstorms is increasing [2]. Such disasters usually exhibit a chain development characteristic, where the initial heavy rainfall event may trigger a series of secondary disasters, such as ground subsidence, roadbed collapse, and house collapse, which further exacerbate the casualties and property losses, making the water safety situation in cities more complex and severe [3]. In flooded environments, roads and transport systems are often severely damaged, leading to disruption of traffic and rescue operations [4]. For example, in August 2023, Beijing, Tianjin, Hebei, Henan, and Shanxi were hit by frequent heavy rainstorms, which triggered frequent floods, posing a serious threat to the safety of people's lives and property and having a significant impact on the normal operation of cities [5]. In the process of coping with flooding, the rapid response of the rescue system and the effective execution of the rescue mission are crucial. Through in-depth research and development of advanced detection technologies, vehicle risks in flooding can be more accurately identified and assessed, thus providing timely and accurate information support for emergency decision-making, improving rescue efficiency, reducing casualties and property losses, and safeguarding the operational stability and safety of cities in the face of flooding [6].

However, current vehicle detection datasets generally suffer from insufficient coverage of flooding scenarios and lack of specialised design, which to a certain extent restricts the development and practical application of vehicle hazard detection algorithms in flooded environments. Existing datasets are usually based on conventional urban traffic environments, which cannot adequately simulate the environmental conditions and phenomena specific to flooding, such as water inundation, the refraction effect of light, and image blurring [7]. Therefore, in order to fill the gap of the vehicle hazard detection dataset in flooding scenarios and to promote the research and development of vehicle detection algorithms in this scenario, this paper proposes a dataset for the detection of vehicle hazards in urban flooding and applies a relevant target detection model to evaluate the performance of this dataset, aiming to provide a targeted data resource to support and optimise the development of vehicle detection technology in flooding environments, which in turn improves flood emergency response capability and public safety.

2 Related Works

Target detection is a key fundamental task in the field of deep learning computer vision and one of the hot topics in current academic research [8]. Its applications widely penetrate into many fields such as daily production and military, including important scenarios such as face recognition, aerospace, security and intelligent surveillance [9].

As a general tool for target detection, deep learning models show a wide range of application potential in vehicle detection tasks. For example, Zhang et al. [10] proposed an improved algorithm based on optimising the YOLO v5 network for the problem of misdetection or omission of vehicle targets due to occlusion, which is suitable for vehicle detection in various traffic scenarios.Dong et al. [11] were concerned about the problem of high computational load and low detection rate of YOLO v5, and their Neck network part of YOLO v5, introduced the C3Ghost and Ghost modules, aiming to reduce the floating-point operations in the feature channel fusion process, thus improving the feature representation performance and achieving more efficient vehicle detection. Pratama et al. [12] implemented real-time vehicle detection on the network by using the YOLOv8 algorithm, and their team constructed a large dataset of vehicle images for training the YOLOv8 model, to ensure that it is capable of recognising and track different types of vehicles.Chen et al. [13], on the other hand, proposed a modified SSD (single-shot multibox detector) algorithm, which is designed for fast vehicle detection in traffic scenarios, further improving detection speed and accuracy. These methods address specific problems in vehicle detection and provide more accurate and efficient solutions for vehicle detection in real traffic scenarios.

There are many datasets that can be used for vehicle detection. The COCO dataset is a large-scale dataset widely used for target detection, segmentation, and keypoint detection tasks, and it is one of the most influential and widely used datasets in the field of target detection [14]. Open Images contains more than 9 million images covering more than 60,000 different categories, and it provides an important resource for target detection algorithm research and evaluation [15]. The KITTI dataset is a widely used dataset for autonomous driving and computer vision research, containing data for tasks such as vehicle detection, target tracking, stereo vision, etc. [16]. The BDD100K dataset is a large-scale dataset for autonomous driving, containing high-definition images and videos from different cities [17]. These datasets provide specially designed images and annotation information for specific application scenarios and tasks, providing valuable benchmarks for related research work.

Numerous datasets and research works have emerged in the field of target detection, which provide rich content and standard references for algorithm training and performance evaluation. Due to the time-sensitive and potentially dangerous process of acquiring data in flooding scenarios, there is a lack of datasets in the field specifically designed for this scenario. Therefore, this paper proposes a dataset named Urban Flooding vehicle hazard Detection dataSet (ISE-UFDS), which is designed for vehicle hazard detection and risk assessment in flooding scenarios. In order to validate the effectiveness and practicality of the ISE-UFDS dataset, its performance will be evaluated by applying relevant detection algorithms in Chapter 4 of this paper.

3 Proposed Dataset

The proposed dataset implementation process is shown in Fig. 1.

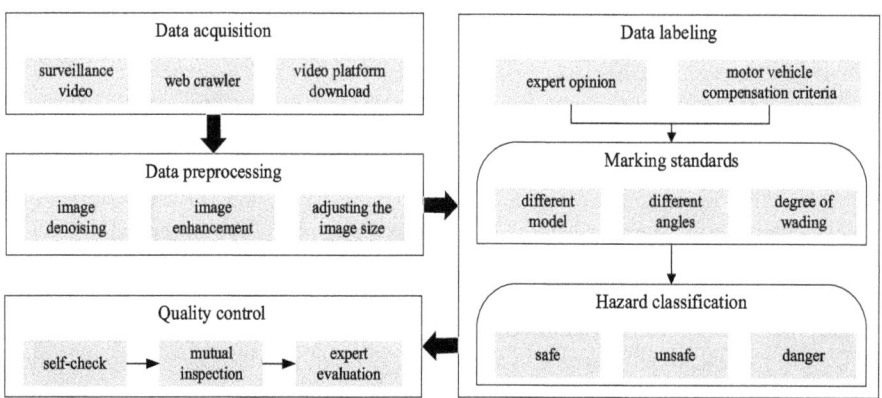

Fig. 1. Flow of dataset realization.

3.1 Data Acquisition

Given the difficulty in acquiring image data of flooded vehicles in flooding scenarios, the source data images in this study come from three main sources. Firstly, we use the road video monitoring privileges of the big data centre of the Ministry of Emergency Management and combine them with the national meteorological warning information to predict the areas where severe weather, such as heavy rainfall, is about to occur, so as to monitor and record the video in the areas where flooding or waterlogging of the roads is likely to occur. Secondly, we write Python crawler scripts to capture relevant video and image data on the web with the keywords of "urban flooding" and "flooded vehicles", and finally collect more than 10,000 images and 8G video clips. Finally, we also borrowed the videos of flooded vehicles taken by relevant bloggers on YouTube to supplement the data set moderately. Screenshots of some of the data clips are shown in Fig. 2, which were used as raw data for subsequent processing.

Fig. 2. Sample of some of the original images.

We decompose the acquired flood video data frame by frame, extracting one frame every 10 s, and then screen all the obtained image files to eliminate images that are too similar and irrelevant to the target to be detected. After the above operation screening, a total of 20, 152 images are retained for subsequent image annotation. At the same time, considering personal privacy issues, we blurred the positions involving faces and licence plate numbers before image annotation.

3.2 Hazard Classification and Data Labelling

Based on the compensation standards of some auto insurance companies for flooded vehicles, combined with professional knowledge of vehicle structures, and after consulting relevant experts and the Big Data Centre of the Ministry of Emergency Management, three labelling levels were developed for the vehicles targeted for detection in the dataset, using the side view perspective as an example:

(1) safe: A vehicle is considered to have no risk of flooding when the water level line is below the horizontal median line of the vehicle's wheel hub.
(2) unsafe: Vehicles are at risk of flooding when the water level line is above the median wheel level but still does not reach under the bonnet.
(3) danger: If the water line exceeds the bonnet of the vehicle, this indicates that flood water may have entered the engine of the vehicle and the vehicle is at serious risk of flooding and stalling.

Taking into account the differences in the water-wading capacity of different car models, the vehicles involved in this dataset were classified into three main categories: ordinary cars, sports cars (low chassis category) and SUVs (high chassis category). In addition, the labelling requirements were classified as side, front and rear of the vehicle according to the angle from which the vehicle enters the picture. The specific labelling requirements are described in detail in Table 1, including the labelling criteria and thresholds for each category of vehicle at different viewing angles.

Table 1. Dataset labelling requirements (based on water level line position)

	car side	car front	car rear
ordinary car	Lv. 1: wheel median Lv. 2: Above wheel median to below bonnet; Lv. 3: Above the bonnet	Lv. 1: below the lower edge of the body; Lv. 2: above the lower edge of the body to below the bonnet; Lv. 3: above the bonnet	Lv. 1: below the lower edge of the body; Lv. 2: above the lower edge of the body to below the upper edge of the for lights; Lv. 3: above the lower edge of the taillights
Sports car		Lv. 1: below the top edge of the licence plate frame; Lv. 2: above the top edge of the licence plate frame to below the bonnet; Lv. 3: above the bonnet	Lv. 1: below the lower edge of the licence plate frame Lv. 2: Above the lower edge of the licence plate frame to below the upper edge of the licence plate frame; Lv. 3: above the upper edge of the licence plate frame
SUV		Lv. 1: below the lower edge of the front end; Lv. 2: above the lower edge of the front end to below the bonnet; Lv. 3: above the bonnet	Lv. 1: below the lower edge of the vehicle body; Lv. 2: above the lower edge of the vehicle body to below the lower edge of the licence plate frame; Lv. 3: above the lower edge of the licence plate frame

Figure 3 provides a schematic representation of the labelling criteria for each type of vehicle at different angles, visually demonstrating how the type of labelling can be determined based on the position of the water level line relative to the critical parts of the vehicle.

Fig. 3. Schematic diagram of the labelling standards for different angles of various types of vehicles.

In this study, we adjusted the labelling for special cases for the dataset of vehicle detection in flooding scenarios. For example, in the case of a transient water level line elevation caused by splashing water when the vehicle is travelling fast, we determine the actual water level line of the vehicle based on its position that is not obscured by splashing water. For passenger cars and lorries with large differences in size and structure, we adjusted the labelling criteria and simplified it to two water level classes: safe and unsafe, without creating a hazard class. In addition, in order to enhance the generalisation ability and adaptability of the dataset, we retained some images with lower image quality or partial occlusion and made fine annotations. Such treatment makes the model better adaptable to complex and changing real-world application scenarios.

The data labelling exercise was carried out after the pre-processing of the dataset was completed. The proposed dataset is labelled using LabelImg tool and the information is saved in YOLO format. Some of the data labelling results are shown in Fig. 4 and the sample distribution is shown in Fig. 5.

Fig. 4. Partial data labelling results.

3.3 Quality Control

When the data completed the labelling work for the relevant experimental tests, it was found that the detection effect deviated from the expected effect. In order to ensure

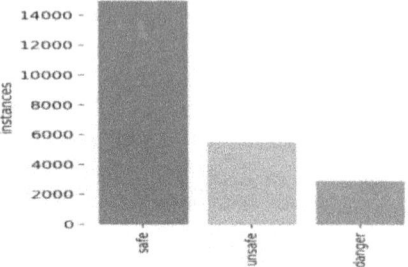

Fig. 5. Sample distribution.

the quality of the dataset annotation, the proposed dataset strictly adopts a three-step verification process for each annotation result:

Self-inspection by the annotator. The self-test can help the annotator to re-examine the results of his/her work, find deviations or errors, and correct the errors in advance to ensure the quality of the dataset.

Cross-checking between annotators. In the manual annotation work, the annotation results will often be affected by the subjective judgement of the annotator, in the cross-checking process, different annotators can check each other's errors, in order to reduce the impact of individual subjective judgement.

Validation by experts. By seeking experts in the relevant fields to evaluate the dataset, it helps to verify the validity of the dataset, and then the annotator modifies the annotation results based on the experts' opinions.

Through a careful review process, changes were made to some of the labelling results to ensure the quality of the labelling and consistency standards for this dataset, with an average improvement of 6.8 per cent in each metric compared to the initial experimental results.

4 Experiments

In order to verify the usability of the proposed dataset for the detection of vehicle hazard level in flooding scenarios, a more classical deep learning approach is used for evaluating the performance of the ISE-UFDS dataset [18]. All experiments were conducted utilizing an NVIDIA GeForce RTX 3090 GPU equipped with 24 GB of graphics memory for model training. The target detection models used were uniformly set to train for 200 epochs, with batch size set to 16, and were trained using the SGD optimiser with a learning rate of 0.001. The evaluation metrics used are precision (P), recall (R), F1-score, average accuracy (AP), and the mean of the AP of different categories of samples (mAP), which are calculated as shown in Eqs. (1)–(5), respectively.

$$Precision = \frac{TP}{TP+FP} \quad (1)$$

$$Recall = \frac{TP}{TP+FN} \quad (2)$$

$$F1 - score = 2 * \frac{P*R}{P+R} \quad (3)$$

$$AP = S_{P-R} \quad (4)$$

$$mAP = \frac{\sum_{i=1}^{k} AP_i}{k} \quad (5)$$

where TP, FP and FN denote true cases, false positive cases and false negative cases, respectively, S_{P-R} denotes the area represented under the PR curve, and k is the number of all detection classes.

In order to verify the performance of the ISE-UFDS dataset, it is applied to the current mainstream target detection network models to verify the validity of the dataset, respectively. In this paper, the proposed dataset is respectively applied to the more classical target detection networks for performance testing to verify the quality of the dataset. The experimental results of multiple network models are shown in Table 2.

Table 2. Experimental results of multiple network models

Model	P	R	F1-score	mAP
YOLOv5s	0.663	0.668	0.665	0.676
YOLOv5s-BiFPN [19]	0.67	0.685	0.677	0.712
YOLOv5s-GIoU [20]	0.649	0.689	0.668	0.718
YOLOv8s	0.653	0.671	0.662	0.68
Faster R-CNN [21]	0.69	0.732	0.710	0.782
Cascade R-CNN [22]	0.70	0.75	0.724	0.789
Mask R-CNN [23]	0.725	0.763	0.744	0.796

The analysis of the experimental results shows that by comparing the performance of several other mainstream target detection algorithms on the ISE-UFDS dataset, the single-stage algorithm is able to achieve a mAP result of more than 0.6 and the two-stage algorithm is able to achieve a mAP result of more than 0.7, which further highlights the fact that the specialised dataset proposed in this study can be used for the detection of the hazardous level of flooded vehicles by the classical target detection network. Combined with the problems of vehicle detection in flooding scenarios, such as varying scales and water occlusion, in the case of the YOLOv5 network, a simple improvement is made by adding the BiFPN module, which alleviates the problem of multi-scale detection, and the GIoU loss function, which helps to solve the problem of occlusion, to the YOLOv5s network, respectively, and it is found that the mAPs are both improved to a certain extent.

Considering the need for high real-time performance in flood search and rescue scenarios, we will focus on the faster YOLOv8s algorithm with higher detection accuracy to improve it in order to balance the speed and accuracy of detection. The main problems encountered in the detection of vehicles in flooding scenarios from surveillance videos are due to the degree of occlusion of the vehicle by the water body i.e. the depth of the flooded vehicle and the presence of multi-scale target detection. In order to solve the above problems, we add the Efficient Multiscale Attention Module (EMA) [24],

Lightweight Generalised Upsampling Operator (CARAFE) [25], Bidirectional Feature Pyramid Network (BiFPN) [19], and Spatial Depth Converted Convolution (SPDConv) [26] one by one to the YOLOv8 base network, and the improved network diagram is shown in Fig. 6.

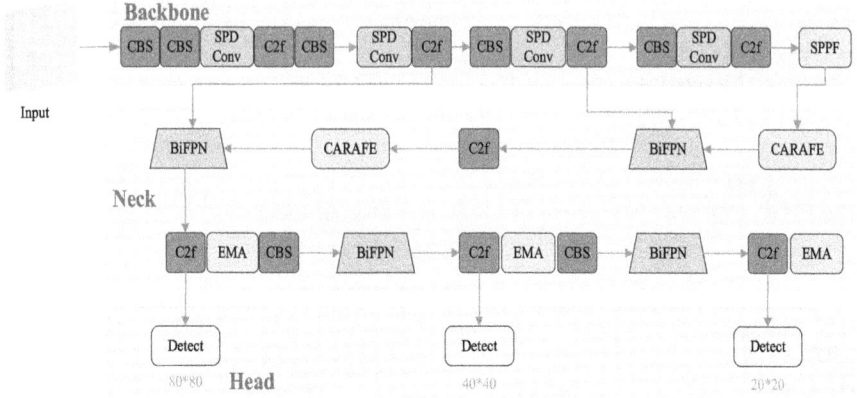

Fig. 6. Improved YOLOv8 network structure.

In this study, we adopt four key techniques to optimise vehicle detection in flooding scenarios: the EMA, CARAFE, BiFPN, and SPDConv. The EMA, as an attentional mechanism, is able to enhance the detection efficiency of small targets by optimising the information channel and reducing the computational overhead, especially when the target is partially occluded or of small size. The CARAFE, on the other hand, optimises feature continuity and detail through content aware up-sampling approach optimises the continuity and details of the features and improves the model's ability to distinguish between targets in complex environments. BiFPN, through its innovative feature fusion strategy, achieves an effective combination of features from different layers and enhances the model's ability to detect targets at different scales. Finally, SPDConv enhances the capture of spatial information by introducing spatial convolution, especially in the case where the target is partially occluded, to more accurately identify the edges and contours of the vehicle. Together, these techniques significantly improve the accuracy and efficiency of vehicle detection in flooding scenarios.

The results of the ablation experiments with the improved YOLOv8 model are shown in Table 3.

The baseline model YOLOv8s reached 0.68 in the mAP index. When we introduced EMA, the mAP was gradually increased to 0.689. Based on this, we introduced CARAFE, BiFPN and SPDConv one by one, and the mAP values were increased to 0.706, 0.694, and 0.724, respectively, which showed that each component had a positive effect. When we use the complete combination of EMA, CARAFE, BiFPN, and SPDConv, the mAP reaches up to 0.775, which is a 9.5% improvement compared to the baseline model.

Table 3. Ablation experiments with YOLOv8s as baseline

Method	EMA	CARAFE	BiFPN	SPDConv	mAP
Baseline	-	-	-	-	0.68
Ours	√	-	-	-	0.689
	√	√	-	-	0.706
	√	-	√	-	0.694
	√	-	-	√	0.724
	√	√	√	-	0.703
	√	-	√	√	0.741
	√	√	√	√	0.775

Through the above ablation experiments, we validate the effectiveness of each component in improving the performance of the flooded vehicle detection model and demonstrate their potential in improving the accuracy of vehicle detection in complex scenarios. These findings provide a valuable reference for designing more efficient deep learning models in similar tasks in the future.

5 Future Challenges and Work

The proposed dataset has shown significant results in the application of vehicle hazard detection in flooded environments, however, the following challenges and improvement directions are worth further exploration:

(1) Balance of labelling classification: During the actual data labelling process, it is found that there is a significant gap between the number of samples in the first category of "safe" and the number of samples in the third category of "dangerous". Therefore, efforts should be made to reduce the difference between the number of samples in each category in the follow-up work.

(2) Response to complex environmental factors: Flooding is often accompanied by severe weather conditions such as cloudy skies or heavy rain, which brings challenges to the detection of water-related vehicles. Issues such as visual perception in low-light environments need to be addressed when assessing the hazard level of a vehicle, as well as improving the recognition ability in cases where the target is partially or completely obscured.

(3) Limitations of data collection: due to the difficulty of acquiring video surveillance data on urban roads, the number of video surveillance videos collected where flooding occurs is still relatively limited. In order to further improve the generalisation performance of the vehicle target detection model, it is necessary to collect more diverse video surveillance data.

6 Conclusion

In this paper, we investigate the key challenges of vehicle detection in flooding scenarios and propose a targeted dataset for flooded vehicle hazard level detection, aiming to fill the gaps of existing datasets in this specific context. By introducing a new dataset and improving the YOLOv8s algorithm, we conduct a series of ablation experiments on our home-built flooded vehicle detection dataset to evaluate the impact of different network components such as EMA, CARAFE, BiFPN and SPDConv. The experimental results show that the gradual addition of these components significantly improves the detection accuracy of the model, with the complete combination of configurations achieving the highest mAP value of 0.775, a 9.5% improvement over the baseline model. This result not only confirms the effectiveness of the components in improving vehicle detection performance in flooding scenarios, but also demonstrates their potential to improve vehicle detection accuracy in complex environments. Future work will focus on further optimising the model architecture and expanding the dataset to improve the generalisation ability and usefulness of the model in more complex scenarios.

Acknowledgments. This study was funded by the National Natural Science Foundation of China (Grant No. 62171042, 62102033), the R&D Program of Beijing Municipal Education Commission (Grant No. KZ202211417048), the Project of Construction and Support for high-level Innovative Teams of Beijing Municipal Institutions(Grant No. BPHR20220121), the National Key R&D Program of China (2022YFC3090603), the Beijing Natural Science Foundation(Grant No. 4232026, 4242020), the Academic Research Projects of Beijing Union University(No.ZKZD202302).

References

1. Tonne, C., Adair, L., Adlakha, D., et al.: Defining pathways to healthy sustainable urban development. Environ. Int. **146**, 106236 (2021)
2. Xiaotao, C., et al.: Evolutionary characteristics of flood risk and urban resilience enhancement strategies in changing environments. J. Water Resour. **53** (07), 757–768+778 (2022)
3. Zongxue, X.U., Chenlei, Y.E., Ruting, L.I.A.O.: Collaborative management of urban floods: research progress and application cases. Adv. Earth Sci. **38**(11), 1107–1120 (2023)
4. Kumar, V., Sharma, K.V., Caloiero, T., et al.: Comprehensive overview of flood modeling approaches: a review of recent advances. Hydrology **10**(7), 141 (2023)
5. Prakash, C., Barthwal, A., Acharya, D.: FLOODWALL: a real-time flash flood monitoring and forecasting system using IoT. IEEE Sens. J. **23**(1), 787–799 (2022)
6. Guofu, Z., et al.: Modelling and solution methods for dynamic scheduling problem of repair teams in disaster-affected road networks. Comput. Eng. **49**(06), 300–313 (2023)
7. Alam, F., Alam, T., Hasan, M.A., et al.: MEDIC: a multi-task learning dataset for disaster image classification. Neural Comput. Appl. **35**(3), 2609–2632 (2023)
8. Zhang, Y., Zhang, H., Huang, Q., et al.: DsP-YOLO: an anchor-free network with DsPAN for small object detection of multiscale defects. Expert Syst. Appl. **241**, 122669 (2024)
9. Li, C., Qu, Z., Wang, S., et al.: A method of cross-layer fusion multi-object detection and recognition based on improved faster R-CNN model in complex traffic environment. Pattern Recogn. Lett. **145**, 127–134 (2021)
10. Zhang, Y., Guo, Z., Wu, J., et al.: Real-time vehicle detection based on improved yolo v5. Sustainability **14**(19), 12274 (2022)

11. Dong, X., Yan, S., Duan, C.: A lightweight vehicles detection network model based on YOLOv5. Eng. Appl. Artif. Intell. **113**, 104914 (2022)
12. Pratama, V., et al.: Car detection over network using Yolov8 in forza horizon 4. In: 2023 17th International Conference on Telecommunication Systems, Services, and Applications (TSSA), 1–5. IEEE, 2023
13. Chen, Z., Guo, H., Yang, J., et al.: Fast vehicle detection algorithm in traffic scene based on improved SSD. Measurement **201**, 111655 (2022)
14. Lin, T Y., et al.: Microsoft coco: common objects in context. In: Computer Vision–ECCV 2014: 13th European Conference, Zurich, Switzerland, September 6-12, 2014, Proceedings, Part V 13. Springer International Publishing, 2014: 740-755. https://doi.org/10.1007/978-3-319-10602-1_48
15. Kuznetsova, A., Rom, H., Alldrin, N., et al.: The open images dataset v4: unified image classification, object detection, and visual relationship detection at scale. Int. J. Comput. Vision **128**(7), 1956–1981 (2020)
16. Geiger, A., Lenz, P., Stiller, C., et al.: Vision meets robotics: the kitti dataset. Int. J. Robot. Res. **32**(11), 1231–1237 (2013)
17. Yu, F., et al. Bdd100k: A diverse driving dataset for heterogeneous multitask learning. In: Proceedings of the IEEE/CVF Conference on Computer Vision and Pattern Recognition, 2636–2645 (2020)
18. Weikun, L., Linhui, W., Dian, Z., et al.: Mars surface image segmentation dataset and performance evaluation. Comput. Eng. **49**(05), 262–268 (2023)
19. Tan, M., Pang, R., Le, Q V.: Efficientdet: scalable and efficient object detection. In: Proceedings of the IEEE/CVF Conference on Computer Vision and Pattern Recognition, 10781–10790 (2020)
20. Rezatofighi, H., et al.: Generalized intersection over union: a metric and a loss for bounding box regression. In: Proceedings of the IEEE/CVF Conference on Computer Vision and Pattern Recognition, 658–666 (2019)
21. Ren, S., et al.: Faster r-cnn: towards real-time object detection with region proposal networks. Adv. Neural Inf. Process. Syst. 28 (2015)
22. Cai, Z., Vasconcelos, N.: Cascade R-CNN: high quality object detection and instance segmentation. IEEE Trans. Pattern Anal. Mach. Intell. **43**(5), 1483–1498 (2019)
23. He, K., et al.: Mask r-cnn. In: Proceedings of the IEEE International Conference on Computer Vision, 2961–2969 (2017)
24. Ouyang, D., et al.: Efficient multi-scale attention module with cross-spatial learning. In: ICASSP 2023–2023 IEEE International Conference on Acoustics, Speech and Signal Processing (ICASSP), 1–5. IEEE, 2023
25. Wang, J., et al.: Carafe: Content-aware reassembly of features. In: Proceedings of the IEEE/CVF International Conference on Computer Vision, 3007–3016 (2019)
26. Sunkara, R., Luo, T.: No more strided convolutions or pooling: a new CNN building block for low-resolution images and small objects. In: Joint European Conference on Machine Learning and Knowledge Discovery in Databases. Cham: Springer Nature Switzerland, 443–459, (2022). https://doi.org/10.1007/978-3-031-26409-2_27

Convergence and Divergence: A New Paradigm for Pedestrian Detection

Yueyan Zhu[1], Hai Huang[1,2(✉)], Shan Yue[1], Shu Zhang[1], and Aoran Chen[1]

[1] School of Information and Communication Engineering, Beijing University of Posts and Telecommunications, Beijing 100876, China
huanghai@bupt.edu.cn
[2] Key Laboratory of Interactive Technology and Experience System, Ministry of Culture and Tourism, Beijing 100876, China

Abstract. Complex backgrounds, scale and occlusion variance have long limited the accuracy of pedestrian detection. In this paper, we propose a pedestrian detector named Convergence and Divergence (CADNet). In "Convergence" network, we propose a cross-scale semantic alignment block (CSAB). CSAB effectively mitigates the background interference and resolves scale variance through multi-scale global contexts aggregation, without extensive computational overhead. In "Divergence" network, we propose a receptive field differentiation block (RFDB) to tackle the challenges of scale and occlusion variance. RFDB generates discriminative features with varying receptive fields, effectively capturing pedestrians across different scales and occlusion conditions. Due to the effectiveness of the proposed components, CADNet achieves an excellent performance of 8.47% and 2.16% MR^{-2} on a Reasonable subset of CityPersons and Caltech, respectively. Extensive experiments demonstrate the robustness and efficiency of CADNet, ensuring its superior performance in various scenarios.

Keywords: Object Detection · Pedestrian Detection · Cross-scale Semantic Alignment · Receptive Field Differentiation

1 Introduction

Computer vision has traditionally struggled with pedestrian detection. In intelligent transportation, pedestrian detection serves as an initial step. Traditional methods, relying on hand-crafted features, struggle to accurately detect pedestrians. The introduction of convolutional neural networks (CNNs) has yielded significant advancements. However, there still remains scope for enhancement in pedestrian detection.

Pedestrian detection has encountered limitations due to complex backgrounds, scale variance and occlusion variance, as shown in Fig. 1. Firstly, the complex background hinders detectors from learning discriminative features. The diverse attire worn by pedestrians, coupled with the inconsistency of low-level features, like color and texture, renders

---

Y. Zhu, H. Huang and S. Yue—Contribute equally to this work.

the reliance on these features for detection problematic. The semantic feature of pedestrians is appearance shape. However, objects such as trees and signage often exhibit shapes similar to human body and can interfere with detectors. It is crucial to weaken the background while strengthening the pedestrian's features. Some researchers leverage semantic labels or vision-language semantics to alleviate interference from surrounding context (e.g., [6, 11]). Whereas, this approach necessitates manual labeling efforts and computational overhead. Secondly, scale variance leads to inconsistent feature representations, with small-scale pedestrians often appearing as rectangular contours, lack of specific details. While large-scale pedestrians exhibit distinct body structures, such as heads and limbs. Previous approaches, such as [4], attempt to enhance feature details for small-scale pedestrians through feature fusion or super-resolution. These methods can not effectively address the issue of feature discrepancies caused by scale variance. Moreover, occlusion variance intensifies the problem of inconsistent features. The shape of pedestrians is relatively uniform when unobstructed. Its width is about 0.41 times of height. Whereas, occlusion results in the invisibility of certain body structures, altering their aspect ratios. Although several studies (e.g., [9, 21]) try to tackle occlusion problem, they still face challenges of intra-class discrepancies among pedestrians in heterogeneous occlusion scenarios. The diverse scales and shapes contribute to intra-class discrepancies, leading to degradation in detector performance.

(a) Complex backgrounds   (b) Scale variance (c) Occlusion variance

Fig. 1. Examples of complex backgrounds, scale variance and occlusion variance. The area in the red box are objects that the detector tends to misrecognize.

In this paper, we propose a pedestrian detector, named convergence and divergence (CADNet). CADNet comprises 3 components, namely feature extract, feature convergence and feature divergence network. We use HRNet-W32 as the feature extraction network to enhance the feature details of small-scale pedestrians. For feature convergence network, we propose a cross-scale semantic alignment block (CSAB). Benefiting from recursive lightweight attention, CSAB effectively aggregates and reconfigures global contexts, thereby mitigating the interference of complex backgrounds without requiring semantic labeling or extensive computation. Natural images inherently exhibit cross-scale feature correlation. Leveraging this prior knowledge, CSAB expand the context from single scale to a multi-scale aspect through cross-scale feature-wise affinity. The established cross-scale convergence of features effectively addresses the scale variance issue. For feature divergence network, we propose a receptive field differentiation block (RFDB). Scale and occlusion discrepancy gives rise to diverse pedestrian patterns, necessitating the network to generate features that accurately capture these variations. RFDB generates a series of features with varying receptive fields by matching and combining multiple-branch convolutional layers, providing flexibility in receptive field shapes and diverse feature selection. Employing a two-layer and cross-branch design, RFDB enables feature reuse and multi-path fusion. Compared to traditional directly-connected multi-branch structure, RFDB achieves the same receptive field combinations with fewer model parameters and facilitates network learning.

Conclusively, this paper makes three contributions:

- We propose a cross-scale semantic alignment block (CSAB) to leverage dense contextual information across multiple scales and globally.
- We propose a receptive field differentiation block (RFDB) to generate a flexible and extensive feature selections to recognize pedestrians with intra-class disparities.
- Extensive experiments demonstrates that CADNet exhibits remarkable robustness and efficiency, ensuring its superior performance across various scenarios.

2 Related Work

2.1 Cross-Scale Visual Attention

Cross-scale visual attention has garnered significant attention across numerous study fields. CrossViT [1] comprises a dual-branch transformer that combines image patches of varying sizes to aid in the learning of multi-scale feature representations. CS-NL [15] is applied to image super resolution. It establishes a mapping between high and low resolution images through the inherent cross-scale feature correlation property in natural images. SMFE [20] introduces multi-scale deformable attention to pedestrian detection, aiming to explore its effectiveness in single-stage object detectors.

2.2 Adaptive Receptive Fields

There are two main approaches to form adaptive receptive fields, parallel multi-branch fusion and attention-based linear combination. RFBNet [12] uses multi-branch convolution to model the magnitude and eccentricity of RFs in human visual systems. SKNet [10], on the other hand, employs softmax attention to combine many branches with varied kernel size. This dynamic selection mechanism allows each neuron to modify its receptive field size based on various input information scales. ODConv [7] utilizes a multi-dimensional attention mechanism to learn a linear combination of convolutional kernels and weight them with input-dependent attention to expand the receptive field.

3 Method

3.1 Overview

The overall architecture of CADNet is illustrated in Fig. 2. CADNet comprises 3 components, feature extraction, feature convergence and feature divergence network. To effectively exploit the features of small-scale pedestrians, we employ HRNet-W32 [18] as the feature extract network. The 4 feature maps extracted from backbone are fed into the cross-scale semantic alignment block (CSAB). CSAB establishes feature correlations between multi-scale pedestrians and aggregates multi-scale contextual information through a cross-scale spatial attention mechanism. Processed by CSAB, the feature maps are concatenated for feature fusion. The fused feature map is then fed to the detection head. The detection head consists of three branches that predict the center, scale, and offset of pedestrians. The receptive field differentiation block (RFDB) is integrated in the center branch to facilitate locating pedestrians. During inference, the predictions of center, scale, and offset are combined to generate the detection results.

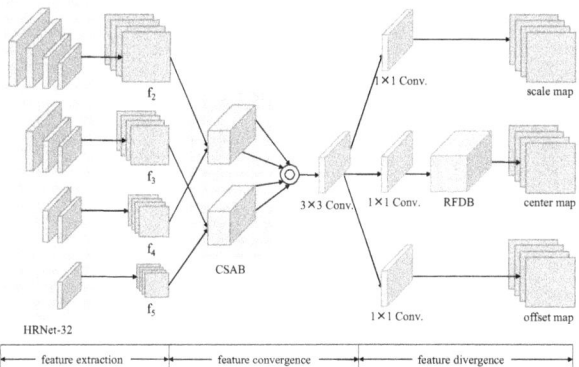

Fig. 2. The overall network architecture of CADNet.

3.2 Cross-Scale Semantic Alignment Block (CSAB)

The performance of pedestrian detectors is limited by the feature quality, both locally and globally. We propose a cross-scale semantic alignment block (CSAB) in the feature convergence network. The CSAB facilitates establishing feature correlations between cross-scale pedestrians and selectively integrates contexts based on a spatial attention map. Contexts and non-local features play a pivotal role in object detection, and CSAB extends their utilization to cross-scale, complementing non-local aggregation on the scale level. By effectively enhancing the feature self-similarity among multi-scale pedestrians, CSAB generates robust features to enhance the detector's performance.

Processing by the feature extraction network, 4 feature maps, denoted as f_2, f_3, f_4, and f_5 are output. The non-local computation [19], though effective, introduces space complexity due to dense feature sampling. To address this challenge, CADNet employs a two-by-two grouping strategy. Instead of performing simultaneous computations, it adopts a recursive sequential approach. This strategy forms two feature map pairs without concurrent computation, as illustrated in Fig. 3. Cross-scale attention is calculated between each pair of feature maps. During iter1, f_2 and f_3 form one pair, while f_4 and f_5 constitute another. This generates fused feature maps f_2' and f_3', f_4' and f_5'. In iter2, f_2' and f_5', with f_3' and f_4', are utilized as new pairs. This computation is conducted recursively, then outputs f_2'' and f_5'', f_3'' and f_4''. In iter3, f_2'' and f_4'' are paired together, while f_3'' and f_5'' form another pair, leading to the final output: $f_2''', f_3''', f_4''',$ and f_5'''.

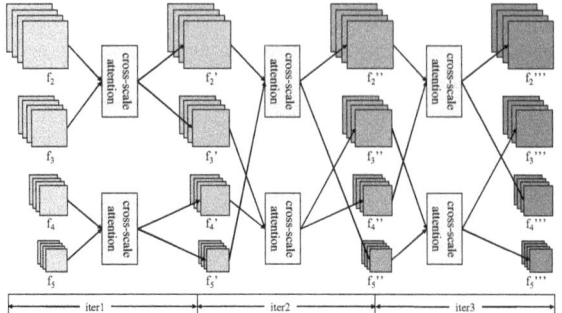

(a) The feature map grouping strategy during the 3 iters of CSAB.

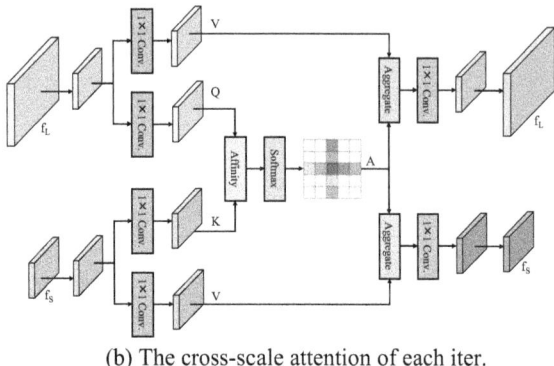

(b) The cross-scale attention of each iter.

Fig. 3. The network architecture of the cross-scale semantic alignment block (CSAB).

The cross-scale attention module is illustrated as Fig. 3. The large-scale feature map, denoted as f_L, serves as the query Q. The small-scale feature map, denoted as f_S, serves as the key K. Both feature maps are concurrently utilized as the value V. To enable affinity operations, the feature maps are resized by downsampling. Then, affinity is performed between Q and K to derive the attention map. A softmax layer is then applied to normalize the attention weights. This normalized attention map A is then used to guide feature aggregation with V. Then a 1×1 convolution is applied for feature reconfiguration. Afterward, f_L and f_S are reinstated to its original scales. Each attention computation focuses on aggregating contexts along criss-cross path, and through two recursive computations, contextual information is gathered for all pixels across the entire map [5]. This approach enables efficient aggregation of contextual information for each pixel across multiple scales while minimizing memory consumption.

After 3 iters, feature map $f_i \in \{f_2, f_3' f_4' f_5\}$ is semantically fused with other feature maps $\{f_j\} 5 \, j = 2, j \neq i$. This fusion ensures cross-scale information effectively integrated. For example, f_2 was fused with f_3 in iter1, and the output f_2' and f_3' both fused the contexts on the criss-cross paths of f_3. On this basis, f_3' was subjected to context aggregation with f_4' in iter2, and the output f_3'' and f_4'' still contain the contexts of f_3. Finally, f_2'' and f_4'' with f_3 features are computed in iter3, and a second recursive computation can aggregate the full context of f_3. The recursive pairwise computation allows the context of the initial feature map to pass along with the iterative computation, effectively generating a multi-scale attention pool. And it does not bring a large computational burden.

3.3 Receptive Field Differentiation Block (RFDB)

To mitigate the intra-class discrepancy caused by scale and occlusion variance, RFDB performs discriminative feature differentiation for pedestrians with various geometric structures. By matching and grouping, six convolutional branches with different receptive fields are formed. The advantage of RFDB is two-fold: 1) Constructing flexible receptive fields to extract pedestrian features of varying scales and occlusions. 2) Reusing shared features to jointly optimize parameters and save computational costs.

In RFDB, there are two stages of convolutional layers, as illustrated in Fig. 4. The multiplexing stage contains 2 branches, 3×1 and 5×3 general convolutions, respectively. A 1×1 convolutional layer is integrated to reduce the number of channels. The differentiation stage contains 3 branches of dilated convolutional layers. The convolutional kernels are 1×1, 3×3, and 3×3, and the dilation rates are set to 1×1, 2×1, and 3×1, respectively. The dilated convolution can be equivalent to a general convolution of size 1×1, 5×3, and 7×3, but with fewer parameters. The multiplexing stage generates two feature maps, which are fed to the differentiation stage to perform feature differentiation, ultimately generating 6 feature maps with heterogeneous receptive fields. The output 6 feature maps are concatenated and fed to 1×1 convolutional layer. A shortcut branch is added to facilitate gradient propagation. For computational simplicity, we replace large convolutions by stacking multiple small convolutions (e.g., 3×3).

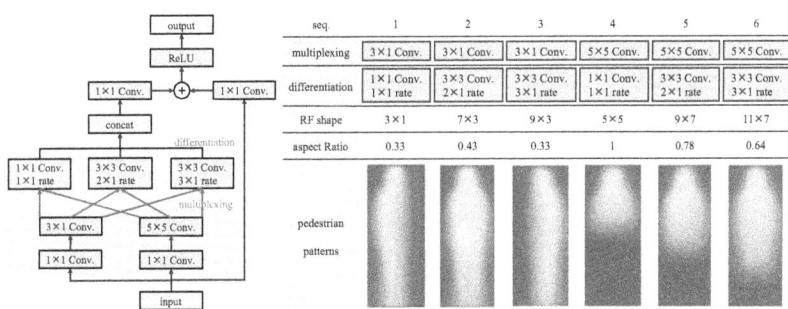

(a) The network architecture of RFDB. (b) The illustration of different receptive fields shapes.

Fig. 4. The network architecture of receptive field differentiation block (RFDB) and illustration of different receptive fields shapes. Pedestrian patterns are from the analysis of [22].

Based on statistics and analysis on pedestrian data [3, 22], it is known that about 80% of pedestrians have a maximum scale variance of 3 times. Having about 10 occlusion patterns, about 94% of pedestrians have aspects ratios from 0.3 to 1.0. By matching and combining the branches of the multiplexing and differentiation stages, we construct flexible convolutional combinations to generate receptive fields of various scales and aspects ratios, which are consistent with the scale and occlusion discrepancies of pedestrian data, as shown in the Fig. 4.

The multiplexing stage forms two shapes of receptive fields and generates reusable features for the differentiation stage. By effectively leveraging the output of the multiplexing stage, RFDB establishes a mechanism for information exchange and feature sharing, allowing for joint optimization of parameters. Typically, generating 6 parallel feature maps would necessitate 6 convolutional branches. While, RFDB's feature reuse mechanism enhances computational efficiency. By utilizing 3×3 general and dilated convolutions, RFDB only requires 6 convolutional layers to create 6 distinct receptive fields. In contrast, traditional multi-scale structure, for the same receptive fields, necessitates a six-way branching structure, totaling 18 layers of 3×3 convolution.

4 Experiments

4.1 Experiment Settings

Datasets. We evaluate CADNet on two datasets, Caltech [3] and CityPersons [22]. The Caltech dataset comprises approximately 10 h of video of urban scene. The frames of the video are partitioned into a training set, containing 42,500 images, and a validation set, including 4,024 images. The CityPersons dataset is a widely used benchmark. It includes 5,000 images captured from urban scenes, of which 2,975 images are allocated for training, 500 images for validation, and 1,525 images for testing.

Evaluation Metrics. We evaluate the performance using the evaluation criterion of Caltech evaluation measure [3], which is the log-average miss rate (MR-2) over false positive per image (FPPI) ranging from 10–2 to 100, denoted as MR-2. The lower MR-2 values indicate higher performance.

Implementation Details. For training, we employ the Adam optimizer, with β1 and β2 are set to 0.9 and 0.999. The initial learning rate is set to 1×10^{-4}. On Caltech, we use 8 NVIDIA A40 GPUs to train the network, with 16 images per GPU. Training is stopped after 10K iterations. On CityPersons, we use 2 NVIDIA A5000 GPUs, with 4 images per GPU. Training is stoped after 37.5K iterations.

4.2 Comparision with the State-Of-The-Art

CityPersons. We present the experimental results on CityPersons in Table 1. The results with best performance are highlighted in red. The results of the baseline method CSP are highlighted in green. CADNet achieves the outperformance in the Reasonable, Partial, and Small subsets. Compared to detectors designed for heavily occlusion, e.g., OAFNet, BGCNet, CADNet's performance in Heavy is impressive. Compared to VLPD and SOLIDER, CADNet does not leverage additional contextual and semantic labels. Compared to the baseline CSP, CADNet has performance improvement on all subsets, which demonstrates the effectiveness of CSAB and RFDB proposed. To visualize the performance of CADNet, we plot the detection results in Fig. 5 and compare them with CSP. It can be seen that CADNet has fewer false positives.

Caltech. We present the experimental results on Caltech, as shown in Table 2. The results with best performance are highlighted in red. The results of the baseline method CSP are highlighted in green. CADNet achieves MR-2 values of 2.16%, 51.47% and 38.31% on the Reasonable, All, and Occ subsets, respectively. CADNet outperforms existing methods in the Reasonable and All subsets. It performs slightly inferior to VLPD in the Occ subset, while VLPD leverages explicit semantic labels. Compared with baseline method CSP, CADNet achieves improvements in all subsets. The performance enhancement indicates that CADNet exhibits robust performance and the ability to facilitate detection in various scenarios.

Table 1. The performance comparison with other state-of-the-art methods on CityPersons dataset. Reason. is short for Reasonable. Med. is short for Medium.

Method	Backbone	Reason.	Heavy	Partial	Bare	Small	Med.	Large
FRCNN[22]	VGG-16	15.4	-	-	-	25.6	7.2	7.9
FRCNN+Seg[22]	VGG-16	14.8	-	-	-	22.6	6.7	8.0
OR-CNN[23]	VGG-16	12.8	-	-	-	-	-	-
TLL+MRF[16]	ResNet-50	14.4	52.0	15.9	9.2	-	-	-
ALFNet[13]	ResNet-50	12.0	51.9	11.4	8.4	19.0	5.7	6.6
CSP[14]	ResNet-50	11.0	49.3	10.4	7.3	16.0	3.7	6.5
BGCNet[8]	HRNet-W32	8.8	43.9	8.0	6.1	11.6	2.6	5.3
APD[21]	DLA-34	8.8	46.6	8.3	5.8	-	-	-
SMFE[20]	ResNet-50	10.9	38.6	-	-	-	-	-
OAFNet[9]	HRNet-W32	9.4	43.1	8.3	5.6	-	-	-
VLPD[11]	ResNet-50	9.4	43.1	8.8	6.1	-	-	-
SOLIDER[2]	Swin-B	9.7	39.4	-	-	-	-	-
CADNet(ours)	HRNet-W32	8.47	42.91	7.26	5.90	10.35	2.89	5.14

Table 2. The performance comparison with other state-of-the-art methods on Caltech dataset.

Method	Reasonable	All	Occ.
FRCNN[22]	8.7	62.6	53.1
OR-CNN[23]	4.1	58.8	45.0
ALFNet[13]	6.1	51.9	51.0
CSP[14]	4.5	56.9	45.8
BGCNet[8]	4.1	-	42.0
SMPD[6]	4.2	55.2	44.8
SMFE[20]	3.7	57.0	42.8
VLPD[11]	2.3	52.4	37.7
CADNet(ours)	2.16	51.47	38.31

4.3 Ablation Study

Component Evaluation. Ablation experiments are conducted on the CityPersons dataset to validate the component effectiveness. The experiments results are shown in Table 3. The optimal results are highlighted in red. The baseline uses ResNet-50 as the feature extraction network, and we replace with HRNet-W32. This improvement in performance is achieved on all 4 subsets. We integrate CSAB into the feature convergence network for cross-scale contextual semantic fusion. Experimental results show that CSAB reduces the MR^{-2} by 0.68%, 1.44%, 0.88%, and 0.32% in Reasonable, Heavy, Partial, and Bare subsets, respectively. It indicates the generality and effectiveness of CSAB. The introduction of RFDB enhances performance on all subsets. Especially on Heavy, RFDB brings significant improvement of 1.96% MR^{-2}. It demonstrates that RFDB effectively balances the intra-class variation caused by occlusion.

(a) CADNet (b) CSP

Fig. 5. The visualization of the detection results of CADNet and CSP.

Table 3. Ablation experiments on CityPersons dataset. Reason. is short for Reasonable.

Method	Backbone	CSAB	RFDB	Reason.	Heavy	Partial	Bare
Baseline	ResNet-50			10.90	48.73	10.15	7.22
CADNet	HRNet-W32			9.58	46.31	8.81	6.36
CADNet	HRNet-W32	✓		8.90	44.87	7.93	6.04
CADNet	HRNet-W32	✓	✓	8.47	42.91	7.26	5.90

Feature Map Grouping Strategy in CSAB. We explore the performance of different feature map grouping strategy in CSAB. Firstly, we evaluate the effectiveness of aggregating global contexts by performing criss-cross attention [5]. For this evaluation, we do not perform cross-scale operations, only single-scale self-attention. Experimental results are shown in the first row of Table 4, and "$f_i f_j$" indicates that f_i and f_j form a pair for contextual feature fusion, and (•) denotes one recursive iteration. Compared with baseline, the introduction of contexts brings performance improvement. Then, we evaluate the performance of cross-scale context fusion, as shown in Table 4. The experimental results show that in iter1, the optimal grouping is pairing f_2f_3 and f_4f_5. In iter2, the best configuration is grouping f_2f_5 and f_3f_4. In iter3, the best grouping is pairing f_2f_4 and f_3f_5. CADNet demonstrates performance enhancements on the Small and Reasonable, underscoring the significance of cross-scale contextual semantic fusion. Some of the grouping strategies fail to outperform, probably due to large gap of scale, which complicates feature similarity computation and hinders feature convergence.

Receptive Field Shapes in RFDB. To verify the effectiveness of RFDB, we conduct ablation experiments as shown in Table 5. Compared to RFB and P-RFB, which are also designed by the receptive fields concept, RFDB creates flexibility of receptive fields with less computation through the cross-combination of convolutional layers. The integration of RFDB achieves an MR^{-2} of 8.47% on Reasonable, also achieving excellent performance on other subsets. In contrast, RFB employs a square convolutional kernel and lacks a pedestrian-specific design, resulting in subpar performance. P-RFB falls short of RFDB in addressing heavily occluded pedestrians on Heavy subset. This may be because P-RFB's receptive fields adhere to a single aspect ratio, lack of diversity. These findings underscore the importance of flexible and comprehensive receptive field combinations in enhancing pedestrian detection performance.

Table 4. Ablation experiments of various grouping configurations in 3 iters.

Feature Map Pairs in 3 iters	Reasonable	Heavy	Small
$(f_2f_2, f_3f_3, f_4f_4, f_5f_5) \rightarrow (f_2f_2, f_3f_3, f_4f_4, f_5f_5)$	9.16	45.92	12.71
$(f_2f_5, f_3f_4) \rightarrow (f_2f_3, f_4f_5) \rightarrow (f_2f_4, f_3f_5)$	9.21	46.20	12.38
$(f_2f_5, f_3f_4) \rightarrow (f_2f_4, f_3f_5) \rightarrow (f_2f_3, f_4f_5)$	9.11	46.34	11.79
$(f_2f_4, f_3f_5) \rightarrow (f_2f_3, f_4f_5) \rightarrow (f_2f_5, f_3f_4)$	8.95	45.42	11.36
$(f_2f_4, f_3f_5) \rightarrow (f_2f_5, f_3f_4) \rightarrow (f_2f_3, f_4f_5)$	9.07	45.13	11.85
$(f_2f_3, f_4f_5) \rightarrow (f_2f_4, f_3f_5) \rightarrow (f_2f_5, f_3f_4)$	8.95	44.71	10.94
$(f_2f_3, f_4f_5) \rightarrow (f_2f_5, f_3f_4) \rightarrow (f_2f_4, f_3f_5)$	8.90	44.87	10.75

Table 5. Ablation experiments of receptive field shapes. Reason. is short for Reasonable.

Method	Receptive Field Shapes	Reason.	Heavy	Partial	Bare
RFB	(3×3),(9×9),(15×15)	8.65	43.85	7.62	5.95
P-RFB	(3×1),(7×3),(11×5)	8.53	44.36	7.43	6.01
RFDB(ours)	(3×1),(7×3),(9×3),(5×5),(9×7),(11×7)	8.47	42.91	7.26	5.90

5 Conclusion

In this paper, we introduce CADNet, a pedestrian detection method proposed to tackle the challenges posed by complex backgrounds, scale and occlusion variance. CADNet comprises 3 components: feature extraction, feature convergence, and feature divergence network. In the feature convergence network, we propose a cross-scale semantic alignment block, CSAB. This module aggregates contexts and non-local features across multi-scales, providing a comprehensive view for the detector. By establishing feature correlations, CSAB ensures feature consistency across scales. In the feature divergence network, we propose a receptive field differentiation block, RFDB. RFDB generates a series of feature maps with various receptive fields by combining multiple-branch convolutional layers. This module extracts diverse patterns to capture pedestrians of different scales and occlusion conditions. Extensive experiments conducted on the Caltech and CityPersons datasets demonstrate the robustness and effectiveness of CADNet.

Acknowledgments. This work was supported by the National Key R&D Program of China under Grant 2022YFF0904300.

References

1. Chen, C.F.R., Fan, Q., Panda, R.: Crossvit: cross-attention multi-scale vision transformer for image classification. In: ICCV, pp. 347–356 (2021)
2. Chen, W., et al.: Beyond appearance: a semantic controllable self-supervised learning frame work for human-centric visual tasks. In: CVPR, pp. 15050–15061 (2023)
3. Dollár, P., Wojek, C., Schiele, B., et al.: Pedestrian detection: an evaluation of the state of the art. IEEE Trans. Pattern Anal. Mach. Intell. **34**(4), 743–761 (2012)
4. Hsu, W.Y., Chen, P.C.: Pedestrian detection using stationary wavelet dilated residual super-resolution. IEEE Trans. Instrum. Meas. **71**, 1–11 (2022)
5. Huang, Z., et al.: Ccnet: criss-cross attention for semantic segmentation. In: ICCV, pp. 603–612 (2019)
6. Jiang, H., Liao, S., Li, J., et al.: Urban scene based semantical modulation for pedestrian detection. Neurocomputing **474**, 1–12 (2022)
7. Li, C., Zhou, A., Yao, A.: Omni-dimensional dynamic convolution. In: ICLR (2022)
8. Li, J., et al.: Box guided convolution for pedestrian detection. In: ACM MM, pp. 1615–1624 (2020)
9. Li, Q., Su, Y., Gao, Y., et al.: Oaf-net: an occlusion-aware anchor-free network for pedestrian detection in a crowd. IEEE Trans. Intell. Transp. Syst. **23**(11), 21291–21300 (2022)
10. Li, X., et al.: Selective kernel networks. In: CVPR, pp. 510–519 (2019)
11. Liu, M., et al.: Vlpd: context-aware pedestrian detection via vision-language semantic self-supervision. In: CVPR, pp. 6662–6671 (2023)
12. Liu, S., Huang, D., Wang, Y.: Receptive field block net for accurate and fast object detection. In: Ferrari, V., Hebert, M., Sminchisescu, C., Weiss, Y. (eds.) ECCV 2018. LNCS, vol. 11215, pp. 404–419. Springer, Cham (2018). https://doi.org/10.1007/978-3-030-01252-6_24
13. Liu, W., Liao, S., Weidong, H., Liang, X., Chen, X.: Learning efficient single-stage pedestrian detectors by asymptotic localization fitting. In: Ferrari, V., Hebert, M., Sminchisescu, C., Weiss, Y. (eds.) Computer Vision – ECCV 2018: 15th European Conference, Munich, Germany, September 8–14, 2018, Proceedings, Part XIV, pp. 643–659. Springer International Publishing, Cham (2018). https://doi.org/10.1007/978-3-030-01264-9_38

14. Liu, W., et al.: High-level semantic feature detection: a new perspective for pedestrian detection. In: CVPR, pp. 5182–5191 (2019)
15. Mei, Y., et al.: Image super-resolution with cross-scale non-local attention and exhaustive self-exemplars mining. In: CVPR, pp. 5689–5698 (2020)
16. Song, T., Sun, L., Xie, D., Sun, H., Shiliang, P.: Small-Scale Pedestrian Detection Based on Topological Line Localization and Temporal Feature Aggregation. In: Ferrari, V., Hebert, M., Sminchisescu, C., Weiss, Y. (eds.) Computer Vision – ECCV 2018: 15th European Conference, Munich, Germany, September 8–14, 2018, Proceedings, Part VII, pp. 554–569. Springer International Publishing, Cham (2018). https://doi.org/10.1007/978-3-030-01234-2_33
17. Tan, Y., et al.: Prf-ped: multi-scale pedestrian detector with prior-based receptive field. In: ICPR, pp. 6059–6064 (2020)
18. Wang, J., Sun, K., Cheng, T., et al.: Deep high-resolution representation learning for visual recognition. IEEE Trans. Pattern Anal. Mach. Intell. **43**, 3349–3364 (2021)
19. Wang, X., Girshick, R., Gupta, A., He, K.: Non-local neural networks. In: CVPR, pp. 7794–7803 (2018)
20. Yuan, J., Panagiotis, B., Stathaki, T.: Effectiveness of vision transformer for fast and accurate single-stage pedestrian detection. In: NIPS. (2022)
21. Zhang, J., Lin, L., Zhu, J., et al.: Attribute-aware pedestrian detection in a crowd. IEEE Trans. Multimedia **23**, 3085–3097 (2021)
22. Zhang, S., Benenson, R., Schiele, B.: Citypersons: a diverse dataset for pedestrian detection. In: CVPR, pp. 4457–4465 (2017)
23. Zhang, S., Wen, L., Bian, X., Lei, Z., Li, S.Z.: Occlusion-aware R-CNN: detecting pedestrians in a crowd. In: Ferrari, V., Hebert, M., Sminchisescu, C., Weiss, Y. (eds.) Computer Vision – ECCV 2018: 15th European Conference, Munich, Germany, September 8–14, 2018, Proceedings, Part III, pp. 657–674. Springer International Publishing, Cham (2018). https://doi.org/10.1007/978-3-030-01219-9_39

Improved YOLOv8-Based Lightweight Object Detection on Drone Images

Maoxiang Jiang, Zhanjun Si(✉), Ke Yang, and Yingxue Zhang

College of Artificial Intelligence, Tianjin University of Science and Technology, Tianjin 300457, China
szj@tust.edu.cn

Abstract. The target detection task of drones requires lightweight algorithms to fully utilize limited resources. Therefore, this paper proposes the YOLOv8-LD model. Firstly, propose the ASBiFPN neck network; Secondly, improve the detection head. Once again, introduce MPDIoU and improve the classification loss function to address the issue of imbalanced data samples. Finally, using pruning algorithms significantly reduces model volume. Improved YOLOv8-LD model in the VisDrone2019 dataset mAP@0.5 Improved by 21%. After pruning, compared with YOLOv8, the model parameters decreased by 81% and the volume decreased by 67%, mAP@0.5 increase by 3%.

Keywords: Object detection · Feature fusion · Pruning · YOLOv8

1 Introduction

In target detection tasks in drone scenarios, due to changes in viewpoint and height, the images in the scene contain the following features, there are many objects of different sizes, with small targets being the majority; The dense arrangement of objects; Lighting issues and complex background structures in images. The significance of the lightweight model is to enable UAVs to efficiently and effectively perform real-time multi-target detection, which is particularly important for missions such as aerial photography, surveillance and search and rescue [1]. A one-stage detector refers to predicting the position and category of the target directly from the input image, usually through dense anchor points or prior boxes for object detection. The advantage of one-stage detectors lies in real-time performance. Alam et al. [2] shift computational tasks from embedded processors to the cloud, alleviating computational pressure. Zhu et al. [3] proposed the TPH-YOLOv5 algorithm. Shao Y et al. [4] proposed target detection of UAV aerial images based on Aero-YOLO. Modern drones are equipped with high-performance processors with abundant computing resources, which deploy YOLO based object detection algorithms for real-time detection, recognition, and classification of task targets when the drone collects data. Even high-performance processors have inherent limitations, especially in terms of resource availability.

2 The Proposed Algorithm

2.1 YOLOv8-LD

This study chose YOLOv8 as the benchmark model. YOLOv8 is the latest version of the YOLO series algorithm. This paper proposes a lightweight object detection algorithm YOLOv8-LD (YOLOv8 Lightweight Target Detection Algorithm in UAV Scene) network for unmanned aerial vehicle scenarios, as shown in Fig. 1.

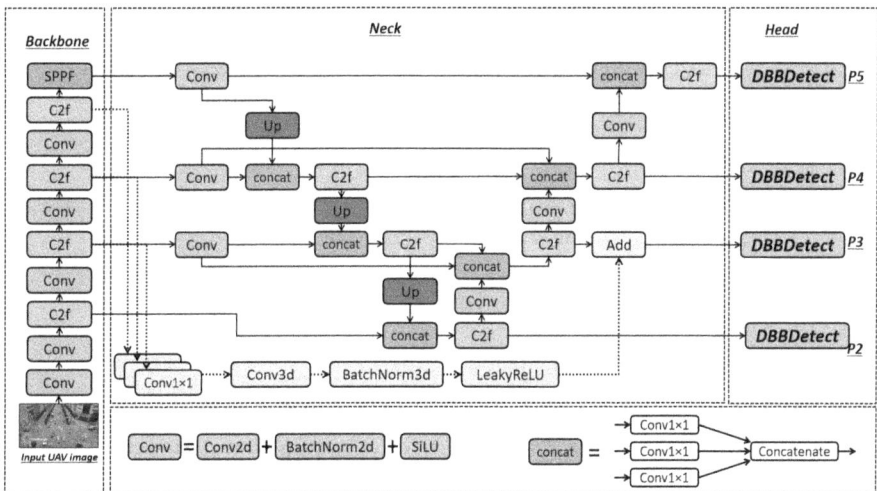

Fig. 1. Network chart of YOLOv8-LD

2.2 Improvement of the Neck Network

After passing through the backbone network, low-level features contain more positional and detailed information, while higher-level features have stronger linguistic information. How to further process and optimize features at different levels is crucial. In paper [5], different popular neck structures are described, as shown in Fig. 2. (a), (b), and (c).

Inspired by the neck network design of BiFPN and ASF-YOLO [6], We propose the ASBiFPN (A Specialized Shape Bidirectional Feature Pyramid Network for Small Target Detection) neck network structure, as shown in Fig. 2. (d) shown. We add detection heads for small targets in ASBiFPN. P4 and P5 are converted to channel number by 1 × 1 convolution, resized to the same size as P3 using interpolation operation, and spliced in the P3 dimension. The new feature maps are processed by passing them sequentially through 3D convolution, batch normalization layer and activation function, downscaled by 3D maximum pooling layer, compressed in the second dimension, and finally superimposed with the P3 detection layer. This approach exploits the application of 3D convolution in feature fusion in the target detection task, where the fused features can act directly on the P3 detection head by superimposing low-level features with semantic information and high-level features with more spatial information. The structure of the feature connection method used in this paper is shown as concat in Fig. 1. The feature mapping is added directly to the spatial and channel dimensions, which helps in the detection of small targets.

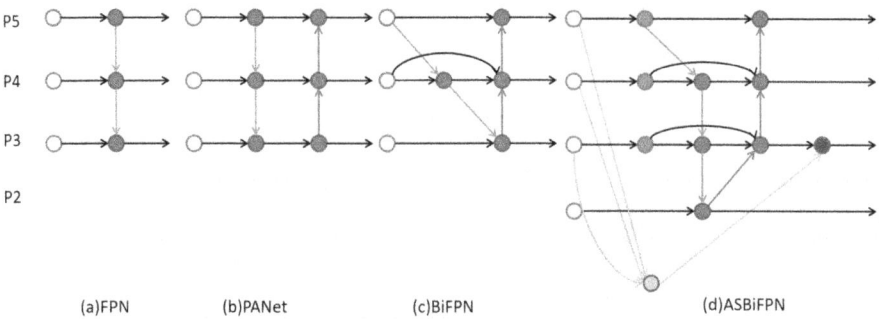

Fig. 2. Feature fusion method

2.3 Improved Detection Head

To improve the performance of convolutional neural networks, DBB convolution is introduced to form the DBBDetect module, as shown in Fig. 3. DBB(Diverse Branch Block) [7] module uses a structure-heavy parameterized design with a multi-branch topology, where each branch mainly consists of a 1 × 1 convolution, a 3 × 3 convolution, an average pooling (AVG), and a bulk normalization (BN) layer. The expressive power of a single convolution is enhanced by combining branches of different sizes and complexity (including tandem convolution, multi-scale convolution, and average pooling layers).

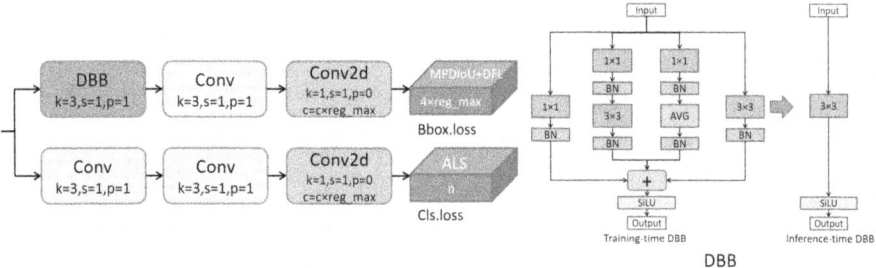

Fig. 3. DBBDetect

2.4 Improvement of the Loss Function

In target detection tasks in drone scenarios, difficult samples are relatively sparse, and samples near the boundaries often suffer significant losses. Reference [8] proposed Slide-Loss to solve this problem. Samples with values less than µ are assigned a negative label, while those with values greater than µ are assigned a positive label, as shown in Fig. 4.

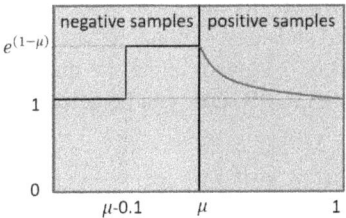

Fig. 4. Slide Loss

In order to enable the model to fully utilize the samples, EMA is introduced to solve the problem. EMA can adaptively adjust weights to better reflect trends. Calculate the exponential moving average of IOU values to smooth out changes in IOU, and then calculate adjustment weights to adjust losses based on different ranges of IOU values, forming the ASL (Average Sliding Loss) in this paper as follows:

$$new\alpha = init\alpha * \left(1 - e^{-\frac{updates}{2000}}\right) \quad (1)$$

$$\lambda = \alpha\lambda + (1 - \alpha)float(\mu.d) \quad (2)$$

$$\mu = \lambda \quad (3)$$

where (1) is the formula for the exponentially varying weighting α. µ.d denotes the detach operation on µ. The parameters as well as the current model parameters are weighted and summed by Eq. (2), and assigned to µ by Eq. (3).

In paper [9], MPDIoU includes all the factors that need to be considered in the loss function, namely overlapping or non overlapping regions, centroid distance, and width height deviation, while simplifying the calculation process. The formula is as follows:

$$d_1^2 = \left(x_1^B - x_1^A\right)^2 + \left(y_1^B - y_1^A\right)^2 \quad (4)$$

$$d_2^2 = \left(x_2^B - x_2^A\right)^2 + \left(y_2^B - y_2^A\right)^2 \quad (5)$$

$$MPDIoU = \frac{A \cap B}{A \cup B} - \frac{d_1^2 + d_2^2}{w^2 + h^2} \quad (6)$$

Where: where A is the real region, B is the predicted region, d_1 and d_2 are the distances corresponding to the upper left and lower right corners of regions A and B.

2.5 Pruning

In order to enable modern models to be deployed in environments with limited resources. We used multiple pruning methods to study the pruning experiment of YOLOv8-LD. The experimental results show that the LAMP (for amplitude based layer adaptive sparse pruning) [10] pruning method shows significant results in the proposed algorithm. To achieve a balance between performance and sparsity, LAMP proposes a pruning score based on layer adaptive amplitude. In order to provide a uniform definition of the LAMP score for both fully connected and convolutional layers, the LAMP method assumes that each weight tensor is expanded (or spread) into a one-dimensional vector. The u-th index of the weight tensor W of the LAMP score can be defined by the following Eq. 7:

$$score(u; W) := \frac{(W[u])^2}{\sum_{v \geq u}(W[v])^2}. \tag{7}$$

$$(W[u])^2 > (W[u])^2 \Rightarrow score(u; W) > score(v; W) \tag{8}$$

where: w[u] denotes the entry of w that indexes the u mapping. After calculating the LAMP score, the connection with the lowest global pruning score is selected until the desired global sparsity constraint is satisfied.

3 Experimental Results and Analysis

3.1 Hyperparameters and Evaluation Metrics

The network environment is Ubuntu, Python 3.9 and PyTorch 2.1.0, the GPU is RTX 4090 (24 GB), and the CUDA version is 12.1. In the hyperparameter setting, the batch is set to 8, and epoch is set to 200, In the hyperparameter settings, batch is set to 8, epoch is set to 200 and image size is 640 × 640. The main evaluation metrics set for the experiment are Param (number of parameters), GFLOPs (amount of computation), mAP@0.5, mAP@0.5-0.95.

3.2 Ablation Study

Table 1 shows the results of ablation experiments on the VisDrone2019 dataset [11]. It can be seen that the performance of each branch and component confirms the effectiveness and superiority of our proposed method.

Figure 5 shows the visualization comparison results of models in different scenarios. It can be seen that the improved YOLOv8-LD model in this paper has significantly improved performance under different environmental conditions (such as different lighting and weather conditions), especially in small object detection (such as pedestrians and vehicles of different categories), it has shown excellent performance. This further proves the effectiveness of the improved method in this paper.

Table 1. Ablation study

Methods	Param	GFLOPs	mAP@0.5	mAP@0.5-0.95
YOLOv8n	3.01	8.1	33.1	19.2
YOLOv8n+ASBiFPN	2.31	17.1	39.3	23.5
YOLOv8n+ASBiFPN+DBBDetect	2.31	17.1	39.6	23.6
YOLOv8n+ASBiFPN+DBBDetect+MPDIoU	2.31	17.1	39.7	23.6
YOLOv8n+ASBiFPN+DBBDetect+MPDIoU+Slide	2.31	17.1	39.7	23.5
YOLOv8n+ASBiFPN+DBBDetect+MPDIoU+ASL	2.31	17.1	39.9	23.8

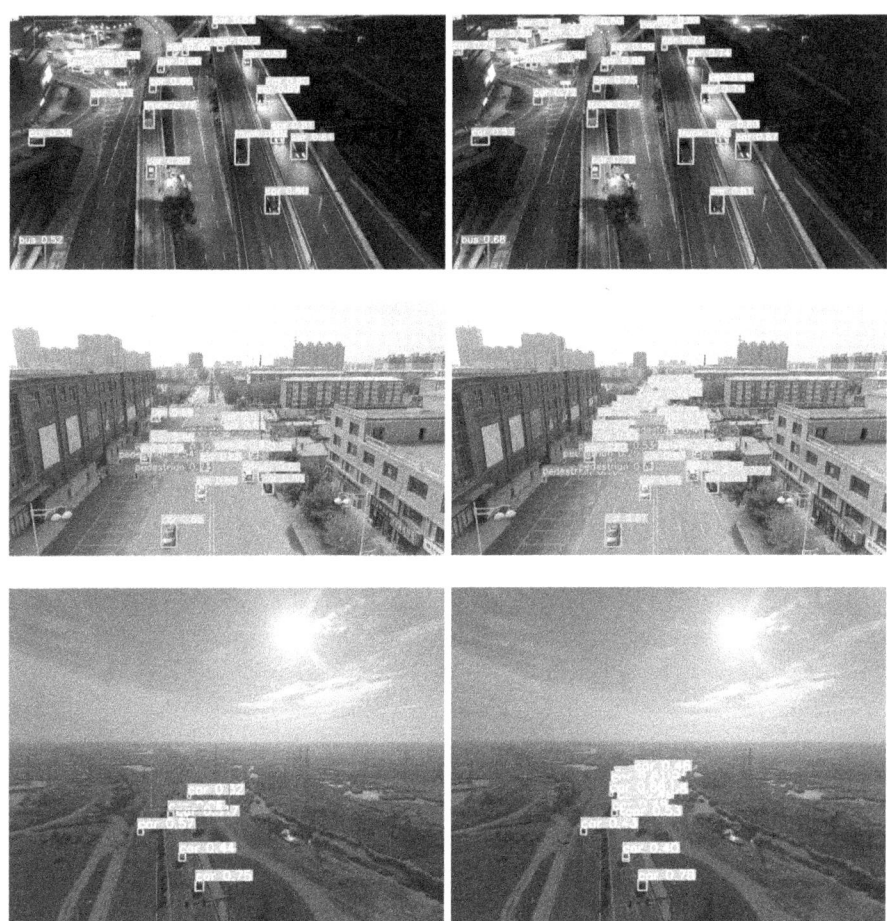

Fig. 5. On the left are the detection results of the YOLOv8 model; The detection results of the YOLOv8-LD model on the right

3.3 Comparative Experiments

To further evaluate the performance of the improved algorithm, comparisons were made in the VisDrone2019 dataset. As shown in Table 2, THP-YOLO is the SOTA algorithm of the YOLO series algorithm in the VisDrone challenge. In this experiment, the latest code released by the author of THP-YOLO is referenced to reproduce the THP-YOLOv5n version. YOLOv8-LD achieved the highest accuracy in different categories. This proves the effectiveness of the improved algorithm in this paper.

Table 2. Comparative experimental results with classical object detection algorithms

Methods	Pedestrian	People	Bicycle	Car	Van	Truck	Tricycle	Awning-tricycle	Bus	Motor	All
Faster R-CNN [12]	17.6	12.0	7.2	50.5	30.1	23.3	14.4	8.9	37.2	18.2	21.9
CenterNet [13]	22.6	20.6	14.6	59.7	24.0	21.3	20.1	17.4	37.9	23.7	26.2
YOLOv6n [14]	30.6	24.4	4.6	73.9	35.5	24.9	17.1	10.1	40.3	31.7	29.3
THP-YOLOv5n [3]	40.3	33.5	10.4	79.3	40.7	28.6	21.5	12.7	48.2	40.8	35.6
YOLOv8n	35.1	28.5	7.6	75.6	38.7	26.1	22.4	12.4	47.7	37.3	33.1
YOLOv8-LD	45.7	37.9	13.3	81.7	45.5	32.2	26.6	14.4	54.2	47.1	39.9

3.4 Pruning Experiments

As shown in Table 3, LAMP achieved the best experimental results compared to other pruning methods. As shown in Table 4, it can be seen that YOLOv8-LD in this paper has a better pruning effect than YOLOv8.

Table 3. Experimental results of different pruning algorithms

Methods	speed_up	Param	GFLOPs	ModelSize	mAP@0.5	mAP@0.5-0.95
LAMP [10]	2.0	0.60M	7.2	2.0 MB	34.1	20.1
group_hessian [15]	2.0	1.29M	7.2	3.4 MB	26.6	15.1
group_taylor [16]	2.0	1.15M	7.3	3.6 MB	26.7	15.0
random	2.0	0.75M	7.2	2.3 MB	31.3	17.9

Table 4. Experimental results of LAMP pruning algorithm

Methods	speed_up	Param	GFLOPs	mAP@0.5	mAP@0.5-0.95
YOLOv8	2.0	0.90M	4.0	32.3	18.7
YOLOv8-LD	2.5	0.43M	5.3	27.5	15.8
	2.0	0.60M	7.2	34.1	20.1

4 Conclusion

This paper proposes a lightweight object detection algorithm YOLOv8-LD suitable for drone scenarios. Proposed the ASBiFPN neck feature fusion network; Improve the detection head; Introducing MPDIoU loss; Propose ASL classification loss; Use pruning algorithms to reduce model volume. And verified the effectiveness of the proposed improvement plan in this paper.

References

1. Zhao, C., Liu, R.W., Qu, J., Gao, R.: Deep learning-based object detection in maritime unmanned aerial vehicle imagery: review and experimental comparisons. Eng. Appl. Artif. Intell. **128**, 107513 (2024)
2. Alam, M.S., Natesha, B.V., Ashwin, T.S., Guddeti, R.M.R.: UAV based cost-effective real-time abnormal event detection using edge computing. Multimed. Tools Appl. **78**(24), 35119–35134 (2019)
3. Zhu, X., Lyu, S., Wang, X., Zhao, Q.: TPH-YOLOv5: improved YOLOv5 based on transformer prediction head for object detection on drone-captured scenarios. In: Proceedings of the IEEE/CVF International Conference on Computer Vision 2021, Montreal, Canada, NJ, pp. 2778–2788. IEEE (2021)
4. Shao, Y., Yang, Z., Li, Z., Li, J.: Aero-YOLO: an efficient vehicle and pedestrian detection algorithm based on unmanned aerial imagery. Electronics **13**(7), 1190 (2024)
5. Tan, M., Pang, R., Le, Q.V.: EfficientDet: scalable and efficient object detection. In: Proceedings of the IEEE/CVF Conference on Computer Vision and Pattern Recognition 2020, Seattle, WA, USA, NJ, pp. 10781–10790. IEEE (2020)
6. Kang, M., Ting, C.M., Ting, F.F., Phan, R.C.W.: ASF-YOLO: a novel YOLO model with attentional scale sequence fusion for cell instance segmentation. Image Vis. Comput., 105057 (2024)
7. Ding, X., Zhang, X., Han, J., Ding, G.: Diverse branch block: building a convolution as an inception-like unit. In: Proceedings of the IEEE/CVF Conference on Computer Vision and Pattern Recognition 2021, Piscataway, Nashville, TN, USA, NJ, pp. 10886–10895. IEEE (2021)
8. Yu, Z., Huang, H., Chen, W., Su, Y., Liu, Y., Wang, X.: YOLO-FaceV2: a scale and occlusion aware face detector. arXiv preprint arXiv:2208.02019 (2022)
9. Siliang, M., Yong, X.: MPDIoU: a loss for efficient and accurate bounding box regression. arXiv preprint arXiv:2307.07662 (2023)
10. Lee, J., Park, S., Mo, S., Ahn, S., Shin, J.: Layer-adaptive sparsity for the magnitude-based pruning. arXiv preprint arXiv:2010.07611 (2020)

11. Cao, Y., et al.: VisDrone-DET2021: the vision meets drone object detection challenge results. In: Proceedings of the IEEE/CVF International Conference on Computer Vision 2021, Montreal, Canada, NJ, pp. 2847–2854. IEEE (2021)
12. Yu, W., Yang, T., Chen, C.: Towards resolving the challenge of long- tail distribution in UAV images for object detection. In: Winter Conference on Applications of Computer Vision 2021, Piscataway, pp. 3258–3267. Virtual. IEEE (2021)
13. Zhou, X., Wang, D., Krähenbühl, P.: Objects as points. arXiv preprint arXiv:1904.07850 (2019)
14. Li, C., et al.: YOLOv6: a single-stage object detection framework for industrial applications. arXiv preprint arXiv:2209. 02976 (2022)
15. LeCun, Y., Denker, J., Solla, S.: Optimal brain damage. In: Advances in Neural Information Processing Systems, vol. 2 (1989)
16. Molchanov, P., Mallya, A., Tyree, S., Frosio, I., Kautz, J.: Importance estimation for neural network pruning. In: Proceedings of the IEEE/CVF Conference on Computer Vision and Pattern Recognition 2019, Long Beach, CA, USA, NJ, pp. 11264–11272. IEEE (2019)

A Multi-dimensional Camera Image Stitching Method Under Large Parallax Conditions

Chuanlei Zhang[1], Yubo Li[1(✉)], Tianxiang Cheng[1], Jianrong Li[1], Haifeng Fan[1], Zhiqiang Zhao[2], Zhanjun Si[1], and Hui Ma[3]

[1] College of Artificial Intelligence, Tianjin University of Science and Technology, Tianjin 300457, China
jaridli@163.com
[2] Qinhuangdao Xinneng Energy & Equipment Co., Ltd., Qinhuangdao 066011, China
[3] Yunsheng Intelligent Technology Co., Ltd., Tianjin 300457, China

Abstract. Image stitching technology, as a critical link in digital image processing, can accurately combine numerous photos with overlapping sections into a panoramic image. Traditional image stitching typically demands that the input image have no parallax or very little parallax. However, in complex settings, spliced images produced by image splicing algorithms based on huge parallax are prone to issues such as ghosting and severe image distortion. This study provides an energy function optimization method for basic texture areas, as well as an enhanced seam quality evaluation algorithm to help with local seam alignment. Firstly, the entropy value based on the grey-scale covariance matrix is used to calculate the texture complexity, followed by region splitting, the penalty value of simple texture region is calculated based on the similarity of overlapping regions to obtain the energy function, secondly, the maximum flow minimum cut algorithm is used to locate the optimal seams, and finally, the simulated annealing algorithm is used to optimize the seam quality assessment algorithm for the algorithm suggested in this research performs well in picture fusion, as evidenced by experimental verification, which greatly enhances image fusion efficiency and final spliced image quality.

Keywords: Energy Function · Stitching Seam Quality Assessment · Local Seam Optimization · Optimal Splicing Seam

1 Introduction

In the real world, the field of vision of a single photo is limited by the physical restrictions of the viewing angles of various camera lenses. There are two approaches to improving it. One example is the employment of wide-angle lenses to directly record large-field images [1]. The second method is to capture numerous photographs using a general camera and then merge them using an image stitching technique to create a panoramic. The second option is more cost-effective.

Gao et al. [2] created an image calculation approach based on seams and found the optimal seams using the results of a seam evaluation algorithm. Li et al. [3] included sensory variables in the energy function, bringing the findings closer to the human sensory experience. Existing seam-cutting techniques [4] often bypass textured sections wherever possible. In this paper, a joint that can pass through simple texture areas is proposed, which can lead to higher overall quality joints.

Liao et al. [5] proposed in their study that traditional seam driving technology is not enough to find the most ideal seams in terms of feel. Therefore, they advocate calculating all points of the seam to obtain a better splicing effect. Liao et al. [6] proposed a local seam optimization strategy based on seam quality assessment, which can effectively reprocess local areas with poor seam processing. Since the seam quality assessment algorithm needs to calculate the quality of the entire seam, it takes a lot of time and affects the efficiency of local seam optimization. In this paper, a seam quality assessment algorithm optimized by a simulated annealing algorithm [7] is proposed, which significantly improves the efficiency of local seam optimization.

In this paper, we find a seam that can perfectly stitch together the left and right images under complex and variable large parallax conditions based on images taken by a multivariate camera, and optimize the efficiency of the algorithm to stitch as fast and well as possible. Our contributions can be summarized as follows:

(1) We propose an energy function optimization method for simple texture regions, which uses entropy value based on the grey-scale co-production matrix to calculate texture complexity, then performs region splitting, calculates the penalty value of simple texture regions based on the similarity of overlapping regions, obtains the energy function, and obtains the globally optimal seam through the graph cut algorithm.
(2) We use a simulated annealing algorithm to quickly find poorly spliced local regions for re-splicing, speeding up seam optimization.
(3) We conducted rich experiments to test the effectiveness of the optimized algorithm and compare it with mainstream algorithms.

2 Methods

The overall idea of our algorithm is to use a region separation algorithm [8] to find the texture simple region [9], followed by using entropy computation based on the grey-scale covariance matrix to improve the texture complexity term in the energy function, to determine the location with the smallest energy value as a seam, and then using simulated annealing algorithm to accelerate the seam quality assessment algorithm to locally optimize the seams, and finally smoothening to get the fused image.

We use a region-growing algorithm to find texture simple regions. Finally, several texture simple regions are obtained. The penalty term is then determined based on the region overlap similarity of the corresponding simple texture region [10]. At higher overlap similarity, it is considered that the seam passing through the simple texture region will be better and the penalty is smaller. At lower overlap similarity, the penalty term for this simple texture region is larger, reducing the seam line passing through the region. For the complex texture region, a smaller penalty term is set, mainly based on the color difference and gradient change can accurately guide the calculation of the seam.

Suppose I_0 and I_1 denote two images respectively, p and q represent a pair of pixel points with adjacent positions in the overlapping region Ω. The energy function is as follows:

$$E = \sum_{p \in \Omega} E_d(p, l_p) + \sum_{(p,q) \in \Omega} E_s(p, q, l_p, l_q) \tag{1}$$

where $E_d(p, l_p)$ represents the data term, $E_s(p, q, l_p, l_q)$ represents the smoothing term.

Then the texture complex term is integrated into the energy function, which is defined as follows:

$$E_s(p, q, l_p, l_q) = (E_c(p, q) + E_g(p, q))|ENT(p) + ENT(q)| \tag{2}$$

where $E_c(p, q)$ represents the grey-scale difference, $E_g(p, q)$ represents the gradient difference, and $|ENT(p) + ENT(q)|$ represents the image texture complexity term.

To solve the problem of low efficiency of the seam quality assessment algorithm, we use the simulated annealing algorithm to improve it and find the bad spots in the seams quickly. The simulated annealing process is shown in Algorithm 1.

Algorithm 1: Finding all bad pixels

Input: random init point set S, temperature set T, seam S_0, multiple B_0, Average of errors N_0
Output: all bad pixels
1: SPC = Sum(S_0), BP = ∅
2: for point in S do
3:   point_SSIM = calculate SSIM(point)
4:   for t in T
5:     if t > 0
6:       step = t * SPC
7:       point_left, point_right = step_instance(point)
8:       if point_left > point.left and point_right < point.right
9:         point_left_SSIM = calculate SSIM(point_left)
10:        point_right_SSIM = calculate SSIM(point_left)
11:        BP_candidate = max(point_SSIM, point_left_SSIM, point_right_SSIM)
12:        if BP_candidate > B_0 * N_0
13:          BP = BP ∪ BP_candidate
14:      End if
15:    End if
16: End if
17: End for
18: End for
Return BP

After the simulated annealing algorithm, we get the location of several bad points, which are extended to the left and right sides to get several bad point segments. As shown in Fig. 1, splice recomputation is performed on these found bad segments using the splice cutting algorithm to get new seams. As shown in Fig. 2, finally image fusion is performed using a weighted average algorithm [11] which achieves smooth blending of pixels using the gradient for a natural transition.

(a) Splice seams with bad pixel   (b) Local bad point segment

Fig. 1. Schematic diagram of a bad pixel segment.

(a) Repaired spliced seam   (b) Localized seam

Fig. 2. Seam weight calculation.

3 Experiments

3.1 Experiments on Splicing Seams Based on Graph Cuts

To make the improved energy function in this paper to achieve the best effect, a series of data test experiments were done. First of all, we use the entropy value in the grey-scale covariance matrix can represent the texture complexity, the smaller the entropy value [12], the simpler the texture is, we need to get the simple texture region, we did some experiments for the definition of the simple texture and the complex texture, and got the following experimental results. As shown in Table 1.

From the experimental results, we can conclude that as the range of entropy values of simple texture regions increases, the number of simple texture regions increases and the total elapsed time is also increased. The result of seam quality assessment is maximum at maximum entropy value of 0.26 for simple texture region. The image is processed by the grey-scale covariance matrix and then the entropy value is used as a criterion for texture complexity. The texture with entropy value between 0 and 0.26, we consider this texture as simple texture region and the rest of the entropy value is considered as complex texture region.

Table 1. Defining the range of entropy values for simple texture regions.

Maximum entropy of a simple texture region	Number of simple texture areas	Total time consumption	Seam quality assessment
0.20	29	34.37	0.83
0.22	30	34.49	0.88
0.24	35	35.08	0.92
0.26	38	35.19	0.94
0.28	39	36.13	0.90
0.30	43	36.56	0.86

To determine the penalty term setting for simple texture areas, we conducted the following experiment. In the simple texture area, we use the contour matching algorithm [13] to measure the overlapping similarity. The higher the degree of contour matching in the simple texture area, the better the match between the two images. The higher the matching degree, the smaller the penalty term, and the greater the probability that the seam passes through this area. We assume that the overlapping similarity and the penalty term are linearly related, assuming that the linear ratio is k, and then we did some experiments to determine the value of this ratio. As shown in Table 2.

Table 2. Relationship between overlapping similarity and penalty terms.

Ratio k	Total time consumption	Seam quality assessment
0.75	36.13	0.90
0.85	36.46	0.93
0.95	36.27	0.91
1.05	35.96	0.90
1.15	35.78	0.85

From the experimental results, we can get the linear proportion k value between the penalty term and the overlapping similarity. It can be seen that the seam quality is the highest when k is near 0.85, and the relationship between the penalty term and the overlapping similarity is finally determined.

We also used the traditional energy function and the energy function improved based on the research in this article for splicing, and obtained the following experimental results. Figure 3 shows two images to be stitched. Figure 4 shows the splicing seam obtained based on the traditional energy function. The left image is the complete splicing seam, and the right image is the detailed display of the key areas of the splicing seam. Figure 5 shows the splicing seam obtained based on the improved energy function. The left image is the complete splicing seam, and the right image is the detailed display of the key areas of the splicing seam.

Fig. 3. Two images to be stitched.

Fig. 4. Spliced seam based on the traditional energy function.

From Fig. 4, it can be seen that the seams obtained by the traditional energy function are more inclined to be along the edges of the object, which means that the search for the best splice seam is based on the structural gradient. From Fig. 5, it can be seen that the seams obtained by the improved energy function can be searched along the texture regularity and the region with uncomplicated texture, and there is no obvious error situation in the place where it enters and leaves the texture regularity region. In this paper, the improved splicing seam passes through areas with uncomplicated textures and can obtain seam splicing with lower energy values. Moreover, there is basically no difference in color and structural gradient after splicing in this part, the texture difference is smaller, and the splicing effect is better.

Fig. 5. Splice seams based on the improved energy function.

3.2 Improved Seam Quality Assessment Experiments

To improve the seam quality assessment algorithm to achieve the best results, a series of experiments were done to determine the values of some of these parameters. First of all, the number of random points we select will directly affect the efficiency of the algorithm, too few random points will lead to poor-quality seams, and the more random points we select, the more time will be consumed. We know that the longer the seam is, the more random points we need to select, so we need to determine a parameter d, indicating the number of d times the total length of the selected seam as the initial number of random points. To address these issues we did a series of experiments on the number of random points, and the results of the experiments are shown in Table 3.

Table 3. Proportion of random points d.

Ratio d	Total time	Seam quality assessment
0.005	3.963	0.885
0.008	4.204	0.906
0.011	4.437	0.922
0.014	4.869	0.930
0.017	5.671	0.931

From the experimental results, we can see that the higher the percentage of random points selected, the longer the algorithm takes and the higher the quality of the seams. We find that the time and seam quality performance is best when d is 0.011. So the final determination of the number of random points selected proportion is 0.011 times the total number of points of the seams.

The selection of temperature is the most important part of the simulated annealing, and whether the temperature is selected appropriately determines the efficiency and effectiveness of the simulated annealing. According to our experience, several groups of simulated annealing temperatures are given [14], the first group of temperatures are 0.3, 0.2, 0.1, 0.06, 0.03, 0.02, 0.01, 0.005, 0.002, 0.001, 0. The second group of temperatures are 0.25, 0.175, 0.125, 0.085, 0.055, 0.03, 0.01, 0.006, 0.003, 0.001, 0. The third set of temperatures were 0.2, 0.135, 0.085, 0.045, 0.025, 0.01, 0.008, 0.006, 0.003, 0.001, 0. Temperatures multiplied by the total length of the seam equaled the number of steps. We used 20 initial random points and did a series of experiments for each of these sets of temperatures, and the results are shown in Table 4.

The experimental findings show that the temperature in the first group has the maximum number of bad points and the best results. After analyzing the reason, it is found that because the temperature of the second and third groups is low, the random points across the local maximum worth of ability are weaker, resulting in fewer poor points. So, eventually, the temperature of the first group is determined.

Table 4. Effect of different temperature groups on the results.

Temperature	Total time	Number of bad points
group 1	4.147	5
group 2	4.104	3
group 3	4.203	2

3.3 Improved Seam Quality Assessment Experiments

The optimized algorithm in this paper is subjected to comparative experiments with algorithms involving seam-driven strategies [15]. We performed sufficient tests on this dataset, including 20 image pairs from [6], in which each image pair has overlapping parts and some parallax, and the dataset picture is shown in Fig. 6.

The method of this paper is compared with some commonly used panoramic image stitching methods, including APAP [16], and iterative seam estimation image stitching method based on quality assessment [17] (SEAGULL). A combination of subjective and objective evaluation is used to compare the different algorithms in the experimental results. The images to be spliced are shown in Fig. 7.

Figure 8 shows the comparison results, it can be seen that the APAP algorithm shows obvious ghosting, the staircase part of the SEAGULL algorithm is spliced unaligned, and the rest of the splicing is better. In addition, we use the information entropy (Entropy), root mean square error (RMSE), average gradient (AG), peak signal-to-noise ratio (PSNR) and program running time (Running Time) as evaluation indexes to objectively evaluate the effect of panorama splicing, and we get the results of Table 5.

From the experimental results, it can be seen that all the indexes of this paper's method perform well. The RMSE, AG and PSNR of this paper's method are the best among several methods. Entropy reacts to the richness of image information after fusion, and Entropy is only second to the SEAGULL method, and the gap between this value

Fig. 6. Dataset Image.

(a) The target images   (b)The reference images

Fig. 7. Two images to be stitched.

(a) APAP   (b) SEAGULL   (c) Our Method

Fig. 8. Experimental results of APAP, SEAGULL and our methods

and the best SEAGULL is very small, but this paper's algorithm takes a lot of time faster than that of SEAGULL. So the panoramic image obtained by the method of this paper is clearer and richer in image information.

The experimental data in this paper confirms that the proposed panoramic image stitching technique effectively handles the common phenomena of ghosting and ghosting, and at the same time can effectively smooth the transition region, thus generating high-quality panoramic images. Comprehensive subjective evaluation and objective

Table 5. Objective evaluation index of panorama stitching effect.

Method	Entropy	RMSE	AG	PSNR	Running Time (seconds)
APAP	8.57	3.31	7.96	18.69	50.56
SEAGULL	6.40	2.76	10.74	20.02	78.69
Our Method	6.46	2.73	11.13	20.39	39.67

analysis show that compared with other existing image stitching techniques, the method proposed in this study not only has the feasibility of practical application, but also demonstrates its unique advantages in terms of the overall stitching effect.

4 Conclusions

In this paper, we use a region separation algorithm to find simple texture regions, use entropy calculation based on gray-level co-occurrence matrices to improve the texture complexity term of the energy function, and find seams. Then the simulated annealing algorithm is used to quickly find the places with poor local seams and perform local re-stitching. Finally, the weighted average algorithm is used for image fusion, which significantly improves the efficiency and quality of image stitching.

Our method can handle the image stitching problem under large parallax well, but it still has limitations. Since there may be a certain amount of time between two captured images, resulting in a moving object in the image appearing at different locations in the overlapping region, this object may appear twice or zero times in the final stitching result, we hope that we can specify the number of times the moving object appears in the panorama by some methods. We leave this as our future work.

References

1. Gao, Z., et al.: Stereo camera calibration for large field of view digital image correlation using zoom lens. Measurement **185** (2021)
2. Gao, J., Li, Y., Chin, T.J., Brown, M. S.: Seam-driven image stitching. In: Eurographics (Short Papers), pp. 45–48 (2013)
3. Li, N., Liao, T., Wang, C.: Perception-based seam cutting for image stitching. SIViP **12**, 967–974 (2018)
4. Chen, J., Li, Z., Peng, C., Wang, Y., Gong, W.: UAV image stitching based on optimal seam and half-projective warp. Remote Sens. **14**(5), 1068 (2022). https://doi.org/10.3390/rs14051068
5. Liao, T., Chen, J., Xu, Y.: Quality evaluation-based iterative seam estimation for image stitching. SIViP **13**, 1199–1206 (2019)
6. Liao, T., Zhao, C., Li, L., Chao, H.: Seam-guided local alignment and stitching for large parallax images (2023). arxiv:2311.18564
7. Beneich, C., Douiri, S.M.: Solving the multi compartment vehicle routing problem using a hybridized simulated annealing algorithm. Int. J. Appl. Comput. Math. **9**(6), 127 (2023). https://doi.org/10.1007/s40819-023-01609-0

8. Zhang, Y., Yuan, Y.: ResNet-based surface normal estimator with multilevel fusion approach with adaptive median filter region growth algorithm for road scene segmentation. Int. J. Comput. Vis. Robot. **14**(1), 99–117 (2024)
9. Balling, J., Herold, M., Reiche, J.: How textural features can improve SAR-based tropical forest disturbance mapping. Int. J. Appl. Earth Obs. Geoinf. **124**, 103492 (2023)
10. Lhermitte, E., Hilal, M., Furlong, R., O'Brien, V., Humeau-Heurtier, A.: Deep learning and entropy-based texture features for color image classification. Entropy **24**(11), 1577 (2022). https://doi.org/10.3390/e24111577
11. Prabukumar, M., Shrutika, S.: Band clustering using expectation–maximization algorithm and weighted average fusion-based feature extraction for hyperspectral image classification. J. Appl. Remote. Sens. **12**(4), 046015 (2018)
12. Xie, C., Wang, J., Haase, D., Wellmann, T., Lausch, A.: Measuring spatio-temporal heterogeneity and interior characteristics of green spaces in urban neighborhoods: a new approach using gray level co-occurrence matrix. Sci. Total. Environ. **855**, 158608 (2023). https://doi.org/10.1016/j.scitotenv.2022.158608
13. Arulananth, T.S., Baskar, M., Sateesh, R.: Human face detection and recognition using contour generation and matching algorithm. Indonesian J. Electr. Eng. Comput. Sci. **16**(2), 709–714 (2019)
14. Shahrin, S.H., Hussin, M. S.: Comparisons of simulated annealing temperature schedule based on QAPLIB instances. In: AIP Conference Proceedings, vol. 1974. AIP Publishing (2018)
15. Chen, X., Mei, Y., Song, Y.: Optimized seam-driven image stitching method based on scene depth information. Electronics **11**(12), 1876 (2022). https://doi.org/10.3390/electronics11121876
16. Zaragoza J., Chin, T.J., Brown, M.S., Suter, D.: As-projective-as-possible image stitching with moving DLT. In: Proceedings of the IEEE Conference on Computer Vision and Pattern Recognition, pp. 2339–2346 (2013)
17. Lin, K., Jiang, N., Cheong, L F., Do, M., Lu, J.: SEAGULL: seam-Guided Local Alignment for Parallax-Tolerant Image Stitching. In: Leibe, B., Matas, J., Sebe, N., Welling, M. (eds.) Computer Vision – ECCV 2016. ECCV 2016. LNCS, vol. 9907. Springer, Cham (2016). https://doi.org/10.1007/978-3-319-46487-9_23

Harmonizing Stable Diffusion and GPT-4 for Mural Expansion with ArtExtend

Dufeng Chen[1], Yuqing Yang[2], Zehua Wang[2,3(✉)], Zishan Xu[2], Jueting Liu[2], Tingting Xu[2], and Wei Chen[2]

[1] Beijing Geotechnical and Investigation Engineering Insititute, Beijing 100080, China
[2] School of Computer Science and Technology, China University of Mining and Technology, Xuzhou 221116, China
zehuaw@cumt.edu.cn
[3] Department of Electrical and Computer Engineering, The University of British Columbia, Vancouver, Canada

Abstract. The Dunhuang murals have a long history. Over the centuries, changes have made it hard to restore them. This study addresses the limitations of existing multimodal learning models in the lack of semantic information on the scene expansion of Dunhuang mural images. A total of 887 groups of Dunhuang mural patterns and their text descriptions were collected for this purpose. A method called ArtExtend was created based on the Stable Diffusion model. It uses BLIP-2 technology to encode keywords in mural images. It uses BLIP-2 technology to encode keywords from mural images and accurately represent mural image features in conjunction with image-text contrast loss. It then optimizes the GPT-4 large model expansion mural keywords through black-box prompt optimization (BPO) technology to generate scene descriptions. Finally, it fine-tunes the Stable Diffusion model and expands Dunhuang mural images with GPT-4 descriptions through LoRA technology. The experimental results show that the proposed method outperforms the benchmark model in terms of LPIPS metric reduction 28.5%, FID metric reduction 30.5%, and CLIPScore score improvement 16.6%. This makes the model better at understanding Dunhuang murals. This study combines deep language understanding and advanced image generation techniques in a new way. This approach reduces the time and cost of traditional restoration work and improves the use of large models in mural painting.

Keywords: Dunhuang Murals · Multimodal Learning · Text-to-Image · Stable Diffusion

1 Introduction

In the digital age, attention to the preservation of ancient murals has increased. These artworks are protected and revitalized through advanced technologies, which also foster the growth of cultural diversity. Digital mural technology applications: Ren et al.[1] applied neural networks for the digitalization of Dunhuang murals, and Xu et al.[2] used Generative Adversarial Networks (GANs) to enhance the precision and quality of the digitalization process. Wang et al.[3] integrated adaptive local convolution and arbitrary shape masks into GAN technology. Xu et al.[4] introduced a novel method based on a new diffusion model for digitizing Dunhuang murals. These studies showcase the application of various technologies in mural digitization.

In the field of image processing, outpainting presents a challenging task. Zhang et al.[5] introduced a new regularization method to encourage diversity sampling in conditional synthesis. Yang et al.[6] designed innovative modules to improve the realism and quality of the generated images. Zhang et al.[7] incorporated prior knowledge to enhance the inference ability of encoders for outpainting. Lu et al.[8] used contextual attention mechanisms and adversarial learning schemes for panorama outpainting. Gao et al.[9] the extrapolated visual context in all directions around the image. Van et al.[10] employed context encoders inspired by common image inpainting architectures and paradigms. Wang et al.[11] extended image borders with plausible structure and details. Zhuang et al.[12] introduced learnable task prompts and fine-tuning strategies, which can utilize different task prompts to accomplish various outpainting tasks.

The Stable Diffusion model[13] offers new ways to share ancient murals. But it still has problems. The expansion process might change the meaning of the generated content. This is because the model doesn't have enough information about the original murals. To make the model work better, we need to add more information. The pre-trained version of the model is not designed to reproduce the style of murals. This paper introduces an innovative approach called "ArtExtend." It employs the following strategies:

1. The multimodal image description function of BLIP-2 [14] and the language generation capability of GPT-4 are combined to provide detailed semantic guidance for Stable Diffusion, thereby ensuring that the generated images are technically advanced and faithful to the mural features. The specific process effects illustrated in Fig. 1.
2. The query is refined through the black-box prompt optimization (BPO) technique [15], thereby enhancing the text generated by GPT-4 and improving the performance and accuracy of Stable Diffusion. The performance and adaptability of Stable Diffusion will be evaluated.
3. The LoRA fine-tuning technique [16] will be employed to make specific adjustments to Stable Diffusion, to generate images that conform to the style of murals.

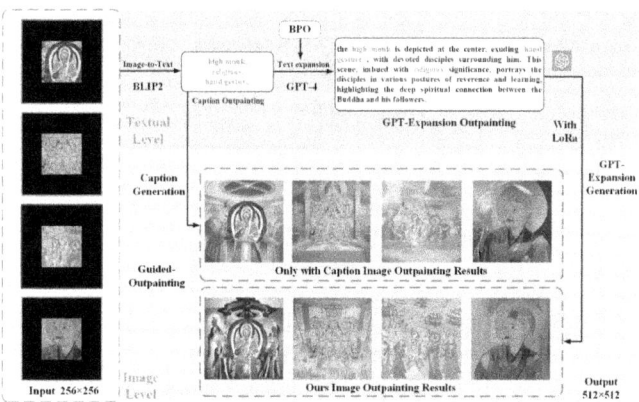

Fig. 1. ArtExtend flow effect diagram.

2 Method

This chapter introduces a comprehensive methodological framework named "ArtExtend" Fig. 2 illustrates that the framework consists of three core components: multimodal visual-language interaction analysis, query optimization, prompt engineering, and model fine-tuning tailored to specific requirements. Initially, large multimodal models are used for visual analysis and text description generation of murals. Then, BPO technology is utilized to optimize GPT-4, finding the optimal prompts that guide GPT-4 to generate the most accurate and relevant mural text descriptions. Subsequently, LoRA technology is applied for the specialized fine-tuning of the Stable Diffusion model to conform to the specific style of the murals. The goal of this comprehensive approach is to efficiently and accurately restore ancient murals, ensuring the preservation of their original artistic value. The specific network structure diagram is shown in Fig. 2.

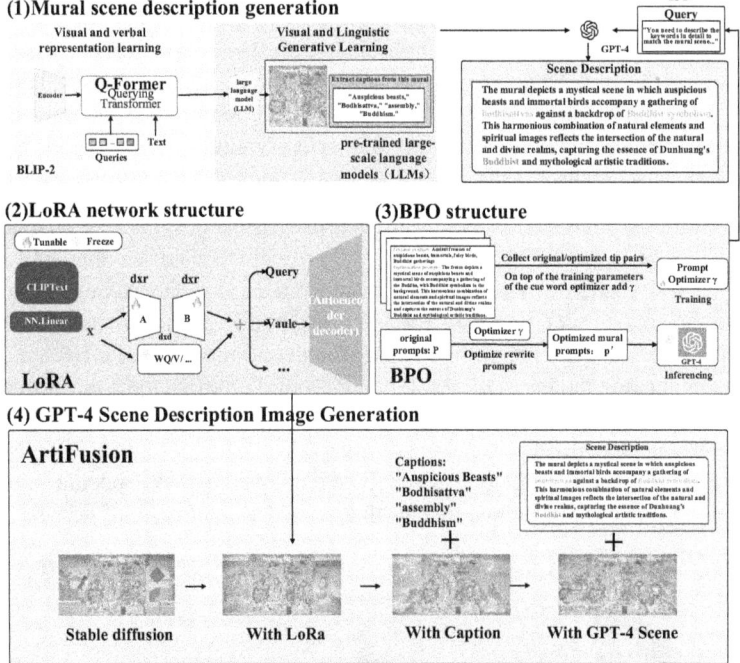

Fig. 2. ArtExtend flow effect diagram

2.1 Multimodal Visual Language Interaction Analysis and Description Generation

In this chapter, the BLIP-2 model is used to visually analyze ancient murals and identify keywords. Special datasets containing 887 images and descriptions are created. The BLIP-2 model is capable of providing more detailed annotations for the mural images, which assists in better understanding the images and generating more detailed descriptions. This is combined with a contrast loss function. The Image-Text Contrast Loss (ITM Loss) is aimed at making matched image-text pairs similar and mismatched pairs different, utilizing binary cross-entropy loss to achieve this objective.

$$L_{ITM} = -\frac{1}{N}\sum_{i=1}^{N}\left[y_i \log(\hat{y}_i) + (1-y_i)\log(1-\hat{y}_i)\right] \quad (1)$$

where N is the number of samples in the batch, y_i is the true label of the ith sample (1 for matching image-text pairs and 0 for mismatches), and $\hat{y}_i$ is the probability of matching predicted by the model. This process involves extracting the most important visual information from an image and turning it into a keyword description. Key elements in mural images can be identified by BLIP-2, and text descriptions are generated accordingly.

2.2 Query Optimization and Prompt Engineering

After obtaining captions, the next step is to make the queries better. At this stage, Blackbox Prompt Optimization technology is used to make simple queries more complex, specific, and information-rich. This process makes the queries better by evaluating the quality of the model's output. It aims to find the best prompts that can make GPT-4 generate the most accurate and relevant mural text descriptions. BPO technology makes queries more effective by adjusting external inputs. This leads to more precise and targeted prompts. This ensures that the prompts match the murals' visual and cultural characteristics and the research objectives. The target function CLIPLoss is used:

$$L = \frac{1}{N}\sum_{i=1}^{N}\log\frac{\exp(sim(i,i)/\tau)}{\sum_{j=1}^{N}\exp(sim(i,j)/\tau)} + \frac{1}{N}\sum_{i=1}^{N}\log\frac{\exp(sim(i,i)/\tau)}{\sum_{j=1}^{N}\exp(sim(j,i)/\tau)} \quad (2)$$

where $sim(i,j)$ represents the similarity between the ith image embedding and the jth text embedding and τ is the temperature parameter (a preset positive number used to control the smoothness of the distribution).

Using the Bayesian optimization algorithm, starting with basic prompts such as "Describe the theme of this mural" and "What story does this mural tell?", 35 iterations are set, with each iteration generating 5–10 prompts for evaluation and comparison. Based on the target function's score, the best prompt is selected for the next round of optimization. The prompts are refined to include information such as historical background and artistic style, with specific instructions like "Use professional terminology" or "Assume you are a Dunhuang mural historian" and diversity constraints to ensure the breadth and accuracy of the generated descriptions. The optimization process can be represented by the following formula:

$$Q_{opt} = BPO(Q_{init}, P, \gamma) \quad (3)$$

Here, Q_{init} is the initial keywords generated based on the formula, P is the auxiliary prompt, and γ represents the optimizer. The formula demonstrates how BPO technology optimizes queries. The key to this step is how effectively the original keywords are transformed into more specific and detailed descriptions of mural scenes, providing richer and more specific input for the textual expansion in the Stable Diffusion model.

2.3 Special Fine-Tuning for Mural Outpainting

To make the Stable Diffusion model match specific mural styles more precisely, we used LoRA technology to make fine adjustments. LoRA adds low-rank matrices to key parts of the model, allowing for efficient adjustments while keeping the majority of the pre-trained model's parameters unchanged. An auxiliary path is added alongside the original Stable Diffusion model, where only the dimensionality reduction matrix A and the dimensionality increasing matrix B are trained. The dimensions of the model stay the same, and the output of BA is combined with the parameters of Stable Diffusion. This fine-tuning strategy can be summarized by the following formula:

$$SD_{tuned} = LoRA(SD_{ori}, LRM, \beta) \tag{4}$$

where SD_{ori} represents the original Stable Diffusion model, LRM refers to the introduced low-rank matrices, β represents the adjustment parameters during the fine-tuning process, and SD_{tuned} is the model after fine-tuning. Through this method, we are able to effectively personalize the model without significantly changing its original structure, thereby generating images that conform more closely to specific artistic style requirements, such as Dunhuang mural style images.

We have created a way to turn text into images. This process involves converting detailed descriptions into images in the style of a mural. The process is as follows:

$$Image = Outpaint(SD_{tuned}, D, K) \tag{5}$$

D represents the detailed description, and K represents the keywords. These text inputs are used to make images. The Outpaint function makes images with specific features. Our Stable Diffusion model can generate images matching the style of Dunhuang murals and ensure the accuracy and richness of the images in terms of cultural and artistic content. This method opens new ways to represent and preserve cultural and artistic works like Dunhuang murals.

3 Experiment

This section explains the Dunhuang mural dataset that was collected to improve image generation technology. In this experiment, a dataset of Dunhuang murals and their descriptions was created. It was ensured that all the mural images had the same resolution to meet the experiment's quality requirements. A V100 GPU was used in the experiments. The experiments were conducted in stages to compare different technologies. The murals were restored through our approach, enhancing their visual and artistic value while preserving their artistic essence. These experiments demonstrated that our method works and can be used to preserve cultural heritage.

3.1 Unsupervised Image Expansion Comparative Experiment

This section presents a comparative experiment of our "ArtExtend" method under unsupervised conditions. We tested four image expansion techniques capable of extending images from a resolution of 512 × 512 to 1024 × 512. It was found that while the "SRN[11]," which optimizes based on image boundary structures, and "IOH-GAN[10]," based on inpainting architecture, performed well in standard tasks, they lacked semantic information during expansion. The "PowerPaint[12]" method, integrating task guidance and fine-tuning strategies, showed improvement but was limited in specific scenarios. In contrast, "ArtExtend" excelled in outpainting Dunhuang murals, generating precise images while retaining the original style, especially adept at handling complex themes. Further comparisons demonstrated the efficacy of "ArtExtend" combining Stable Diffusion technology, BLIP-2 for extracting key descriptions, BPO-optimized GPT-4, and LoRA style fine-tuning. As illustrated in Fig. 3, "ArtExtend" showcased its superior ability and potential value in the field of unsupervised image expansion of murals, offering more reasonable and precise scene generation.

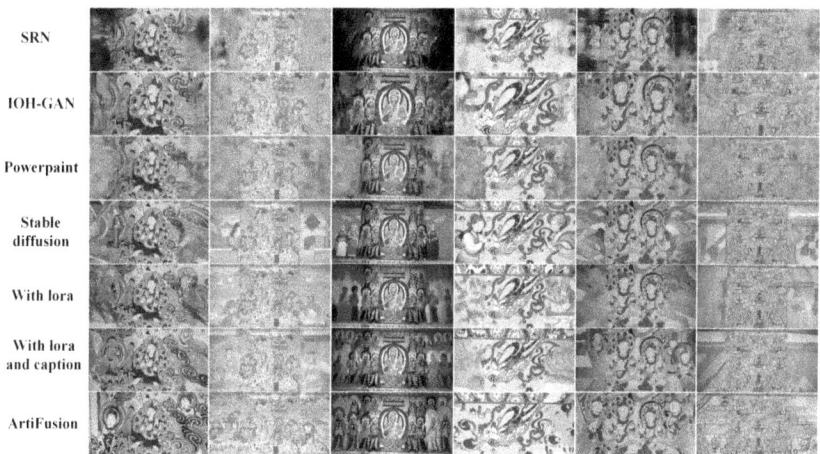

Fig. 3. Unsupervised image expansion comparative diagram

3.2 Comparative Analysis of Text-Guided Expansion Experiment

This section compares our "ArtExtend" mural image expansion technique with popular methods like "Wide-Context," "Image Outpainting," and "PowerPaint". The main goal was to outpaint 256 × 256 pixel images to 512 × 512 pixels and evaluate each model under the same training and testing conditions. A version of "PowerPaint" with prompt words was specifically tested, using LPIPS, FID, and CLIPscore as evaluation metrics. These metrics measure the quality of the generated images, their semantic consistency with the original images, and visual similarity, important criteria for assessing image generation model performance. Considering potential FID inflation due to sample limitations, "ArtExtend" ensures effective reflection of image quality and diversity even with limited samples by enhancing image details and overall consistency.

Detailed comparative analysis through Fig. 4 and Table 1 shows that, although some technologies perform well in general image expansion, they lack semantic information in

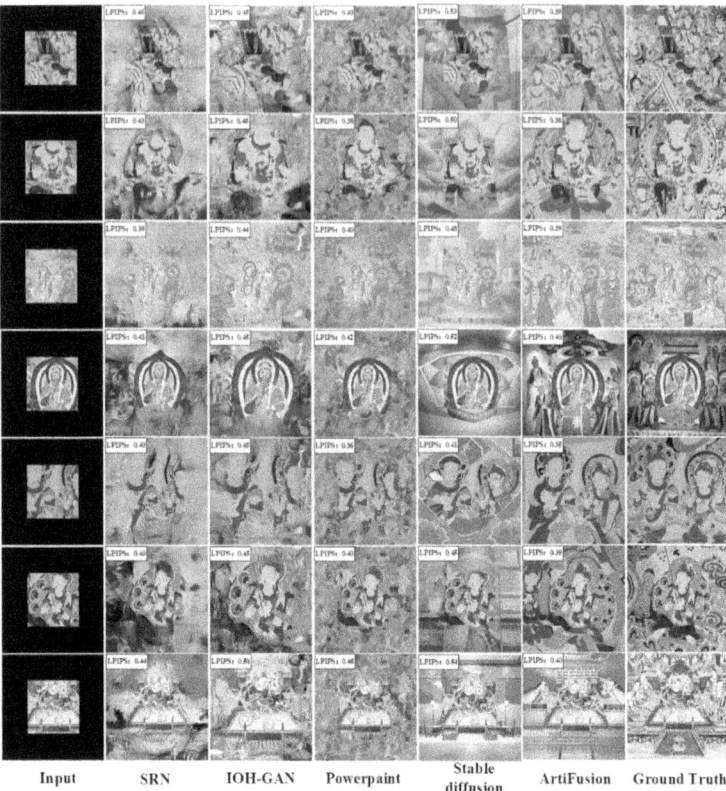

Fig. 4. Comparison diagram of results with other methods

Table 1. Comparative analysis table for evaluation of the effectiveness of outpainting

Methods	Lpips↓	Fid↓	Clipscore↑
Wide-Context	0.43	341	/
Image Outpainting	0.47	250	/
Powerpaint with Caption	0.40	259	26.32
Powerpaint with expantion	0.39	223	30.43
Stable Diffusion	0.49	285	/
ArtExtend	**0.35**	**198**	**31.50**

complex mural processing, compromising accuracy. "PowerPaint" attempts to enhance performance through mural keywords and descriptions but is limited in style and detail handling, demonstrating ArtExtend's superiority in specific scenarios and highlighting potential limitations of advanced technologies when facing challenges.

3.3 Comparative Ablation Study Experiment

This section evaluates the effects of Stable Diffusion, LoRA, BLIP-2, and GPT-4 optimized by BPO in mural image expansion tasks through ablation studies.

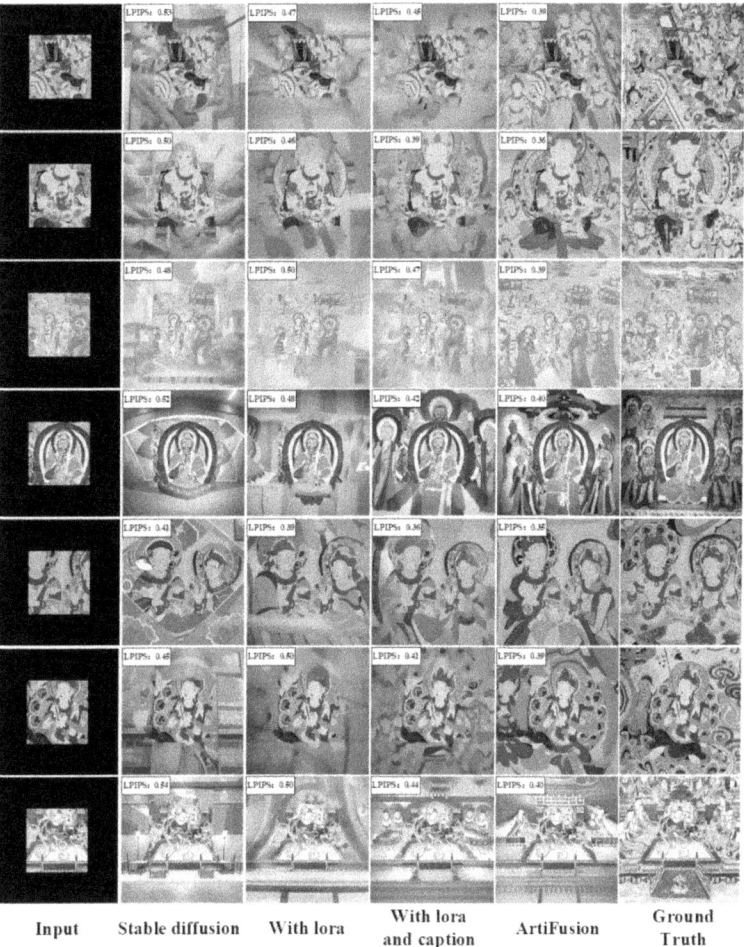

Fig. 5. Ablation experiment effect diagram

The results, displayed in Fig. 5, showcase the performance of each technology individually and in combination, confirming the outstanding effects of integrating GPT-4, BLIP-2, Stable Diffusion, and LoRA in mural expansion.The experiment demonstrates that GPT-4, optimized by BPO, can refine BLIP-2 text descriptions, effectively guiding Stable Diffusion and LoRA in image expansion to produce images that closely match the original mural style and are highly consistent visually and semantically. The results in Table 2 reflect the excellent performance of the "ArtExtend" method on FID, CLIP-Score, and LPIPS metrics, highlighting its strong capabilities in image quality, semantic relevance, and perceptual similarity, offering an efficient and creative solution for mural image expansion.

Table 2. Ablation comparison study effectiveness assessment table

	Lpips↓	Fid↓	Clipscore↑
Stable Diffusion	0.49	285	/
With LoRA	0.48	275	/
with Caption	0.42	231	27.02
ArtExtend	**0.35**	**198**	**31.50**

4 Conclusion

The main contribution of this study lies in combining deep language understanding with advanced image generation technology, offering a new perspective for the digital outpainting of ancient murals and paving a new technical path for the preservation and outpainting of cultural heritage. This research not only opens up new possibilities at a technical level but also provides fresh approaches and tools for the protection, education, and dissemination of global cultural heritage. However, ensuring cultural and historical accuracy remains a key challenge. Although artificial intelligence technology can restore and expand murals, it is crucial to ensure the authenticity and appropriateness of these works in cultural and historical aspects, which requires a deep understanding of the cultural background and historical context behind the murals. Additionally, the adaptability and universality of the technology pose another challenge, necessitating further development and optimization to ensure its applicability to ancient murals of various styles and periods. When using AI technology for cultural heritage preservation, it is imperative to respect and protect the integrity of the original art pieces.

Acknowledgments. This study was funded by the National Natural Science Foundation of China (grant number 52274160, 51874300), the Funding for the "Jiangsu Distinguished Professor" project in Jiangsu Province (grant number 140923070) and the Fundamental Research Funds for the Central Universities(2023QN1079).

Disclosure of Interests. The authors have no competing interests to declare that are relevant to the content of this paper.

References

1. Xiaokang, R., Peilin, C.: Murals inpainting based on generalized regression neural network. Comput. Eng. Sci. **39**, 1884–1889 (2017)

2. Xu, H., Kang, J., Zhang, J.: Digital mural inpainting method based on feature perception. Comput. Sci. **49**, 217–223 (2022)
3. Wang, N., Wang, W., Hu, W., Fenster, A., Li, S.: Thanka mural inpainting based on multi-scale adaptive partial convolution and stroke-like mask. IEEE Trans. Image Process. **30**, 3720–3733 (2021)
4. Xu, Z., et al.: Restoration of Dunhuang Murals on Large-scale pretraining. In: Proceedings of the 2023 6th International Conference on Signal Processing and Machine Learning, pp. 106–111 (2023)
5. Zhang, L., Wang, J., Shi, J.: Multimodal image outpainting with regularized normalized diversification. In: Proceedings of the IEEE/CVF Winter Conference on Applications of Computer Vision, pp. 3433–3442 (2020)
6. Yang, Z., Dong, J., Liu, P., Yang, Y., Yan, S.: Very long natural scenery image prediction by outpainting. In: Proceedings of the IEEE/CVF International Conference on Computer Vision, pp. 10561–10570 (2019)
7. Zhang, X., Chen, F., Wang, C., Tao, M., Jiang, G.-P.: Sienet: Siamese expansion network for image extrapolation. IEEE Signal Process. Lett. **27**, 1590–1594 (2020)
8. Lu, C.-N., Chang, Y.-C., Chiu, W.-C.: Bridging the visual gap: Wide-range image blending. In: Proceedings of the IEEE/CVF Conference on Computer Vision and Pattern Recognition, pp. 843–851 (2021)
9. Gao, P., et al.: Generalized image outpainting with U-transformer. Neural Netw. **162**, 1–10 (2023)
10. Van Hoorick, B.: Image outpainting and harmonization using generative adversarial networks. arXiv preprint arXiv:1912.10960 (2019)
11. Wang, Y., Tao, X., Shen, X., Jia, J.: Wide-context semantic image extrapolation. In: Proceedings of the IEEE/CVF Conference on Computer Vision and Pattern Recognition, pp. 1399–1408 (2019)
12. Zhuang, J., Zeng, Y., Liu, W., Yuan, C., Chen, K.: A task is worth one word: learning with task prompts for high-quality versatile image in painting. arXiv preprint arXiv:2312.03594 (2023)
13. Rombach, R., Blattmann, A., Lorenz, D., Esser, P., Ommer, B.: High-resolution image synthesis with latent diffusion models. In: Proceedings of the IEEE/CVF Conference on Computer Vision and Pattern Recognition, pp. 10684–10695 (2022)
14. Li, J., Li, D., Savarese, S., Hoi, S.: BLIP-2: bootstrapping language-image pre-training with frozen image encoders and large language models. In: International Conference on Machine Learning, pp. 19730–19742. PMLR (2023)
15. Cheng, J., et al.: Black-box prompt optimization: Aligning large language models without model training. arXiv preprint arXiv:2311.04155 (2023)
16. Hu, E.J., et al.: LoRA: Low-rank adaptation of large language models. arXiv preprint arXiv:2106.09685 (2021)

MuralRescue: Advancing Blind Mural Restoration via SAM-Adapter Enhanced Damage Segmentation and Integrated Restoration Techniques

Zishan Xu[1], Dufeng Chen[2], Qianzhen Fang[1], Wei Chen[1(✉)], Tingting Xu[1], Jueting Liu[1], and Zehua Wang[1]

[1] China University of Mining and Technology, Xuzhou 221116, China
chenwdavior@163.com

[2] Beijing Geotechnical and Investigation Engineering Insititute, Beijing 100080, China

Abstract. In this paper, we introduce an innovative method for blind mural restoration, named "MuralRescue," which demonstrates a systematic approach to progressively restore and enhance the quality of Dunhuang mural images by integrating damaged area segmentation, inpainting processing, and super-resolution techniques. In the process of mural damage segmentation, we employ the SAM-Adapter to optimize the "Segment Anything" model and to enhance the performance of mural damage segmentation. Specifically, we use an adapter module containing two layers of MLP to fine-tune the "Segment Anything" model, thereby increasing the accuracy of segmenting mural cracks. Through extensive experiments, we have proven the adapter's effectiveness in detecting small targets and fine-grained mural cracks. Additionally, by combining detected cracks with image restoration, we have significantly improved the superiority of blind image restoration tasks without reference.

Keywords: Segment Anything · Blind mural restoration · SAM-Adapter

1 Introduction

Mural images are a long-standing art form that records significant aspects of human history and reflects the uniqueness of different cultures. Despite their historical significance, many ancient murals have suffered severe damage due to natural and human factors. Traditionally, restoring these murals required extensive manual labor, and the results heavily depended on the skill of the restorers. With the rapid development of computer vision and deep learning technologies, new methods have emerged, offering possibilities to automate and improve the restoration process.

This paper introduces "MuralRescue," a comprehensive approach for automated blind mural segmentation and restoration. The method integrates area segmentation, advanced inpainting, and super-resolution techniques to systematically restore Dunhuang mural images. "MuralRescue" involves identifying and segmenting damaged areas, applying advanced inpainting technologies to fill these damages, and employing super-resolution techniques to enhance the clarity and detail of the images. The method leverages the Segment Anything Model (SAM) enhanced by a specially designed SAM-Adapter, which improves the accuracy of detecting fine cracks and segmentation of damaged areas.

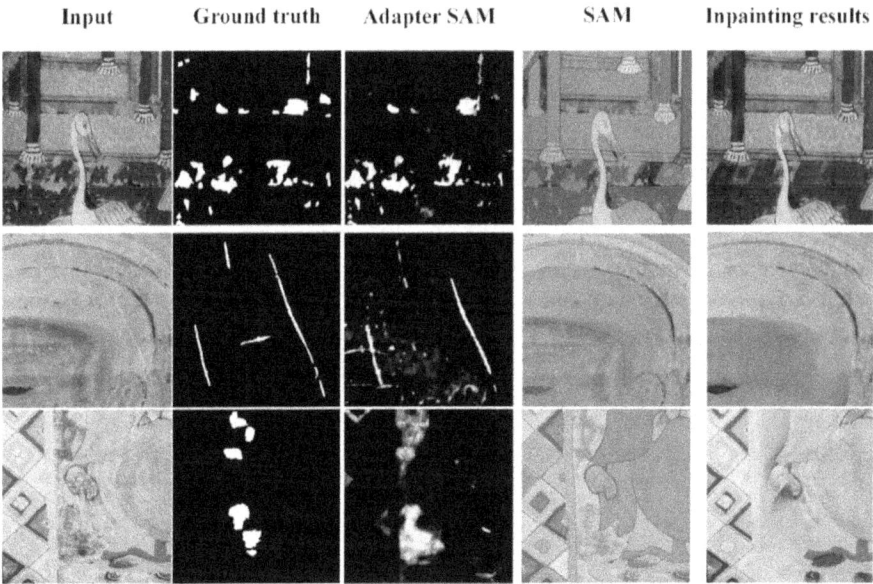

Fig. 1. The results of MuralRescue on Mural dataset, the ground truth is our marked damaged mask, and through Adapter SAM, the detected damage is more detailed, and the unmarked damage of the ground truth can also be detected so that the restored result is closer to reality.

Digital restoration of murals has gained attention globally. Initial digital restoration efforts by Pan et al. [1] have been refined by subsequent researchers such as Shen et al. [2], who utilized MCA decomposition for Tang Dynasty tomb murals. Further advancements were made using sequential similarity detection and cuckoo optimization by Chen et al. [3], and the disease extraction and in-painting algorithm for digital grotto murals by Zhang et al. [4]. Additional studies by Chen et al. [5] and Yang et al. [6] on improving algorithms for intricate disrepaired regions of murals have furthered the field. Moreover, Jiao et al. [7] have advanced mural inpainting based on an improved block matching algorithm.

The "Inpaint Anything" (IA) approach [9], which utilizes the Segment Anything Model (SAM) [10], combines state-of-the-art image painters and AI-generated content models for diverse restoration tasks. SAM's zero-shot performance has been demonstrated in a wide range of applications, including medical imaging [11–13], remote sensing [14], and camouflaged object detection [15]. SAM has also been adapted for non-Euclidean domains, which presents new research opportunities [16].

The results of MuralRescue are illustrated in Fig. 1. The main contributions of this paper are:

- Development and implementation of "MuralRescue," an automated mural restoration method that preserves the original texture and artistic style while improving the accuracy and efficiency of restoration.
- A novel blind image restoration method using the SAM-Adapter, which significantly enhances the segmentation and restoration of damaged mural areas.

2 Method

The main workflow of this study is implemented in three steps for the automatic restoration of murals: First, we use our designed SAM-adapter to segment the damaged areas in the murals; second, we employ the LAMA [20] inpainting algorithm to inpaint these damaged areas. Lastly, we choose Real-ESRGAN [21] to perform super-resolution on the inpainted mural images. The entire process is encapsulated within our "MuralRescue" method, presented in an end-to-end format. The implementation process of these three steps is detailed below. The structure of "MuralRescue" is illustrated in Fig. 2.

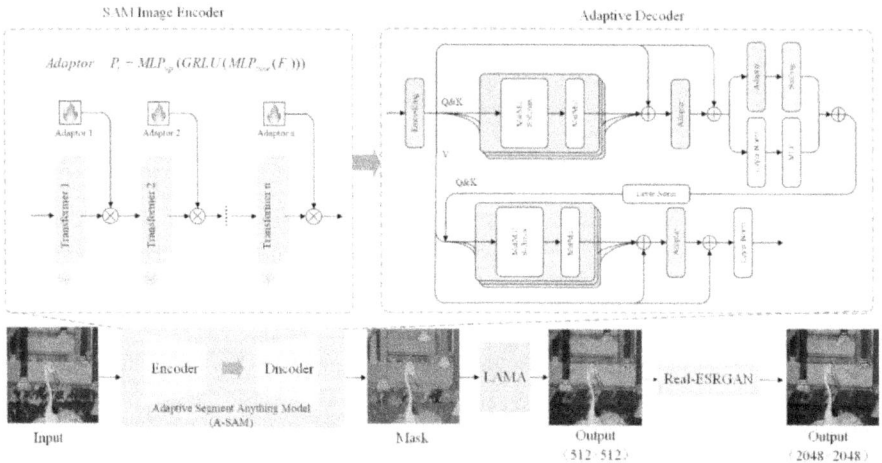

Fig. 2. The structure of MuralRescue

2.1 Segmentation of Damaged Areas

We input the mural image I into the model SAM and obtain the segmentation result S of the broken region:

$$S = SAM(I) \tag{1}$$

Segment Anything model (SAM) is used to accurately segment broken regions, We designed an Adapter to adapt to the specific needs of mural breakage detection. The adapter is a lightweight model that can be trained using relatively little data and inject task-specific bootstrap information into the SAM network. This information is communicated to the network through visual cues, demonstrating efficiency and effectiveness in adapting to many downstream tasks.

Specifically, SAM's image encoder used the ViT-H/16 model with a 14 × 14 window of attention and four uniformly distributed global attention blocks. We keep the weights of the original model frozen and add the adapter module between each transformer layer separately. Each adapter consists of two MLPs and an activation function. Specifically, the adapter receives task-related information F_i and then generates a cue P_i with the expression:

$$P_i = MLP_{up}(Gelu(MLP_{tune}(F_i))) \qquad (2)$$

In this formulation, MLP_{tune} denotes the linear layer used to generate task-specific cues for each Adapter, and MLP_{up} is an up-projection layer shared among all Adapters that adjusts the dimensionality of Transformer features. *Gelu* denotes the GELU activation function [8].

In SAM's mask decoder, we deploy three adapters for each ViT block. The first Adapter is deployed after cueing to the cross-attention of the image embedding, and it is fine-tuned to integrate the cueing information. The second Adapter is used to adapt the MLP-enhanced embedding. The third Adapter is deployed after the cross-attention of the image embedding to the cue, and then the final result is output by additional residual connections and layer normalization. The second decoder block and the mask prediction head are adapted to the given data.

For the training process, we used a dataset containing more than 5000 murals, of which 1000 murals containing broken regions were manually annotated with detailed semantics. In this way, our model can better learn and understand the features of the broken regions of the murals for more accurate segmentation.

2.2 Restoration of Damaged Areas

After completing the segmentation of the broken regions, we used the LAMA [20] algorithm to automate the repair of these regions. We input the original image I, and the segmentation results S into the LAMA algorithm to obtain the repaired image I':

$$I' = LAMA(I, S) \qquad (3)$$

LAMA is an algorithm with powerful restoration capability, which employs a multi-level texture synthesis and area expansion strategy to effectively restore the texture and colour of the mural while maintaining its original artistic style.

After obtaining the repaired image I' using the LAMA algorithm, we further enhance its resolution by employing the Real-ESRGAN [21] algorithm to upscale the image from 512 × 512 pixels to 2048 × 2048 pixels. This process is formulated as follows:

$$I'' = Real-ESRGAN(I') \qquad (4)$$

Image I'' is the final result of our blind restoration approach. The choice of the Real-ESRGAN method is motivated by its training on a real-world scene dataset, which, when combined with adversarial loss, improves the visual effects of super-resolution. This model is particularly suited for reconstructing lines, making it an ideal choice for enhancing mural lines which are critical to preserving the artistic integrity and details of the mural.

3 Experimental Results

In order to fully evaluate the performance of our proposed "MuralRescue" method on the mural restoration task, we designed and executed a series of detailed experiments. In this section, our experimental design, the obtained results, and the related data analysis are discussed in detail.

3.1 Experimental Setup and Dataset

The experiments were conducted on an A40 GPU. We collected and manually labelled a mural image dataset by ourselves, which was used as the data source for the experiments. The dataset includes more than 5000 images of frescoes, of which 1000 images have been manually annotated with detailed semantic annotations of the damaged areas. For model training and testing, we divided these data into a training set and a test set in the ratio of 80% : 20%.

3.2 Comparison Experiments

In our experiments (Fig. 3), we demonstrated the exceptional efficacy of our "MuralRescue" method in the automatic labeling and repair of defective mural areas, surpassing the performance of the popular inpaint anything approach. Our method, enhanced by integrating an adapter module into SAM for precise damage segmentation and employing the LAMA algorithm followed by Real-ESRGAN for super-resolution, produces high-resolution, high-quality mural restorations at 2048 × 2048 pixels. This approach ensures the restored murals exhibit significant improvements in texture, color fidelity, and line sharpness, closely mirroring their original state with superior detail and clarity. The final results set a new benchmark in digital heritage conservation, effectively preserving the intricate details and aesthetic values of ancient artworks.

3.3 Ablation Study

Ablation Study of Segment Model. We conducted ablation experiments to understand how our "MuralRescue" approach can improve mural restoration. We focused on segmenting defective areas using SAM with different adapter settings: (1) using SAM for mural segmentation only; (2) adding an adapter to the image encoder and training for 70 epochs; (3) adding an adapter to the image encoder and training for 100 epochs; (4) adding adapters to both the image encoder and mask decoder and training for 100 epochs. We examined and compared the defective areas of the murals under these four conditions (Table 1).

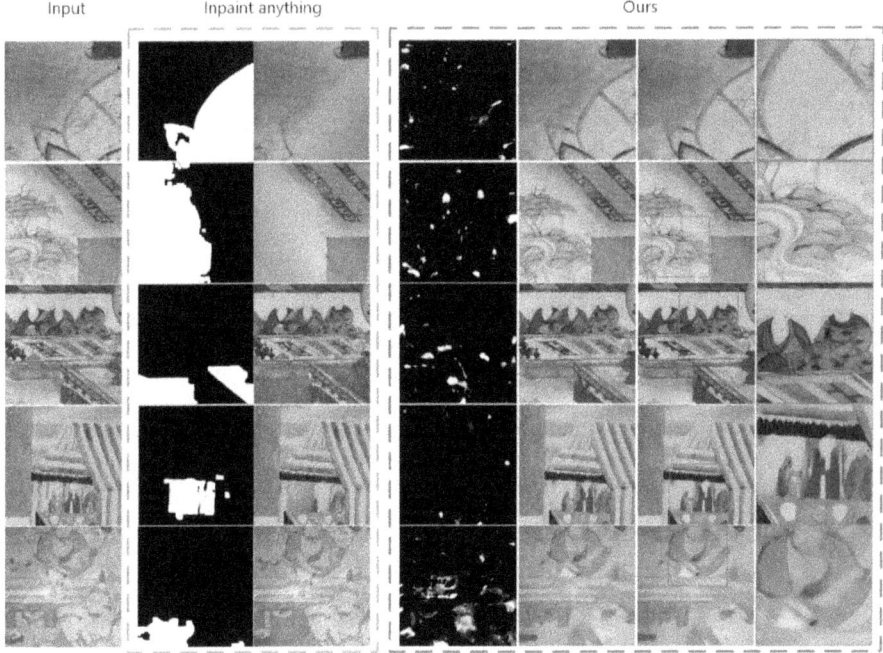

Fig. 3. The compare results with Inpainting-anything on Mural dataset

Table 1. Abaltion study of MuralRescue on Mural dataset (Frozen and Fintune)

Method	Epoch	Averge IoU score ↑	Average Dice Coeffcient ↑
Bring Old Life [19]		0.0790	0.5310
Encoder Adapter	70	0.1390	0.7610
Encoder Adapter	100	0.1366	0.7050
Encoder+Decoder Adapter	100	**0.1518**	**0.7459**

The results (Fig. 4) show that direct detection using the SAM method can segment many categories, but segmenting the damaged areas in the mural is challenging. The segmentation effect is greatly improved when we add the adapter to the image encoder in the SAM method. Not only can we bifurcate the damaged areas in the mural, but the damaged areas in the mural can also be segmented to a very detailed accuracy. The significant damages are peeling, scratching, fading, etc. When we add Adapter to SAM's mask decoder, our method achieves another significant improvement in segmenting the defective areas of the mural. Since many damaged areas of the mural are difficult to mark manually, but our "MuralRescue" can segment them, the semantic segmentation indexes IOU and DSI computed with ground truth are not of the reference value.

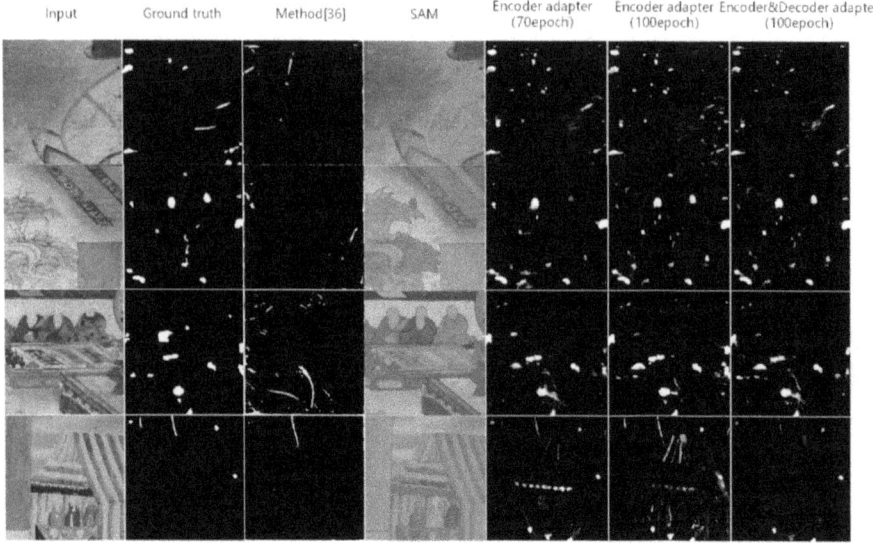

Fig. 4. The ablation study of Segment model on Mural dataset

4 Conclusion

In this paper, we introduce an innovative mural restoration method that combines the Segment Anything model and SAM-Adapter to improve the accuracy of mural restoration. Experimental results on a self-constructed mural dataset show that our method performs excellently on mural restoration tasks.

However, there is still room for improvement, including improving the accuracy of the segmentation stage and optimizing the restoration algorithm to enhance the visual effect. In the future, we plan to expand the application of this method to a broader range of restoration tasks, such as old building restoration, to achieve a greater impact in ancient art restoration work.

Acknowledgments. This study was funded by the National Natural Science Foundation of China (grant number 52274160, 51874300), the Funding for the "Jiangsu Distinguished Professor" project in Jiangsu Province (grant number 140923070).

Disclosure of Interests. The authors have no competing interests to declare that are relevant to the content of this paper.

References

1. Pan, Y.H., et al.: Digital Protection and Restoration of Dunhuang Mural. J. Syst. Simul. **15**(3), 310–314 (2003)

2. Jingni, S.H.E.N., et al.: Tang Dynasty Tomb Murals Inpainting Algorithm of MCA Decomposition. J. Front. Comput. Sci. Technol. **11**(11), 1826 (2017)
3. Chen, et al.: Dunhuang mural inpainting algorithm based on sequential similarity detection and cuckoo optimization. Laser Optoelectronics
4. Zhang, et al.: Research on disease extraction and inpainting algorithm of digital grotto murals. Appl. Res. Comput. **38**(08), 2495–2498+2504 (2021). https://doi.org/10.19734/j.issn.1001-3695.2020.09.0395
5. Yong, C., et al.: Inpainting Algorithm for Dunhuang Mural Based on Improved Curvature-Driven Diffusion Model. J. Comput.-Aided Des. Comput. Graph. **32**(5), 787–796 (2020)
6. Xiaoping, Y., Shuwen, W., et al.: Dunhuang mural inpainting in intricate disrepaired region based on improvement of priority algorithm. J. Comput.-Aided Des. Comput. Graph. **23**(2), 284–289 (2011)
7. Jiao, L.J., et al.: Wutai mountain mural inpainting based on improved block matching algorithm. J. Comput.-Aided Des. Comput. Graph. **31**(1), 118–125 (2019)
8. Hendrycks, D., Gimpel, K.: Gaussian error linear units (GELUs). arXiv preprint arXiv:1606.08415 (2016)
9. Yu, T., Feng, R., Feng, R., et al.: Inpaint anything: segment anything meets image inpainting. arXiv preprint arXiv:2304.06790 (2023)
10. Kirillov, A., Mintun, E., Ravi, N., et al.: Segment anything. arXiv preprint arXiv:2304.02643 (2023)
11. Ma, J., Wang, B.: Segment anything in medical images. arXiv preprint arXiv:2304.12306 (2023)
12. Zhang, K., Liu, D.: Customized segment anything model for medical image segmentation. arXiv preprint arXiv:2304.13785 (2023)
13. Roy, S., Wald, T., Koehler, G., et al.: SAM.MD: zero-shot medical image segmentation capabilities of the segment anything model. arXiv preprint arXiv:2304.05396 (2023)
14. Wang, D., Zhang, J., Du, B., et al.: Scaling-up remote sensing segmentation dataset with segment anything model. arXiv preprint arXiv:2305.02034 (2023)
15. Chen, T., Zhu, L., Ding, C., et al.: SAM fails to segment anything?–SAM-adapter: adapting SAM in underperformed scenes: camouflage, shadow, and more. arXiv preprint arXiv:2304.09148 (2023)
16. Jing, Y., Wang, X., Tao, D.: Segment anything in non-euclidean domains: challenges and opportunities. arXiv preprint arXiv:2304.11595 (2023)
17. Peng, J., Liu, D., Xu, S., Li, H.: Generating diverse structure for image inpainting with hierarchical VQ-VAE. In: Proceedings of the IEEE/CVF Conference on Computer Vision and Pattern Recognition, pp. 10775–10784 (2021)
18. Wan, Z., Zhang, J., Chen, D., Liao, J.: High-fidelity pluralistic image completion with transformers. arXiv preprint arXiv:2103.14031 (2021)
19. Wan, Z., Zhang, B., Chen, D., et al.: Bringing old photos back to life. In: Proceedings of the IEEE/CVF Conference on Computer Vision and Pattern Recognition, pp. 2747–2757 (2020)
20. Zhao, S., Cui, J., Sheng, Y., et al.: Large scale image completion via co-modulated generative adversarial networks. arXiv preprint arXiv:2103.10428 (2021)
21. Wang, X., Xie, L., Dong, C., et al.: Real-ESRGAN: training real-world blind super-resolution with pure synthetic data. In: Proceedings of the IEEE/CVF International Conference on Computer Vision, pp. 905–1914 (2021)

Full-Range Fusion Network with Local-Global Attention for Change Detection in Remote Sensing Images

Shuting Niu, Yingxue Zhang(✉), and Zhanjun Si

College of Artificial Intelligence,
Tianjin University of Science and Technology, Tianjin 300457, China
yxzhang@tust.edu.cn

Abstract. Remote sensing image change detection (CD) is an important technology used to monitor changes in surface features and objects over time, widely applied in fields such as land use planning, environmental monitoring, and disaster management. Although traditional change detection methods are effective in certain scenarios, they are often limited by high sensitivity to noise and computational complexity, making them unsuitable for the rapidly evolving demands of big data. In response, this paper proposes an efficient local-global context fusion network (LGCF-Net) based on a Siamese architecture, aimed at enhancing the accuracy and efficiency of change detection in remote sensing images. LGCF-Net incorporates efficient local-global context aggregator (ELGCA) module and cross fusion attention module (CFAM) to effectively improve the performance of change detection. The proposed method is evaluated on the SYSU-CD dataset, achieving accuracy and recall of 93.21% and 95.39%, respectively, which confirms the effectiveness of the proposed method.

Keywords: Remote sensing image · Change detection · Siamese architecture · Efficient Local-global context aggregator module · Cross fusion attention module

1 Introduction

Change detection(CD) in remote sensing images refers to the use of multitemporal remote sensing data to identify and analyze temporal and spatial changes in land surfaces or features, such as changes in land cover types, alterations in buildings, and impacts of natural disasters. This process aims to extract change information from remote sensing images, convert it into understandable data, and support applications across various fields [1].

Traditional methods of remote sensing image change detection primarily rely on pixel-level difference analysis or object-based change detection. However, inaccuracies often arise from factors such as seasonal variations in background colors, displacement changes caused by moving objects, and minor shooting errors between images. With the advancement of deep learning technologies, numerous deep learning-based methods have been proposed for change detection. SNUNet-CD [2] is a densely connected

Siamese network that reduces information loss during depth information loading by facilitating tight information transfer between the encoder and decoder. There are also networks that improve accuracy by incorporating an attention mechanism. STANet-CD [3] generates superior feature representations by capturing spatio-temporal dependencies at different scales through a spatio-temporal attention module. Similarly, DASNet [4] employs a dual attention mechanism to enhance the robustness of the model and addresses the sample imbalance problem by adjusting the loss function weights. And DSAMNet [5] combines the CBAM [6] attention mechanism with the metric module to improve the feature extraction capability and generate more useful features. In recent years, Transformer has garnered widespread attention in the field of remote sensing image change detection. ICIFNet [7] proposed an integrated CNN and Transformer network for intra-scale interaction and inter-scale feature fusion. WNet [8] combined CNNs and Transformers in a W-shaped dual-branch tiered network and developed a Differential Enhancement Module (DEM). BIT_CD [9] combined spatial attention and a Transformer encoder to convert images from different times into semantic labels, which were then remapped to the pixel space by the decoder, enhancing features to generate pixel-level change predictions.

The aforementioned methods demonstrate outstanding performance, yet some issues persist. Firstly, it remains challenging to suppress background interference in change detection while effectively capturing both global and local contextual information to detect subtle and significant structural changes between image pairs. Secondly, most current CD-based methods focus solely on the images themselves, overlooking temporal clues between images collected at different times. To overcome these challenges, we propose a change detection method based on the Siamese architecture named Efficient Local-Global Context Fusion Network (LGCF-Net). Specifically, we introduce a efficient local-global context aggregator (ELGCA) module [12] to capture contextual information, which uses various aggregation strategies for fine-grained optimization of features, enhancing the model's receptive field. To leverage temporal clues for addressing the change detection task, we further propose the cross fusion attention module (CFAM) that allows for the useful exchange and fusion of information between images taken at two different time points.

2 The Proposed Method

The proposed change detection framework mainly comprises a Siamese encoder, cross fusion attention module (CFAM), Dual Attention Module (DAM), and decoder, as illustrated in Fig. 1. The Siamese encoder takes a pair of satellite images as input, initially down-sampling them through a patch embedding layer, and then processing them through four pairs of encoding modules to output four pairs of multi-scale feature maps. Feature maps of the same size enter the CFAM, where fused feature maps are generated and subsequently sent to the DAM for further feature enhancement. The four feature maps enhanced by the DAM are fed into the fusion module, where simple linear projections, feature concatenation, and 1x1 convolution operations are performed to reduce the number of channels. Finally, these fused features are passed to the decoder module to produce more accurate change map predictions.

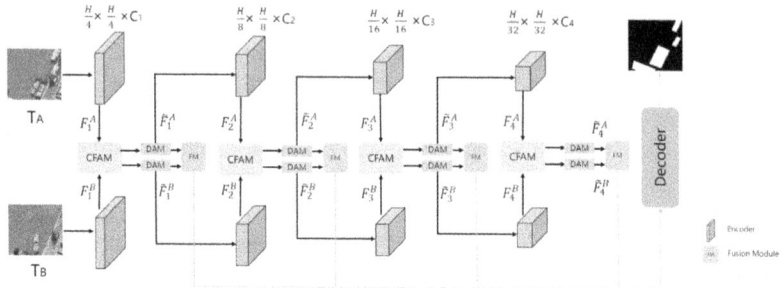

Fig. 1. Overall framework of the LGCF-Net

2.1 ELGCA Module

The encoding module consists of an efficient local-global context aggregator (ELGCA) module and an MLP module and utilizes a residual connection structure to mitigate the vanishing gradient problem. Our ELGCA module is designed to capture both local and global contextual information while reducing computational complexity, as illustrated in Fig. 2. The input features $f^i \in R^{H^i \times W^i \times C^i}$ are split into two halves channel-wise, resulting in f_{lo}^i and $f_{gl}^i \in R^{H^i \times W^i \times (C^i/2)}$. These are separately fed into individual context aggregators to obtain local and global contextual information, where H^i, W^i and C^i denote the width, height, and number of channels, respectively.

$$f_{lo}^i, f_{gl}^i = Split(f^i) \tag{1}$$

The X_{gl}^i feature of our ELGCA module initially undergoes a 1x1 convolution, dividing it into Z^i, Q^i, K^i and V^i features. Here, Z^i is used for multi-channel feature aggregation, while Q^i, K^i and V^i serve as the query, key, and value for the PT attention mechanism, aimed at capturing global contextual information. The PT attention mechanism first performs average pooling on the query Q^i and max pooling on K^i, capturing the average and maximum values of the input features. This process is designed to obtain feature representations $\overline{Q}^i$ and $\overline{K}^i$ that are robust to subtle changes, thereby more effectively capturing essential information from the input data. Subsequently, using the averaged features $\overline{Q}^i$, maximum features $\overline{K}^i$ and the value features V^i a transpose attention operation (G) is applied, resulting in the feature representation A_{att}^i.

$$A_{att}^i = V^i \times \left[\sigma \left(\overline{K}^{iT} \times \overline{Q}^i \right) \right] \tag{2}$$

The f_{lo}^i feature undergoes a 3x3 depthwise separable convolution, resulting in the locally aggregated contextual feature $\overline{f}_{lo}^i$. The purpose of this step is to capture local contextual information, and the use of depthwise separable convolution reduces both the number of model parameters and the computational complexity.

Finally, the feature A_{att}^i processed by the PT attention mechanism, the locally aggregated contextual feature $\overline{f}_{lo}^i$, and the multi-channel aggregated feature Z^i are concatenated. This results in a rich feature representation $\overline{f}^i$ that combines both local and global contextual information. This fusion of context information at different levels and through different methods provides a more comprehensive feature representation for subsequent full-range feature fusion.

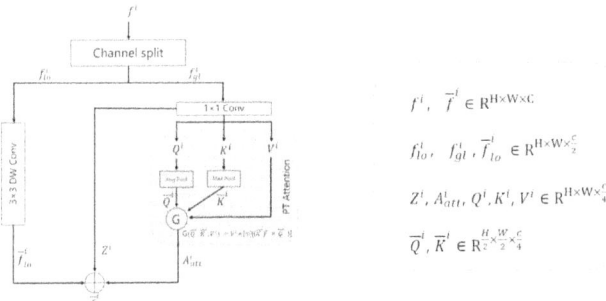

Fig. 2. Efficient local-global context aggregator (ELGCA) module

2.2 CFAM

Cross fusion attention module (CFAM) is shown in Fig. 3. Its primary function is to allow the useful exchange and fusion of information between bi-temporal remote sensing images. CFAM facilitates the mutual integration of information between two input data pairs, allowing the encoder processing Image A to concurrently consider information from Image B. This enables the encoder to comprehensively understand the relationship between images at different time points, thereby detecting change areas more accurately. For the input tensors $X, Y \in R^{H^i \times W^i \times C^i}$ they are fed into the CFAM for information interaction. In this module, we use a dot product operation to calculate the similarity matrix between the query Q from tensor X and the key K from tensor Y, and then normalize it using the softmax function. The purpose of this is to obtain normalized attention weights, allowing each pixel in tensor X to focus on important pixels in tensor Y. The process can be represented by the following formula:

$$Attention(X, Y) = softmax\left(\frac{Q_y K_x^T}{\sqrt{d_{kx}}}\right) V_x \qquad (3)$$

In the formula, d_k represents the dimension of the key K. For the fused features, we perform a linear transformation to map them to a higher-dimensional feature space. Then, the result of this linear transformation is added to the original query features of tensor X to retain the original feature information of image X, making the final feature representation richer. After the addition, we apply layer normalization to standardize the distribution of the features. Subsequently, a Multi-Layer Perceptron (MLP) is used to perform a nonlinear mapping of the features, enhancing their expressive power and distinctiveness. The same operations are performed for tensor Y. Ultimately, the CFAM outputs two cross-fused feature maps, each representing the remote sensing images at two different time points, and highlighting the common and differentiating features between them.

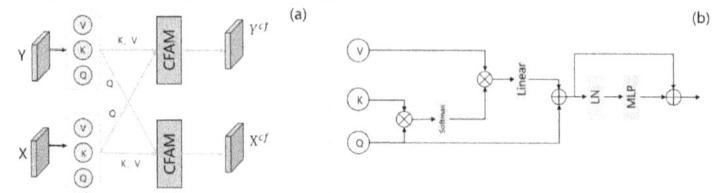

Fig. 3. Cross fusion attention module (CFAM)

2.3 Dam

For the two cross-fused feature maps, a Spatial and Channel Dual Attention Module is used to enhance the model's feature representation ability, effectively capturing and utilizing key features in the image to improve the model's ability to recognize and analyze changes in terrain. First, the channel attention module identifies which channels are more important by utilizing features from global average pooling and max pooling to generate a channel attention map. This map is used to adjust the response strengths of the individual channels. Next, the spatial attention module focuses on which areas within the feature map are more significant. It uses the previously channel-weighted feature map to perform max pooling and average pooling operations, creating a two-dimensional attention map that emphasizes important spatial regions in the feature map. Finally, the spatially attentive feature map is multiplied by the channel attentive feature map to produce a feature map with dual attention.

2.4 Decoder

The decoder is composed of convolutional and transposed convolutional layers, as shown in Fig. 4. Initially, four feature maps of different scales are merged along the channel dimension, and a 1x1 convolutional layer adjusts the number of channels and reorganizes the features. Subsequently, the transposed convolutional layer's upsampling operation increases the spatial resolution of the feature maps and restores image details, bringing the processed feature maps closer to the original image size. To further enhance feature expression, a residual block containing two 3x3 convolutional layers is introduced, where skip connections prevent information loss and ensure the accurate transfer of deep features. Moreover, the combination of transposed convolution and residual blocks is cascaded twice consecutively to progressively expand the spatial dimensions of the feature maps until they match the input size. This process not only improves spatial resolution but also enhances the feature hierarchy for change detection. The decoder ultimately outputs a binary change map through the convolutional layers.

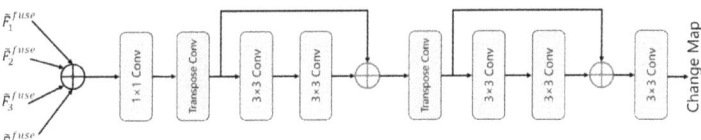

Fig. 4. Decoder

2.5 Loss Function

The cross-entropy loss function is used as shown in the following equation. The cross-entropy loss function is a method for measuring the difference between two probability distributions, primarily used to evaluate the proximity between model prediction results and true labels.

$$Loss = -\frac{1}{N}\Sigma_{i=1}^{N} q_n \log(P_n) + (1 - q_n)\log(1 - p_n) \tag{4}$$

where q_n represents the probability of the true label, P_n represents the model's predicted probability, N represents the total number of samples, and n represents the nth sample, with the value ranging from 1 to N.

3 Experimental Results

3.1 Dataset

The SYSU-CD [5] dataset consists of 20,000 pairs of image patches collected between 2007 and 2014, each with a size of 256 × 256, sourced from ortho-rectified aerial images in Hong Kong. The SYSU-CD dataset not only includes common change information in urban and suburban areas but also provides specific details regarding high-density building changes and marine construction changes, offering rich data support for spatial change research in the urbanization process. This dataset is randomly divided with 60% used for model training, and 20% each for model validation and testing.

3.2 Experimental Results

We employed four evaluation metrics: Precision (P), Recall (R), F1 score (F1), and Intersection over Union (IoU) to quantitatively assess the experimental results of our proposed network. To validate the effectiveness of our proposed network, we compare it with five mainstream deep learning-based change detection methods, including SNUNet [2], DSAMNet [5], LCDNet [10], GeSANet [11], and ELGC-Net [12]. From the results in Table 1, it is clear that our method has achieved improvements in all the metrics. For example, our LGCF-Net achieves 93.21% and 95.39% in precision and recall, respectively, successfully surpassing the existing methods being compared. It indicates that our model has a significant advantage in detecting changes in targets of different sizes in complex scenes.

Figure 5 presents a visual comparison of various methods on the SYSU-CD dataset, illustrating that our method visually outperforms others in detecting change areas. The

Table 1. Comparative experimental results of the SYSU-CD dataset

Method	P	R	F1	IoU
SNUNet [2]	82.86	74.87	78.50	64.16
DSAMNet [5]	83.86	73.32	78.24	64.25
LCDNet [10]	81.71	83.79	82.57	70.31
GeSaNet [11]	90.80	92.93	90.68	86.64
ELGCNet [12]	92.34	94.81	93.85	88.42
Ours	**93.21**	**95.39**	**93.97**	**88.63**

first row shows the changes in the road extension, and from the figure, it can be observed that some models incorrectly recognize the shadows as areas of change and there are missed detections. Our model, however, shows the most complete performance in detailed segmentation. The second displays the change comparison images for suburban expansion. It is evident that some models incorrectly identify the area in the middle of the houses as a changing area, while only our model provides the most accurate segmentation. The third row shows the change comparison for oceanic construction, revealing that for large and irregularly shaped change areas, most methods produce detection results that lack clarity in shape and contours, with significant missed areas. Our model, however, effectively maintains the integrity of large targets while somewhat restoring edge details. The fourth row displays the changes in newly constructed urban buildings, where the rooftop textures and contours of buildings are complex. The segmentation results from the other five methods are too coarse to accurately delineate the correct shapes. In contrast, our method identifies more detailed change information, generates change prediction maps with clear and continuous boundaries, and detects small targets missed by other methods. From the visual results, our model, by incorporating the ELGCA module, effectively captures both local and global information, thus expanding the model's receptive field. After introducing the CFAM, the model more effectively captures changes between two-time points, resulting in more precise segmentation of small objects. DAM effectively identifies hidden key information, further reducing the loss of edge details.

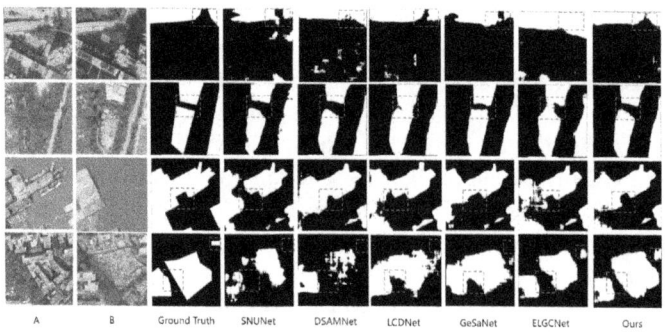

Fig. 5. Visualization results of the SYSU-CD dataset

4 Conclusions

In this paper, we introduce an Efficient Local-Global Context Fusion Network (LGCF-Net) based on the Siamese architecture. The ELGCA module leverages both local and global information to capture image changes more comprehensively. The CFAM enables dense fusion of bi-temporal features, while the DAM identifies hidden crucial information to improve feature extraction capabilities. Our method has been validated on the SYSU-CD dataset and demonstrates superior performance across multiple evaluation metrics compared to existing technologies. However, despite the excellent performance of our LGCF-Net in change detection, its high computational resource consumption is a significant drawback, leading to slower processing speeds. Future work will therefore explore lightweight models.

References

1. Bin, Y.A.N.G., et al.: Review of remote sensing change detection in deep learning: bibliometric and analysis. Nat. Remote Sens. Bull. **27**(9), 1988–2005 (2023)
2. Fang, S., et al.: SNUNet-CD: a densely connected Siamese network for change detection of VHR images. IEEE Geosci. Remote Sens. Lett. **19**, 1–5 (2021)
3. Chen, H., Shi, Z.: A spatial-temporal attention-based method and a new dataset for remote sensing image change detection. Remote Sens. **12**(10), 1662 (2020)
4. Chen, J., et al.: DASNet: dual attentive fully convolutional Siamese networks for change detection in high-resolution satellite images. IEEE J. Sel. Top. Appl. Earth Observations Remote Sens. **14**, 1194–1206 (2020)
5. Shi, Q., et al.: A deeply supervised attention metric-based network and an open aerial image dataset for remote sensing change detection. IEEE Trans. Geosci. Remote Sens. **60**, 1–16 (2021)
6. Woo, S., et al.: CBAM: convolutional block attention module. In: Proceedings of the European Conference on Computer Vision (ECCV) (2018)
7. Feng, Y., et al.: ICIF-Net: intra-scale cross-interaction and inter-scale feature fusion network for Bitemporal remote sensing images change detection. IEEE Trans. Geosci. Remote Sens. **60**, 1–13 (2022)
8. Tang, X., et al.: WNet: W-shaped hierarchical network for remote sensing image change detection. IEEE Trans. Geosci. Remote Sens. **61**, 1–14 (2023)
9. Chen, H., Qi, Z., Shi, Z.: Remote sensing image change detection with transformers. IEEE Trans. Geosci. Remote Sens. **60**, 1–14 (2021)
10. Li, J., Li, S., Wang, F.: LCDNet: lightweight change detection network with dual attention guidance and multiscale feature fusion for remote sensing images. IEEE Geosci. Remote Sens. Lett. **21**, 1–5 (2023)
11. Zhao, X., et al.: GeSANet: geospatial-awareness network for VHR remote sensing image change detection. IEEE Trans. Geosci. Remote Sens. **61**, 1–14 (2023)
12. Noman, M., et al.: ELGC-Net: efficient local-global context aggregation for remote sensing change detection. IEEE Trans. Geosci. Remote Sens. **62**, 1–11 (2024)

Author Index

C
Cao, Dehua 41
Cao, Fengping 77
Cao, Shitong 312
Chen, Aoran 414
Chen, Dufeng 124, 446, 456
Chen, Mengjie 345
Chen, Minglang 218
Chen, Siyi 279
Chen, Wei 446, 456
Chen, Zhanglu 15
Chen, Zhongyue 29
Cheng, Tianxiang 435

D
Deng, Ruting 15
Deng, Yifan 15
Dong, Chen 184
Dong, Feng 234
Dongye, Changlei 333
Du, Qiaoqiao 147
Duan, Wensi 41
Duan, Wen-Tao 134
Duan, Wentao 53

F
Fan, Bangkui 208
Fan, Haifeng 435
Fang, Qianzhen 456
Fu, Yaowen 300
Fu, Yutian 234

G
Gao, Lijun 89
Gao, Xueyan 300
Gong, Guoliang 172
Guo, Haozhe 345
Guo, Hui 218
Guo, Yitong 124

H
Hao, Weijie 147
He, Jie 218
Hu, Wei 53, 134
Huang, Hai 414
Huang, Lingfeng 266
Huang, Yangyang 65, 101
Huo, Wanli 29
Huo, Xiangzuo 197

J
Jiang, Maoxiang 426
Jiang, Peng 41
Jin, Xiao 89
Jin, Yu 41

K
Kang, Zhiqing 15
Kong, Xiangyu 369

L
Li, Aolun 197
Li, Cheng 41
Li, Jianrong 435
Li, Kaijiang 345
Li, Yachao 234
Li, Yubo 435
Li, Zhan 15
Li, Zhenhua 279
Lian, Zhe 53, 134
Liang, Dong 234, 266, 279
Liang, Qi 3
Lin, Yangde 323
Lin, Zhehao 184
Ling, Sai Ho 160
Liu, Hongzhe 402
Liu, Juan 41
Liu, Jueting 446, 456
Liu, Xiang 3
Long, Hang 15
Long, Qian 257

long, Qian 381
Lu, Huijuan 29
Lu, Yingying 390
Luo, Ronghua 65, 101
Lv, Pei 345
Lyu, Juan 160

M

Ma, Hui 435
Mei, Yijing 113, 124
Meng, Jinpeng 160
Meng, Xianghong 172
Mi, Zeng 134
Miao, Yi 77

N

Ni, Yuliang 357
Niu, Shuting 464

P

Pan, Gang 113, 124, 246
Pan, Xiangyu 246
Pang, Baochuan 41

Q

Qi, Lin 390
Qi, Tianyang 300
Qi, Xuan-Hao 134
Qi, Yaping 29
Qiu, Zhichao 15
Qu, Hongwei 257, 381

S

Shen, Sheng 323
Shi, Haoshan 300
Shi, Jinyu 291
Si, Zhanjun 291, 426, 435, 464
Su, Hao 345
Sun, Di 113, 124, 246, 323
Sun, Jiwu 402
Sun, Lin 160
Sun, Yue 266
Sun, Zeyang 89

T

Tang, Ying 29
Tian, Shengwei 197
Tie, Yun 390

W

Wan, Yuxuan 184
Wang, Daole 369
Wang, Gaihua 257, 381
Wang, Guibao 3
Wang, Jiahao 246
Wang, Jin 312
Wang, Lang 41
Wang, Lanmei 3
Wang, Lizhe 3
Wang, Pengfei 402
Wang, Qihang 323
Wang, Suran 89
Wang, Wenjun 369
Wang, Xiaoliang 172
Wang, Yiping 381
Wang, Yu 357
Wang, Yumei 333
Wang, Yunxiang 113
Wang, Zehua 446, 456
Wang, Zhihui 357
Wu, Pengnian 208
Wu, Weiye 65, 101

X

Xi, Xing 65, 101
Xie, Di 218
Xin, Qin 89
Xu, Caixu 218
Xu, Cheng 402
Xu, Qiaozhi 53
Xu, Tingting 446, 456
Xu, Yulong 208
Xu, Zishan 446, 456
Xue, Dong 208

Y

Yang, Ke 426
Yang, Na 53
Yang, Tingting 113, 246
Yang, Xinbin 291
Yang, Xinqi 172
Yang, Yuqing 446
Yao, Chaojie 124
Yao, Jingxuan 257
Ye, Minchao 29
Yin, Yan-Jun 134
Yin, Yanjun 53
Yu, Lei 53

Yu, Long 197
Yue, Shan 414

Z

Zeng, Zhiliang 323
Zhang, Cheng 402
Zhang, Chuanlei 435
Zhang, Ruiyu 208
Zhang, Shizhao 323
Zhang, Shu 414
Zhang, Wangyi 77
Zhang, Wenyin 147
Zhang, Xuejie 312
Zhang, Yingxue 291, 426, 464
Zhang, Youzhi 89
Zhang, Yu 160, 172
Zhang, Yue-Ning 134
Zhang, Zhaojuan 29
Zhang, Zhongwei 172
Zhao, Wenxiu 333
Zhao, Xiuyang 369
Zhao, Yanchen 147
Zhao, Zhiqiang 435
Zhi, Min 53, 134
Zhou, Bingming 197
Zhou, Xiaobing 312
Zhu, Bolun 257, 381
Zhu, Qi 266
Zhu, Yueyan 414
Zou, Yifei 300

Printed in the USA
CPSIA information can be obtained
at www.ICGtesting.com
CBHW051934180824
13382CB00003B/47